INDUSTRIAL ELECTRONICS
Devices and Systems

INDUSTRIAL ELECTRONICS
Devices and Systems

DALE R. PATRICK

STEPHEN W. FARDO

Eastern Kentucky University

A RESTON BOOK
Prentice-Hall
Englewood Cliffs, New Jersey

Library of Congress Cataloging in Publication Data

Patrick, Dale R.
  Industrial electronics.

  ''A Reston book.''
  Includes index.
  1. Industrial electronics. I. Fardo, Stephen W.
II. Title.
TK881.P38 1986   621.381   85-19265
ISBN 0-8359-3197-8

Editorial/production supervision and interior design
by Barbara J. Gardetto

A Reston Book
Published by Prentice-Hall
A Division of Simon & Schuster, Inc.
Englewood Cliffs, N.J. 07632

Printed in the United States of America

To our wives,
Kay and Helen,
for their forbearance, understanding, and help
in the preparation of this manuscript

Contents

3
OPERATIONAL AMPLIFIERS 75

4
UJT THYRISTORS AND SCRs 98

7
INDUSTRIAL TIMING SYSTEMS 227

8
OPTOELECTRONIC SYSTEMS 273

9

THERMAL SYSTEMS 321

10

DIGITAL ELECTRONIC SYSTEMS 364

11

MICROPROCESSOR SYSTEMS 414

12

PROGRAMMABLE CONTROLLERS 444

13

INDUSTRIAL ROBOTIC SYSTEMS 468

Industrial electronics is a special branch of the electronics field that deals with electronic power control procedures and systems that relate to some form of manufacturing. This part of electronics has undoubtedly gone through some of the most significant changes of the entire field. The demand for personnel trained in this area is almost overwhelming today.

At one time, industrial electronics was limited to motor-control systems and devices that altered the flow of high-current equipment. Gaseous tubes, magnetic contactors, and electrical switchgear served as the nucleus of the field at this time. Recent developments in solid-state electronics, microminiaturization, computers, microprocessors, programmable controllers, and robotics have had a significant impact on the field. A person working in industrial electronics must be knowledgeable of these things and the systems that use them in the manufacture of a product. *Industrial Electronics: Devices and Systems* was developed for this type of person.

The systems concept of this presentation served as the basis of our approach to industrial electronics. We first divided a system into a number of essential blocks or parts. Each block of the system plays a significant role in the operation of the overall system. Each block was further divided into discrete components and presented in more detail. The reader will be able to look at specific systems to see how they respond. A common format was used to classify the system. This includes such areas as thermal, timing, digital, optoelectronic, microprocessor, computer, robotic, and industrial environment systems. Through this approach, we should eventually be able to see how the pieces of an industrial electronic system fit together. This method of presentation is closely associated with the gestalt, or "big picture," approach in the psychology of learning.

The explanations used in this approach are essentially nonmathematical and apply to typi-

Preface

cal industrial equipment that is designed to achieve specific manufacturing operations. When math is used, it is presented only to show a practical relationship in the explanation of a process.

This book is intended for use in vocational/technical schools, college-level industrial technology courses, industrial training, and self-study pursuits. Chapter organization includes an introductory section, the main text, and study questions. Many of the chapters have mathematical problems and laboratory activities.

The authors feel that an industrial technician should be a generalist in order to work in the industrial electronics field. A rather broad scope of information is presented here in order to acquaint the reader with various systems and devices that will be encountered. Through this approach the reader should be better equipped to meet the demands of the industrial electronics field.

A number of the illustrations in this manuscript have been provided by industrial manufacturing concerns. We gratefully acknowledge the cooperation and courtesy of these concerns. A great deal of credit must also be extended to our wives, Kay Patrick and Helen Fardo, for their helpful criticism and excellent work in typing the manuscript to its completion.

Dale R. Patrick
Stephen W. Fardo

All industrial electronic systems require certain voltage and current values for operation. The energy source of the system is primarily responsible for this function. As a rule, the energy source is more commonly called a *power supply*. In some systems the power supply may be simply a battery or some dry cells. Portable systems are generally energized in this way. Fixed or stationary systems are usually energized by the ac power source. These systems normally require large amounts of energy in their operation. Most industrial systems are energized by the ac power line.

In general, most industrial electronic systems require some form of direct current or dc energy in order to be operational. This energy is primarily used to supply such things as transistors, integrated circuits, computers, optoelectronic devices, and thermal components. Direct current can be produced chemically by batteries and cells, mechanically by generators, or by rectification of the ac power source. Most industrial electronic systems are energized by rectified power sources. These systems are supplied by ac, and they change this energy into a usable form of dc. The primary source of energy is ac and the operational source is dc.

ALTERNATING-CURRENT SOURCES

A very high percentage of all the electrical power produced in the United States is alternating current. Massive generators at power plants throughout the country provide the necessary power to sustain industrial operations. Most generators produce three-phase alternating current. This is supplied to an industrial site through a massive electrical power distribution system. When ac is supplied to a specific system, it may be three phase or single

1

Industrial Electronic Sources and Power Supplies

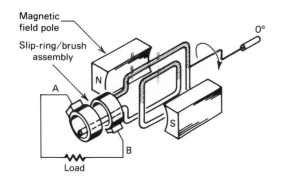

Position A

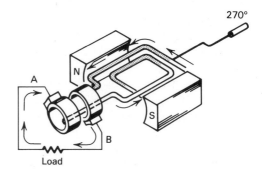

Position B

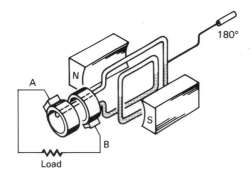

Position C

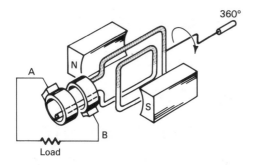

Position D

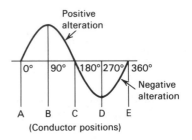

Position E

Resulting output waveform

FIGURE 1–1
Basic principle of operation of a single-phase alternator.

phase according to the circuitry of the distribution system. As a rule, systems that require large amounts of power are energized by a three-phase source, whereas smaller systems are supplied by a single-phase source. Three-phase and single-phase ac sources are very important in the operation of an industrial electronic system.

Single-phase AC Generators

Electrical energy can be produced by single-phase ac generators, commonly called *alternators*. The principle of operation of a single-phase alternator is illustrated in Figure 1–1. For a generator to convert mechanical energy

into electrical energy, three conditions must exist: (1) a magnetic field must be developed; (2) a group of conductors must be within the magnetic field; (3) relative motion must exist between the magnetic field and the conductors. Two methods can be used to meet these conditions for electrical energy production: the rotating armature method and the rotating field method. These methods are illustrated in Figure 1–2.

In the *rotating armature method*, shown in Figure 1–2(A), ac voltage is induced into conductors of the rotating portion of the machine. The magnetic field is developed by a set of stationary pole pieces. Relative motion between the conductors and the magnetic field is provided by a prime mover or mechanical energy

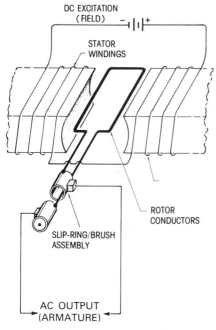

(A) Rotating armature method.

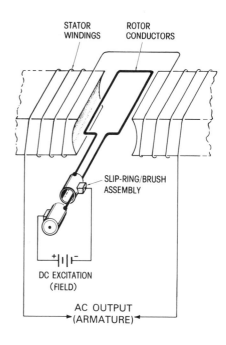

(B) Rotating field method.

FIGURE 1–2
Two basic methods of generating single-phase alternating current.

source connected to the shaft, which is part of the rotor assembly. Prime movers may be gasoline or diesel engines, hydroturbines, steam turbines, or possibly electrical motors. Generators convert mechanical energy into electrical energy.

Electrical energy produced by the rotating armature method is in the form of a sinusoidal wave form. This wave form is referred to as a *sine wave* due to its trigonometric origin. The voltage induced into the conductors of the armature varies as the sine of the angle of rotation between the conductors and the magnetic field (see Figure 1–3). The instantaneous voltage induced into an armature conductor can be expressed as

$$V_i = V_{max} \times \sin \theta$$

where

V_i = instantaneous induced voltage

V_{max} = maximum induced voltage

θ = angle of conductor rotation from the zero reference

For example, at the 30° position, if the maximum voltage is 100 volts *(V)*, then

$$V_i = 100 \times \sin \theta$$

Since the sine of 30° = 0.5,

$$V_i = 100 \times 0.5$$

$$= 50 \text{ V}$$

The frequency of the sinusoidal wave forms produced by an alternator is usually 60 hertz (Hz). Since a cycle of ac is generated as the armature passes a set of north and south field poles, a speed of 60 revolutions per second (3600 r/min) must be maintained to produce a frequency of 60 Hz. The frequency of an alternator can be expressed as

$$f = \frac{\text{number of poles} \times \text{speed of rotation (r/min)}}{120}$$

where f is the frequency in hertz. Note that if the number of poles is increased the speed of rotation can be reduced while still maintaining a 60-Hz frequency.

As the electrical load of an alternator is increased, the alternator tends to slow down and the generated (terminal) voltage tends to decrease. The amount of change depends on the design of the alternator and the type of load connected to its terminals. The amount of change in generated voltage from a no-load condition to a rated full-load condition is referred to as *voltage regulation*. Voltage regulation can be expressed as

$$VR = \frac{V_{NL} - V_{FL}}{V_{FL}} \times 100$$

TRIGONOMETRIC SINE VALUES

Degrees	Sine	Degrees	Sine
0/360	0.000	180	0.000
30	0.500	210	0.500
60	0.866	240	0.866
90	1.000	270	1.000
120	0.866	300	0.866
150	0.500	330	0.500

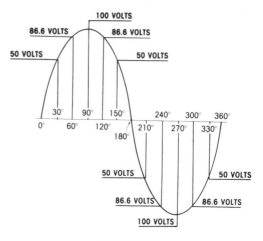

FIGURE 1–3
Trigonometric origin of the ac sine wave.

where

VR = voltage regulation in percent

V_{NL} = no-load terminal voltage

V_{FL} = rated full-load terminal voltage

Alternator efficiency is the ratio of the power output in watts to the power input in horsepower. The efficiency of an alternator can be expressed as

$$\text{Efficiency (\%)} = \frac{P_{out}}{P_{in}} \times 100$$

where

P_{in} = power input in horsepower

P_{out} = power output in watts

To convert horsepower to watts, remember that 1 horsepower (hp) = 746 watts (W). Al-

ternator efficiencies generally range from 70% to 85%.

The basic operation of single-phase alternators has been explained by referring to the rotating armature method. However, this type of alternator can only be used to produce relatively small amounts of power. The major disadvantage is that the ac voltage is extracted from the slip-ring/brush assembly [see Figure 1–2(A)]. A high voltage could produce tremendous sparking or arc-over between the brushes and slip rings. The maintenance involved to replace the brushes and repair the slip-ring assembly would be very time consuming and expensive. Therefore, this method is used only for alternators with low power ratings.

The *rotating field method,* illustrated in Figure 1-2(B), is used for alternators capable of producing larger amounts of power. The dc ex-

Courtesy General Electric Co.

FIGURE 1–4
A large, commercial, three-phase ac
generator. (Courtesy of General Electric Co.)

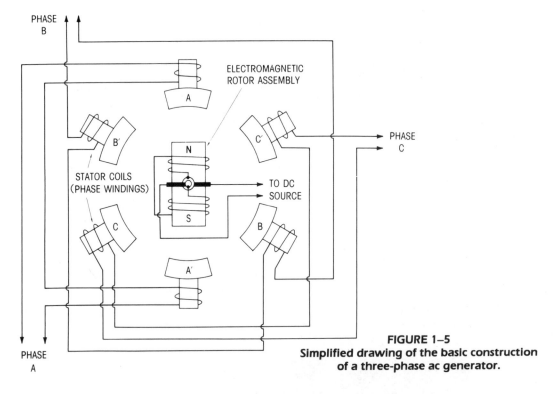

FIGURE 1–5
Simplified drawing of the basic construction of a three-phase ac generator.

citation voltage, which develops the magnetic field, is applied to the rotating portion of the machine. The ac voltage is induced into the stationary conductors of the machine. Since the dc excitation voltage is a much lower value than the ac voltage produced, the maintenance problems associated with the slip-ring/brush assembly are minimized. The conductors of the stationary portion of the machine can be made larger to handle more current since they do not rotate.

Three-phase AC Generators

A large, commercial, three-phase ac generator is shown in Figure 1–4. Most large commercial generators in the United States produce a three-phase voltage. Due to their large power ratings, three-phase generators utilize the rotating field method. A typical three-phase gener-

ator in a power plant might have 250 V dc excitation applied to the rotating field through a slip-ring/brush assembly, while 13.8 kilovolts (kV) ac is induced into the stationary conductors.

The basic construction of a three-phase gen-

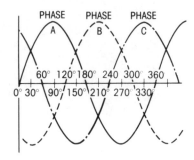

FIGURE 1–6
Output wave forms of a three-phase ac generator.

erator is illustrated in Figure 1–5, and its resulting output wave form is illustrated in Figure 1–6. Note that three-phase generators must have at least six stationary poles, or two poles per phase. In Figure 1–5, poles A′, B′, and C′ represent the beginnings of each of the phase windings. Poles A, B, and C represent the ends of each of the windings. Two methods can be used to connect these windings together. These methods, called *wye* (or star) and *delta* connections, are illustrated in Figure 1–7.

In the wye connection of Figure 1–7(A), the beginnings or the ends of each winding are connected together. The other sides of the windings become the ac lines from the generator. The voltage across the ac lines (V_L) is equal to the square root of 3 (1.73) multiplied by the voltage across the phase windings (V_P), or

$$V_L = V_P \times 1.73$$

The line currents (I_L) are equal to the phase currents (I_P), or

$$I_L = I_P$$

In the delta connection of Figure 1–7(B), the end of one phase winding is connected to the beginning of the adjacent phase winding. The line voltages (V_L) are equal to the phase voltages (V_P). The line currents (I_L) are equal to the phase currents (I_P) multiplied by 1.73.

The power developed in each phase (P_p) for either a wye or a delta circuit is expressed as

$$P_p = V_p \times I_p \times \text{pf}$$

where pf is the power factor (phase angle between voltage and current) of the load. The total power developed by all three phases of a three-phase generator (P_T) is expressed as

$$P_T = 3 \times P_p$$
$$= 3 \times V_p \times I_p \times \text{pf}$$
$$= 1.73 \times V_L \times I_L \times \text{pf}$$

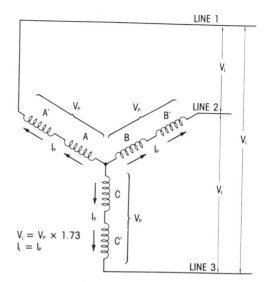

$$V_L = V_P \times 1.73$$
$$I_L = I_P$$

(A) The wye (or star) connection.

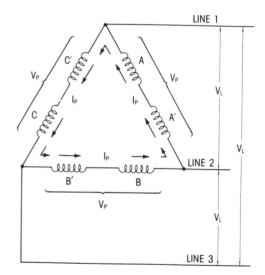

$$V_L = V_P$$
$$I_L = I_P \times 1.73$$

(B) The delta connection.

FIGURE 1–7
Two methods of connecting three-phase stator coils.

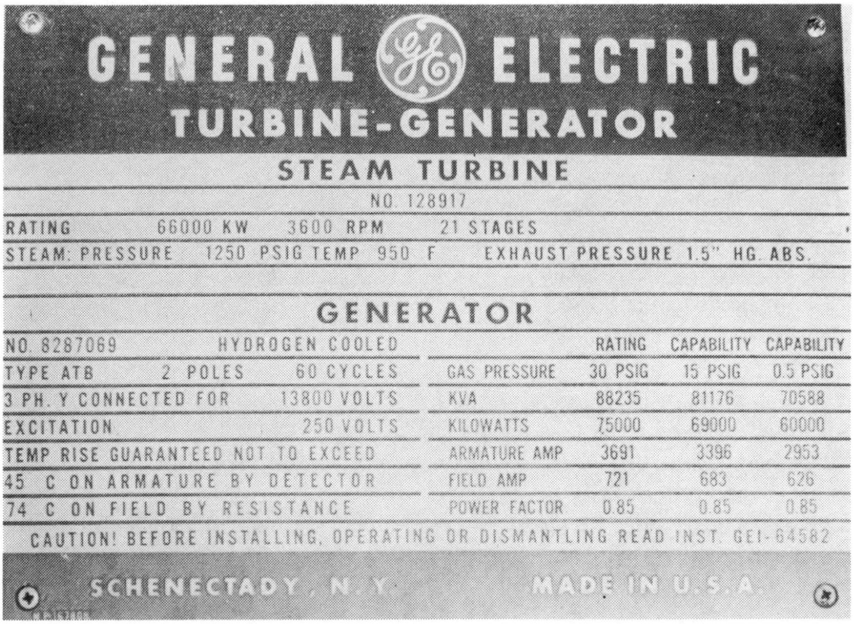
GENERAL ELECTRIC
TURBINE-GENERATOR
STEAM TURBINE
NO. 128917
RATING 66000 KW 3600 RPM 21 STAGES
STEAM: PRESSURE 1250 PSIG TEMP 950 F EXHAUST PRESSURE 1.5" HG. ABS.
GENERATOR
NO. 8287069 HYDROGEN COOLED
RATING CAPABILITY CAPABILITY
TYPE ATB 2 POLES 60 CYCLES
GAS PRESSURE 30 PSIG 15 PSIG 0.5 PSIG
3 PH. Y CONNECTED FOR 13800 VOLTS
KVA 88235 81176 70588
EXCITATION 250 VOLTS
KILOWATTS 75000 69000 60000
TEMP RISE GUARANTEED NOT TO EXCEED
ARMATURE AMP 3691 3396 2953
45 C ON ARMATURE BY DETECTOR
FIELD AMP 721 683 626
74 C ON FIELD BY RESISTANCE
POWER FACTOR 0.85 0.85 0.85
CAUTION! BEFORE INSTALLING, OPERATING OR DISMANTLING READ INST. GEI-64582
SCHENECTADY, N.Y.
MADE IN U.S.A.

FIGURE 1–8
Nameplate data for a commercial three-phase alternator. (Courtesy of General Electric Co.)

Commercial power systems use many three-phase alternators connected in parallel to supply regional load requirements. Industrial loads represent a large portion of the total load on our power systems. Due to the vast loads to be met by power systems, generators have high power ratings. Nameplate data for a commercial three-phase alternator are shown in Figure 1–8. Note the large quantities for each of the nameplate ratings.

DIRECT-CURRENT SOURCES

Direct current is a rather common source of energy for many industrial electronic systems. It is, however, not very readily available for industrial applications. Alternating current is the most abundant source of electrical energy delivered to an industrial facility. It must therefore be changed to a usable form of dc. The process of changing ac to dc is called *rectification*. In the past, rectification was largely achieved by vacuum tubes, gaseous tubes, mercury pool devices, and metal-plated rectifiers. By modern-day standards, these devices are considered to be somewhat inefficient. Rectification is largely achieved today by silicon diodes. Most power supplies are classified as rectified sources of energy.

The rectification process is quite varied and can be used in a variety of applications depending on the system. First, it can be supplied by either a single- or three-phase source. Second, it can utilize only half of the ac wave form or both alternations of the wave form. Half-wave rectification is the easiest to obtain

but has problems with efficiency and filtering. Full-wave rectification is somewhat more complex but has improved efficiency and produces a purer form of dc output. Current and voltage regulation is also an important consideration in dc power supplies. As a rule, most dc power sources of the industrial type are achieved by rectification.

Single-phase Rectification

The simplest system for converting alternating current to direct current is single-phase rectification. A single-phase rectifier changes alternating current to pulsating direct current. This process can be accomplished by using either semiconductors, vacuum tubes, gaseous tubes, or rotary converters. The most common and economical method in industry today is the use of low-cost silicon rectifiers. Since semiconductors are so prevalent in industry today, it is desirable to review the action of a semiconductor diode before we look at specific rectifier circuits.

Semiconductor Diode

We know that certain materials (conductors) conduct electrical current easily and other materials (insulators) do not. Between these two extremes are other materials that are neither good conductors nor good insulators. These materials, such as silicon and germanium, have characteristics between those of conductors and insulators.

Silicon and germanium are crystalline materials whose electrical characteristics can easily be altered in the manufacturing process. Elements called impurities are added to pure silicon or germanium to form either *n*-type or *p*-type materials. These materials are used in various combinations to form many types of semiconductors, such as diodes, transistors,

silicon-controlled rectifiers, triacs, and diacs. An *n*-type material possesses an abundance of electrons or negative charge carriers that do not take part in covalent bonding. A *p*-type material has an excess of positive charge carriers or holes that are not influenced by covalent bonding. By controlling the impurities added to silicon, these conditions can be altered.

The most basic semiconductor device is the diode, which performs the function of rectification. A diode is merely a *pn* junction device formed by adjacent *p*- and *n*-type materials, as shown in Figure 1–9(A). The junction formed by the adjacent *p*- and *n*-type materials allows current to pass in one direction but offers a high resistance to current in the other direction. This device is called a *junction diode*. Some *pn* junction diodes are shown in Figure 1–9(C).

The current carriers of a *pn* junction diode are in a state of equilibrium when an external potential is not applied. It is possible that, due

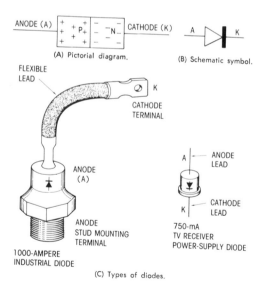

FIGURE 1–9
PN junction diodes.

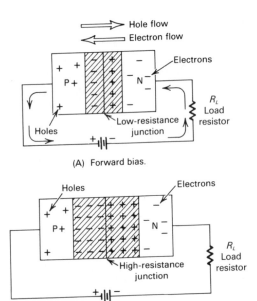

(A) Forward bias.

(B) Reverse bias.

FIGURE 1–10
Forward and reverse bias of a *pn* junction diode.

to temperature, some electrons will cross the junction from the *n*-type region to the *p*-type region. Likewise, some holes will diffuse from the *p*-type region to the *n*-type region. After this diffusion has taken place, an electrical barrier is developed between the two regions. Thus the further movement of charge carriers is prohibited and the diode is in a state of equilibrium.

In an electronic power supply, diodes are connected to an ac source of electrical energy. The instantaneous polarity of the potential connected to each terminal of the diode determines the action performed by the diode. To best see the basic operation of a rectifier, a simple dc circuit is connected to a silicon diode. Figure 1–10 shows a battery used as the energy source and a resistor as the load device. The polarity of the battery is used to bias the diode.

With the positive battery terminal connected to the *p*-type material and the negative battery terminal connected to the *n*-type material, the diode is said to be *forward biased*. During forward bias, as shown in Figure 1–10(A), a low-resistance *pn* junction is developed. The low-resistance junction permits electrons in the *n*-type material to drift into the *p* region since they are attracted by the positive terminal of the battery. Likewise, holes drift in the opposite direction into the *n* region since they are attracted by the negative battery terminal. The continuous movement of electrons and holes constitutes an electrical current when a diode is forward biased.

If we reverse the battery polarity, as shown in Figure 1–10(B), the diode is said to be *reverse biased*. Electrons in the *n*-type material are pulled away from the junction by the positive battery terminal, and holes are drawn away from the junction by the negative terminal of the battery. The area near the junction develops an electrical barrier that blocks the movement of charge carriers. Only a very slight current, which is barely measurable, flows in the reverse-biased condition. Since the *pn* diode conducts while forward biased and does not conduct while reverse biased, it exhibits the properties of a rectifier.

Single-phase, Half-wave Rectification

A single-phase, half-wave rectifier circuit, shown in Figure 1–11, converts an alternating current into a pulsating direct current. Let us assume that during the positive alternation of the ac cycle the anode of the diode is positive. The diode will then conduct since it is forward biased and the junction resistance is low. The positive alternation of the ac will then appear across the load device (represented by a resistor).

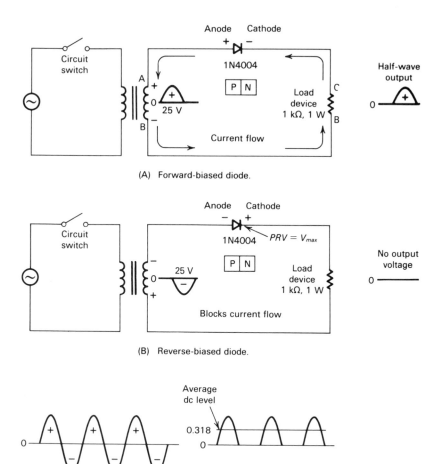

(A) Forward-biased diode.

(B) Reverse-biased diode.

(C) Input/output voltage waveforms

FIGURE 1–11
Single-phase, half-wave rectifier circuit.

During the negative alteration of the ac cycle, the anode of the diode becomes negative. The diode is now reverse biased and no significant current will flow through the load device. Therefore, no voltage will appear across the load. The input and resulting output wave forms of the half-wave rectifier circuit are shown in Figure 1–11(C). The pulsating direct current of the output has an average dc level. The average value of the pulsating dc produced by single-phase, half-wave rectification is expressed as

$$V_{dc} = 0.318 \times V_{max}$$

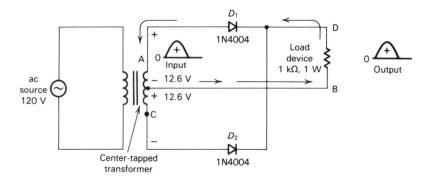

(A)   Diode D_1 forward biased.

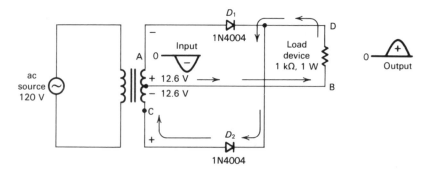

(B)   Diode D_2 forward biased.

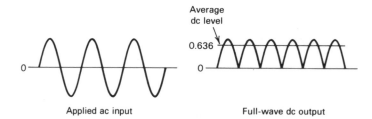

(C)   Input/output voltage waveforms

FIGURE 1–12
Single-phase, full-wave rectifier circuit.

where

V_{dc} = average value of rectified voltage

V_{max} = peak (maximum) value of applied ac voltage

Certain diode ratings should be considered for half-wave rectifier circuits. The maximum forward current (I_{max}) is the largest current that can flow through the diode while it is forward biased without damaging the device. The peak

inverse voltage (p_{iv}) or peak reverse voltage (p_{rv}) is the maximum voltage across the diode while it is reverse biased. For the half-wave rectifier, the maximum voltage developed across the diode is V_{max} of the applied ac. As shown in the preceding formula, the p_{rv} of a diode used in a half-wave circuit must be much larger than the dc voltage developed.

Single-phase, Full-wave Rectification

To obtain a purer form of dc energy, it is possible to improve on half-wave rectification systems. Figure 1–12 shows a single-phase, full-wave rectifier circuit that uses two diodes and produces a dc output voltage during each alternation of the ac input. The rectified output of the full-wave rectifier has twice the dc voltage level of the half-wave rectifier.

The full-wave rectifier utilizes a center-tapped transformer to transfer ac source voltage to the diode rectifier circuit. During the positive alternation of the ac source voltage, the instantaneous charges on the transformer secondary are as shown in Figure 1–12(A). The peak voltage (V_{max}) is developed across each half of the transformer secondary. At this time, diode D_1 is forward biased and diode D_2 is reverse biased. Therefore, conduction occurs from the center tap, through the load device, through D_1, and back to the outer terminal of the transformer secondary. The positive half-cycle is developed across the load as shown.

During the negative alternation of the ac source voltage, diode D_1 is reverse biased and diode D_2 is forward biased by the instantaneous charges shown in Figure 1–12(B). The current path is from the center tap, through the load device, through D_2, and back to the outer terminal of the transformer secondary. The negative alternation is also produced across the load, developing a full-wave output as illustrated in the waveforms in Figure 1–12(C).

Each diode in a full-wave rectifier circuit must have a p_{rv} rating of twice the value of the peak voltage developed at the output, since twice the peak voltage $(2V_{max})$ is present across the diode when it is reverse biased. The average voltage for a full-wave rectifier circuit is

$$V_{dc} = 2(0.318 \times V_{max})$$
$$= 0.636 \times V_{max}$$

This type of rectifier circuit produces twice the dc voltage output of a half-wave rectifier circuit. Its construction requires a center-tapped transformer and two diodes that have a p_{rv} rating of twice the peak value of applied ac voltage.

Single-phase Bridge Rectification

One disadvantage of the full-wave rectifier discussed previously is the requirement of a center-tapped transformer. To overcome this disadvantage, four diodes can be used to form a full-wave bridge rectifier as shown in Figure 1–13. In addition, the diode p_{rv} rating is only required to be the peak output voltage value (V_{max}).

During the operation of a bridge rectifier, two diodes are forward biased during each alternation of the ac input. When positive alternation occurs, as shown in Figure 1–13(A), diodes D_1 and D_3 are forward biased, while diodes D_2 and D_4 are reverse biased. This biasing condition is due to the instantaneous charges occurring during the positive alternation. The conduction path is from the instantaneous negative side of the ac source, through diode D_3, through the load device, through diode D_1, and back to the instantaneous positive side of the ac source.

During the negative alternation of the ac in-

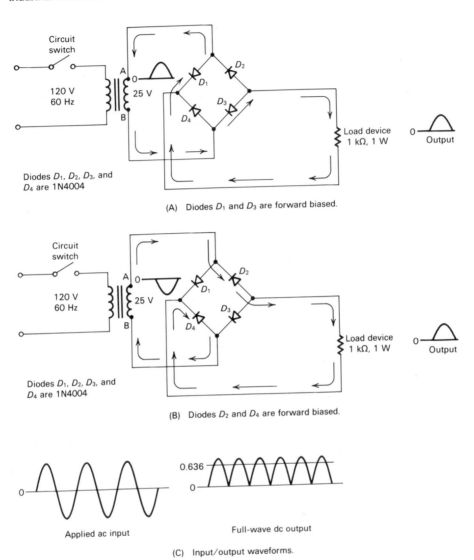

(A) Diodes D_1 and D_3 are forward biased.

(B) Diodes D_2 and D_4 are forward biased.

(C) Input/output waveforms.

FIGURE 1–13
Single-phase, full-wave bridge rectifiers.

put, diodes D_2 and D_4 are forward biased, while diodes D_1 and D_3 are reverse biased. Conduction occurs, as is shown in Figure 1–13(B), from the instantaneous negative side of the source, through D_2, through the load device, through D_4, and back to the instantaneous positive side of the ac source. Since a voltage is developed across the load device during both half-cycles of the ac input, a full-wave output is produced, as shown in Figure

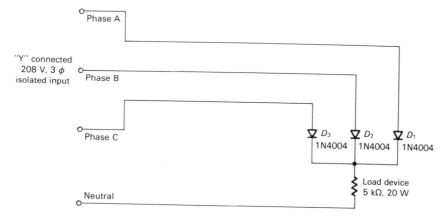

(A)   Schematic diagram.

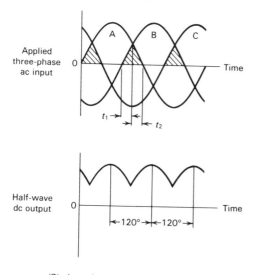

(B)   Input/output voltage waveforms.

FIGURE 1–14
Three-phase, half-wave rectifier circuit.

Three-phase, Half-wave Rectification

Most industries are supplied with three-phase alternating current. Therefore, due to the inherent advantages of three-phase power, it is beneficial to use three-phase rectifier circuits to supply dc voltage for industrial use. Single-phase rectifier circuits are ordinarily used where small amounts of dc power are required. To supply large amounts of dc power for industrial requirements, a three-phase rectifier circuit, such as that shown in Figure 1–14, could be employed. Three-phase rectifier circuits produce a purer dc voltage output than single-phase rectifier circuits do, thus wasting less power.

Figure 1–14(A) shows a three-phase, half-wave rectifier circuit that does not use a transformer. Phases A, B, and C of the wye-connected, three-phase source supply voltage to the anodes of diodes D_1, D_2, and D_3. The load device is connected between the cathodes of the diodes and the neutral of the wye-connected source. When phase A is at its peak positive value, maximum conduction occurs through diode D_1, since it is forward biased.

1–13(C), that is similar to that of the full-wave rectifier discussed previously. For high values of dc output voltage, the use of a bridge rectifier is desirable since the diode p_{rv} rating is one-half that of other single-phase, full-wave rectification methods.

No conduction occurs through D_1 during the negative alternation of phase A. The other diodes operate in a similar manner, conducting during the positive ac input alternation and not conducting during the associated negative ac alternation. In a sense, this circuit combines three single-phase, half-wave rectifiers to produce a half-wave dc output, as shown in Figure 1–14(B). Of course, the voltages appearing across the diodes are 120° out of phase. There is a period of time during each ac cycle when the positive alternations overlap one another, as shown in the shaded areas of the diagram. During overlap time period t_1, the phase A voltage is more positive than the phase B voltage, whereas during the t_2 interval, phase B is more positive. Diode D_1 will conduct until time period t_1 ends; then D_2 will conduct beginning at the end of t_1 until the next area of overlapping is reached.

Note that the voltage across the load device rises to a peak value twice during each phase alternation of the ac input voltage. These peaks are 120° apart. Since the dc output voltage never falls to zero, less ac ripple is present, which results in a purer form of dc than single-phase rectifiers produce. The average dc output voltage (V_{dc}) is expressed as

$$V_{dc} = 0.831 \times V_{max}$$

which compares very favorably with single-phase, full-wave rectifier circuits.

A disadvantage of this type of three-phase rectifier circuit is that the ac lines are not isolated. This lack of isolation, which is a direct connection to the ac lines, could be a hazardous safety factor. To overcome this disadvantage, a transformer can be used, as shown in Figure 1–15, to form a similar three-phase, half-wave rectifier. The secondary voltage can either be increased or decreased by the proper selection of the transformer. This will permit a variety of different values to be made available. The circuit illustrated uses a delta-to-wye connected transformer. The operation of this circuit is identical to that of the three-phase, half-wave circuit previously discussed; however, line isolation has been accomplished.

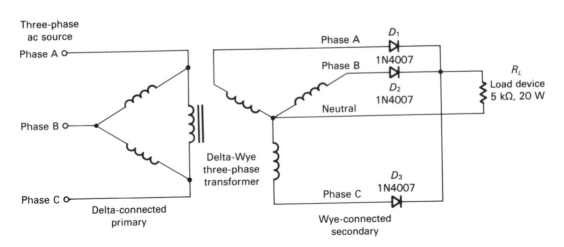

FIGURE 1–15
Three-phase, half-wave rectifier circuit using a transformer.

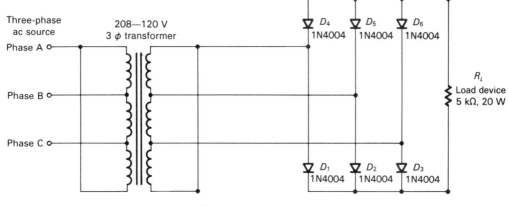

(a) Schematic diagram.

Three-phase, Full-wave Rectification

The full-wave counterpart of the three-phase, half-wave rectifier circuit is shown in Figure 1–16(A). This type of circuit is popular for many industrial applications. Six rectifiers are required for operation of the circuit. The anodes of D_4, D_5, and D_6 are connected together at point A, while the cathodes of D_1, D_2, and D_3 are connected together at point B. The load device is connected across these two points. The three-phase ac lines are connected to the anode–cathode junctions of D_1 and D_4, D_2 and D_5, and D_3 and D_6. This circuit does not require the neutral line of the three-phase source; therefore, a delta-connected source could be used.

The resulting dc output voltage of the three-phase, full-wave rectifier circuit is shown in Figure 1–16(B). The operation of the circuit is similar to a single-phase bridge rectifier in many respects. At any single instant of time along the three-phase ac input cycle, the anode voltage of one of the diodes is more positive than all others, while the cathode voltage of another diode is more negative than all others. These two diodes will then form the conduc-

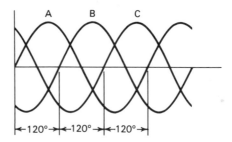

Applied three-phase ac input

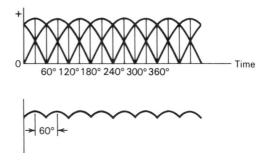

Full-wave dc output

(b) Input/output voltage waveforms.

FIGURE 1–16
Three-phase, full-wave rectifier circuit.

(A) Physical appearance.

(B) Schematic symbol.

(C) Basic SCR circuit.

FIGURE 1–17
Silicon-controlled rectifier.

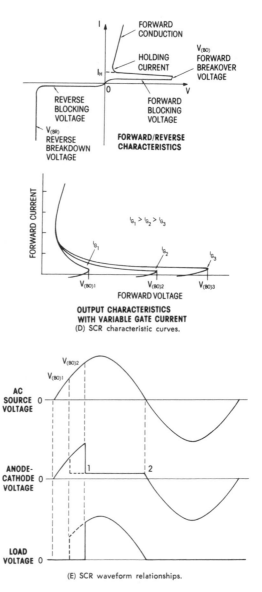

FORWARD/REVERSE
CHARACTERISTICS

OUTPUT CHARACTERISTICS
WITH VARIABLE GATE CURRENT
(D) SCR characteristic curves.

(E) SCR waveform relationships.

tion path for that time period. This conducting action is similar to a bridge rectifier, since two diodes conduct during a time interval. Each rectifier in this circuit conducts during one-third of an ac cycle (120°). Peak positive dc output voltage occurs during every 60° of the three-phase ac input.

Three-phase Rectification Using SCRs

The rectification circuits previously discussed have no means of controlling the output voltage and current levels. In the circuit shown in Figure 1–17, silicon-controlled rectifiers

(SCRs) are used in place of semiconductor diode rectifiers. The conduction time of a silicon-controlled rectifier can be varied to control dc output voltage and current levels.

The use of an SCR as a controlled rectifying device is illustrated in Figure 1–18. The SCR conducts when its forward breakover voltage (V_{BO}) is reached. The V_{BO} is determined by the gate control circuit. When the SCR conducts, current flows through the load device as shown in Figure 1–18(D). When the ac source voltage level drops to that shown at point 2 (holding current level), the SCR turns off and remains off during the negative half-cycle of the ac input.

Voltage is developed across the load only from point 1 to point 2 in Figure 1–18(E). When the gate control circuit is used to change the V_{BO} value, the result is to change the conduction time of the SCR, as shown by the dotted lines in Figure 1–18(E). The dotted lines illustrate the effect of a reduced V_{BO} on the anode–cathode voltage of the SCR and the corresponding voltage developed across the load.

Similar rectifying action can be accomplished by using gaseous thyratron tubes in place of SCRs.

To control the conduction time of the SCRs of the three-phase rectifier, a phase-shift network is used. In Figure 1–17, R_1C_1, R_2C_2, and R_3C_3 are identical RC phase-shifting networks. The three rheostats are ganged together so that control is accomplished by varying only one knob. The conduction time of the circuit is increased by increasing the resistance of the rheostats. Operationally, this circuit is the same as the three-phase, half-wave rectifier discussed previously. However, the dc output can be easily controlled by varying the rheostat setting.

Direct-current Filtering Methods

The pulsating direct current produced by both single- and three-phase rectifier circuits is not pure direct current. A certain amount of alternating-current ripple is evident in each type of

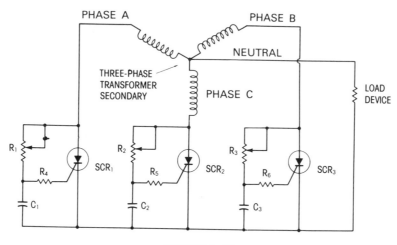

FIGURE 1–18
Three-phase, half-wave rectifier circuit using SCRs.

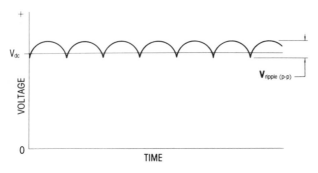

FIGURE 1–19
Rectifier output voltage.

rectifier. For many applications, a smooth dc output voltage with the ac ripple removed is required. Circuits used to remove ac variations of rectified direct current are *filter* circuits.

The output of a rectifier has a dc value and an ac ripple value as shown in Figure 1–19. To gain a relative index of the amount of ac variation, the ripple factor of the output wave form of a rectifier can be determined by

$$r = \frac{V_{r\ (rms)}}{V_{dc}}$$

where

r = ripple factor

$V_{r\ (rms)}$ = rms value of the ac component

V_{dc} = average value of the rectified dc voltage

Another index used to express the amount of ac variation in the output of a rectifier is the percentage of ripple. Ripple percentage can be determined by

$$\%\ ripple = \frac{V_{r\ (rms)}}{V_{dc}} \times 100$$

A full-wave rectified voltage has less percentage of ripple than does a half-wave rectified voltage. When a dc supply must have a low amount of ripple, a full-wave rectifier circuit should be used.

Capacitor Filter

A simple capacitor filter can be used to smooth the ac ripple of a rectifier output. Figure 1–20 shows the result of adding a capacitor across the output of a 60-Hz, single-phase, full-wave bridge rectifier. The output wave form after the capacitor has been added is shown in Figure 1–20(C).

The ideal filtered dc voltage would have no ac ripple and a value equal to the peak voltage (V_{max}) from the rectifier output. Note in Figure 1–20(C) that the value of V_{dc} is approaching that of V_{max}. Compare this value to the full-wave rectified voltage of Figure 1–20(B). Note also that two time intervals are shown in Figure 1–20(C). Time period t_1 represents diode conduction, which charges the filter capacitor (C) to the peak rectified voltage (V_{max}). Time period t_2 is the time required for the capacitor to discharge through the load (R_L).

A different value of filter capacitor would result in a change in the rate of discharge. If C discharged a very small amount, the value of V_{dc} would be closer to the value of V_{max}. With light loads (high resistance), the capacitor filter

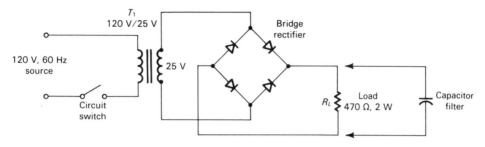

(A) Bridge rectifier circuit with filter capacitor.

will supply a high dc voltage with little ripple. However, with a heavy (low resistance) load connected, the dc voltage level will drop due to a greater ripple. The increased ripple is caused by the lower resistance discharge path for the filter capacitor. The effect of a heavier load on the filter capacitor is shown in Figure 1–20(D).

By utilizing the values indicated on the wave forms of Figure 1–20, it is possible to express V_{dc} and $V_{r \text{ (rms)}}$ as

$$V_{dc} = V_{max} - \frac{V_{r \text{ (p-p)}}}{2}$$

$$V_{r \text{ (rms)}} = \frac{V_{r \text{ (p-p)}}}{2\sqrt{3}}$$

We can also express the amount of ripple of a 60-Hz, full-wave filter-capacitor circuit with a light load as

$$V_{r \text{ (rms)}} = \frac{2.4 I_{dc}}{C}$$

or $$V_{r \text{ (rms)}} = \frac{2.4}{R_L C}$$

where

I_{dc} = load current in milliamperes

C = filter capacitor value in microfarads

R_L = load resistance in kilohms

(B) Full-wave output waveform with no filter capacitor.

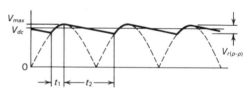

(C) Full-wave output waveform with filter capacitor across load.

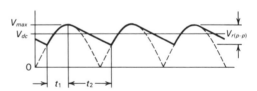

(D) Full-wave output waveform with filter capacitor across heavier (lower resistance) load.

FIGURE 1–20
Filter capacitor operation.

The average dc voltage output can be expressed as

$$V_{dc} = V_{max} - \frac{4.16 I_{dc}}{C}$$

Again, the value of V_{dc} is for a 60-Hz, full-

wave filter-capacitor circuit with a light load.

With a heavier load (lower resistance) connected to the filter circuit, more current (I_{dc}) is drawn. As I_{dc} increases, V_{dc} decreases. However, if the value of filter capacitor C is made larger, the value of V_{dc} becomes closer to that of V_{max}. The value of C for a 60-Hz, full-wave rectifier can be determined by using the equation

$$C = \frac{2.4I_{dc}}{V_{r\,(rms)}}$$

It should be pointed out, however, that as the value of C increases the peak value of the current through the diodes will also increase. There is, therefore, a practical limit for the value of C that is reflected in the foregoing equation.

The filter capacitor produces a high dc voltage with low ac ripple for light loads. However, its major disadvantages are higher ripple and lower V_{dc} at heavier loads, poor voltage regulation, and high peak current through the diodes.

RC Filter

It is possible to improve on the previous filter circuit by using an RC filter. Figure 1–21 shows an RC filter stage. This filter has lower ripple than a capacitor filter does, but it has a lower average dc voltage due to the voltage

dropped across R_1. The purpose of R_1 and C_2 is to add another filter network, which further reduces the ripple. This circuit also operates best with light loads connected. It is possible to have many stages of RC filters to further reduce ac ripple.

Pi-type Filter

The use of a resistor (R_1) in the RC filter is not desirable in many cases since it reduces the average dc output of the circuit. To compensate for the dc voltage reduction, a pi (π) type of filter can be used. Figure 1–22 shows this type of filter. The advantage of the choke coil (L_1) over the resistor (R_1) of the RC filter is that it offers only a small dc series resistance, but its ac impedance is much larger. Therefore, it passes dc and blocks the ac component of the rectified voltage. Several sections of this type of filter can also be used to further reduce ac ripple.

Voltage-multiplier Circuits

The purpose of a voltage multiplier circuit is to increase the value of rectified dc voltage output applied to a load. Voltage-multiplier circuits are modifications of filter circuits. The applications of these circuits are limited in industry; however, specific types of equipment use voltage-multiplier circuits.

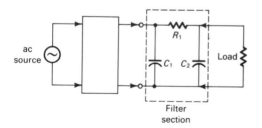

FIGURE 1–21
RC filter circuit.

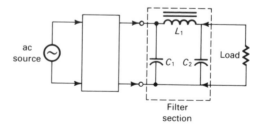

FIGURE 1–22
Pi-type filter circuit.

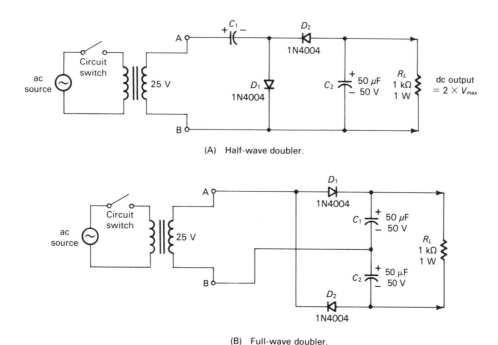

(A) Half-wave doubler.

(B) Full-wave doubler.

FIGURE 1–23
Voltage-doubler circuits.

The basic voltage-multiplier circuits are the voltage doublers shown in Figure 1–23. In the half-wave doubler circuit, shown in Figure 1–23(A), when point A has an instantaneous positive charge, diode D_1 will conduct and diode D_2 will be reverse biased. Capacitor C_1 will charge to the peak rectified voltage (V_{max}). The right side of capacitor C_1 will obtain a positive charge. During the next half-cycle of ac input, the instantaneous polarities will be reversed, placing point B at a positive potential. Diode D_2 will now conduct while D_1 will be reverse biased, placing a charge on capacitor C_2 equal to V_{max}. During the next half-cycle of ac input, the charge on capacitor C_1 will accumulate on capacitor C_2 by discharging through D_2. Also during this half-cycle, capacitor C_2 will discharge through the load. The sum of the voltages accumulated on C_2 will be equal to $2V_{max}$.

The output is similar to a half-wave rectified wave form that has a simple capacitor filter. The p_{rv} rating of the diode must be $2V_{max}$ in value.

The operation of the full-wave voltage double of Figure 1–23(B) is similar to the half-wave doubler. When point A has a positive potential, diode D_1 will conduct, allowing C_1 to charge to the value of V_{max}. The next half-cycle of ac input will place an instantaneous positive charge on point B. Diode D_2 will then conduct, charging capacitor C_2. With no load connected, the dc voltage at the output terminals is $2V_{max}$. The p_{rv} rating of the diodes must also be $2V_{max}$. More sections of these diode–capacitor circuits can be connected together to form voltage-tripler or voltage-quadrupler circuits. Extremely high dc voltages can be produced in this way.

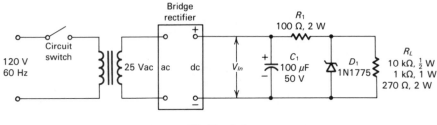

(A)   Circuit diagram.

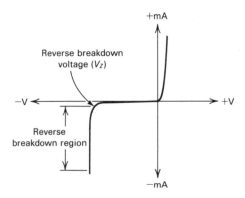

(B)   Zener diode characteristic curve.

FIGURE 1–24
Zener-diode regulator.

Direct-current Regulation Methods

The concept of voltage regulation can best be understood by referring to the formula

$$VR = \frac{V_{NL} - V_{FL} \times 100}{V_{FL}}$$

where

VR = voltage regulation in percent

V_{NL} = no-load terminal voltage

V_{FL} = rated full-load terminal voltage

In an ideally regulated circuit, V_{NL} would equal V_{FL}.

In all types of power supplies that convert ac to dc, the dc output levels are affected by variations in the load. Lower percentage values, approaching 0%, indicate better regulation. For instance, power supplies are capable of having a voltage regulation of less than 0.01%, which means that the value of the load has little effect on the dc output voltage produced. A well-regulated dc power supply is necessary for many industrial applications.

Zener Diode Regulators

A simple voltage regulator circuit uses a zener diode as shown in Figure 1–24. This circuit consists of a series resistor (R_1) and a zener diode (D_1) connected to the output of a rectifier

FIGURE 1–25
Series transistor voltage regulator.

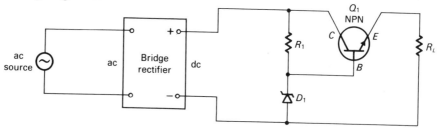

circuit. We should review zener diode operation before discussing the circuit operation.

Zener diodes are similar to *pn* junction diodes when they are forward biased. When reversed biased, no conduction takes place until a specific value of reverse breakdown voltage (or zener voltage) is reached. The zener diode is designed so that it will operate in the reverse breakdown region of its characteristic curve [see Figure 1–24(B)]. The reverse breakdown voltage is predetermined by the manufacturer. When used as a voltage regulator, the zener diode is reverse biased so that it will operate in the breakdown region. In this region, changes in current through the diode have little effect on the voltage across it.

The constant-voltage characteristic of a zener diode makes it desirable for use as a regulating device. The circuit of Figure 1–24(A) is a zener-diode shunt regulator. The zener establishes a constant voltage across the load resistance within a range of rectified dc voltages and output load currents. Over this range, the voltage drop across the zener remains constant. The current flow through the zener (I_z) will vary to compensate for changes in load resistance, since $I_z = I_T - I_L$. Thus the output voltage will remain constant.

Transistor Voltage Regulators

An improvement over the zener-diode voltage regulator is a transistorized regulator such as the circuit of Figure 1–25. This regulator has

a transistor (Q_1) placed in series with the load device (R_L). Transistor Q_1 acts as a variable resistance to compensate for changes in input voltage. The collector–emitter resistance of Q_1 varies automatically with changes in the circuit conditions. The zener diode establishes the dc bias placed on the base of Q_1. When this circuit is operating properly, if the voltage across the load (R_L) increases, the rise in emitter voltage makes the base less positive. The current through Q_1 will then be reduced, which results in an increase in the collector–emitter resistance of Q_1. The increase in resistance will cause a larger voltage drop across Q_1, which will now compensate for the change in voltage across the load. Opposite conditions would occur if the load voltage were to decrease. Many variations of this circuit are used in regulated power supplies today.

Shunt transistor regulators are also used in dc power supplies. The circuit of Figure 1–26 is a shunt voltage regulator. Again, the zener diode (D_1) is used to establish a constant dc bias level. Therefore, voltage variations across the dc output will be sensed only by resistor R_2. If the dc output voltage rises, an increased positive voltage will be present at the base of Q_1. The increased forward bias on Q_1 will cause it to conduct more, which makes the base of Q_2 more positive. Transistor Q_2 will then conduct more heavily. Increased current flow through both transistors causes an increase in the voltage drop across R_1, which will then counterbalance the rise in output volt-

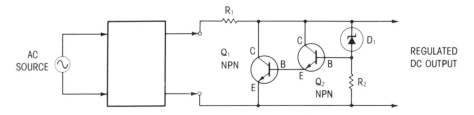

FIGURE 1–26
Shunt transistor voltage-regulator circuit.

age. Thus the dc output voltage will remain stabilized. Decreases in dc output voltage will cause the circuit action to reverse. Shunt transistor voltage-regulator circuits are used exten-sively in independent power supplies. Some examples of commercial regulated dc power supplies are shown in Figures 1–27 through 1–29.

IC Regulators

A rather recent innovation in power supply circuitry is the integrated-circuit (IC) regulator chip. This chip accepts an unregulated dc input and develops a regulated output. Some IC reg-

FIGURE 1–27
Regulated dc power supply. (Courtesy of Kepco, Inc.)

FIGURE 1–28
Microprocessor power supply. (Courtesy of Lambda Electronics)

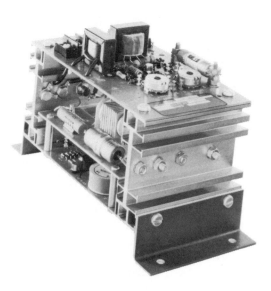

FIGURE 1–29
AC to dc power controller. (Courtesy of Honeywell, Inc.)

ulators are designed to deliver one fixed output voltage. A typical series of regulators is available in values of 5, 8, 12, 15, 18, and 24 V. Adjustable regulated voltage outputs can also be obtained with the addition of a few extra components. Current output of 1 ampere (A) or more can be delivered to a load by a representative chip of this type.

The internal structure of an IC regulator is somewhat complex. In general, it contains a series-pass transistor, reference voltage source, feedback amplifier, and short-circuit protection. Figure 1–30 shows a block diagram of the internal structure of a representative three-terminal regulator.

Operation of the three-terminal regulator is based on the applied input voltage and devel-

oped output voltage. Output voltage is compared with a reference voltage by a high-gain error amplifier. Any difference in voltage will be sensed by the error amplifier. The output of the error amplifier then controls conduction of the series-pass transistor. This transistor responds as a variable resistor. It changes inversely with the load current to maintain the output voltage at a constant value. An increase in output voltage would cause a corresponding increase in the conduction of the series-pass transistor. This in turn would cause more voltage drop across the series resistor, which would lower the output voltage. A decrease in output voltage would cause less conduction of the pass transistor. Reduced current through the series resistor will cause less voltage drop.

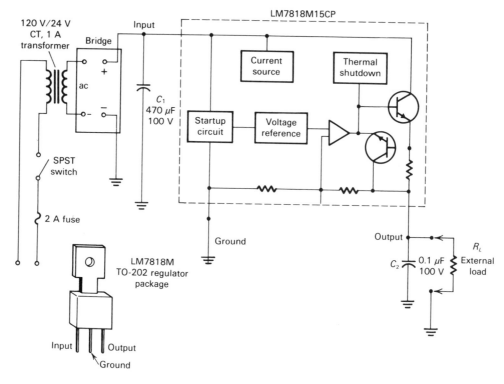

FIGURE 1–30
Three-terminal IC regulator.

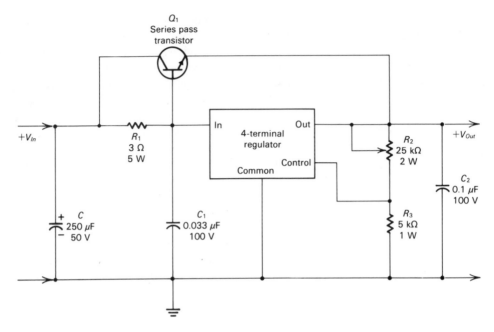

FIGURE 1–31
Four-terminal regulator with pass transistor.

The output voltage would therefore increase in value to compensate for the decrease in voltage.

Integrated-circuit regulators are usually equipped with some type of current overload protection. This function prevents damage to the series-pass transistor. The three-terminal regulator of Figure 1–30 has a thermal shutdown circuit. The temperature of the series-pass transistor is sensed. If its operating temperature exceeds 175°C, the regulator turns off. Removing an excessive load will lower the output current and permit the transistor to cool down. Operation will be restored when the temperature returns to normal. Protection of this type makes the chip virtually indestructible.

A variety of different IC regulators is now being used in industrial power supplies. Larger IC regulators with increased current-handling capabilities are readily available. In addition to

this, ICs are now designed for external series-pass transistor connections. The chip has a sensing circuit, reference source, and error amplifier. The IC simply achieves regulation by altering conduction of the series-pass transistor. Figure 1–31 shows the circuitry of a four-terminal regulator. This particular circuit has variable dc output capabilities with a current output of 30 A. For circuits that demand more current, the power dissipation (P_D) rating of the series-pass transistor can be increased. Regulators of this type can control extremely large amounts of current.

Switching Regulators

Switching power supplies provide a rather unusual method of dc voltage regulation. A simplification of the switching regulator power supply is shown in Figure 1–32. Note in this

circuit that all the unregulated dc must flow through the series-pass transistor. This transistor responds as a switch that turns on and off very rapidly. The dc output at this point has a *chopped* or square-wave characteristic. Chopped dc is then fed into a transformer that changes it to high-frequency ac. This ac is then applied into a second bridge rectifier, which produces the regulated dc output.

Operation of a switching regulator is controlled by a sensing circuit that detects a change in dc output voltage. An increase in the power supply load, caused by a decrease in resistance, normally reduces the output voltage.

This condition is detected immediately by the sensor circuit. The sensor then controls the frequency of the voltage-controlled oscillator (VCO). A decrease in voltage causes an increase in frequency. The VCO output is then applied to the base of the series-pass transistor. An increase in base frequency causes a corresponding increase in the chopped output. This in turn causes a corresponding increase in dc output to compensate for the change in load. The frequency of the chopping circuit normally operates at 20 kHz.

A decrease in the load, caused by less resistance, normally increases the output voltage.

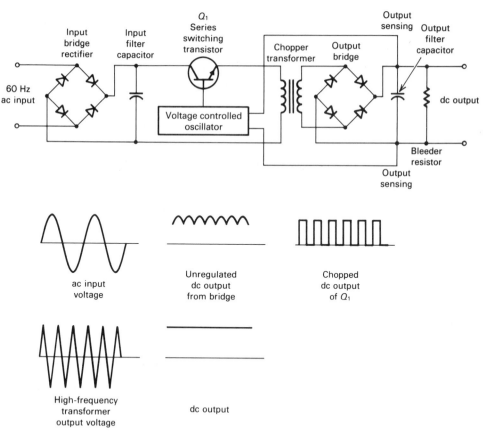

FIGURE 1–32
Switching regulated power supply.

To compensate for this, the increased output voltage is detected by the sensor. Its output is used to control the frequency of the VCO. An increase in output voltage causes a decrease in VCO frequency. Applied to the series-pass transistor, this causes a decrease in chopping rate. Lower frequency ac causes a corresponding reduction in dc output. In a sense, the dc output is regulated by the value of its chopping frequency.

Switching regulator power supplies are much more efficient than the conventional series-pass transistor voltage regulator. Less power, for example, is consumed by the series-pass transistor. In effect, the transistor does not produce as much heat during its operation. In addition, switching supplies are usually much smaller physically than the conventional regulated power supplies. Components operating at 20kHz are generally much smaller than those responding to 50 to 60 Hz. Switching power supplies are therefore particularly well suited for applications where compactness, efficiency, and moderately accurate regulation are required.

Switching power supplies have some disadvantages. For example, they produce more electrical and audible noise than a conventional power supply. In many applications, a great deal more filtering and shielding are needed when employing a switching supply. In addition, the switching supply is somewhat more costly to produce. In general, the advantages tend to outweigh the disadvantages. Today, high operational efficiency is of primary concern in selecting a power supply for a particular application.

QUESTIONS

1. What are the three most widely used electrical energy sources in an industrial system?

2. What three conditions must be met to convert mechanical energy into electrical energy?

3. Describe the rotating armature and rotating field methods of producing electrical energy.

4. Define voltage regulation of an alternator.

5. Define efficiency regulation of an alternator.

6. Make a sketch of the wye and delta systems for connecting three-phase alternator windings.

7. What are the voltage and current relationships in wye and delta systems?

8. What methods may be employed to convert alternating current to direct current?

9. Discuss the operation of a semiconductor diode.

10. Describe the following types of rectification systems:
    a. Single phase, half-wave
    b. Single phase, full wave
    c. Single phase, bridge
    d. Three phase, half-wave
    e. Three phase, full wave

11. What methods may be used to filter direct current?

12. What is a voltage multiplier?

13. What are some methods used for voltage regulation?

PROBLEMS

1. If the peak voltage of a 60-Hz ac generator is 170 V, what is the instantaneous voltage after a conductor has rotated 70°?

2. What is the instantaneous voltage after the

conductor in Problem 1 has rotated 140°? 220°? 310°?

3. At what speed must a two-pole ac alternator rotate in order to produce a frequency of 50 Hz?

4. What is the voltage regulation of a generator that has a full-load output of 240 V and a no-load output of 260 V?

5. What is the efficiency of a generator whose rated output is 60 kW when the input is 80 hp?

6. The phase voltage of a three-phase, wye-connected generator is 277 V. What is the line voltage?

7. If a wye-connected generator has a phase voltage of 120 V, what is the line voltage?

8. The phase current of a delta-connected generator is 82 A. What is the line current?

9. Three loads, each having a resistance of 10 ohms (Ω), are placed across the output of a wye-connected generator. The generator output is 480 V. Find the line current and total three-phase power.

10. Calculate the line current and total three-phase power for the generator of Problem 8 if it is delta connected.

11. What is the average value of dc output voltage of a half-wave rectified voltage of 20 V peak value?

12. If a 120-V (rms) voltage is rectified by a half-wave circuit, what is the equivalent output voltage before filtering?

13. What is the dc voltage obtained from a full-wave rectifier if the peak ac input is 169 V?

14. Calculate the ripple factor and percentage of ripple of a filtered rectifier circuit whose dc voltage is 20 V and ac ripple voltage is 1.5 V (rms).

15. The no-load voltage of a dc power supply is 160 V. The full-load voltage is 150 V. What is the voltage regulation?

16. What is the ripple voltage of a full-wave rectifier with a capacitor filter of 25 microfarads (μF) and a load current of 50 milliamperes (mA)?

17. In the circuit of Problem 16, if the peak ac voltage input is 150 V, what is the filtered dc voltage?

18. A three-phase, half-wave rectifier has an ac voltage input of 240 V (rms). What is the average dc voltage output?

ACTIVITIES

ACTIVITY 1–1: Half- and Full-wave Rectification

Objective: Construction of half-wave, full-wave, and bridge rectifier circuits, evaluation of each circuit, calculation of respective output voltages, and observation of wave forms.

Procedure:

1. Construct the half-wave rectifier circuit of Figure 1–11(A).

2. Turn on the circuit switch and measure the rms input at points *A–B*. Calculate the equivalent dc output for this circuit.

3. Measure and record the dc output across R_L or at points *C–B*.

4. With an oscilloscope, observe the wave forms at points *A–B* and *B–C*. Make a sketch of the observed wave forms. Record the amplitude of the ripple voltage.

5. Disconnect the circuit of Figure 1–11(A)

and connect the full-wave rectifier of Figure 1–12(A).

6. Turn on the circuit switch and measure the rms input at points A–B–C. Calculate the equivalent dc output for this circuit. Measure and record the dc output appearing at points D–B.

7. With an oscilloscope, observe the wave forms at points A–B, C–B, and D–B. Make a sketch of the observed wave forms and record the amplitude of the ripple voltage.

8. Disconnect the circuit and connect the bridge rectifier of Figure 1–13(A).

9. Turn on the circuit switch and measure the rms input at points A–B. Calculate the equivalent dc output for this circuit. Measure and record the dc output appearing at points D–B.

10. With an oscilloscope, observe the wave forms at points A–B and C–D. Make a sketch of the observed wave forms and record the amplitude of the ripple voltage.

11. Briefly explain the differences in the three rectifier circuits using your collected data and wave forms.

ACTIVITY 1–2: Three-phase, Half-wave Rectification

Objective: Construction of a three-phase, half-wave rectifier power supply and evaluation of the circuit.

Procedure:

1. Construct the three-phase, half-wave rectifier power supply of Figure 1–15. It is imperative that a three-phase isolation transformer be used in this circuit. The primary may be delta connected and the secondary wye connected. If possible, a variable three-phase ac should be used to reduce the input voltage.

2. Apply isolated three-phase ac to the circuit.

3. Measure and record the dc voltage across R_L.

4. Connect an oscilloscope across R_L and observe the wave form. Make a sketch of the wave form and indicate the value of the ripple.

5. Turn off the three-phase ac source and disconnect the voltage going to diode D_1. Turn on the ac and repeat steps 3 and 4.

6. Repeat step 5, but disconnect the voltage feeding both D_1 and D_2.

7. How does the output of a half-wave, three-phase power supply differ from that of a single-phase power supply?

ACTIVITY 1–3: Three-phase, Full-wave Rectification

Objective: Construction of a three-phase, full-wave rectifier power supply and evaluation of its output.

Procedure:

1. Construct the three-phase, full-wave rectifier power supply of Figure 1–16(A). It is imperative that a three-phase isolation transformer be used in his circuit. The transformer should be connected delta to delta. If at all possible, the ac input should be stepped down to a lower value.

2. Apply isolated three-phase ac to the circuit.

3. Measure and record the rectified dc across R_L.

4. Measure the phase-to-phase input voltage and calculate the dc output. How closely do the measured and calculated values compare?

5. Connect an oscilloscope across R_L and observe the wave form. Make a sketch of the wave form and indicate the value of the ripple.

6. Turn off the ac source and temporarily disconnect D_1. Turn on the source and again measure the dc output and observe the wave form across R_L.

7. Using the same procedure as in step 6, disconnect both D_1 and D_2. Measure and record the dc voltage across R_L and observe the wave form. Using the same procedure, disconnect D_1, D_2, and D_3. Measure and record the dc voltage across R_L and observe the wave form.

8. How does the output of a full-wave, three-phase power supply differ from that of a half-wave, three-phase power supply?

ACTIVITY 1–4: Filtering Circuits

Objective: Construction of a rectifier power supply and evaluation of different filter circuits.

Procedure:

1. Construct the full-wave bridge rectifier circuit of Figure 1–20(A). Connect a 470-Ω, 2-W resistor as the load.

2. Apply power to the circuit and turn on the circuit switch.

3. Measure and record the dc output voltage and load current.

4. Connect an oscilloscope across R_L and make a sketch of the observed wave form. Measure and record the ripple of the output.

5. Turn off the circuit switch. Connect a 100-μF, 50-V capacitor across RL. Be certain

to observe the polarity of C and dc source. Repeat the procedures in steps 3 and 4 for the C filter.

6. Turn off the circuit switch. Connect a CRC filter using a 100-μF, 50-V capacitor, 200-Ω, 2-W resistor, and 50-μF, 50-V capacitor. Repeat the procedures in steps 3 and 4 for the CRC filter.

7. Turn off the circuit switch. Connect a CLC filter using the same capacitors in step 6 with a 4-henry (H), 200-mA inductor in place of the 200-Ω resistor. Repeat steps 3 and 4 for the CLC filter.

8. Using collected data, evaluate the performance of the R, C, CRC, and CLC filter circuits.

ACTIVITY 1–5: Voltage-doubler Power Supplies

Objective: Construction and evaluation of half-wave and full-wave voltage-doubler power supplies.

Procedure:

1. Construct the half-wave voltage-doubler power supply of Figure 1–23(A).

2. Turn on the circuit switch; measure and record V_{RL} and I_L. With an oscilloscope, observe V_{RL} and make a sketch of the wave form.

3. Turn off the circuit switch and construct the full-wave voltage-doubler circuit of Figure 1–23(B).

4. Turn on the circuit switch, measure and record V_{RL} and I_L. With an oscilloscope, observe V_{RL} and make a sketch of the observed wave form.

5. Explain the difference between the two circuits of this activity.

ACTIVITY 1–6: Zener-diode Voltage Regulation

Objective: Construction of a zener-diode regulator and evaluation of its circuit operational characteristics.

Procedure:

1. Construct the zener-diode voltage-regulator circuit of Figure 1–24.

2. Connect a 10-kΩ, 0.5-W resistor as R_L.

3. Measure and record V_{in}, V_{RL}, I_z, and I_{RL}.

4. Turn off the circuit switch and exchange the 10-kΩ load resistor for a 1-kΩ, 1-W R_L. Apply power to the circuit and repeat step 3.

5. Turn off the circuit switch and exchange the 1-kΩ load resistor for a 270-Ω, 2-W R_L. Apply power to the circuit and repeat step 3.

6. Determine the percentage of regulation using the 10-kΩ as no load and the 270-Ω resistor as full load.

7. Explain how a zener diode achieves regulation.

ACTIVITY 1–7: Three-terminal IC Regulators

Objective: Construction of a three-terminal IC regulator and evaluation of the circuit's output.

Procedure:

1. Construct the IC regulator of Figure 1–30. It is imperative that the bridge, regulator IC, and filter C_2 be connected correctly or there will be some damage to the circuit or devices.

2. Energize the circuit and turn on the circuit switch. Use a 1-kΩ load initially.

3. Measure and record the voltage across R_L and the load current.

4. With an oscilloscope, observe the wave form across R_L. Make a sketch of the wave form and indicate the dc value and ac ripple.

5. Exchange the 1-kΩ, 0.5-W load with a 100-Ω, 5-W load.

6. Repeat steps 2 through 4 for the new R_L.

7. Exchange the 100-Ω load with a 10-Ω, 25-W load. Connect a voltmeter across R_L and turn on the circuit switch. This should cause thermal overload of the IC and cause it to shut down. Disconnect the 10-Ω load and connect the 100-Ω load again. After a short cooling down time, energize the circuit. How does it respond?

The word "transistor" was coined to describe the action of a transfer resistor developed by Walter H. Brattain and John Bardeen of Bell Telephone Laboratories in 1948. The transistor is capable of achieving amplification of an electrical signal by transferring it from a low-resistance to a high-resistance circuit. This device is primarily responsible for the solid-state electronics era that we are in today.

Since the invention of the original transistor on December 23, 1947, a variety of transistor-like devices has been developed. The earlier transistor, known as a point-contact device, is rarely used in contemporary circuits. The technology created by the device is, however, responsible for a wide range of new transistors, the operation of which is distinctly different from that of the original device. Three general classifications of transistors are used in industrial electronics circuits:

1. Bipolar junction transistors (BJT)

2. Junction field-effect transistors (JFET)

3. Insulated-gate field-effect transistors (IGFET)

These devices are all capable of signal gain or amplification and can be used as switches to turn a circuit on and off. Transistors are used independently in many circuit applications and are the construction basis of an integrated circuit.

2

AMPLITUDE CONTROL

Transistors

A major electronic control function that is designed to alter the size of a voltage or current signal as it passes through a system is called *amplitude control*. This type of control is primarily achieved by either active or passive devices. When the amplitude or magnitude of a signal is increased, it is said to have amplifi-

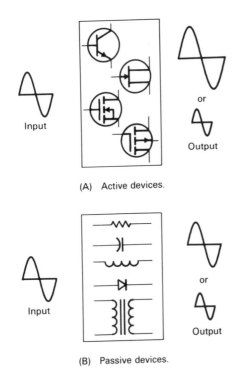

(A) Active devices.

(B) Passive devices.

FIGURE 2–1
Active–passive device control.

transformation process. When electric current passes through a resistor, a certain amount of it is changed into heat energy, which is a loss of system energy. Heat energy of this type cannot be effectively recovered and used by the system to do work. Amplitude control of this type has a rather low level of operational efficiency.

When electricity is applied to a capacitor, it causes an energy change to take place. In a passive device of this type, some of the applied energy is changed into electrostatic energy, which is stored between the plates of the capacitor. A small amount of heat energy is also developed by the dielectric material of the capacitor when it becomes charged. Stored electrostatic energy is normally released by a capacitor when the system is turned off. In an operating system, energy that is not recovered represents a system loss similar to the heat energy of a resistor.

Passing electric energy through an inductor also produces a loss of system energy. In this case, a major portion of the loss appears as electromagnetic energy. This energy is stored in the inductor's magnetic field. Not all energy of this type is released when the inductor is turned off. In addition, a small amount of heat energy is generated by the inductor's resistance. A combination of both heat and electromagnetic energy represents a loss to the regular system.

When passive devices are used in an electrical system to achieve attenuation, it is important to know the relationship of input and output characteristics. Inductors, capacitors, and resistors are commonly described as having *linear* characteristics. This means that a component value remains constant regardless of the voltage or current applied as long as ratings are not exceeded. When the input voltage applied to a passive device is doubled, its output will increase an equal amount. Ambient temperature and construction materials have

cation. Control of this type is accomplished by active devices. Passive devices, by comparison, only decrease the amplitude of an electrical signal. Passive devices are also called *attenuators* because they can only reduce signal amplitude. Figure 2–1 shows a comparison of active and passive control devices and functions.

Passive Device Control

If electrical energy is applied to a passive device, it will cause the signal to be reduced or attenuated to some extent according to its value. For this to occur, the control device must consume a certain amount of the applied energy. This means that a passive device performs a certain amount of work in this energy

some influence on the linear characteristics of a passive device.

A number of diode devices have passive characteristics very similar to those of resistors, capacitors, and inductors. These devices, however, only conduct an electric current effectively in one direction. Diodes are normally classified as *nonlinear* devices. Linear parts of the characteristic curve can be used quite effectively with the proper selection of components and operating voltages. Diodes are used more today as wave-shaping devices than in passive applications.

Active Device Control

If electrical energy is applied to an active device, it has the capability of accepting a very weak signal and using it to control power at a higher level. An amplitude control function called *amplification* can be achieved through the use of this device. The amount of amplification accomplished by an active device is called *gain*. Electronically, gain is the ratio of the output signal to the input signal. Transistors are widely used to achieve this function in industrial systems.

When an active device is used as an amplifier, its primary function is to accept a small input signal and cause a reasonable increase in its amplitude. Ideally, the output of an amplifier should reflect only a change in signal amplitude. Improper component selection, voltage values, or circuit design, however, may cause the output to be somewhat distorted. The amount of distortion permitted is based largely on the application of the amplifier.

For an active device to achieve power gain, it must have a source of operating energy and a signal to process. Typically, direct current is used as the operating energy source for this type of device. In a strict sense, an amplifier could be considered as a small electrical system achieving the control function of a larger system. In this regard, the amplifier must have an energy source, path, control, and load device to function properly. When an input signal is applied to an amplifier, it causes the operating energy source to change somewhat. A small change in input signal strength can cause a rather substantial change in the output signal. The input signal source may be either ac or dc and still be processed through the amplifier.

Small-signal Versus Large-signal Amplifiers

Practically all the active devices that achieve amplitude control can be classified as either small- or large-signal amplifiers. This particular classification usually indicates the location of the amplifier in the system. Initially, the input signal of a system is quite small and requires a great deal of amplification. Small-signal amplifiers are designed to accept a weak signal and amplify it to some predetermined value. Voltage gain is a primary function of the small-signal amplifier. As a rule, this refers to the total voltage change that takes place between the input and the output of the amplifier. An equation for voltage gain or amplification is

$$\text{Amplification voltage} = \frac{\text{output voltage}}{\text{input voltage}}$$

$$A_v = \frac{V_o}{V_{in}}$$

When uppercase letters, as in V_o/V_{in}, are used it usually denotes dc voltage values. AC voltages are expressed by lowercase letters, as in v_o/v_{in}. Small-signal amplifiers are generally capable of amplifying a wide range of signals.

A small-signal amplifier that produces an output current that is greater than the input is called a *current amplifier*. Bipolar transistors

FIGURE 2–2
Internal structure of a bipolar power
transistor. (Courtesy of General Electric Co.)

are capable of achieving current gain. Alpha and beta are used to describe the current-gain function of a specific transistor. Current amplification is dependent on the transistor and all its circuit components. Current amplification is expressed by the formula

$$\text{current amplification} = \frac{\text{output current}}{\text{current input}}$$

$$A_i = \frac{I_o}{I_{\text{in}}}$$

After a signal voltage or current value has been amplified, it can be used to control larger amounts of power. Large-signal amplifiers are primarily designed to achieve this system function. These devices are substantially larger in physical size and often include special heat-dissipating devices. Figure 2–2 shows the internal structure of a bipolar power transistor. This device is capable of controlling several amperes of collector current, as compared with the few milliamperes controlled by the small-signal transistor.

Large-signal amplifiers are more commonly called *power amplifiers*. Increased amounts of current are usually controlled by a power amplifier. Ordinarily, larger input voltages are needed to control an increased current flow. Power amplifiers must therefore be capable of

dissipating a great deal more heat than a small-signal amplifier. An expression of power amplification is given by the formula

$$\text{Power amplification} = \frac{\text{output power}}{\text{input power}}$$

$$A_p = \frac{P_o}{P_{\text{in}}}$$

Power amplification may also be expressed as the product of voltage and current. The formula is

$$\text{Power amplification} = \text{voltage amplification} \times \text{current amplification}$$

$$A_p = A_v \times A_i$$

The power amplification formula shows a rather interesting relationship for A_v and A_i. Both values do not need to be large in order to achieve power amplification. In some power amplifier circuits, large A_i values are developed with an A_v of less than 1. Essentially, this means that A_p must take into account the values of both A_v and A_i to be meaningful.

BIPOLAR JUNCTION TRANSISTORS

Today, industrial electronic systems employ several devices that are described by the term transistor. Each type of transistor has different characteristics and operational conditions that are used to distinguish it from others. In the first part of this discussion, we are concerned with the bipolar junction transistor. Structurally, this transistor is described as *bipolar* because it has two different current-carrier polarities. Holes are positive current carriers, whereas electrons are negative current carriers. Two distinct kinds of semiconductor crystals

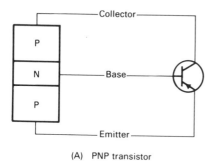

(A) PNP transistor

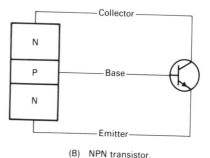

(B) NPN transistor.

FIGURE 2–3
PNP and *NPN* transistors.

are connected together by a common element. The structure of this device is similar to that of two diodes connected back to back, with one crystal being common to both junctions. The center material is usually made thinner than the two outside pieces. Figure 2–3 shows the crystal structure, element names, and schematic symbols of two distinct types of bipolar transistors.

Bipolar transistors are now available in a variety of package styles and enclosures. The outward appearance and internal structure of this device vary a great deal between different manufacturers. Figure 2–4 shows the structure of a plastic-encapsulated small-signal transistor. This type of packaging is widely used in industrial electronic systems.

A bipolar transistor is primarily used as an amplifying device that regulates the amount of current that passes through it. Current from the energy source enters the emitter, flows through the base region, and exits through the collector. Variations in collector current are usually identified as the output of a transistor. Collector current is controlled by a small change in base current. This relationship is described as *current gain* or *beta*. Expressed mathematically,

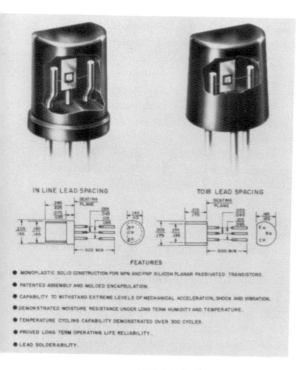

FIGURE 2–4
Internal workings of a plastic-encapsulated transistor. (Courtesy of General Electric Co.)

$$\text{Current gain} = \frac{\text{collector current}}{\text{base current}}$$

$$\text{(Beta)} = \frac{I_C}{\Delta I_B}$$

The Greek letter delta of this formula indicates a change value. This is used to denote the re-

sponse of a transistor when ac values are applied. Conditions of this type are called *dynamic* characteristics. Omission of the delta sign in a formula denotes dc or *static* operating conditions.

All the current entering a transistor at the emitter is identified as emitter current, or I_E. The collector current, or I_C, is always somewhat less than I_E. The difference between I_E and I_C is due to base current. Mathematically, this is

Base current (I_B) = emitter current

− collector current

$$I_B = I_E - I_C$$

Example 2–1: Determine the base current of a bipolar transistor with an I_E of 11 mA and an I_C of 10.95 mA.

Solution:

$$I_B = I_E - I_C$$

$$= 11 \text{ mA} - 10.95 \text{ mA}$$

$$= 0.05 \text{ mA} \quad \text{or} \quad 0.05 \times 10^{-3} \text{ A}$$

Npn Transistor Circuits

Figure 2–5 shows the circuit connections of a simple *npn* silicon transistor. Operation of this circuit is based on a forward-biased emitter–base junction and a reverse-biased collector. Forward biasing of the emitter–base junction is accomplished by connecting the negative side of the dc source to the emitter and the positive side through R_b to the base. Reverse biasing of the collector occurs when it is connected to the positive side of the source through resistor R_L. Collector current through R_L is controlled by the forward-bias voltage of the emitter–base junction.

In the operation of a single *pn* diode junction, forward biasing causes conduction and reverse biasing causes nonconduction. In a transistor, this rule does not apply directly because two junctions are involved. For example, when the emitter–base junction is forward biased, it causes a large amount of I_E to enter the base region. Reverse biasing of the base–collector junction would ordinarily restrict this current. But due to the thin base structure, I_E will immediately enter into the collector when it reaches the base area. Ultimately, this current passes through the collector and appears as collector current I_C or output current. Forward biasing of the emitter–base junction therefore alters or reduces the reverse biasing effect of the base–collector junction in normal transistor operation.

A transistor is primarily classified as a current-operating device. This means that the output or collector I_C will occur only when the emitter–base junction is forward biased and producing base current. When the base current ceases, collector current stops and the transistor becomes nonconductive. This condition is called *cutoff*. On the other hand, if an excessive amount of base current occurs, the transistor is driven into *saturation*. When this condition occurs, a further increase in I_B will not cause a corresponding change in I_C. When amplitude control is being achieved, a transistor is rarely operated in the saturation region. When a transistor is used as a switch, it usually operates in the saturation region.

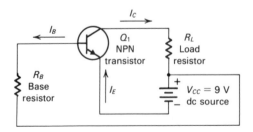

FIGURE 2–5
NPN transistor circuit.

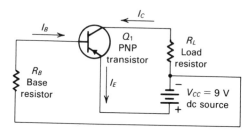

FIGURE 2–6
PNP transistor circuit.

Pnp Transistor Circuit _____

The transistor amplifier circuit of Figure 2–6 is a *pnp* counterpart of the previous *npn* circuit. The battery of this circuit is connected in a reverse direction in order to achieve proper biasing. Performance is basically the same as that of the *npn* circuit. Currents I_C, I_B, and I_E are represented in this diagram by arrows. The emitter current of this circuit still provides the largest current value. The composite of I_C plus I_B also equals I_E in this circuit.

Alpha–Beta Characteristics _____

When a transistor is developed, the manufacturer produces operating specifications and characteristics that are used to predict its performance. A typical family of collector curves is shown in Figure 2–7. The *x* axis or horizontal part of the graph shows the collector–emitter voltage, or V_{CE}. The *y* axis or vertical part of the graph represents different I_C values. Individual lines of the graph indicate different base current values. The zero I_B line is usually omitted because it represents the cutoff condition of operation.

A family of collector curves tells a great deal about the operation of a transistor. The values of I_C, V_{CE}, and I_B, for example, are all related. Assume now that the V_{CE} voltage of a

transistor is held at a constant value of 10 V. This is shown on the graph by an arrow extending up from the 10-V_{CE} point. A base current value of 20 μA will, for example, cause approximately 2.5 mA of I_C. This represents the current gain or *beta* of the transistor. Beta is the ratio of collector current to base current. This is demonstrated by the following example.

Example 2–2: Determine the beta for the indicated I_C and I_B values on the I_C–V_{CE} curves of Figure 2–7.

Solution:

$$\beta = \frac{I_C}{I_B} \text{ or } \frac{2.5 \text{ mA}}{20 \text{ μA}}$$

$$= 0.125 \times 10^2$$

$$= 125$$

The beta of a transistor is not represented by a specific unit. It is based on a ratio of two

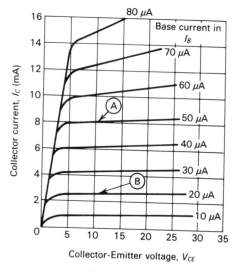

FIGURE 2–7
Family of I_C/V_{CE} characteristic curves for a transistor.

independent current values. Typical values of beta can be observed at various points on the family of curves. As a general rule, small-signal transistors have beta values of 40 to 300. Power transistors have values in the range of 10 to 30.

Beta can also be used to determine I_C or I_B values. I_C can be determined by multiplying beta and I_B. By transposing this formula, I_B can be determined by dividing I_C by beta. These expressions are

$$I_C = \beta \times I_B$$

$$I_B = \frac{I_C}{\beta}$$

The collector curves of a transistor can also be used to determine a characteristic known as *alpha*. This characteristic compares the values of collector current with emitter current. Alpha is expressed by the formula:

$$\alpha = \frac{\text{collector current}}{\text{emitter current}}$$

$$= \frac{I_C}{I_E}$$

To show the relationship of alpha on a characteristic curve, refer to point A of the I_C curves of Figure 2–7. Note that this point indicates the intersection of 10 V_{CE}, 8 mA of I_C, and 50 μA of I_B. In Example 2–1, we indicated that $I_B = I_E - I_C$. By transposing this expression, we find that $I_E = I_B + I_C$. To determine the alpha of a particular transistor, we need to know I_C and I_E values. This is determined by Example 2–3.

Example 2–3:   Referring to the I_C family of curves in Figure 2–7, determine the I_E and alpha for transistor operation at reference point A. At point A, $I_C = 8$ mA and $I_B = 50$ μA.

Solution:

$$I_E = I_B + I_C$$

$$= 50 \text{ μA} + 8 \text{ mA}$$

$$= 0.05 \text{ mA} + 8 \text{ mA}$$

$$= 8.05 \text{ mA}$$

The alpha at this test point is

$$\alpha = \frac{I_C}{I_E}$$

$$= \frac{8 \text{ mA}}{8.05 \text{ mA}}$$

$$= 0.99379$$

It is important to note that the alpha of a transistor is always less than unity or 1. This is due to the fact that I_E is always somewhat greater than I_C. Alpha does not, therefore, show a current gain between the input and output of a transistor. Alpha may be used in some amplifier circuit configurations to show voltage gain and power gain. If the ac or dynamic alpha of a transistor is to be calculated, all values would be expressed as lowercase letters or the uppercase letter would be preceded by the Greek letter delta (Δ). In this case, delta refers to a change in value. Alternating current is representative of a constant changing value.

The alpha and beta of a given transistor are directly related because of the values I_E, I_C, and I_B. This relationship is often expressed by the formula

$$\beta = \frac{\alpha}{1 - \alpha}$$

If the alpha of the transistor is known, it could be used to determine the beta. Example 2–4 shows this relationship.

Example 2–4:   Determine the beta for the transistor represented by point A of Figure 2–

7 using the alpha value. Then calculate beta by the I_C/I_B method. The previous alpha value was determined to be 0.9938.

Solution:

$$\beta = \frac{\alpha}{1 - \alpha}$$

$$= \frac{0.9938}{1 - 0.9938}$$

$$= 160.29$$

By the I_C/I_B method,

$$\beta = \frac{I_C}{I_B}$$

$$= \frac{8 \text{ mA}}{50 \text{ } \mu\text{A}}$$

$$= \frac{8 \times 10^{-3}}{50 \times 10^{-6}}$$

$$= 160.0$$

The small value difference between the two methods of calculation is primarily due the rounding off of alpha. Essentially, the two values are equal.

Graphical Amplifier Data _____

Manufacturers often supply information about the characteristics and parameters of transistors in graphical form. This type of information is usually more valuable than conventional numerical data. Operating conditions can be readily predicted by analyzing graphical data. Graphs can also be used to plot the behavior of a specific device in an actual circuit. It is important at this point to realize that graphical information is considered to be only typical data rather than specific or exact device data.

Many different transistor graphs are avail-able. Some are widely used in transistor circuit analysis. Others are only used when a transistor is being designed for a specific circuit application. As a rule, a person working with transistor circuits should be familiar with the more important forms of graphic data. Circuit modification, component replacement, and response predictions in a different operational environment may call for evaluation of a transistor's graphical data.

Figure 2–8 shows representative data graphs for a silicon power transistor. A typical I_C–V_{CE} family of characteristic curves is shown in part A. This graph has collector current (I_C) plotted as a function of collector-to-emitter voltage (V_{CE}), for various values of base current (I_B). Dc and ac circuit operating conditions can be determined from these data. When a transistor has dc voltage supplied to its elements and no signal applied to the input, it is considered to be in a static or dc operating state. When a signal is applied to the input of a properly energized transistor, it responds in the dynamic state. Static and dynamic operation can both be determined from an I_C–V_{CE} family of curves.

Figure 2–8(B) shows the I_B–V_{BE} characteristic curve for the same silicon power transistor. This graph shows how the base current (I_B) changes for different values of base–emitter voltage (V_{BE}). It should be noted that a small change in V_{BE} causes a very substantial change in I_B. For most circuit applications, this graph shows how the input of a transistor will respond.

The I_{CBO}–T_j characteristic of Figure 2–8(C) displays transistor leakage current. I_{CBO} refers to the amount of reverse current that flows through the collector–base junction with the emitter open circuited. The resulting current flow is directly dependent on junction temperature (T_j). It should be noted that at normal room temperature (21°C or 70°F) the leakage current is considered to be negligible. As the

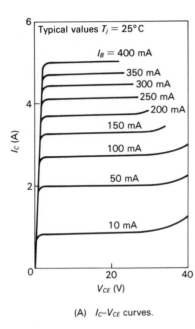

(A) I_C–V_{CE} curves.

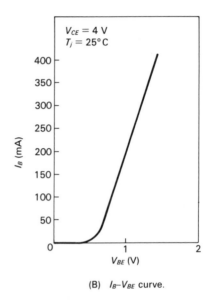

(B) I_B–V_{BE} curve.

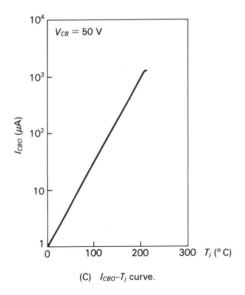

(C) I_{CBO}–T_j curve.

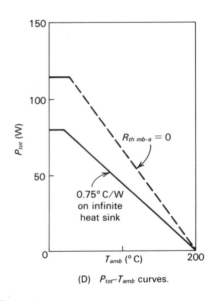

(D) P_{tot}–T_{amb} curves.

FIGURE 2–8
Data graphs of a silicon transistor.

junction temperature of a power transistor increases, its I_{CBO} increases rather significantly. High T_j values may ultimately alter the normal operating characteristics of transistor base current.

The graph of Figure 2–8(D) shows the P_{tot}–T_{amb} curves of the silicon power transistor. P_{tot} is the maximum permissible collector power dissipation in watts, and T_{amb} is the ambient temperature. These two curves show how the transistor will respond with or without a heat sink. This graph is used to see how the transistor will respond when it is operated at an elevated temperature.

Graphical Transistor Analysis

One very important application of graphical transistor data involves the I_C–V_{CE} characteristic curves. Assume that the collector curves of Figure 2–9 represent the silicon transistor being used in the amplifier circuit of Figure 2–10. Analysis of these data will show how the

transistor will respond when it is connected to a load.

The static or dc operating condition of the amplifier is observed first. In Figure 2–10, static operation is based on the values of V_{CC}, the collector resistor (R_C), and the base resistor (R_B). Note that V_{CC} supplies forward-bias voltage to the base–emitter junction through R_B and reverse bias to the collector through R_C. Specifically, V_{CC} is 30 V, R_C is 1000 Ω, and V_{RB} is 500 kΩ.

When a transistor is operated in the dc state, its V_{CE} is determined by the equation:

$$V_{CE} = V_{CC} - I_C \times R_C$$

This expression is called the *load-line equation*. It shows that the output operating voltage values are directly related. A straight line can be used to show this relationship on the collector curves. The two connecting points of the line represent the extreme conditions of operation. These occur when the transistor is in its nonconductive state and when it is fully conductive or saturated. Nonconduction occurs when $I_C = 0$ and $V_{CC} = V_{CE}$. Full conduction takes place when the maximum value of I_C flows through R_C. This means that $I_C = V_{CC}/R_C$ and $V_{CE} = 0$.

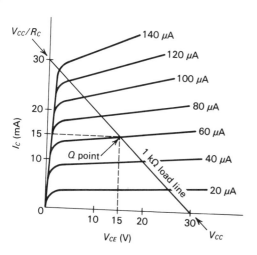

FIGURE 2–9
Collector curves of transistor Q_1.

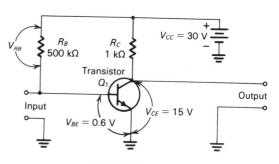

FIGURE 2–10
Transistor amplifier.

Example 2–5: Determine the two extreme conditions of operation for the transistor amplifier circuit of Figure 2–10. Locate corresponding points on the collector curves of Figure 2–9.

Solution: For the nonconductive condition,

$$V_{CC} = V_{CE} \quad \text{when } I_C = \text{zero}$$

$$30 \text{ V} = 30 \text{ V} \quad \text{when } I_C = 0 \text{ mA}$$

For the full conduction condition,

$$I_C = \frac{V_{CC}}{R_C} \quad \text{when } V_{CE} = \text{zero}$$

$$= \frac{30 \text{ V}}{1000 \text{ }\Omega}$$

$$= 0.03\text{A} \quad \text{or} \quad 30 \text{ mA} \quad \text{when } V_{CE} = 0 \text{ V}$$

A straight line connecting the two extreme operating points together is called a load line. In Figure 2–9, a diagonal line is drawn across the collector curves connecting these points. This represents a 1-kΩ load line for the amplifier circuit. This shows that the maximum range of collector current being controlled is 0 to 30 mA. The V_{CE} voltage of the amplifier is permitted to change from 0 to 30 V.

The base current (I_B) of our amplifier circuit is determined by the value of R_B and V_{CC}. Mathematically, this is determined by the formula

$$I_B = \frac{V_{CC}}{R_B}$$

Base current for static operation of the amplifier in Figure 2–9 is 30 V/500 kΩ or 60 μA. This condition of operation is located graphically at the intersection of the load line and the 60-μA base current line. In junction transistor circuit analysis, this is called the *bias operating point* or *Q-point*. "Q" means quiescent or point at rest. This represents the point where our transistor is fully energized and opera-

tional, but does not have a signal applied to its input.

The Q-point of the collector curves of Figure 2–9 is used to show the static operation of our transistor amplifier circuit. Projecting a line to the left of the graph from Q shows an I_C of 15 mA. This indicates that an I_B of 60 μA will cause an I_C of 15 mA. The V_{CE} of the circuit is determined by projecting a line down from the Q point. A V_{CE} of 15 V is indicated by this procedure. This means that the voltage across the transistor is 15 V when V_{CC} is 30 V and I_B is 60 μA. Graphically, this shows how the transistor amplifier responds in its static state.

Dynamic Transistor Operation

When an ac signal is applied to a transistor, it causes the current and voltage values to be in a continuous state of change. Operation of this type is usually described as being in the *dynamic state*. For this to take place, an ac signal must be applied to the input of the transistor circuit. Action of this type first causes a change in the emitter–base voltage (V_{BE}). This change in turn causes a change in base current. Ultimately, this controls the amount of collector current passing through R_C and the value of V_{CE}. Figure 2–11 shows a silicon bipolar transistor circuit that responds as an ac amplifier.

To demonstrate the operation of a transistor amplifier, it is important to see how an ac signal alters the input characteristic. As a rule, this type of information is shown on an input characteristic curve. A representative input curve for the transistor of Figure 2–11 is shown in Figure 2–12. Note that this curve plots base current (I_B) against emitter–base voltage (V_{BE}). This shows how a change in input signal voltage alters the value of I_B. The static operating point for the amplifier is 0.6

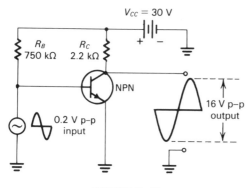

FIGURE 2–11
AC amplifier.

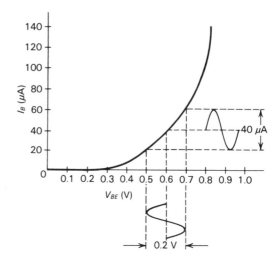

FIGURE 2–12
Input characteristic curve.

V. The resulting I_B at the operating point is 40 μA. Locate these two points on the input curve.

Assume now that a 0.2-V peak-to-peak input signal is applied to the transistor amplifier circuit. During the positive alternation of the signal, the V_{BE} increases in value from 0.6 to 0.7 V. This action causes the I_B to increase from 40 to 60 μA. In a similar manner, the negative alternation lowers the value of V_{BE} from 0.6 to 0.5 V. The resulting I_B in turn changes from 40 to 20 μA. Essentially, this means that a 0.2-V p–p input signal voltage causes a 40-μA change in I_B.

Dynamic Load-line Analysis

Dynamic load-line analysis is used to show how the output of a transistor responds when an ac signal is applied to its input. In this, case, the I_C–V_{CE} curves of Figure 2–13 are for the transistor of Figure 2–11. A load line and Q-point for the circuit have been plotted on the curves. Figure 2–11 shows that R_C is 2.2 kΩ and V_{CC} is 30 V. The Q-point is based on the value of I_B and V_{CE}. This corresponds with the static operating point of Figure 2–11. The

value of I_B is indicated as 40 μA. Operation at this point causes an I_C of 6.2 mA and a V_{CE} of 16 V.

When an ac signal voltage is applied to the input of our amplifier, it causes the value of I_B to change to an ac rate. A 0.2-V peak-to-peak input signal will therefore cause an I_B of 40 μA peak-to-peak. These data are transferred to the I_C–V_{CE} curves as a change in I_B from 60 to 20 μA. The positive alternation of the input voltage causes I_B to rise in value to 60 μA. The resulting I_C is 10 mA and V_{CE} is 8 V. The negative alternation of the input causes I_B to change from 40 to 20 μA. This causes a decrease in I_C to 2.8 mA and increases V_{CE} to 24 V. The ac beta and voltage amplification (A_v) of the amplifier are shown graphically as wave forms.

Example 2–6: Determine the ac beta and A_v for the transistor amplifier on Figure 2–11. Use data from the I_C–V_{CE} curve and V_{BE}–I_B curve.

Solution:

$$\text{ac beta} = \frac{\Delta I_C}{\Delta I_B}$$

$$= \frac{10 \text{ to } 2.8 \text{ mA}}{60 \text{ to } 20 \text{ } \mu A}$$

$$= \frac{7.2 \text{ mA}}{40 \text{ } \mu A}$$

$$= 180$$

$$A_v = \frac{\Delta V_{CE}}{\Delta V_{BE}}$$

$$= \frac{24 \text{ to } 8 \text{ V p-p}}{10.5 \text{ to } 0.7 \text{ V p-p}}$$

$$= \frac{16 \text{ V p-p}}{0.2 \text{ V p-p}}$$

$$= 80$$

FIGURE 2–13
Dynamic load-line analysis.

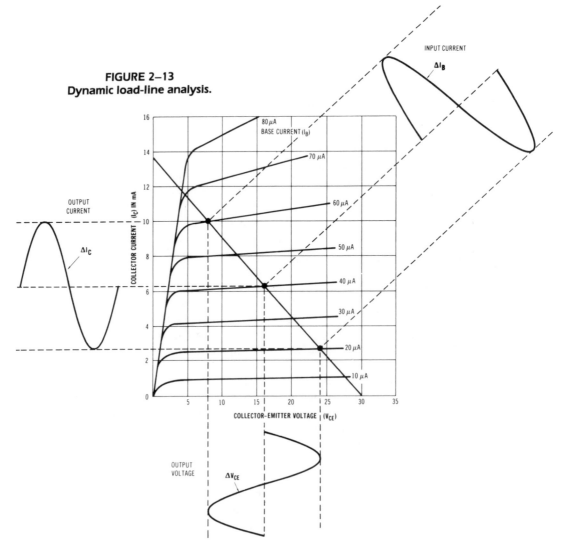

Graphical analysis of a transistor amplifier can also be used to demonstrate the phase relationship of different current and voltage values. The input signal voltage V_{BE} and I_B are, for example, in phase (see Figure 2–12). The I_B and I_C of an amplifier are also in phase as shown by Figure 2–13. The V_{BE} and V_{CE} of this amplifier circuit configuration are out of phase by 180°. In many applications the phase relationships of current and voltage values are extremely important.

Linear and Nonlinear Operation

Ideally, the output of a transistor amplifier should be a duplicate of the input signal with some gain. Normally, the input signal should show an increase in amplitude without distorting the signal. Amplification of this type is considered to be linear. Linear amplification is achieved by operating an amplifier near the center of its I_C–V_{CE} curves. Nonlinearity occurs when operation is in either the saturation or cutoff regions of the curves. Selection of a bias operating point near either of the extreme operating regions usually causes nonlinearity.

Figure 2–14 shows how a bipolar silicon transistor responds at three different operating points. Part A shows operation near the center of the I_C–V_{CE} curves. This shows linear operation. Note that the input and output waves are duplicates. Part B shows operation near the saturation region. This shows distortion of the top or positive alternation of the I_C and V_{CE} waves. Part C shows operation near the cutoff region. This shows distortion of the bottom or negative alternation of I_C and V_{CE}. In some industrial applications, nonlinear distortion can be tolerated.

An amplifier with its operating point near the center of the I_C–V_{CE} curve can become distorted if its input signal is too large. Figure 2–15 shows distortion of this type. Note that the

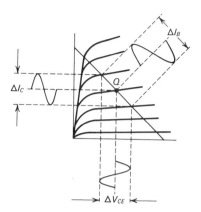

(A) Linear operation.

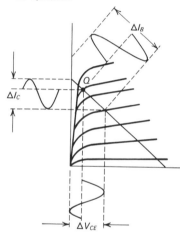

(B) Operation near saturation.

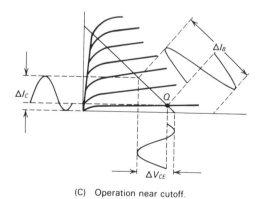

(C) Operation near cutoff.

FIGURE 2–14
Transistor operating point response.

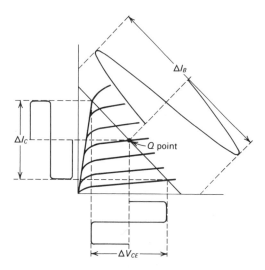

FIGURE 2–15
Overdriving amplifier distortion.

input signal swings into the saturation region during the positive alternation and into the cut-off region during the negative alternation. Both alternations of the input can become distorted. The term *overdriving* is commonly used to describe this condition of operation. Overdriving can be reduced by lowering the level of the input signal.

Transistor Circuit Configurations

A transistor amplifier can be connected in any one of three different circuit element configurations. These are usually described as common-emitter, common-base, or common-collector circuits. One of the three leads is commonly connected to both the input and output. This lead generally serves as a reference point and may be connected to ground. Configurations of this type are often called *grounded* emitter, base, or collector circuits. The designations *ground* and *common* refer to the same type of circuit configuration. In some circuits

a specific element is connected directly to ground. This means that the element is referenced to both dc and ac ground potential. Leads passing through resistors or batteries may be referenced to ac ground when they are bypassed by a capacitor.

Common-emitter Amplifiers

A very high percentage of all bipolar transistor amplifiers are connected in the common-emitter circuit configuration. The input of this amplifier is applied to the base and the output is taken from the collector. The emitter is the common reference electrode. This circuit configuration is capable of having high current and voltage gain. *Npn* and *pnp* common-emitter amplifiers are shown in Figure 2–16.

Operation of the common-emitter amplifier is based on the application of a signal to the emitter–base junction, with the output being developed across the emitter–collector. A small change in the V_{BE} causes a corresponding change in I_B. Changes in I_B then control the I_C flowing through the collector resistor. This in turn causes a change in the value of V_{CE}.

An important consideration of the common-emitter amplifier is its phase-inversion characteristic. The input and output signals are inverted or 180° out of phase. A positive-going input signal will, for example, produce a negative-going output signal. Inversion occurs in both ac and dc signal applications.

The common-emitter amplifier has a number of unique characteristics that distinguish it from the other circuit configurations. The current gain or beta of this amplifier is based on the collector current divided by the base current. Typical values of beta are in the range from 10 to 100. Voltage gain is expressed as output voltage (V_{CE}) divided by input voltage (V_{BE}). A_v values of up to 500 are possible. Power amplification (A_p) is $A_v \times$ beta. A_p values up to 10,000 can be achieved with this

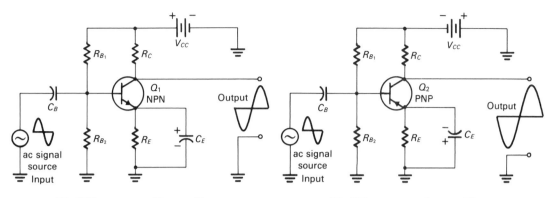

(A)   NPN common emitter amplifier.   (B)   PNP common emitter amplifier

FIGURE 2–16
Common-emitter amplifiers.

type of amplifier. The input impedance (Z_{in}) is determined by a forward-biased emitter–base junction. Typical Z_{in} values are in the range of 1 kΩ. The output resistance or impedance (Z_o) is developed across the reverse-biased collector. Representative Z_o values are 50 kΩ. As a rule, the characteristics of a common-emitter circuit tend to favor its use in small-signal applications or as voltage amplifiers.

Common-base Amplifiers

A common-base circuit configuration is shown in Figure 2–17. This particular circuit has the base commonly connected to both the input and output. The circuit configuration may also be described as a grounded-base amplifier. Operation depends on the emitter–base being forward biased and the collector–base reverse biased. Current flows according to the arrows of the diagram. The forward-biased emitter–base junction usually has a rather large I_E. Approximately 5% of the total I_E flows into the base when holes and electrons recombine. This causes the flow of some base current (I_B). The remaining I_B flows into the reverse-biased collector. The resulting I_C is approximately 95%

of the I_E. This means that the output current I_C is slightly less than the input current I_E. The current gain of a common-base amplifier is therefore always less than 1. This relationship is called *alpha*. Mathematically, alpha is determined by dividing the collector current by the emitter current.

Operation of the common-base amplifier is controlled by the dc values of V_{EE} and V_{CC}. Resistor R_E is the emitter current limiting resistor. The input operating point is established by the value of I_E and R_E. The collector resistor R_{CL} and V_{CC} reverse bias the collector. The output signal is reflected as a change in the value of V_{CB} and I_C. Note that an *npn* transistor is used in this circuit configuration.

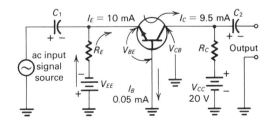

FIGURE 2–17
Common-base amplifier.

When an ac signal is applied to the input of our common-base amplifier, it changes the value V_{EE} and I_E. The positive alternation of the input signal, for example, reduces the value of V_{EE} and I_E. This in turn reduces I_C and the voltage drop across R_C. With less voltage drop across R_C, the value of V_{CB} increases rather significantly. The output voltage therefore increases or becomes more positive. In effect, V_{CB} changes in the same direction as the input voltage. This shows that V_{in} and V_o are in the same direction or in phase. The negative alternation of the input signal likewise produces an in-phase output signal. A sine wave applied to the input of this amplifier has gain but no phase shift.

A common-base amplifier has a variety of characteristics that distinguish it from other circuit configurations. The current gain or alpha is always less than 1. Typical values are in the range from 0.96 to 0.99. Voltage gain is based on the output voltage (V_{CB}) divided by the input voltage (V_{BE}). Typical A_v values range from 100 to 2500 depending on the resistance ratio of R_E and R_C. Power amplification (A_p) has a value range very similar to A_v. A_p is determined by the product of A_v and alpha. Typical A_p values are 1500. The input impedance (Z_{in}) of a common-base amplifier is usually quite low. Values of 10 to 200 Ω are normal. The output impedance (Z_o) of the amplifier is developed across the reverse-biased collector–base junction. Values are rather moderate and in the range from 5 to 40 kΩ. The characteristics of a common-base circuit tend to favor its use in impedance-matching applications. Low-impedance input devices can be coupled into a circuit through a common-base amplifier.

Common-collector Amplifiers

In a common-collector amplifier circuit configuration, the collector is connected to both the input and output. A representative amplifier of this type is shown in Figure 2–18. The input circuit is essentially the same as the common-emitter amplifier. The collector is, however, commonly connected to one side of the input and output. In effect, the collector is connected to ground through V_{CC}. Thus it does not operate at a dc ground potential. With capacitor C_2 connected from collector to ground, the collector is at an ac ground potential. A unique feature of the circuit is its output connection. Output is developed across a load resistor connected to the emitter. Common-collector amplifiers do not ordinarily have a collector resistor.

When an ac signal is applied to the input of a common-collector amplifier, it either adds to or reduces the value of V_{BE} and I_B. The positive alternation of a sine wave increases both V_{BE} and I_B. The negative alternation reduces the value of V_{BE} and I_B. The positive alternation also causes an increase in the value of I_E and I_C. With an increase in I_E, there is more voltage drop across the emitter resistor (R_L). The top side of R_L and the emitter therefore become more positive. In effect, the positive alternation of the input produces a corresponding positive alternation across the load resistor or output. The negative alternation of the input in the same manner produces a reduction of signal across R_L. Essentially, this means that

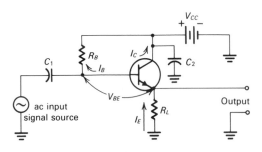

FIGURE 2–18
Common-collector amplifier.

the input and output signals of the amplifier are in phase. The output voltage at the emitter therefore follows the input signal voltage. A common-collector amplifier is frequently called an emitter-follower because of this condition.

A common-collector amplifier is capable of developing current gain. A small change in the value of I_B, for example, causes a rather substantial change in the value of I_E. This current gain does not have a general descriptive term, such as alpha or beta. Normally, this current gain is described as *beta plus one*. This means that the current gain can be in the range from 10 to 100 depending on the value of the emitter resistor.

The common-collector amplifier has a number of other characteristics that distinguish it from the other circuit configurations. The voltage amplification (A_V), for example, is less than 1. This is due to the degenerative effect of the load resistor connected to the emitter. Since the input and output signals are in phase, the output signal tends to oppose changes in the input circuit bias produced by the incoming signal. An increase in V_{BE} and I_B, for example, causes a corresponding increase in I_E and V_E. An increase in V_E causes reverse biasing of the emitter. In effect, an increase in the input lowers or reduces the output of the transistor. This is called *degeneration* or *negative feedback*. The resulting output voltage will therefore always be lower than the input voltage.

The power amplification (A_p) of a common-collector amplifier is determined by the product of current gain and voltage gain. Power gain is moderately high. Typical values are in the range from 10 to 50. This range is primarily based on the ratio of input impedance (Z_{in}) to output impedance (Z_o). Representative Z_{in} values are in the range from 50 to 300 kΩ. Z_o values are rather small because of the location of the load resistor in the emitter. Typical output impedance values are in the range from 10 to 500 Ω.

Common-collector amplifiers are primarily used in impedance-matching circuits. They are used to match a high-impedance input to a low-impedance output. Typical applications are power amplifiers and transistor driver amplifiers. In these applications a rather large input current is needed to deliver maximum power to the output or load device.

BIPOLAR TRANSISTOR SWITCHING

Switching is an electronic control function that is used to make, break, or change connections in an electrical circuit. Normally, this function is achieved by some form of mechanical action, such as flipping a toggle switch, pushing a button, or sliding an electrical contact. Ideally, the switch should have zero resistance across its contacts when closed and infinite resistance when open. Mechanical action switches respond very well in this type of operation.

In high-speed switching applications, mechanical action switches have some very serious operational problems. Moving parts have a tendency to wear out with continued use, contacts arc, and the inherent spring action of a switch causes contact bounce. In addition, mechanical switches have a very slow response time. These problems can be reduced and in many cases overcome by using electronic devices as switches. Transistors are the operational basis of many switching applications.

Transistor Switching Characteristics

When a transistor is used as a switch, there is a rather significant change in its operation compared with that of an amplifier. As a switch, operation is either fully conductive or

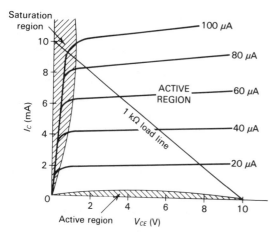

FIGURE 2–19
V_{CE}/I_C curves of a common-emitter amplifier.

cut off. In the on or conductive state, a transistor usually operates in the saturation region. This produces the lowest possible resistance between the emitter–collector. When a transistor is cut off, the emitter–collector is infinite. This is achieved by reverse biasing the base, shorting the emitter–base together, or opening the base lead. Normally, this action stops the flow of collector current. In effect, a transistor switch is either fully conductive or cut off.

A family of characteristic curves for an *npn* transistor connected in a common-emitter configuration is shown in Figure 2–19. A load line for the circuit is drawn to show the switching response of the transistor from cutoff to saturation. The characteristics are divided into three operational regions. The bottom or lower horizontal area represents the cutoff region. The left vertical part of the curve indicates the saturation region. Between these two extreme areas of operation is the active region. When a transistor responds as a switch, it must change very quickly from cutoff to saturation or from saturation to cutoff. As a rule, a switching transistor does not operate in the active region.

The emitter–collector resistance of a transis-

tor is another important characteristic of a switching transistor. Ideally, this resistance should be zero when forward biased and infinite when reverse biased. In a functional switching circuit, these values are only approximated. A saturated transistor, for example, has some emitter–collector resistance. In many applications this resistance is considered negligible. Practical values of resistance are in the range from 10 to 50 Ω. In the same manner, a nonconductive transistor does represent an infinite resistance. Practical values of internal resistance are in the range from 500 kΩ to 5 MΩ. This resistance is temperature dependent to some extent.

Saturation Region Operation

Figure 2–20 shows a simplified transistor switch operating in the saturation region. The emitter–base junction is forward biased by resistor R_B and the collector is reverse biased by R_L. The value of base current or the operating point of the transistor is determined by R_B. In this circuit, 100 μA of base current occurs when the transistor is switched into conduction. The values of R_L and V_{CC} determine the collector current of the transistor. An I_C of 10 mA in this case causes the transistor to reach

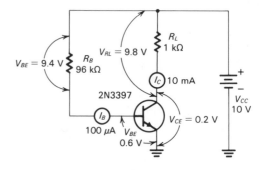

FIGURE 2–20
Transistor switch operating in saturation.

saturation. Note this region of the I_C–V_{CE} curves of Figure 2–19.

A transistor switch usually has current gain that approximates the beta of an amplifier. In the switch of Figure 2–20, the beta is 100. An I_B of 100 μA therefore produces an I_C of 10 mA. This is shown by the expression

$$\text{Beta} = \frac{I_C \text{ (saturation)}}{I_B \text{ (saturation)}}$$

$$= \frac{10 \text{ mA}}{100 \text{ μA}}$$

$$= 100$$

The beta of this circuit is an expression of the dc current gain. If the base current has an ac control signal, the current gain is described as ac beta. As a rule, there is some difference in the two gain expressions. AC beta is generally greater than a dc beta value. Beta is generally not a significant parameter in the selection of a transistor as a switch.

The voltage and current values of the circuit in Figure 2–20 tell a great deal about the operation of a transistor as a switch. When the emitter–base junction is forward biased, I_B causes a suitable value of I_C to flow through R_L. When the saturation region is reached, a very small value of V_{CE} appears across the transistor. Typical values are in the range from 0.15 to 0.2 V. This means that the internal resistance (R_{CE}) of the transistor drops to a rather small value. It can be determined by the formula

$$\text{Resistance emitter–collector} = \frac{\text{saturation voltage}}{\text{saturation current}}$$

$$R_{CE} = \frac{V_{CE \text{ sat}}}{I_{C \text{ sat}}}$$

For the transistor switch, the internal or saturation resistance is

$$R_{CE} = \frac{V_{CE}}{I_C}$$

$$= \frac{0.2 \text{ V}}{10 \text{ mA}}$$

$$= 20 \text{ Ω}$$

This shows that a small value of internal resistance is present in a conductive transistor switch. In a practical circuit there will always be some V_{CE} appearing across a conductive transistor. Operation in the saturation region minimizes this voltage.

Cutoff Region Operation

Transistor cutoff is representative of switch operation in the off or nonconductive state. For this to occur the base–emitter junction must be reverse biased, shorted together, or allowed to float by disconnecting the base resistor. All three of these methods will stop the flow of base current and eliminate nearly all the collector current. The internal resistance of the transistor approaches infinity and practically no current is delivered to the load resistor. Virtually all the source voltage (V_{CC}) appears across the emitter–collector of the transistor. At cutoff, $V_{CE} = V_{CC}$.

Figure 2–21 shows a switching transistor

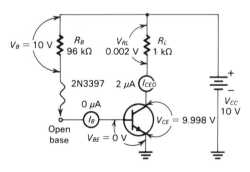

FIGURE 2–21
Switching transistor in cutoff region.

operating in the cutoff region. In this circuit configuration the base resistor is left open or floating. The collector is reverse biased through R_L, and the emitter is forward biased by connection to ground. With the base resistor open, no I_B flows in the emitter–base junction. Normally, we would expect this condition to stop all the collector current. However, when the base is allowed to float in an open state, there will be a small amount of leakage current between the collector and emitter. Leakage current, in this case, is described as I_{CEO}, which is collector–emitter current with the base open. With improved transistor construction techniques, general-purpose silicon transistors of the low- to medium-power range have an extremely low value of leakage current. High-power switching transistors have I_{CEO} values in the microampere range. Leakage current in all applications is temperature dependent. In most switching applications, leakage current can be ignored.

The voltage and current values of the circuit in Figure 2–21 tell a great deal about the response of a transistor in its cutoff state. With the base open or reverse biased, practically no I_C will flow to the load resistor. The internal resistance of the transistor is extremely high, with values approaching several million ohms. In this circuit we show a leakage current of 2 μA. This causes a very small voltage to appear across R_L. V_{RL} is determined by the formula

$$V_{RL} = I_{CEO} \times R_L$$
$$= 2 \ \mu A \ \times \ 1 \ k\Omega$$
$$= 0.002 \ V$$

With 0.002 V across R_L, the V_{CE} of the transistor is

$$V_{CE} = V_{CC} - V_{RL}$$
$$= 10 \ V \ - \ 0.002$$
$$= 9.998 \ V$$

Knowing the value of V_{CE} permits us to determine the internal resistance of the transistor. The internal resistance at cutoff is

$$R_{int} = \frac{V_{CE}}{I_{CEO}}$$
$$= \frac{9.998 \ V}{2 \ \mu A}$$
$$= 4.999 \times 10^6 \quad or \quad 4.999 \ M\Omega$$

Thus the actual internal resistance of our transistor switch is 4.999 MΩ instead of an infinite value. In low-voltage switching applications, an internal resistance of this value responds as an infinite condition. This means that all the source voltage will appear across the transistor with no V_{RL}. For a large majority of industrial switching applications, a cutoff transistor responds as an ideal switch.

FIELD-EFFECT TRANSISTORS

Industrial electronic systems utilize a number of devices known by the name field-effect transistor or FET. This type of active device is quite different from the bipolar junction transistor. Only one type of current carrier is used in the operation of an FET. This current passes through a single piece of semiconductor material. The piece of material is called a *channel*. Today, *N*-channel and *P*-channel FETs are both available. Operation of the device is based on the control of current carriers passing through the channel. Current flow is altered by the strength and polarity of an electrostatic field that is developed around the channel.

There are two distinct classes of active devices known by the term *field-effect transistor*. One division is called a *junction* field-effect transistor (JFET) and the other, an *insulated gate* field-effect transistor (IGFET). A JFET

has a piece of opposite polarity semiconductor material attached to its channel. A semiconductor junction is formed by this piece of material and the channel. This element of the JFET is called the *gate*. A JFET has a *PN* or *NP* junction formed by the gate and channel. IGFETs have a different type of construction. The gate is insulated from the channel by a thin layer of silicon dioxide. No junction is formed by the channel and the gate. IGFETs are generally called metal oxide semiconductor field-effect transistors or MOSFETs. The gate of a MOSFET is not made of a semiconductor material. JFETs and MOSFETs are widely used today as amplitude control devices.

Junction Field-Effect Transistors

The JFET is a three-element active device. Its operation is based on the conduction of majority current carriers through a piece of N or P semiconductor material. It is fabricated from a bar or strip of doped silicon with connection terminals at each end. Figure 2–22 shows the crystal construction, element names, and schematic symbols of N- and P-channel JFETs. Current carriers flow from the source terminal through the channel to the drain. The gate material is of an opposite polarity to that of the channel. A *PN* or *NP* junction is formed by the gate and channel. The gate–channel junction of a JFET is reverse biased during its operation. Current flowing through the channel is based on the value of the reverse-bias voltage. A large reverse-bias gate voltage (V_G) can cutoff the flow of drain current (I_D). Full conduction or maximum I_D occurs when V_G is zero. Drain current is controlled by altering the value of V_G.

N- and P-channel JFETs are both used in industrial circuits. As a general rule, N-channel JFETs tend to be more popular than P-

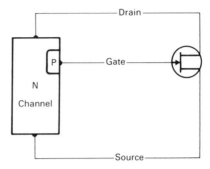

(A)   N channel JFET.

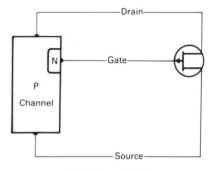

(B)   P-channel JFET.

FIGURE 2–22
Construction and symbol of a JFET.

channel devices. Electrons, which are the current carriers of the N-channel device, have greater mobility than the holes of a P-channel device. N-channel JFETs respond better to high-frequency signals. Manufacturers tend to have a wider selection of these devices available for circuit applications. We will discuss only the N-channel device in this section. Keep in mind that the P-channel device is primarily the same in nearly all respects. The major difference in operation is in voltage polarities and the type of channel current carriers.

A cross-sectional view of an N-channel JFET and its operating voltages are shown in Figure 2–23. In Figure 2–23(A), only the ex-

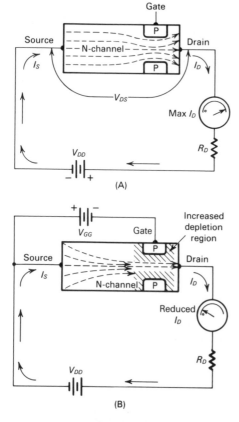

FIGURE 2–23
JFET cross-sectional view.

at the same time. Note that the gate source junction is reverse biased by the V_{GG} battery. This voltage causes an increase in the area of the depletion region near the gate. As a result, the number of current carriers in the channel is reduced. An increase in V_{GS} causes a corresponding decrease in I_D. Reducing the value of V_{GS} causes a substantial increase in I_D. Thus a change in the value of V_{GS} can be used to control the internal resistance of the channel. Variations in V_{GS} are therefore used to control channel current or I_D.

JFET Characteristic Curves

The circuit of Figure 2–24 could be used to develop a family of characteristic curves for a JFET. Figure 2–25 shows a typical I_D–V_{DS} family of characteristic curves for a small-signal JFET. Notice that this grpah shows the relationship of drain current to drain–source voltage for different values of gate–source voltage. The $V_{GS} = 0$ curve indicates how the device responds when the gate is open or with no voltage applied. When V_{GS} is increased, there is a decided decrease in I_D. Notice the position difference between 0 V_{GS} and the -1 V curves. Increasing the value of V_{GS} reverse biases the gate with respect to the source. This essentially increases the area of the depletion region near the gate. With a larger depletion

ternal voltage source V_{DD} is connected. This voltage energizes the source–drain channel circuit path. A maximum value of current flows through the channel. This is called *drain current* and is indicated by the I_D meter. I_D is limited only by the internal resistance of the channel and the value of V_{DD}. Small-signal JFETs usually have an internal channel resistance of a few hundred ohms. With no gate voltage applied, the channel is fully conductive. A JFET is considered to be a normally on device.

Figure 2–23(B) shows how the JFET will respond when V_{DD} and V_{GG} are both connected

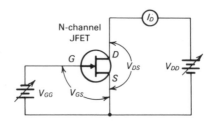

FIGURE 2–24
Circuit for developing I_{DS}/V_{DS} curves.

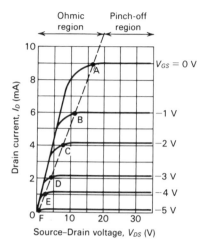

FIGURE 2–25
I_D/V_{DS} **curves for a JFET.**

Load-Line Analysis

Figure 2–26 shows a small-signal amplifier and a family of curves for the JFET used in the circuit. A load line is plotted using the same procedure outlined for the bipolar transistor. The two intersecting points of the load line show how the JFET responds when it is either fully conductive or cut off. Full conduction occurs when $I_D = V_{DD}/R_L$ and V_{DS} is zero. Cutoff occurs when $V_{DD} = V_{DS}$ and $I_D = 0$ mA.

region, less current passes through the channel. Additional increases in V_{GS} cause a greater reduction of I_D. The drain current of this device is completely cutoff for V_{GS} values in excess of -5 V.

Another interesting characteristic of the JFET is also shown on the I_D–V_{DS} curves of Figure 2–25. For any of the V_{GS} curves, a small increase in V_{DS} causes a very substantial increase in drain current. I_D rises very quickly and then levels off. This is indicated by a lettered point on each V_{GS} curve. An increase in V_{DS} beyond this point causes very little change in I_D. The area to the left of the indicated point is called the *ohmic region*. Operation of a JFET in this region is very similar to that of a linear resistor. A small change in V_{DS}, for example, causes a large change in I_D.

The area to the right of the lettered point is called the *pinch-off region*. An increase in V_{DS} in this region does not cause an increase in the flow of I_D. In effect, the channel becomes saturated with electrons. The value of I_D remains the same regardless of the value of V_{DS}. JFET amplifiers are designed to operate in the pinch-off region.

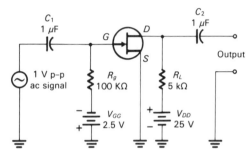

(A)   N-channel JFET amplifier.

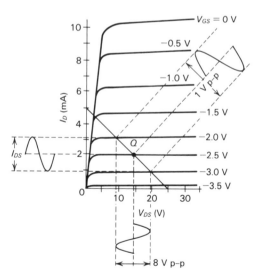

(B)   Drain family of curves.

FIGURE 2–26
Family of I_{DS}/V_{DS} curves and JFET amplifier.

The operating point of a JFET amplifier is determined by different values of gate–source voltage. For the amplifier of Figure 2–26, V_{GS} is supplied by the V_{GG} battery. V_{GS} in this case is equal to V_{GG} or -2.5 V. As a rule, the static operation of the device is established by the value of V_{GS}. This operating state compares with that of a bipolar transistor. The term *quiescent* or *Q-point* is also used to denote this condition of operation.

When an ac signal is applied to a JFET amplifier, it causes the current and voltage values to be in a continuous state of change. An amplifier operating in this manner is considered to be in its dynamic state. An ac signal must be applied to the input of the device in order for this type of operation to take place. This signal will cause a change in the value of V_{GS}. The reverse-bias voltage of the gate will then change in value at an ac rate. This in turn changes the value of the drain current passing through the channel. A variation in I_D causes a corresponding change in V_{DS}. The output of the amplifier is based on the changing value of V_{DS}. Note the relationship of V_{GS}, I_D, and V_{DS} on the I_D–V_{DS} curves of Figure 2–26.

Transfer Characteristics _____

Another way to analyze the operation of a JFET is through the study of its dynamic transfer characteristics. A typical dynamic transfer curve is shown in Figure 2–27. This curve plots drain current and gate–source voltage for a given value of drain–source voltage. A constant value of 10 V_{DS} is used for this particular curve.

A dynamic transfer curve is developed from the data of an I_D–V_{DS} family of curves. Refer to the 10-V_{DS} line of the curves in Figure 2–26. The intersection of each V_{GS} curve and the 10-V_{DS} line represents an I_D value. These I_D values are then plotted on a graph for each value of V_{GS}. The intersecting points are then

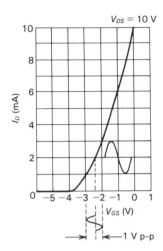

FIGURE 2–27
Dynamic transfer characteristic or input curve.

connected to form the *transfer characteristic*. Essentially, this characteristic shows how a change in V_{GS} causes a change in I_D.

For the amplifier of Figure 2–26, the Q-point is -2.5 V_{GS}. Note the location of this point on the transfer curve. A 1-V p-p change in V_{GS} will cause a change of 2 mA in I_D. This shows a graphic display of the input/output characteristics of a JFET. Nonlinear distortion of the output wave can be readily observed with this type of graph.

A very useful operating parameter of the JFET can be obtained from a dynamic transfer curve. This property is described as the *forward transconductance* (g_m). Transconductance is a measure of the ease with which current passes through the channel of a JFET. It is defined as the ratio of a small change in drain current to a small change in gate–source voltage for a given value of V_{DS}. This is expressed by the formula

$$\text{Transconductance} = \frac{\text{drain current change}}{\text{gate–source voltage change}}$$

$$g_m = \frac{\Delta I_D}{\Delta V_{GS}}$$

Transconductance is indicated in seimens. A seimens (S) is the fundamental unit of conductance. Previously, this unit was known as mho, the reciprocal of an ohm.

Example 2–7: Determine the transconductance of the amplifier of Figure 2–26 using the data from the dynamic transfer curve of Figure 2–27.

Solution:

$$g_m = \frac{\Delta I_D}{\Delta V_{GS}}$$

$$= \frac{1 \text{ to } 3 \text{ mA}}{3 \text{ to } 2 \text{ V}}$$

$$= \frac{2 \times 10^{-3}}{1 \text{ V}}$$

$$= 0.5 \times 10^{-3} \text{ S} \quad \text{or} \quad 500 \text{ μS}$$

MOS Field-Effect Transistors _____

Metal oxide semiconductor FETs or MOSFETs are a unique variation of the basic transistor family. MOSFETs are designed so that the gate is completely insulated from the channel by a thin layer of silicon dioxide. Operation of the device is based on the application of a correct voltage value and polarity to the gate. The gate is simply a coating of metal deposited on a layer of insulation attached to the channel. Voltage applied to the gate causes it to develop an electrostatic charge. No current is permitted to flow between the gate and the channel. The control of current carriers through the channel is based on the polarity and value of the gate voltage.

The channel of a MOSFET has an unusual construction feature. One type of MOSFET responds to the depletion of current carriers that pass through its channel. *Depletion-type* MOSFETs have an interconnecting channel built in

another piece of semiconductor material known as the *substrate*. The source and drain are directly connected by the channel. Channel construction of this device is very similar to that of a JFET.

A second type of MOSFET is called an *enhancement type* of device. The channel of this device is produced when it operates. The source and drain are not directly connected through a common channel. Current carriers are pulled from the substrate and form an induced channel. Gate voltage is used to control the size of the induced channel. The channel is only present when the device is energized. E- and D-MOSFETs are both widely used in industrial electronic systems.

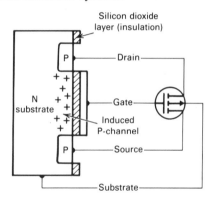

(A) P-channel E-MOSFET.

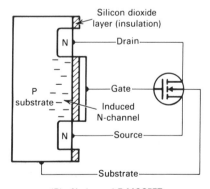

(B) N-channel E-MOSFET.

FIGURE 2–28
P- and N-channel E-MOSFETs.

Figure 2–28 shows a cross-sectional view of the crystal structure, element names, and schematic symbols of the *P*- and *N*-channel E-MOSFETs. A defined channel connection does not exist between the source and drain. The schematic symbol shows this by having independent source, substrate, and drain leads. The middle electrode, which has an arrowhead, shows the polarity of the substrate. When the arrow *Points* i*N* toward the channel, it indicates that the substrate is *P* and the channel is *N*. When the arrow does *Not Point* toward the channel, it shows that the substrate is *N* and the channel is *P*. The entire device is built on the substrate. Gate construction is designed to span the entire space between the source and drain. A thin layer of metal is used in the construction of the gate.

An E-MOSFET is classified as a normally off device. This means that no drain current flows through the channel without gate voltage applied. When the gate of an *N*-channel device is made positive, electrons are pulled from the *P* substrate into the source–drain region. This condition causes the channel region to have a high concentration of current carriers. Completion of the channel provides a conduction path for current carriers to flow between the source and drain. The drain current, in effect, is aided or enhanced by the gate voltage. The absence of gate voltage (V_G) does not permit the channel to form. The size of the channel and density of the current carriers are directly related to the value of V_G.

The operation of an E-MOSFET is primarily based on the voltage value and polarity of its elements. Figure 2–29 shows the correct voltage polarity for *N*- and *P*-channel E-MOS-FETs. The *P*-channel device has the source and drain energized by V_{DD}. The source is positive and the drain is negative. The gate is made negative with respect to the source by battery V_{GG}. A negative gate will pull holes from the *N*-substrate material, forming the in-

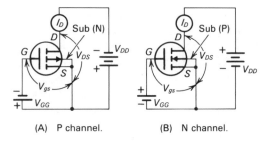

(A) P channel.   (B) N channel.

FIGURE 2–29
E-MOSFET voltage polarities.

duced channel. Current flow through the channel is achieved by hole movement. The *PN* junction formed by the *P* source and drain and the *N* substrate must be reverse biased. The substrate is usually connected to the same polarity as the source.

A family of characteristic curves for an E-MOSFET is shown in Figure 2–30. This set of curves is for an *N*-channel device. A set of curves for a *P*-channel device would be very similar. The primary difference is the polarity of the gate voltage. Note that an increase in V_{GS} causes a corresponding increase in drain current. An individual curve is represented for

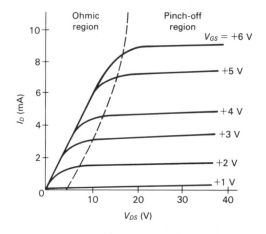

FIGURE 2–30
I_D/V_{DS} **curves for an *N*-channel E-MOSFET.**

each value of V_{GS}. Increasing the source–drain voltage causes an increase in I_D. The leveling off of I_D indicates the pinch-off region of the device. The pinch-off region and the ohmic region of this device are similar to those of the JFET. A family of I_D–V_{DS} curves of this type could be used to develop a load line for a representative amplifier. The procedure to be followed is primarily the same as that of a JFET.

Depletion-type MOSFETs

Figure 2–31 shows a cross-sectional view of the crystal structure, element names, and symbols of P- and N-channel D-MOSFETs. In the N-channel device shown, a channel of N material is formed on a P substrate. The source

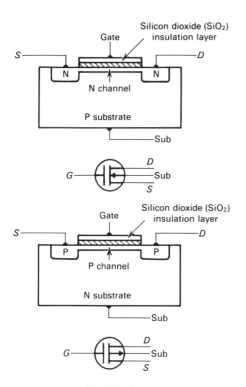

FIGURE 2–31
N- and P-channel D-MOSFETs.

and drain are connected by this channel. A layer of silicon dioxide (SiO_2) insulates the gate from the channel. The gate is simply a strip of metal that has been deposited on the SiO_2 layer. The entire assembly is built on a P substrate. The schematic symbol of the device shows the source, substrate, and drain all connected together. This indicates that the source and drain are connected by a piece of channel material that is all formed on a piece of substrate material. The substrate of the symbol is represented by an arrow. When the arrow Points iN toward the channel it indicates that the substrate is P and channel is N. The current carriers of an N-channel device are electrons.

P-channel device construction is very similar to that of the N-channel device. The crystal material of the channel and substrate are of a different polarity. In a P-channel device, the current carriers are holes. The schematic symbol shows that the source, drain, and substrate are commonly connected. The substrate arrow does Not Point toward the channel. This indicates that the substrate is N and the channel is P material.

The operation of a D-MOSFET is quite unusual when compared with other active devices. With voltage applied to the source and drain only, drain current flows through the channel. In this condition of operation, the gate does not need voltage to produce conduction. A D-MOSFET is therefore classified as a normally on device. Channel current (I_D) is, however, controlled by different values of gate voltage. When the channel and gate voltage are of the same polarity, there is a reduction or depletion of current carriers. This condition of operation increases the depletion region of the channel. Depleting the number of current carriers in the channel causes a corresponding reduction in I_D. The depletion mode of operation represents only one form of control that can be achieved.

If the gate and channel of a D-MOSFET

have a different polarity, the number of channel current carriers increases. This means that the device is capable of both depletion and enhancement modes of operation. Making the gate positive in an *N*-channel device increases the number of current carriers. In effect, this pulls electrons into the channel from the substrate. A negative gate voltage depletes the number of current carriers. This action increases the depletion region of the channel, which reduces I_D. A zero V_G divides the depletion and enhancement modes of operation. In a strict sense, this device could be called an enhancement–depletion MOSFET.

A family of characteristic curves for an *N*-channel D-MOSFET is shown in Figure 2–32. A family of *P*-channel curves would be primarily the same with the exception being the gate polarity. The top V_G lines would be negative values and the bottom lines would be positive values. Note in this display that 0 V_G is near the center of the curves. This divides the enhancement and depletion modes of operation. For ac amplification, an ideal operating point would be 0 V_G. For the *N*-channel

display, the positive alternation of an input signal causes an increase in I_D. The negative alternation produces a decrease in I_D.

Today, *P*-channel D-MOSFETs are not as readily available as *N*-channel devices. *P*-channel devices are somewhat more difficult to fabricate than *N*-channel devices. In general, the *P*-channel device is more costly to produce. Most industrial applications tend to favor the *N*-channel D-MOSFET. *N*-channel devices have better current mobility. This is a desirable feature in high-frequency ac signal amplification. These devices are widely used as high-frequency amplifiers.

V-MOS Field-effect Transistors

A new generation of the field-effect transistor is finding its way into solid-state active device technology. This type of device is largely used to replace the bipolar power transistor. Power FETs are now being used in power supplies and solid-state switching applications. Collectively, these devices are called V-MOSFETs or V-FETs. The ''V'' designation finds its origin

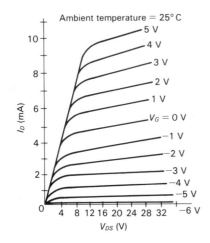

FIGURE 2–32
Characteristic curves for an *N*-channel D-MOSFET.

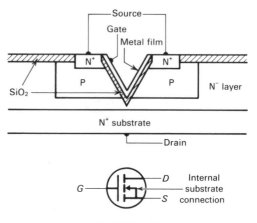

FIGURE 2–33
Cross-sectional view of an *N*-channel V-MOSFET.

in vertical-groove MOS technology. The device has a V-shaped groove etched into the substrate. Construction of this type requires less area than a horizontally assembled device. The geometry of a V-MOS device also permits greater heat dissipation and high-density channel areas. V-MOSFETs have fast switching speeds and lower channel resistance.

Figure 2–33 shows a cross-sectional view of the crystal structure, element names, and schematic symbol of an N-channel V-MOSFET. Notice that a V-groove is etched in the surface of the structure. From the top, the V-cut penetrates through N^+, P, and N^- layers and stops near the N^+ substrate. The two N^+ layers are heavily doped, and the N^- layer is lightly doped. A thin layer of silicon dioxide covers both the horizontal surface and the V-groove. A metal film deposited on top of the groove serves as the gate. The gate is insulated from the groove. The source leads on each side of the groove are connected internally. The bottom layer of N^+ material serves as a combined substrate and drain. Current carriers move between the source and drain vertically.

A V-MOSFET responds as an enhancement MOSFET. No current carriers exist in the source and drain regions until the gate is energized. An N-channel device, such as the one of Figure 2–33, does not conduct until the gate is made positive with respect to the source. When this occurs, an N channel is induced between the two N^+ areas near the groove. Current carriers can then flow through the vertical channel from source to drain. When the gate of an N-channel device is made negative, no channel exists and the current carriers cease to flow.

P-channel V-MOSFETs are also available today for use in industrial system applications. The current carriers of a P-channel device are holes. In general, hole flow has less mobility than electron flow. These devices do not respond as well to high-frequency ac. The primary characteristics and theory of operation are, however, very similar to those of an N-channel device. Differences exist only in voltage polarity and current-carrier flow. As a rule, a wider variety of N-channel devices is manufactured today. Industrial applications tend to favor the N-channel devices a great deal more than P-channel units. Only N-channel devices will be discussed here.

Characteristics of V-MOSFETs

The characteristics of a V-MOSFET are very similar to those of an enhancement MOSFET. Figure 2–34 shows the I_D–V_{DS} curves and the transfer characteristics of an N-channel device. This particular device is a power V-FET. The I_D–V_{DS} characteristic shows that V_{GS} must be positive with respect to the source if there is to be an increase in I_D. The value of V_{GS} also controls I_D for an increase in V_{DS}. Note that V-MOSFETs have ohmic and pinch-off regions very similar to those of an E-MOSFET.

The transfer characteristic of a V-MOSFET plots V_{GS} and I_D for a single V_{DS} value. A change in V_{GS} is considered to be a variation in the input voltage. I_D is used to denote an output condition. A transfer curve shows how the output responds to a change in input voltage. This curve is nearly linear over its entire length. The forward transconductance (g_m) can be obtained from the data of this curve.

Example 2–8: Determine the forward transconductance from the transfer characteristic curve for an input voltage change of 2 V p-p with an operating point of 7 V_{GS}.

Solution: Refer to the I_D–V_{DS} curves of Figure 2–34. Locate the 7-V_{GS} operating point. A 2-V p-p input signal will cause the operating point to change from 6 to 8 V. Trace the V_{GS} values upward to the curve. The resulting I_D

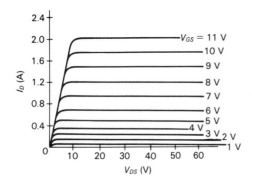

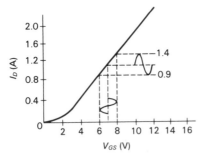

FIGURE 2–34
E-type V-MOSFET characteristics.

values are 0.9 A to 1.4 A. This represents an I_D of 0.5 A. The g_m is determined to be

$$g_m = \frac{\Delta I_D}{\Delta V_{GS}}$$

$$= \frac{0.9 \text{ to } 1.4 \text{ A}}{6 \text{ to } 8 \text{ V}}$$

$$= \frac{0.5 \text{ A}}{2}$$

$$= 0.25 \text{ S} \quad \text{or} \quad 250 \text{ mS}$$

Note that the g_m of a V-MOSFET is quite large. Compared with other FETs, this is a very significant condition of operation. The voltage gain (A_V) of an FET amplifier is based on $g_m \times R_L$. With high values of g_m, it is possible to achieve a great deal more voltage gain with a V-MOSFET than with other types of FETs. This feature, its power-handling capa-

bility, and high switching speed make the V-MOSFET an extremely attractive amplitude control device for industrial control applications.

Circuit applications of the V-MOSFET are very similar to those of a bipolar transistor or any general-purpose FET. Amplifiers can be connected in three different circuit configurations. The common-drain circuit configuration is the most widely used. An input signal voltage is inverted 180° in the output. The gate polarity must be positive with respect to the source. Input impedance is very high. The *on* resistance of the channel may be as little as a few tenths of an ohm. These devices are capable of a rather substantial power gain. Up to 100 V and tens of amperes of I_D can be switched safely. V-MOSFETs can be used as switches or as linear amplifiers. Circuit operation can be predicted by plotting a load line and establishing an operating point. In general, this device has a very promising future as a control element.

FIELD-EFFECT TRANSISTOR SWITCHES

Field-effect transistors are frequently used in industrial circuits as switching devices. As a rule, these devices have a number of advantages and fewer disadvantages than a conventional bipolar transistor switch. Bipolar transistors are current-actuated devices, which means that they tend to alter the input and cause an *offset* between the input and resulting output signals. FETs by comparison are voltage-controlled devices, which have no offset problem and do not load down the input control signal. This makes it possible to control a switching device from one or an unlimited number of inputs. The internal resistance of an FET is quite small compared with bipolar devices. With no minority current carrier storage in an FET,

switching time is very fast. It therefore responds extremely well in high-speed switching applications. The FET also has high input impedance to reduce circuit loading, high reliability, and a very long operational life expectancy.

FET switches are probably used more today in the construction of integrated circuits than they are used as discrete device switches. Contemporary applications of the FET switch are called *gates* in digital ICs and *analog switches* in linear ICs. As a rule, there is a great deal of similarity in FET switches regardless of the name or application. The type of device used to achieve switching is where the difference occurs. JFETs, MOSFETs, and CMOSFETs are used to achieve switching. We will discuss the JFET first and then point out some specific differences in the other switching devices.

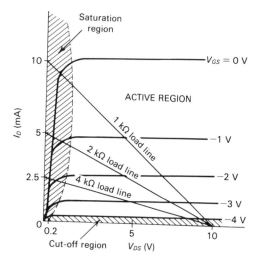

FIGURE 2–35
Family of I_D/V_{DS} curves for an *N*-channel JFET.

JFET Switching

A junction field-effect transistor has operating states of *off* and *on* when it responds as a switch. In the *off* or nonconductive state, a JFET operates in the cutoff region. No drain current (I_D) flows through the channel. The load device does not receive current and practically all the source voltage appears across the source–drain as V_{DS}. The off state is achieved by reverse biasing the gate. Conduction or on-state operation is best when a JFET is saturated. It is important that operation be in the saturation region to achieve the lowest internal channel resistance. Decreasing the gate–source voltage (V_{GS}) increases the drain current I_D until saturation occurs. An open or floating gate is an easy way to cause saturation in a JFET. The value of I_D needed to cause saturation depends on the value of the load resistor (R_L).

A family of characteristic curves for an *N*-channel JFET with three different load lines is shown in Figure 2–35. The resistance of R_L has a decided influence on the angle of each

load line. The greatest degree of conduction occurs when R_L is of the smallest value. The load lines are used to show the switching response of the JFET from cutoff to saturation. Note also that the characteristics are divided into three operational regions. The bottom or lower horizontal area is the cutoff region of operation. The left vertical part of the curve shows the saturation region. Between these extreme areas is the active or linear region. When a JFET responds as a switch, it must change quickly from cutoff to saturation or from saturation to cutoff. Switching applications do not generally operate in the active region.

Saturation Region Operation

Figure 2–36 shows a JFET switch operating in the saturation region. The source and drain elements are connected in series with the load resistor and the dc energy source V_{DD}. Decreasing the gate–source voltage (V_{GS}) to zero

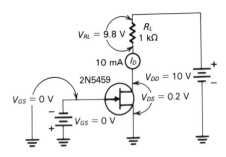

FIGURE 2–36
JFET switch operation in saturation region.

causes full conduction of drain current. For a 1-kΩ load resistor, the I_D reaches saturation at approximately 10 mA. When saturation occurs, the V_{DS} voltage drops to a value of 0.2 V. This voltage is representative of the internal channel resistance of the source and drain. It can be determined by the formula

$$\text{Source–drain resistance} = \frac{\text{saturation voltage}}{\text{saturation current}}$$

$$R_{DS} = \frac{V_{DS}}{I_D}$$

For our JFET switch, the saturation resistance is

$$R_{DS} = \frac{V_{DS}}{I_D}$$

$$= \frac{0.2 \text{ V}}{10 \text{ mA}}$$

$$= 20 \text{ }\Omega$$

This resistance represents the lowest value that can be achieved by a conductive JFET. In practical circuits, some V_{DS} will always appear across the source and drain. Operation in the saturation region keeps this resistance at a minimum value.

A common fault or limitation of the JFET switch in its conductive or on state is its power-handling capability. At its optimum conduction level, the internal resistance of the device is in the range of 5 to 20 Ω. The channel can therefore only handle a few hundred milliamperes of I_D at best. In addition, a JFET has a rather low standoff voltage. Seldom do voltage values exceed 40 V. For logic gates, communication switches, and instrumentation applications, the power-handling capability and low-standoff-voltage limitations are not serious problems. When switching applications call for greater levels of power control, other FETs should be used. The V-MOSFET is widely used today in high-power switching applications.

Cutoff Region Operation

JFET operation in the cutoff region is representative of a switch in its *off* or nonconductive state. For this condition of operation to be established, the source drain is energized and the gate–source junction must be reverse biased. When this occurs, the internal source–drain resistance approaches infinity and practically no drain current will pass through the load resistor. In an actual circuit, a very small amount of leakage current flows even when cutoff is achieved. Thus a very small voltage appears across the source–drain. At cutoff, the V_{DS} of the JFET nearly equals the value of the source voltage V_{DD}.

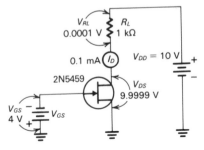

FIGURE 2–37
JFET switch operation in cutoff region.

Figure 2–37 shows a JFET switch operating in the cutoff region. In this circuit, the gate is reverse biased by the value of V_{GS}. When this condition occurs, the I_D drops to an extremely small value. In our circuit a leakage current of 0.1 mA is indicated. Leakage current is a variable that changes with temperature. At 25°C, typical values of leakage current are 0.1 to 2 mA for representative JFETs. In most switching applications, leakage current is ignored.

The voltage and current values of the switching circuit in Figure 2–37 tell a great deal about the response of a JFET in its cutoff state. With the gate–source reverse biased, practically no I_D will flow in the source–drain and load resistor. A reverse-biased gate–channel junction, however, does cause some minority current carriers to enter the channel. These current carriers are responsible for leakage current or off I_D. In this circuit, the off I_D is 0.1 μA at 25°C. Current of this value is generally considered insignificant in normal circuit operation. In this circuit we are using leakage current to permit the calculation of other circuit values. V_{RL} for example, is the voltage drop across the load resistor due to leakage current. It can be determined by the formula

$$V_{RL} = I_D \text{ (off)} \times R_L$$
$$= 0.1 \text{ μA} \times 1 \text{ k}\Omega$$
$$= 0.1 \times 10^{-6} \times 1 \times 10^3$$
$$= 0.1 \times 10^{-6} \quad \text{or} \quad 0.0001 \text{ V}$$

With 0.0001 V across R_L, the V_{DS} of the JFET in its off state is

$$V_{DS} = V_{DD} - V_{RL}$$
$$= 10 \text{ V} - 0.0001 \text{ V}$$
$$= 9.9999 \text{ V}$$

Knowing the off V_{DS} of a JFET permits the calculation of its internal resistance or off R_{DS}. At cutoff the R_{DS} is

$$R_{DS} = \frac{V_{DS}}{I_D \text{ (off)}}$$
$$= \frac{9.9999 \text{ V}}{0.1 \text{ μA}}$$
$$= \frac{9.9999 \text{ V}}{0.1 \times 10^{-6}}$$
$$= 99.999 \times 10^6 \quad \text{or} \quad 99.999 \text{ M}\Omega$$

This indicates that the internal resistance of an off JFET is actually 99.999 MΩ instead of an infinite value. In most low-voltage switching applications, an internal resistance of this value is practically the same as being infinite. This means that a practical switching circuit has all the source voltage across the source–drain, with no V_{RL}. In most industrial switching applications, a cutoff JFET responds as an ideal switch.

MOSFET Switching

Metal oxide semiconductor FETs are widely used as switching devices in logic gates and as discrete device switches. In general, the operation of this device is very similar to that of a JFET switch. Differences exist, however, in biasing procedures and channel construction. The gate of a MOSFET, for example, is insulated from the channel. Switching is controlled by altering the polarity of the gate–source voltage. The channel of a depletion-type device is directly interconnected, whereas the enhancement device has an induced channel. A D-MOSFET is a normally on device or conductive without biasing. The E-MOSFET is classified as a normally off device without biasing. Control of the MOSFET as a switching device is primarily determined by the device being used. E-MOSFETs tend to be more widely used in industrial applications than are the D-MOSFETs.

CMOS Switching

A rather common modification of MOSFET technology is the *complementary* or CMOS device. CMOS switching is used in digital devices to provide 0- or +5-V outputs while consuming very little power from the source. CMOSFET switching technology is the operational basis of an integrated-circuit logic family.

Figure 2–38 shows a cross-sectional view of a CMOS switch and a schematic representation of its internal construction. Note that the switch consists of complementary connected P-MOS and N-MOS enhancement MOSFETs. The two devices are constructed on a common substrate and interconnected. Only four terminal connections are needed for the assembly. The input lead is commonly connected to the gate of both transistors. The output of each transistor is also connected to a common lead.

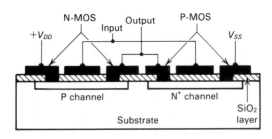

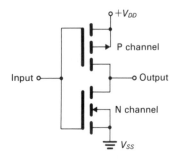

FIGURE 2–38
CMOS switch.

The drain of the N device is connected to the source of the P device in a series configuration. Operational energy is supplied through the two remaining source–drain leads.

Operation of the CMOS switch of Figure 2–38 is based on the polarity or value of voltage applied to the common-gate terminal. A positive voltage applied to the input drives the N-MOS transistor *on* and the P-MOS device *off* and changes the output to its low or 0 V state. A load resistor connected to the output would be nonconductive or in the off state. Changing the input to a low-level or negative value drives the P-MOS device *on* and the N-MOS device *off*, and switches the output high or to its +V_{DD} value. Current flows through the load resistor, indicating conduction or on-state operation. A CMOS switch is unique when compared with single-component FETs. The switch esentially controls or alters voltage to a load resistor. When voltage is supplied to the load, the switch is nonconductive. No output voltage represents the *off* or conductive state. The internal resistance of this device approximates that of an ideal switch. The entire assembly can be made extremely small, which is a very desirable feature in IC construction.

QUESTIONS

1. Briefly explain the difference between power control by passive devices and active devices.

2. How does an *npn* bipolar transistor achieve amplification?

3. What are the alpha and beta of a transistor amplifier? Use the data at point A on the V_{CE}–I_C curves of Figure 2–7.

4. How could the IE of a bipolar transistor be determined from a family of V_{CE}–I_C curves?

5. What is meant by the term *quiescent* or *Q-point* on a family of V_{CE}–I_C curves?

6. What are the two extreme conditions of operation of a bipolar transistor represented by a load line?

7. How is the input curve of a bipolar transistor used to show the response of an ac input signal?

8. Explain the differences in common-base, common-emitter, and common-collector amplifiers with respect to A_V, A_i, Z_o, Z_{in}, and phase.

9. What is the construction difference between a bipolar transistor and a JFET?

10. Explain how amplification is achieved with a JFET.

11. What are the ohmic and pinch-off regions of a JFET?

12. What is a dynamic transfer curve of a JFET?

13. How does a MOSFET differ from a JFET?

14. What is meant by the term *enhancement-MOSFET*?

15. Explain how an E-MOSFET achieves amplification.

16. What is meant by the term *depletion-MOSFET*?

17. Explain how a D-MOSFET achieves amplification.

18. What is meant by the term *V-MOSFET*?

19. What are some of the advantages of a V-MOSFET over bipolar transistors or general-purpose FETs?

20. Why is it desirable for a JFET switch to operate in the saturation region when in the on state?

21. How is CMOS switching different from that of a single JFET?

PROBLEMS

1. Determine the voltage amplification (A_V) of an active device when the input voltage (V_{in}) is 0.2 V p-p and the output voltage (V_o) is 10 V p-p.

2. What is the current amplification (A_i) of an active device with input current (I_{in}) of 5 μA and an output current (I_o) of 10 mA?

3. In a common-emitter amplifier, a change in base current from 0.1 to 0.5 mA causes a change in collector current of 15 to 60 mA. How much beta does this indicate?

4. If the base current of a transistor reads 0.4 mA when the emitter current is 31 mA, what is the collector current?

5. What are the alpha and beta of the transistor in Problem 4?

6. In a JFET, a V_G change of 3 to 4 V causes a change in I_D from 2 to 5 mA. What is the forward transconductance or g_m?

7. The leakage current of the JFET switch in Figure 2–37 changes to 400 μA when the temperature rises to 50° C. What influence does this have on the value of R_{DS}?

ACTIVITIES

ACTIVITY 2–1: Load-line Development

Objective: To develop a load line for a bipolar junction transistor amplifier in order to see how it responds graphically.

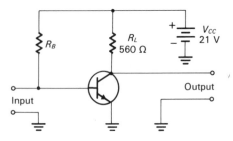

FIGURE 2–39
Circuit.

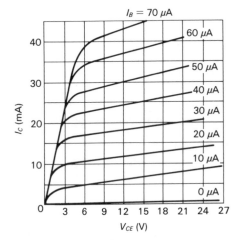

FIGURE 2–40
V_{CE}/I_C **curves.**

Procedure:

1. Develop a load line for the circuit in Figure 2–39 on the $I_C–V_{CE}$ curves of Figure 2–40. If possible, make a duplicate copy of the curves instead of marking in the book.

2. Determine the two extreme conditions of operation for the load line. Connect these two points on the curves with a straight line.

3. Select an operating point of 30 μA. Label this as point Q.

4. Determine the V_{CE} and I_C values for the operating point. This represents the static condition of operation.

5. Assume that a 0.2 V p-p ac signal causes I_B to change from 50 to 10 μA. What is the resulting V_{CE} and I_C? Determine the ac beta and A_v when this occurs.

ACTIVITY 2–2: DC Amplification with a BJT

Objective: To construct a BJT dc amplifier and measure its operating voltages.

Procedure:

1. Connect the dc amplifier of Figure 2–41. A variety of general-purpose *npn* transistors can be used for the circuit.

2. Before applying dc power to the circuit, adjust the potentiometer (R_1) to its mid-range. Turn on V_{CC} and adjust R_1 to produce 100 μA. Then measure V_{CE}, V_{BE}, and I_C.

3. Determine the dc beta and A_v for the circuit.

4. Adjust R_1 to produce different values of I_B such as 200 μA, 500 μA, and 1 mA. Measure and record the value of V_{CE}, I_C, and V_{BE} for each value of I_B.

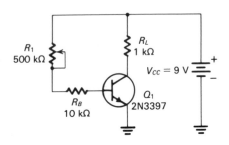

FIGURE 2–41
DC amplifier.

5. If possible, connect an oscillosope to the output of the circuit and observe the dc voltage level. Alter the value of R_1 while observing the change in dc level. Describe your observations.

ACTIVITY 2–3: AC Amplification with a BJT

Objective: To build an ac amplifier with a BJT and test its operation.

Procedure:

1. Construct the ac amplifier of Figure 2–42. A 2N3397 *npn* transistor is recommended for this circuit. It is possible to use a variety of other general-purpose transistors, however.

2. Adjust the ac signal source to produce a 1-V p-p signal at 1 kHz. Turn on the V_{CC} source.

3. Measure the ac input voltage and output voltage. Determine the A_v for this condition of operation.

4. With an oscilloscope, observe the input and output signals of the circuit. Make a sketch of your findings.

5. Prepare your oscilloscope for external sync

operation. Connect the sync input lead to the collector of the transistor. Observe the wave forms across R_E, R_2, and the output. Make a sketch of your observations showing signal levels and phase relationships.

6. Move the vertical probe of the oscilloscope to the output of the amplifier and increase the signal input level until the wave becomes distorted. Describe the distortion.

ACTIVITY 2–4: Transistor Switching

Objective: To build a bipolar junction transistor switch and measure current and voltage values for on and off operating conditions.

Procedure:

1. Construct the BJT switch of Figure 2–20. A variety of general-purpose *npn* transistors can be used for this circuit. Use a 100-kΩ resistor for R_b.

2. To turn on the transistor, connect R_B to the base. To turn off the transistor, disconnect the base resistor. Prepare the transistor for *on* operation.

3. Apply V_{CC} to the circuit and turn on the transistor. Measure and record the V_{CE}, V_{RL}, V_{BE}, V_B, I_C, and I_B.

4. Turn off the transistor. Measure and record V_{CE}, V_{RL}, V_{BE}, V_B, I_C, and I_B.

5. Calculate the internal resistance of the transistor for each condition of operation.

ACTIVITY 2–5: JFET Amplifiers

Objective: To build a JFET small-signal amplifier and test its operation.

Procedure:

1. Construct the JFET small-signal amplifier of Figure 2–43.

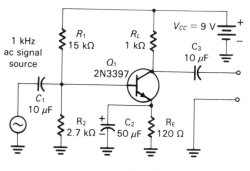

FIGURE 2–42
AC amplifier.

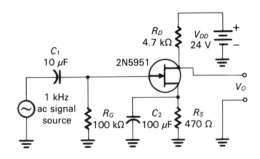

FIGURE 2–43
Small-signal amplifier.

2. Before applying operating power to the circuit, adjust the signal source to produce a 1-V p-p, 1-kHz signal. This should be measured across the gate resistor R_G.

3. Turn on the V_{DD} source and adjust it to 24 V.

4. Connect an oscilloscope across the output. Adjust the input signal voltage to produce the greatest output with a minimum of distortion. Make a sketch of the output wave form and record the output signal level.

5. Move the vertical probe of the oscilloscope to the gate to observe the input signal level. Make a sketch of the observed wave form and record its value. Calculate the A_v for the amplifier.

6. Measure the ac voltage across R_s and calculate the drain current (I_D). This should be an rms value.

7. Measure the rms input voltage across R_G.

8. Calculate the transconductance (g_m) of the circuit.

ACTIVITY 2–6: JFET Switching

Objective: To build and test the operation of a JFET switch.

Procedure:

1. Construct the JFET switch of Figure 2–37.

2. Note that the gate is energized by an independent dc source. Adjust V_{GS} to a value of approximately -4 V. Turn on the V_{DD} source.

3. Measure and record the value of V_{DS}, V_{R_L}, V_{GS}, and I_D. What operating condition do these measurements represent?

4. Adjust V_{GS} to produce 0 V. This can be accomplished by disconnecting V_{GS} or reducing its value to 0 V. Calculate the internal resistance of the JFET for this condition of operation.

5. Measure and record the value of V_{DS}, V_{R_L}, V_{GS}, and I_D. Calculate the internal resistance of the JFET for this condition of operation. What condition of operation does this represent?

The amplitude control function of an industrial system is largely achieved today by operational amplifiers. An operational amplifier or op-amp is a high-performance, directly coupled amplifier circuit containing several transistor devices. The entire assembly is built on a small silicon substrate and packaged as an integrated circuit. ICs of this type are capable of high-gain signal amplification from dc to several million hertz.

An op-amp is a modular, multistage amplifying device with differential input. The assembled unit approximates the characteristics of an ideal amplifier. This includes such things as infinite voltage gain, infinite impedance, zero output impedance, zero output voltage when the two inputs are equal, and high bandwidth.

In practice, an operational amplifier does not actually achieve the properties of an ideal amplifier. It does, however, approximate these properties rather closely. It has open-loop gain capabilities in the range of 200,000 with an input impedance of approximately 2 MΩ. The output impedance is rather low, with values in the range of 50 Ω or less. Its bandwidth or ability to amplify different frequencies is rather good. The gain does, however, have a tendency to drop or *roll off* as the frequency increases. This roll-off characteristic occurs at a rate of -6 dB/octave or -20 dB/decade. An *octave* is a point where the frequency doubles its value while a decade is ten times the previous value. The decrease in amplification continues with frequency until the output equals the input.

3

Operational Amplifiers

INSIDE THE OP-AMP

The internal construction of an op-amp is quite complex and usually contains a large number of discrete components. A person working

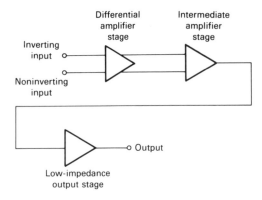

FIGURE 3-1
Op-amp diagram.

with an op-amp does not ordinarily need to be concerned with its internal construction. It is helpful, however, to have some general understanding of what the internal circuitry accomplishes. This permits the user to see how the device performs and indicates some of its limitations as a functioning unit.

The internal circuitry of an op-amp can be divided into three functional units. Figure 3-1 shows a simplified diagram of the internal functions of an op-amp. Notice that each function is enclosed in a triangle. Electronic schematics use the triangle to denote the amplification function. This diagram shows that the op-amp has three basic amplification functions. These functions are generally called *stages* of amplification. A stage of amplification contains one or more active devices and all the associated components needed to achieve amplification.

The first stage or input of an op-amp is usually a differential amplifier. This amplifier has two inputs, which are labeled V_1 and V_2. It provides high gain of the signal difference supplied to the two inputs and low gain for common signals applied to both inputs simultaneously. The input impedance is high to any applied signal. The output of the amplifer is generally two signals of equal amplitude and

180° out of phase. This could be described as a push–pull input and output.

One or more intermediate stages of amplification follow the differential amplifier. Figure 3-1 shows an op-amp with only one intermediate stage. Functionally, this amplifier is designed to shift the operating point to a zero level at the output and has high current and voltage gain capabilities. Increased gain is needed to drive the output stage without loading down the input. The intermediate stage generally has two inputs and a single-ended output.

The output stage of an op-amp has a rather low output impedance and is responsible for developing the current needed to drive an external load. Its input impedance must be great enough that it does not load down the output of the intermediate amplifier. The output stage can be an emitter-follower amplifier or two transistors connected in a complementary-symmetry configuration. Voltage gain is rather low in this stage with a sizable amount of current gain.

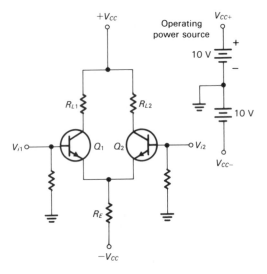

FIGURE 3-2
Simplified differential amplifier.

Differential Amplifier Stage

A differential amplifier is the key or operational basis of most op-amps. This amplifier is best described as having two identical or balanced transistors sharing a single emitter resistor. Each transistor has an input and an output. A schematic diagram of a simplified differential amplifier is shown in Figure 3–2. Notice that the circuit is energized by a dual-polarity or split-power supply. The source leads are labeled $+V_{cc}$ and $-V_{cc}$ and measured with respect to a common ground lead.

Operation of a differential amplifier is based on its response to input signals applied to the base. Grounding one base and applying an input signal to the other base produces two output signals. These signals have the same amplitude but are inverted 180°. This type of input causes the amplifier to respond in its differential mode of operation.

When two signals of equal amplitude and polarity are applied to each base at the same time, the resulting output is zero. This type of input causes a difference or canceling voltage to appear across the commonly connected emitter resistor. In a sense, the differential amplifier responds as a balanced bridge to identical input signals. There is no output when the circuit is balanced and output when it is unbalanced. This is called the *common-mode condition* of operation. A differential amplifier is designed to reject signals common to both inputs. The term *common-mode rejection ratio* (CMRR) is used to described this action of the amplifier. CMRR is a unique characteristic of the differential amplifier. Undesirable noise, interference, or ac hum can be rejected by this operating condition.

Figure 3–3 shows a simplified schematic of a differential amplifier connected for differential mode operation. In this circuit an input signal is applied to the base of Q_1, and the base of Q_2 is left open or in a floating state. This condition causes signals to be developed at both outputs and across the emitter resistor. The emitter signal, as indicated, is in phase with the input. The two output signals are out of phase with each other and have a substantial degree of amplification. Output V_{o1} is out of phase with the input and V_{o2} is in phase.

A differential amplifier will produce two output signals when only one input signal is applied. Coupling of the input signal from Q_1 to Q_2 is accomplished through the emitter resistor. The positive alternation of the input signal, for example, causes increased forward bias of Q_1. This causes an increase in the conduction of Q_1. With more I_E, there is a greater voltage developed across the emitter resistor. This in turn causes both emitters to be less negative. The conduction of Q_1 is not appreciably influenced by this voltage because it has an external signal applied to its input. Q_2 is, however, directly influenced by the reduced negative voltage to its emitter. This causes the conduction of Q_2 to be reduced. A reduction in current through Q_2 causes less voltage drop across R_{c2} and the collector voltage to swing in the positive direction. In effect, an input signal

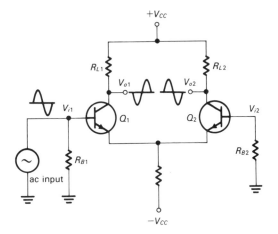

FIGURE 3–3
AC differential amplifier.

applied to the base of Q_1 reduces the V_E of Q_2, which in turn increases the value of the output voltage V_{o2}. An input signal is therefore coupled to Q_2 by the commonly connected emitter resistor.

The negative alternation of the input signal causes a reversal of the action just described. Q_1, for example, will be less conductive and Q_2 will have increased conduction. This action causes a reduction of I_c through Q_1 and an increase swing in the value of V_{o1}. Increased conduction of Q_2 causes a corresponding reduction in V_{o2}. The two output signals continue to be 180° out of phase. In effect, both alternations of the input appear in the output. A differential amplifier connected in the differential mode will develop two output signals that are reflective of the entire input signal.

Differential amplifiers respond in primarily the same way when the inputs are reversed. In this case, an input signal is applied to the base of Q_2 with the base of Q_1 open or floating. V_{o2} is out of phase with the input and V_{o1} is in phase. The amplitude or output signal level of the amplifier is still based on the signal difference between the two inputs. With only one signal applied to the input at a time, the amplifier sees a very large differential input and developes a sizable output voltage.

The differential amplifier of Figure 3–3 is rarely used in op-amp construction today. Ordinarily, the resistance of R_E needs to be quite large in order to have good coupling and common-mode rejection capabilities. Large resistance values are rather difficult to fabricate in IC construction. R_E can, however, be replaced with a transistor. This transistor and its associated components are called a constant-current source.

Figure 3–4 shows a differential amplifier with a constant-current source in the emitter circuit. Transistor Q_3, in this case, has a fixed or constant bias voltage. This voltage maintains the internal resistance of Q_3 at a rather

high value. In some op-amps the constant-current source can be altered by an external base bias voltage. This is achieved by having an external lead connection to the base of Q_3. The current source of the differential amplifier can then be altered to some extent. The resistance or impedance of Q_3 can be adjusted to meet the design parameters of a specific circuit application. When the impedance of Q_3 is high, the common-mode gain of the amplifier is very low and signal coupling is good. The constant-current source of an input differential amplifier is an important part of op-amp construction.

The differential amplifier of an op-amp can be made with other transistor devices and connected in a variety of different configurations. Two rather common configurations are shown in Figure 3–5. The amplifier of Figure 3–5(A) is achieved with bipolar junction transistors connected in a Darlington-pair configuration.

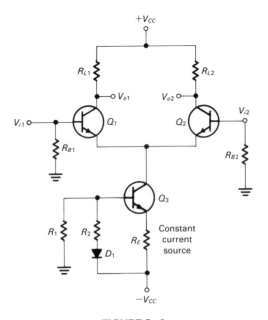

FIGURE 3–4
Differential amplifier with constant-current source in the emitter.

The input impedance of this circuit is increased by a factor of 1.5 times the beta. The beta of each transistor branch is also increased by the same value. Darlington-pair devices respond at high speed to a wide range of frequencies.

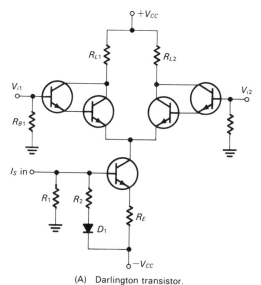

(A) Darlington transistor.

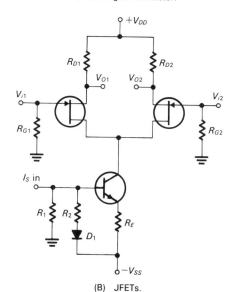

(B) JFETs.

FIGURE 3–5
Differential amplifiers.

The differential amplifier of Figure 3–5(B) employs JFETs instead of bipolar junction transistors (BJTs) in its input. The JFET input is extremely high resistant when compared with the BJT. Typical input impedance values are 10 MΩ for this type of differential input. Op-amps employing the JFET input are widely used in process control, medical instrumentation, and other applications requiring very low input current values.

Intermediate Amplifier Stage

The intermediate amplifier stage of an op-amp follows the input differential amplifier stage and feeds the output stage. This part of the op-amp is primarily responsible for additional circuit gain and dc voltage stabilization. Figure 3–6 shows a simplification of the internal circuitry of a representative op-amp. Note that the intermediate amplifier stage is in the center of the circuit. It contains a differential amplifier with a constant-current source transistor. The amplifier has a push–pull differential input and a single-ended output. Transistors Q_3, Q_4, Q_7, and diode D_2 make up this part of circuit. As a rule, the intermediate differential amplifier has rather high gain capabilities compared with the input differential amplifier.

The intermediate amplifier stage of Figure 3–6 is also equipped with a voltage-stabilizing transistor Q_5. This transistor evaluates the signal at the emitters of Q_3 and Q_4. Since the intermediate differential amplifier is driven by a push–pull signal, there should be a zero reference level at its input when the first differential amplifier is operating properly. If an operational error occurs, a correcting voltage is developed by Q_5 across R_5 of the input amplifier. Q_5 also feeds the error bias voltage to the constant-current transistor Q_7. This voltage further reduces the error and improves the common-

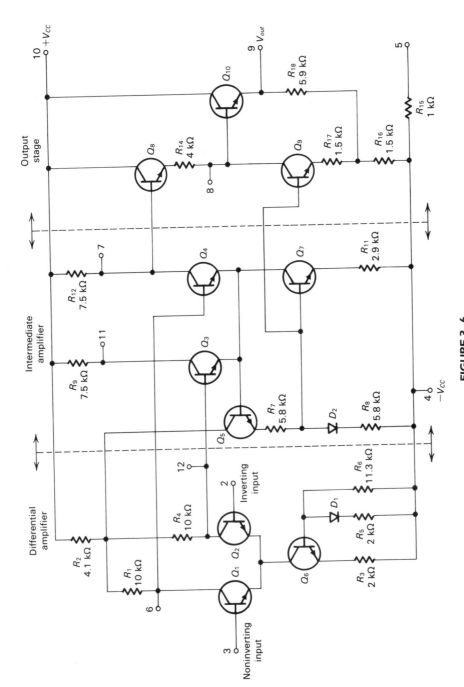

FIGURE 3–6
Internal circuitry of a general-purpose op-amp.

mode rejection capabilities of the amplifier. The output of the intermediate amplifier stage is zero voltage level corrected and appears at the collector of Q_4.

Output Stage

The output stage of an op-amp is primarily designed to develop the power needed to drive an external load device. In accomplishing this function, there must be a maximum output voltage signal developed across a low-impedance load. The output of an op-amp may be single ended or two transistors connected in a complementary-symmetry power amplifier.

The output stage of Figure 3–6 is a single-ended emitter-follower amplifier. This part of the op-amp is on the right side of the schematic diagram. Transistors Q_8, Q_9, and Q_{10} make up the output stage. Q_8 is an emitter-follower driver transistor. Q_9 serves as a constant-

current source for the output transistor Q_{10}. The single-ended output of the intermediate differential amplifier stage drives the base of Q_8. This transistor matches the output impedance of Q_4 to the low output impedance of Q_{10}. Maximum signal transfer is accomplished through Q_8.

The signal gain of a single-ended output stage must be controlled or limited to some extent in order to provide good stability. Transistor Q_9 performs this function in the output stage of Figure 3–6. Functionally, this transistor has a dual role. It responds as a constant-current source for the driver transistor Q_8 and as a feedback regulator for the output transistor. Feedback is regulated by maintaining the current through R_{16} at a rather constant level by conduction of Q_9. The constant-current function of Q_9 maintains the emitter of Q_8 at a consistent level to reduce level shifting and improve common-mode rejection.

Many op-amps employ two transistors in a complementary-symmetry output circuit instead of the single-ended emitter-follower circuit. The emitter resistor of a single-ended emitter-follower output generally consumes a great deal of power at high current levels. The complementary-symmetry output circuit overcomes this problem by using two transistors. The transistors are *NPN* and *PNP* complements that have the same or symmetrical characteristics. Figure 3–7 shows a simplification of the complementary-symmetry power amplifier used in many op-amps today.

The output of the complementary-symmetry amplifier of Figure 3–7 is developed across an external load connected to pin 8. Note that this terminal is connected directly to the emitters of Q_{10} and Q_{11}. These transistors are connected in a common-collector circuit configuration. This type of configuration has a low-impedance output.

A resistive divider network is connected across $+V_{cc}$ and $-V_{ee}$. The base of each tran-

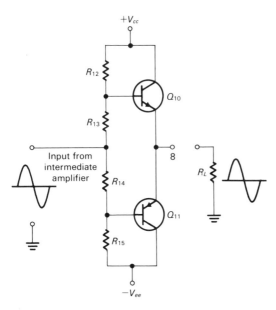

FIGURE 3–7
Complementary-symmetry output of an op-amp.

sistor is biased at cutoff or slightly above cut-off by this network. A signal applied to the input is fed directly to the base of each transistor. The positive alternation of an ac signal causes the *NPN* transistor Q_{10} to be conductive. Conduction current flows from ground through R_L, Q_{10}, and to $+V_{cc}$ for this alternation. Q_{11} is driven further into cutoff by this alternation and has no output. For the negative alternation, Q_{11} is forward biased and goes into conduction. Q_{10} is reverse biased by this alternation and goes into a nonconductive state. Conduction of Q_{11} is from $-V_{ee}$ through Q_{11} and R_L to ground. The negative alternation develops output across R_L. This means that each transistor goes into conduction for one alternation. The output current through R_L is a combination of the current flow produced by each transistor. This type of amplifier can develop large amounts of current with good power gain and low output impedance.

Op-amp Schematic Symbol

An op-amp has at least five terminals or connections in its construction. Two of these are for the power supply voltage, two for differential input, and one for the output. There may be other terminals in the makeup of this device depending on its internal construction or intended work function. Each terminal is generally attached to a schematic symbol at some convenient location. Numbers located near each terminal of the symbol indicate pin designations.

The schematic symbol of an op-amp is generally displayed as a triangular-shaped wedge. The triangle symbol in this case denotes the amplification function. Figure 3–8 shows a typical symbol with its terminals labeled. The point or apex of the triangle identifies the output. The two leads labeled $-$ and $+$ identify the differential input terminals. The $-$ sign indicates inverting input and the $+$ sign denotes

noninverting input. A signal applied to the $-$ input will be inverted 180° at the output. Standard op-amp symbols usually have the inverting input located in the upper-left corner. A signal applied to the $+$ input will not be inverted and remains in phase with the input. The $+$ input is located in the lower-left corner of the symbol. In all cases, the two inputs are clearly identified as $+$ and $-$ inside the triangle symbol.

Connections or terminals on the sides of the triangle symbol are used to identify a variety of functions. The most significant of these are the two power supply terminals. Normally, the positive voltage terminal ($+V$) is positioned on the top side and the negative voltage ($-V$) on the bottom side. In practice, most op-amps are supplied by a split or divided power supply. This supply has $+V$, ground, and $-V$ terminals. It is important that the correct voltage polarity be supplied to the appropriate terminals or the device may be permanently damaged. A good rule to follow for most op-amps is not to connect the ground lead of the power supply to $-V$. An exception to this rule is the current-differencing amplifier or CDA op-amp. These op-amps are made to be compatible with digital logic ICs and are supplied by a straight 5-V voltage source.

The actual schematic symbol of an op-amp generally has its terminals numbered and the element names omitted. There is a pin-out key

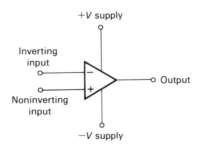

FIGURE 3–8
Op-amp schematic symbol.

schematic and connection diagrams

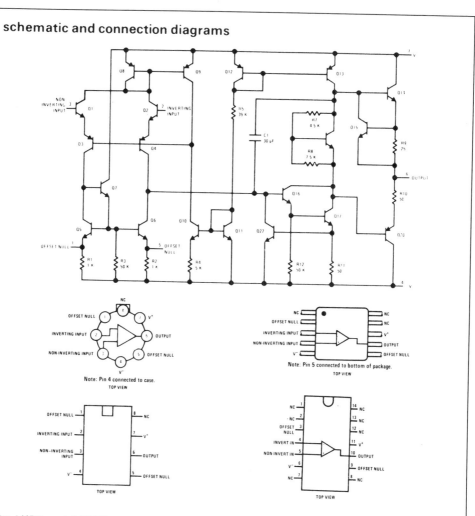

The LM741 and LM741C are general purpose operational amplifiers which feature improved performance over industry standards like the LM709. They are direct, plug-in replacements for the 709C, LM201, MC1439 and 748 in most applications.

The offset voltage and offset current are guaranteed over the entire common mode range. The amplifiers also offer many features which make their application nearly foolproof: overload protection on the input and output, no latch-up when the common mode range is exceeded, as well as freedom from oscillations.

The LM741C is identical to the LM741 except that the LM741C has its performance guaranteed over a 0°C to 70°C temperature range, instead of -55°C to 125°C.

FIGURE 3–9
Schematic diagram of an operational amplifier. (Courtesy of National Semiconductor Corp.)

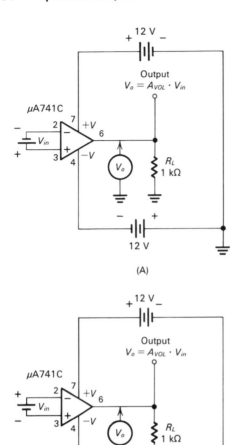

FIGURE 3–10
Inverting dc amplifiers.

solute maximum ratings, electrical characteristics, and typical performance curves.

Figure 3–10 shows the schematic symbol of a uA741 connected as an open-loop amplifier. The power supply voltage terminals are labeled $+V$, $-V$, and ground. Typical supply voltages are ± 15, ± 12, and ± 6 V. The absolute maximum voltage that can be applied to this particular op-amp is 36 V between $+V$ and $-V$ or ± 18 V. The output of an op-amp circuit is generally connected through an external load resistor to ground. R_L, in this case, serves as an external load for the uA741. All the output voltage developed by the op-amp appears across R_L. This type of connection is described as a single-ended output. The operational load current for this device will be of a value between 10 and 15 mA. The maximum output or saturation voltage that can be developed is approximately 90% of the supply voltage. For a $+15$ V supply, the saturation voltage is $+13.5$ V. An ac output would be $+13.5$ and -13.5 or 27 V p-p. The current and voltage limits of the output restrict the load resistance to a value of approximately 1 kΩ. Most op-amps have a built-in load current limiting feature. The uA741 is limited to a maximum short-circuit current of 25 mA. This feature prevents the device from being destroyed in the event of a direct short in the load.

The inputs of an op-amp are labeled minus $(-)$ for inverting and plus $(+)$ for the noninverting function. This is also used to denote that the inputs are differentially related. Essentially, this means that the polarity of the developed output is based on the voltage difference between the two inputs. In Figure 3–10(A), the output voltage is positive with respect to ground. This is the result of the inverting input being made negative with respect to the noninverting input. Reversing the input voltage, as in Figure 3–10(B), causes the output to be negative with respect to ground. For this connection, the noninverting input is negative

to identify the name of each terminal. The manufacturer of the device supplies information sheets that identify the pin-out and operating data. Figure 3–9 shows part of the data sheet for a uA741 linear op-amp. Note the package styles, symbol location, and pin-out key for the device. This sheet also shows ab-

when the inverting input is positive. This condition of operation holds true for both input possibilities. In some applications one input may be grounded. The difference voltage is then made with respect to ground. The inputs of Figure 3–10 are connected in a *floating configuration* that does not employ a ground. For either type of input, the resulting output polarity is always based on the voltage difference. This characteristic of the input makes the op-amp an extremely versatile amplifying device.

Open-loop Voltage Gain

The open-loop voltage gain characteristic of an op-amp refers to an output that is developed when only a difference voltage is applied to the input. The two uA751C op-amps of Figure 3–10 are connected in an open-loop circuit configuration. The open-loop voltage gain (A_{vol}) is a ratio of the output voltage (V_o) divided by the differential input voltage (V_{in}). This is expressed by the formula

$$A_{vol} = \frac{V_o}{V_{in}}$$

The open-loop voltage gain of an op-amp is usually quite large. Typical values are in the range of 10,000 to 200,000. When the differential input voltage is zero, the output voltage is also zero. If a slight difference in input voltage occurs, the output voltage increases accordingly. The output voltage, however, cannot exceed 90% of the source voltage. When the output voltage reaches this level, the amplifier is said to be *saturated*. Due to the high A_{vol} of an op-amp, only a few millivolts of V_{in} are needed to cause it to go into saturation. As a rule, op-amps are rarely used in an open-loop circuit configuration.

To see how an op-amp responds in the open-loop mode of operation, refer to Example 3–1.

Example 3–1: Assume that the op-amps of Figure 3–10 have an A_{vol} of 100,000. The supply voltage is ± 15 V as indicated. What value of V_{in} is needed to cause this amplifier to reach saturation?

Solution: For a representative op-amp, saturation occurs when the output voltage (V_o) reaches approximately 90% of the source voltage. For this circuit, the saturation voltage would be

$$V_{sat} = 0.90 \times +15 \text{ V} = +13.5 \text{ V}$$

Transposing the previous A_{vol} formula for input voltage (V_{in}) causes it to be

$$V_{in} = \frac{V_{sat}}{A_{vol}}$$

The value of V_{in} needed to cause saturation of an op-amp is approximately

$$V_{in} = \frac{+13.5 \text{ V}}{100,000}$$

$$= 135 \text{ }\mu\text{V} \quad \text{or} \quad 135 \times 10^{-6} \text{ V}$$

Input Offset Voltage

Ideally, the output voltage (V_o) of an op-amp should be 0 V when the input voltage is 0 V. In the internal construction of an op-amp, it is extremely difficult to develop perfectly balanced differential amplifiers that will eliminate this problem. Thus there is actually some output voltage even when the input is zero. Values range from microvolts (μV) to millivolts (mV) in a typical circuit.

An input offsetting voltage is used to overcome the unwanted output voltage of an op-amp. The net effect is 0 V at the output when no voltage is applied to the input. This voltage is called the *input offset voltage (V_{io})*. Typical V_{io} values are in the range from a few microvolts to several millivolts. The uA741C op-amp of Figure 4–10 has a V_{io} of 1 mV. As a

general rule, the lower the input offset voltage, the better the quality of the op-amp.

Input Bias Current

The internal construction of an op-amp generally causes input current values of the differential amplifier to be unequal to some extent. Input bias current (I_b) is the average current flowing into or out of the two inputs. This parameter describes the relationship of the two input current values. In general, smaller values of I_b are used with better-quality op-amps.

The type of transistor device used in the construction of the input differential amplifier has a great deal to do with its input bias current. Op-amps with JFET inputs have lower I_b values than bipolar junction transistor inputs. Typical I_b values for the uA741 are in the range of 80 nanoamperes (nA). For a JFET input op-amp such as the LH0042, I_b values drop down to the 5- to 10-picoampere (pA) range. Input bias current values are often used when comparing the quality of different devices.

Input Impedance

The input impedance of an op-amp is the equivalent resistance that an input source sees when connected to the differential input terminals. Normally, the input impedance (Z_{in}) of a conventional op-amp is quite high. Typical values are in the range from 10 kΩ to 1 MΩ. If the Z_{in} of a specific device is unknown, an estimate of the value would be 250 kΩ. Impedance in this case refers to the opposition encountered by either an ac or dc signal voltage.

Input Current

The input current (I_{in}) of a conventional op-amp is usually quite small. A voltage source connected to the differential input sees an extremely high input impedance. Typical I_{in} values are in the range of a few nanoamperes (nA). A nanoampere is one-billionth or 1×10^{-9} amperes. To see how a representative input current of this value occurs, consider the following example.

Example 3–2:   Using one of the op-amps of Figure 3–10, determine the input current for circuit operation at or near the point of saturation. Assume that the Z_{in} is estimated to be 250 kΩ. The input voltage that produces saturation was previously determined to be 135 μV.

Solution:

$$I_{in} = \frac{V_{in}}{Z_{in}}$$

$$= \frac{135 \ \mu V}{250 \ k\Omega}$$

$$= 0.54 \text{ nA} \quad \text{or} \quad 0.00054 \ \mu A$$

With input current values being this small, they are often considered to be negligible in most op-amp circuit calculations.

Slew Rate

The *slew rate* of an op-amp refers to the rate at which its output will change from one voltage to another in a given time. This parameter is extremely important at high frequencies because it indicates how the output responds to a rapidly changing input signal. Slew rate depends on such things as amplifier gain, compensating capacitance, and the polarity of the output voltage. The worse case or slowest slew rate occurs when the gain is at 1 or unity. As a rule, slew rate is generally indicated for unity amplification. Mathematically, slew rate is expressed as

Slew rate (SR) =

$$\frac{\text{Maximum change in output voltage } (\Delta V_o)}{\text{Change in time } (\Delta t)}$$

Slew rate is primarily an indication of how an op-amp responds to different frequencies. A slew rate of 0.5 V/μs means that the output only has time to rise 0.5 V in 1 μs. Since frequency is time dependent, this indicates where certain input frequencies will not have enough time to produce a corresponding output signal. The resulting output is a distorted version of the input. The maximum frequency at which we can obtain an undistorted output is determined by the expression

Frequency (f) =

$$\frac{\text{Slew rate}}{6.28 \times \text{peak output voltage } (V_o)}$$

For the uA741 op-amp, the slew rate is 0.5V/μs. This is used to determine the undistorted output frequency of the op-amp.

Example 3–3: At what maximum frequency can you get an undistorted output voltage of 1 V with the uA741 op-amp?

Solution:

$$f = \frac{\text{SR}}{6.28} \times V_o$$

$$= \frac{1}{6.28} \times \frac{0.5 \text{ V}}{1 \text{ } \mu\text{s}}$$

$$= 0.15924 \times \frac{0.5 \text{ V}}{1 \times 10^{-6}}$$

$$= 0.15924 \times 0.5 \text{ V} \times 10^6$$

$$= 79,620 \text{ Hz}$$

The slew rate of an op-amp is primarily determined by a compensating capacitor that is either internal or externally connected. Essen-

tially, it takes a certain period of time for the capacitor to develop a charge voltage. The value of the capacitor and the charging current determine the response of the capacitor. Since the op-amp has internal constant-current sources to limit the current, the capacitor can only charge at a specified rate. The input signal must occur at a slower rate than the capacitor charge time or some other type of distortion will then occur. When the input frequency is higher than the slew rate limit, the square wave appears as a slope and the sine wave becomes a triangle.

DIFFERENTIAL VOLTAGE COMPARATORS

Op-amps are rarely used in an open-loop circuit configuration. The A_{vol} is generally so high that it is rather difficult to prevent the output (V_o) from being driven into saturation. One application of an op-amp in an open-loop circuit configuration is the differential voltage comparator. Used in this manner, the op-amp simply compares voltage values applied to its two inputs and indicates which is greater.

In Figure 3–11(A), the output voltage swings into full saturation for an extremely small change in input voltage (V_{in}). Note that the noninverting input is referenced at ground or 0 V. If V_{in} swings slightly positive, V_o goes into negative saturation $(-V_{sat})$. A small change in the value of V_{in} in the negative direction causes the output to go into positive saturation $(+V_{sat})$. Used in this manner, the op-amp compares the voltage difference between its inverting input and a zero reference value. An ac voltage applied to the same circuit configuration causes a square wave to appear in the output. The output is inverted or 180° out of phase with the ac input. A com-

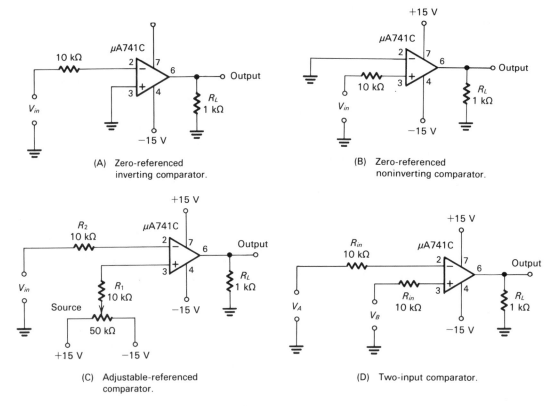

(A) Zero-referenced
inverting comparator.

(B) Zero-referenced
noninverting comparator.

(C) Adjustable-referenced
comparator.

(D) Two-input comparator.

FIGURE 3–11
Op-amp differential comparators.

parator circuit of this type is often called a *wave-shaper*.

Figure 3–11(B) shows a zero voltage referenced comparator for noninverting output. In this type of circuit the V_o detects or indicates the polarity of the input voltage. When V_{in} is positive, the output swings into $+V_{sat}$. A negative value of V_{in} likewise causes the output to reach $-V_{sat}$. An ac input causes an in-phase square wave to appear in the output.

In Figure 3–11(C), V_{in} is compared with a variable reference voltage value. The output voltage only goes positive if V_{in} is made more positive than the voltage level setting of R_3. It also swings negative if V_{in} is more negative than the voltage value adjusted by R_3. A com-

parator of this type has an adjustable reference level. This circuit is designed to produce an output when the input exceeds its referenced level adjustment value.

The circuit of Figure 3–11(D) compares the voltage value of signals applied to both inputs of an op-amp. If V_A is more positive than V_B, at the same time, the output is negative. In the same manner, the output is positive if V_A is more negative than V_B. A similar response occurs if V_B is greater than V_A. In this case, however, the output is of the same polarity as the input to V_B. A comparator of this type is generally used to detect specific voltage values.

An interesting characteristic of the two-input comparator of Figure 3–11(D) is its com-

mon-mode rejection ratio (CMRR). If a signal of the same voltage value and polarity is applied to both inputs at the same time, the output is null or zero. This type of signal is therefore attenuated and will not appear in the output. The CMRR is used in industrial systems to reject noise or to reduce unwanted ac signal voltage values.

INVERTING CONFIGURATION

One of the most widely used industrial op-amp circuit configurations is the inverting amplifier. An amplifier of this type is defined as a circuit that receives a signal voltage at its input and delivers a large undistorted version of the signal at its output. The phase or polarity of the output signal is an inversion of the input. Operation does not ordinarily permit the output to reach saturation. The level of amplification is controlled by a feedback resistor connected between the output and inverting input. This causes the amplifier to have negative feedback. The addition of a feedback resistor permits the amplifier to have a controlled level of amplification. Performance is no longer dependent on the open-loop gain or A_{vol} of the device. Closed-loop voltage gain (A_{vcl}), or simply A_v, can be controlled or adjusted by altering the value of the feedback resistor.

A typical inverting op-amp circuit is shown in Fig. 3–12. This basic circuit consists of an op-amp and three resistors. The noninverting input is connected to ground. Input to the amplifier is applied to the inverting input through resistor R_{in}. The output signal is developed across the load resistor (R_L) and ground. A portion of the output signal is also returned to the inverting input through the feedback resistor (R_f). The value of the inverting input signal is therefore determined by a combination of V_{in} and the output signal fed back through R_f.

To assess the operation of an inverting amplifier, we will describe a number of events that occur rather quickly when it is placed into operation. Assume, for example, that the op-amp of Figure 3–12 is energized by ±15 V. Let us also assume that no signal is initially applied to the input. In this operational state, with no differential input signal applied, the output will be zero or show no output voltage. This represents the quiescent condition or steady state of operation.

Assume now that an input signal of +1 V is applied to the inverting input of our op-amp. With this voltage applied, the inverting input immediately goes positive. This action causes V_o to immediately swing in the negative direction. At the same instant, a negative-going voltage is fed back to the inverting input through R_f. This immediately reduces the original +1 V applied to the inverting input. The feedback signal does not completely cancel the V_{in} signal. It simply reduces the value. The +1 V signal is immediately changed to a value of only a few microvolts. This means that the inverting input is now controlled or limited to a rather low voltage value. As a general rule, the input is considered to be at ap-

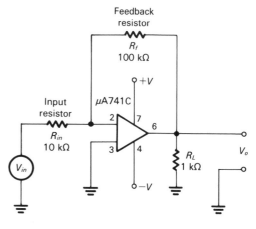

FIGURE 3–12
Inverting op-amp.

proximately zero. Through the feedback loop, the inverting input voltage is held to approximately zero regardless of the value of V_{in}.

To see how an inverting op-amp responds to an input signal, we must consider the virtual ground concept. A *virtual ground* is the point of a circuit which is at zero potential (0 V) but is not actually connected to ground. In an inverting op-amp circuit, a virtual ground appears at the inverting input terminal. With the noninverting input grounded, the voltage at the inverting input will never be greater than a fraction of a millivolt. V_{in}, V_{out}, R_{in}, and R_f all tend to hold the voltage of the inverting input to practically zero. With this condition existing, the inverting input responds as if it were grounded. It is a common practice to refer to this point of an op-amp as a virtual ground.

Refer now to the inverting op-amp and its equivalent circuit in Figure 3–13. Keep in mind that the voltage at the inverting input terminal is nearly zero and its input impedance is approximately 1 MΩ. Assume now that an input of +1 V is applied to V_{in}. This condition causes 1 mA of current to flow through R_{in}. Note the I_{in} calculations near the input of the equivalent circuit. This shows that a 1-V drop will appear across R_{in}. The inverting input continues to remain at zero or virtual ground. The 1 mA of current entering the equivalent circuit at the V_G point must therefore all flow through the feedback resistor (R_f). Very little input control flows into the inverting input. This means that practically all the 1 mA flows through the 10-kΩ feedback resistor. The voltage drop across R_f will be 1 mA times 10 kΩ, or 10 V. Note the calculation near R_f of the equivalent circuit. As indicated, the polarity of the output voltage is negative with respect to the V_G point. This shows the inverting characteristic of the op-amp.

At this point it may be asked, how does an op-amp control a −10-V output signal if the inverting input voltage and current are both

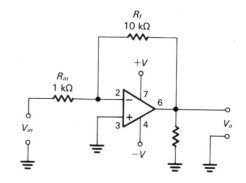

(A)   Inverting operational amplifier.

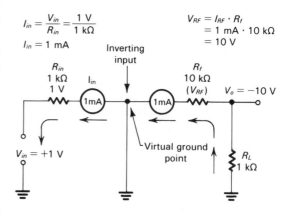

(B)   Equivalent circuit.

FIGURE 3–13
Inverting op-amp.

zero? In response to this question, it should be pointed out that the inverting input terminal is considered to be at a virtual zero. In a circuit, a signal applied to V_{in} will always cause some voltage and current to appear at the inverting input terminal. The actual value of it is so small that it is considered to be zero. In practice, these values are usually not measurable. In effect, this means that the right side of R_{in} is considered to be zero and the left side is V_{in}. Across the feedback resistor, the right side is V_o and the left side is zero.

The closed-loop voltage amplification of an inverting amplifier is primarily determined by the value of R_{in} and R_f. For the op-amp of Figure 3–13, this would be based on the formula

$$A_{vcl} = \frac{-R_f}{R_{in}}$$

$$= \frac{-10 \text{ k}\Omega}{1 \text{ k}\Omega}$$

$$= -10 \text{ V}$$

The negative sign of the formula denotes the inversion function of the op-amp. Industrial applications of the inverting amplifier have A_v values that range from -1 to $-10,000$.

SUMMING OPERATIONS

A slight modification of the inverting op-amp will permit it to achieve the mathematical operation of addition. Used in this manner, it can add dc voltages or ac wave forms. Adding or summing operations are very useful in analog computers and in analog-to-digital conversion functions.

Summing can be achieved when two or more voltage values are applied to the input of an op-amp. A representative schematic diagram of an adder is shown in Figure 3–14. Note that circuit is an inverting op-amp with two inputs. The resistor values are all 1 kΩ. The resulting output voltage that appears across R_1 is the sum of the input voltages applied to V_1 and V_2. For simplicity, the circuit shows the addition of dc voltage values. Keep in mind that it can add ac voltage values equally as well.

The voltage gain of our summing op-amp is 1. This is based on the resistance values of R_{in} and R_f. The output, however, will be -1 due to the inversion characteristic of the op-amp. If a positive value is desired, the output of the adder can be followed by an op-amp with a gain of 1.

The voltage applied to each input of a summing amplifier responds as an independent source. Input V_1 does not alter or change the input of V_2. This is primarily due to the virtual ground appearing at the inverting input terminal. In Figure 3–14, note that input V_1 causes 3 mA of current to flow through input resistor R_1. With only this voltage applied, the feedback resistor R_f would have a resulting 3 mA through it. The load resistor R_4 would likewise have 3 mA and develop an output voltage of 3 V. An applied input voltage of $+3$ V produces a corresponding -3 V output. Therefore, 3 V $+$ 0 V equals 3 V.

Applying $+3$ V to V_1 and $+2$ V to V_2 causes 3 mA and 2 mA to flow through the respective resistors. Current flow at the inverting input will be the sum of these two values or 5 mA. This point of the circuit is usually called the *summing point* instead of the virtual ground. In effect, this common point isolates V_1 from V_2. The combined current from this

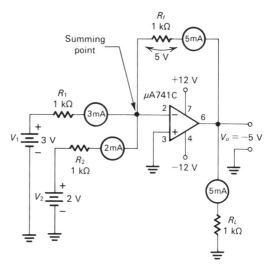

FIGURE 3–14
Op-amp summing operation.

point must all pass through the feedback resistor R_f. Thus R_f has 5 mA of current. The voltage drop across R_f will be 5 V with V_o being -5 V due to the inverting characteristic. A similar current value flows through the load resistor R_1. In effect, an input of $+3$ V and $+2$ V causes the output to increase to -5 V. The summing function is expressed by the formula

$$V_o = -(V_1 + V_2)$$

This formula is used only when the input resistors are of the same value. Any number of input voltages may be added by this circuit. The

input resistors must be the same value for each input voltage.

Figure 3–15 shows three variations of the summing circuit. Circuit A shows the standard adding function. This particular circuit simply adds the input voltages and produces the sum at the output. All resistors must be of an equal value in order for the circuit to respond correctly.

The op-amp of Figure 3–15(B) achieves both summing and gain. The input resistors are of the same value. The feedback resistor is a multiple of the input resistors. The sum of V_1,

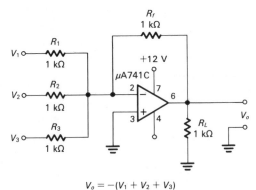

$$V_o = -(V_1 + V_2 + V_3)$$

(A) Standard adder.

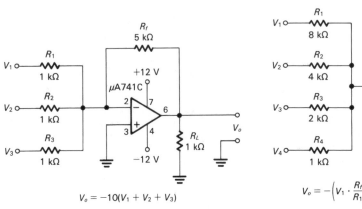

$$V_o = -10(V_1 + V_2 + V_3)$$

(B) Adder with gain.

$$V_o = -\left(V_1 \cdot \frac{R_f}{R_1} + V_2 \cdot \frac{R_f}{R_2} + V_3 \cdot \frac{R_f}{R_3} + V_4 \cdot \frac{R_f}{R_4}\right)$$

(C) Scaling adder.

FIGURE 3–15
Summing amplifiers.

V_2, and V_3 in this case is multiplied by a factor of 5. Note the formula for this mathematical operation.

Figure 3–15(C) is a scaling adder. The input to this circuit sees different weighting factors in the input resistors. An input of $+1$ V applied to V_1 would produce a 1 V output. In the same manner, V_2 would be 2 V, V_3 would be 4 V, and V_4 would be 8 V. This means that the inputs are scaled down by the powers of 2. The resulting output of V_4 carries eight times more weight than V_1. Scaling adders are frequently used in digital-to-analog converter functions. The formula for determining the output of a scaled adder notes the difference in the weighting factor. It should be apparent that voltages fed into the smaller-valued input resistors are more heavily scaled because they produce a larger voltage output.

NONINVERTING OP-AMPS

A noninverting op-amp can provide controlled voltage gain with high input impedance and no inversion of the input–output signals. Voltage gain is dependent on the input voltage and feedback resistors. An unusual feature of the noninverting op-amp circuit configuration is the placement of the feedback resistor network. It is placed in the inverting input with a resistor connected to ground. The input voltage (V_{in}) is applied to the noninverting input.

A representative noninverting amplifier is shown in Figure 3–16. In this circuit the signal voltage (V_{in}) to be amplified is applied to the noninverting input $(+)$. A fraction of the output voltage (V_o) is returned to the inverting input $(-)$ through a voltage-divider network composed of R_f and R_1. In theory, we will again assume that very little current flows into the $+$ and $-$ inputs due to the virtual ground concept. This means that the differential input

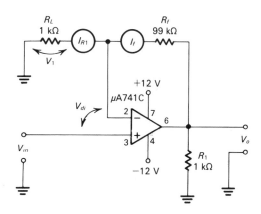

FIGURE 3–16
Noninverting op-amps.

voltage (V_{di}) is essentially zero. The voltage (V_1) developed across resistor R_1 is therefore equal to the input voltage (V_{in}). This means that the current (I_{R1}) passing through R_1 is either equal to

$$I_{R1} = \frac{V_{in}}{R_1} \quad \text{or} \quad I_{R1} = \frac{V_1}{R_1}$$

The feedback current (I_f) is also considered to be the same as I_{R1}. This means that

$$V_o = I_f(R_1 + R_f)$$

or

$$V_o = I_{R1}(R_1 + R_f)$$

In terms of voltage gain, we can then say that

$$A_v = \frac{V_o}{V_{in}}$$

or

$$\frac{V_o}{V_{in}} = \frac{R_1 + R_f}{'R_1}$$

In an actual circuit, the closed-loop voltage gain of a noninverting amplifier depends almost entirely on the external circuit components. In this regard, A_v is usually determined

by the values of R_1 and R_f. The standard voltage gain formula for a noninverting circuit configuration is expressed as

$$A_v = \frac{R_1 + R_f}{R_1} \quad \text{or} \quad \frac{R_f}{R_1 + 1}$$

Example 3–4:   Determine the voltage-amplifying capabilities of the noninverting amplifier of Figure 3–16 by the resistor method.

Solution:

$$A_v = \frac{R_f}{R_1 + 1}$$

$$= \frac{99 \text{ k}\Omega}{1 \text{ k}\Omega}$$

$$= 100$$

QUESTIONS

1. Describe the functional parts of a basic op-amp.

2. Explain how a differential amplifier responds with:

   a. One input grounded and a signal applied to the other input.

   b. The same signal applied to both inputs at the same time.

3. What are the features of an op-amp that approximate an ideal amplifier?

4. Where would the CMRR of an op-amp be used to some advantage in industrial circuits?

5. In the output stage of an op-amp, what is the difference between an emitter-follower output and a complementary-symmetry output?

6. What are included in the five essential terminal connections of an op-amp?

7. What is meant by the term *virtual ground*?

8. What is meant by the term *open-loop voltage gain* of an op-amp?

9. Explain how an op-amp is used as a zero referenced inverting comparator.

10. What is meant by controlled gain or closed-loop voltage amplification A_{vcl}?

11. Explain how an op-amp is used as a summing amplifier.

12. What causes the output of an op-amp to go into saturation?

13. Explain how an op-amp achieves summing.

PROBLEMS

1. An op-amp has an open-loop voltage gain of 200,000 with a supply voltage of ± 12 V. What value of input is needed to cause saturation?

2. What is the controlled gain of an op-amp using an R_{in} of 4.7 kΩ and an R_f of 100 kΩ?

3. A noninverting op-amp has an R_{in} of 10 kΩ and an R_f of 120 kΩ. With a $+0.6$-V p-p input voltage, what is the V_o?

4. An inverting op-amp has an R_{in} of 22 kΩ and an R_f of 68 kΩ. With a $+0.5$-V p-p input signal, what is the V_o?

5. Refer to the summing amplifier of Figure 4–15(A). If $V_1 = +2$ V, $V_2 = +3$ V, and $V_3 = -1$ V, what is the value of V_o?

6. Refer to the scaling amplifier of Figure 3–

15(C). If $V_1 = +200$ mV, $V_2 = +300$ mV, $V_3 = +300$ mV, and $V_4 = +300$ mV, what is V_o?

ACTIVITIES

ACTIVITY 3–1: Input Offset Voltage

Objective: To measure the output offset voltage of a μA741C op-amp and calculate the input offset voltage.

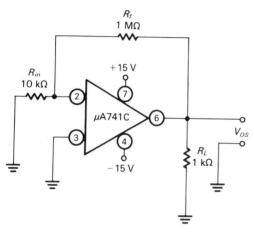

FIGURE 3–17

Procedure:

1. Connect the circuit of Figure 3–17.

2. Apply operational energy from a well-filtered split power supply.

3. Measure and record the output offset voltage V_{os}. Typical values are less than 60 mV.

4. Calculate the input offset voltage V_{oi}. For a μA741C, the V_{oi} should not exceed 6 mV.

ACTIVITY 3–2: Slew Rate

Objective: To determine the slew rate of a μA741C.

Procedure:

1. Connect the slew rate test circuit of Figure 3–18. Apply power from a well-filtered split power supply.

2. Adjust the square-wave generator for 10 kHz with a 5-V p-p output.

3. Measure and record the peak-to-peak output voltage (ΔV).

4. Determine the time change (Δt) that it takes the signal to change from a minimum to a

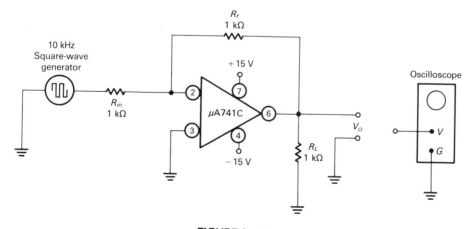

FIGURE 3–18

maximum value on a calibrated horizontal sweep oscilloscope.

5. Calculate the slew rate and record its value.

6. If time permits, use an op-amp with a different slew rate and perform the same evaluation. Suggested types are LM218D and LF356.

ACTIVITY 3–3: Inverting Op-amps

Objective: To build an inverting op-amp and evaluate its performance.

Procedure:

1. Construct the inverting op-amp circuit of Figure 3–12. Apply power from a well-filtered split power supply.

2. V_{in} is an independent dc power source with the positive terminal connected to the inverting input. Adjust V_{in} to a value of 0.2 V.

3. Measure and record the dc output voltage V_o and its polarity.

4. Change the value of V_{in} to 0.5, 0.7, and 1 V while recording the measured V_o values.

5. Reverse the polarity of V_{in} and repeat steps 2 through 4.

6. Disconnect the dc V_{in} source and connect an ac signal of 1 kHz at 1 V p-p.

7. With an oscilloscope, observe the wave forms at the input and output. Make a sketch of the observed waves showing peak-to-peak values and phase relations.

8. If possible, increase the value of V_{in} until the output becomes distorted. Describe the change in the wave form.

ACTIVITY 3–4: Noninverting Op-amps

Objective: To build a noninverting op-amp and evaluate its performance.

Procedure:

1. Construct the noninverting op-amps of Figure 3–16.

2. V_{in} is an independent dc power source with the positive terminal connected to the noninverting input. Adjust V_{in} to a value of 0.2 V.

3. Measure and record the dc output voltage V_o and its polarity.

4. Change the value of V_{in} to 0.5, 0.7, and 1 V while recording the measured V_o values.

5. Reverse the polarity of V_{in} and repeat steps 2 through 4.

6. Disconnect the dc V_{in} source and connect an ac signal of 100 Hz at 1 V p-p.

7. With an oscilloscope, observe the wave forms at the input and output. Make a sketch of the observed waves showing the peak-to-peak values and phase relations.

8. Increase the amplitude of V_{in} until V_o becomes distorted. Describe the wave-form changes observed.

ACTIVITY 3–5: Differential Comparators

Objective: To build a differential comparator and evaluate its performance.

Procedure:

1. Construct one of the zero-referenced comparators of Figure 3–11.

2. Connect a variable dc source to V_{in}.

3. Adjust V_{in} to 0 V and measure and record V_o.

4. Change the value of V_{in} while observing V_o. What value of V_{in} causes a change in V_o?

5. Remove the dc supply from V_{in} and replace it with a 1-kHz ac signal.

6. Adjust the amplitude of the ac signal until it produces V_o. What value of V_{in} is needed to produce V_o?

7. Change the frequency and amplitude of V_{in} while observing V_o. How do these factors alter V_o?

ACTIVITY 3–6: Adjustable Referenced Differential Comparators

Objective: To build an adjustable differential comparator and evaluate its performance.

Procedure:

1. Construct the adjustable referenced comparator of Figure 3–11(C).

2. Connect an independent variable dc voltage source with the positive terminal connected to V_{in}.

3. Adjust the reference voltage source to $+1$ V at the $+$ input.

4. Starting at 0 V, increase the dc value of V_{in} until a V_o is produced. At what value of V_{in} does V_o occur?

5. Reverse the polarity of V_{in} with the reference voltage remaining at $+1$ V. Starting at 0 V, increase the dc value of V_{in}. Does this alter the V_o?

6. Change the reference voltage source to -1 V. Starting at 0 V, increase the value of V_{in} until an output occurs. At what V_{in} value does V_o occur?

7. Try a different reference value such as -0.5 V and repeat the procedure. Describe your findings.

ACTIVITY 3–7: Op-amp Summing

Objective: To build an op-amp summing circuit and evaluate its operation.

Procedure:

1. Complete construction of the op-amp adder of Figure 3–14.

2. Adjust V_1 to produce 3 V and V_2 to produce 2 V.

3. Measure and record the output voltage (V_o).

4. If time permits, measure and record the current values at the designated points.

5. Adjust V_1 and V_2 to different values and measure V_o.

6. The adder will also respond to different polarities of input voltage. Change the circuit so that V_1 is $+3$ V and V_2 is -1 V. Measure and record V_o.

7. The circuit will also add ac signal voltages. Replace V_1 and V_2 with an ac signal. Adjust the signals so that V_1 is 3 V and V_2 is 2 V. The frequency and phase of the ac signals must be the same.

8. Measure and record V_o.

The term thyristor refers to a rather general classification of solid-state devices that are used as electronic switches. Thyristors can be two-, three-, or four-terminal devices. In this chapter we are concerned with the conductivity capabilities of these devices. Devices placed in this classification operate through a type of regenerative feedback. When conduction is initiated, the device will latch or hold in its *on state*. Momentarily removing or reducing the energy level of the source will cause nonconduction or switching to the *off state*. In general, a unidirectional thyristor is classified as a voltage-controlled switch.

UJT THYRISTORS

Thyristors should not be confused with bipolar junction transistors or field-effect transistors. BJTs and FETs are both capable of performing switching operations. As a rule, these devices are not as efficient as a thyristor and do not have the power-handling capability. Thyristors are used as power control devices, whereas transistors are primarily used in amplifying applications.

A variety of unidirectional thyristors is now being used in industrial electronic applications. One of the first to be developed was the silicon-controlled rectifier (SCR). The SCR was designed as a solid-state counterpart of the thyratron gaseous tube. The term thyristor was derived from the words *thy*ratron–trans*istor*. An SCR is classified as a reverse blocking triode thyristor. This means that the device has conductivity in only one direction. When its anode and cathode are reverse biased, the device will not conduct. The silicon-controlled switch (SCS) and the programmable unijunction transistor (PUT) are two other thyristors of this classification. A Shockley diode is classified as a reverse blocking diode thyristor.

4

UJT Thyristors and SCRs

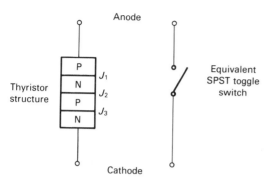

FIGURE 4–1
Four-layer thyristor structure.

Thyristor Structure

The crystal structure of a thyristor is unique when compared with other solid-state devices. Most thyristors are classified as *PNPN* devices. This type of structure consists of four alternately doped semiconductor layers and three *PN* junctions. The number of terminals attached to the structure is based on the function of the device. The two outer terminals are usually called the *anode* and *cathode*. Conduction between these two terminals is the same in nearly all thyristors.

The basic structure of a four-layer thyristor is shown in Figure 4–1. Notice that the anode terminal is connected to the *P* region on one end of the structure. The cathode is connected to the *N* region on the other end. Three junctions are formed between the top and bottom terminals. Conduction between the anode–cathode is similar to that of a mechanical toggle switch. This means that the device must have two operational states. In its on state the three junctions are low resistant. The off state has an infinite resistance between the anode–cathode.

A unique feature of the thyristor structure is its latching characteristic. Latching refers to a condition that holds the device in its on state after conduction has been initiated. Removal of the original actuating signal does not necessarily cause conduction to stop. This action permits the thyristor to be used as an electronic switching device. When the device has been triggered, it usually takes a different procedure for it to be turned off. Switching techniques vary a great deal in thyristors. Diode thyristors change states due to a change in anode–cathode voltage. State changes in a three-element device are initiated by an independent triggering signal.

Thyristor Operation

Description of the operation of a basic *PNPN* thyristor is often simplified by the two-transistor anology. This method divides the *PNPN* structure into two imaginary transistors. Junctions J_1 and J_2 form a *PNP* transistor, while J_2 and J_3 form an *NPN* device. The J_2 junction is common to both transistor structures. See the two-transistor equivalent of the *PNPN* structure in Figure 4–2. Note also the schematic symbol representation of the same structure.

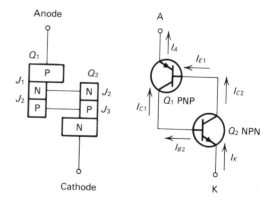

FIGURE 4–2
Two-transistor equivalent of a *PNPN* structure.

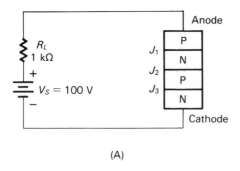

(A)

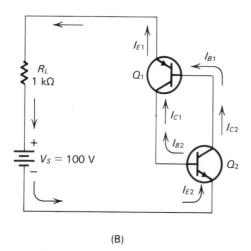

(B)

FIGURE 4–3
Thyristor connected to an energy source.

Assume now that a thyristor is connected to an energy source and a load resistor. Figure 4–3(A) shows the positive side of the source connected through R_L to the anode and the negative side to the cathode. Connected in this manner, junctions J_1 and J_3 are forward biased and J_2 is reverse biased. This means that J_2 will have an infinite resistance, while J_1 and J_3 are low resistant. J_2 will therefore have practically all of V_S appearing across it, while J_1 and J_3 will have zero voltage. Very little current

will flow through the structure. This means that $I_A = I_K$ with a current value of approximately zero. This condition will exist as long as V_{AK} is below the breakdown voltage of junction 2.

Refer now to the two-transistor analogy of the thyristor structure in Figure 4–3(B). Connected in this manner, the emitter–base (E–B) junctions of Q_1 and Q_2 are both slightly forward biased by the source. The E–B junction of Q_1 is the equivalent of J_1, and E–B of Q_2 is representative of J_3. The J_2 junction is equivalent to the collection–base (C–B) junctions of both Q_1 and Q_2. These two junctions are both reverse biased. Connected in this manner, the two transistors are properly biased for conduction. However, the two E–B junctions have practically no forward bias voltage. This will permit very little or practically no current to flow through the structure. A thyristor connected in this manner is considered to be in its off or nonconductive state.

Note the element current designations for the two-transistor equivalent circuit of Figure 4–3(B). The emitter current of Q_1 is representative of the anode current (I_A). I_{B1} is indicative of the base current of Q_1. I_{B1} is determined by the expression

$$I_{B1} = (1 - \alpha \text{ of } Q_1)I_A - I_{CBO1}$$

where α = current gain of Q_1
   $I_A = I_{E1}$
   I_{CBO1} = collector–emitter leakage current of Q_1

For transistor Q_2, the emitter current I_{E2} is equal to the cathode current (I_K). The base current of Q_2 is designated as I_{B2}. The collector current of Q_1 is equal in value to the base current of Q_2. I_{C1} therefore equals I_{B2}. The collector current (I_{C2}) can be determined by the formula

$$I_{C2} = (\alpha \text{ of } Q_2)I_K + I_{CBO2}$$

where α = current gain of Q_2
$I_K = I_{E2}$
I_{CBO2} = collector–emitter leakage current of Q_2

Note that I_{C2} of Q_2 and I_{B1} of Q_1 are of the same value. This permits the two previous expressions to be equated. The combined expression then becomes

$$I_{B1} = I_{C2}$$

or

$$(1 - \alpha \text{ of } Q_1)I_A - I_{CBO2} = (\alpha \text{ of } Q_2)I_K + I_{CBO2}$$

Combining the two expressions permits us to solve for either I_A or I_K. This is given by the formula

$$I_A \text{ or } I_K = \frac{I_{CBO1} + I_{CBO2}}{1 - (\alpha Q_1 + \alpha Q_2)}$$

The combined $I_A = I_K$ expression is an extremely important concept in the operation of all thyristors. We will use this expression to show how a thyristor responds in its nonconductive state. A small modification of the alpha values will cause a thyristor to change into its conductive state. Example 4–1 shows how this applies to a thyristor in its nonconductive or off state.

Example 4–1: When a thyristor is in its off state, the alpha of each equivalent transistor is substantially less than 1. This is primarily due to the extremely low forward bias voltage of J_1 of Q_1 and J_3 of Q_2. For the two-transistor equivalent circuit of Figure 4–3, assume that the alpha of Q_1 is 0.5 and Q_2 is 0.4. The leakage current of a silicon transistor is usually very small. Typical values are in the range of 0.1 μA. This means that the values of I_{CBO1} and I_{CBO2} should each be 0.1 μA. Using these values, determine the conduction current (I_A or I_K) for the two-transistor equivalent circuit.

Solution:

$$I_A \text{ or } I_K = \frac{I_{CBO1} + I_{CBO2}}{1 - (Q_1\alpha + Q_2\alpha)}$$

$$= \frac{0.1 \text{ μA} + 0.1 \text{ μA}}{1 - (0.5 + 0.4)}$$

$$= \frac{0.2 \text{ μA}}{0.1} \text{ or } \frac{0.2 \times 10^{-6}}{0.1}$$

$$= 2 \times 10^{-6} \text{ or } 2 \text{ μA}$$

The thyristor circuit of Figure 4–3 is energized by a source voltage of 100 V. If an I_A or I_K of 2 μA occurs in this state, what is the internal resistance of the thyristor or its two-transistor equivalent? The internal resistance (R_i) is determined by dividing V_S by I_A or I_K. For the off or nonconducting state, R_i is

$$R_i = \frac{V_S}{I_A} = \frac{100 \text{ V}}{2 \text{ μA}} = \frac{100 \text{ V}}{2 \times 10^{-6}}$$

$$= 50 \times 10^6 \text{ or } 50 \text{ MΩ}$$

An internal resistance of 50 MΩ will primarily cause the thyristor to respond as an open circuit. In its off state, the thyristor is considered to be nonconductive, and the full value of V_S will appear across the anode–cathode.

For a thyristor to become conductive, its alpha Q_1 + alpha Q_2 value must be equal to 1. When this occurs, the internal resistance of the device drops to an extremely small value. Some thyristors may drop in value to 0.01 Ω in the conductive state. Device current can increase to an extremely high value. I_A or I_K must be limited by an external series resistor. Note also that the conduction current through a thyristor has a regenerative effect. The emitter–base current of Q_1 causes saturation of Q_1.

This causes an immediate increase in I_{C1}. Since I_{C1} equals I_{B2}, Q_2 goes into saturation. I_{C2} then flows back into I_{B1}, which causes Q_1 to hold its saturation condition. The feedback currents of Q_1 to Q_2 and Q_2 to Q_1 cause the thyristor to latch and hold its conduction state. The device will remain in its latched state as long as a reasonable value of conduction current can be maintained.

There are several ways that the alpha values of Q_1 and Q_2 can be increased to cause a thyristor to change from off to an on state. A change in temperature is one method. An increase in temperature increases the leakage current, which in turn increases the respective I_C and I_B of each transistor. As a rule, this method of triggering a thyristor into conduction is not very practical. An increase in anode–cathode voltage will also cause a thyristor to become conductive. Each thyristor has a forward breakover voltage (V_{BO}) that causes conduction. This voltage causes J_2 or the C_1–B_1 and C_2–B_1 junctions of the two transistors to become conductive. This method of triggering a thyristor into conduction is relatively easy to achieve. Another method of starting conduction is called gate triggering. This is used in thyristors that employ one additional terminal or lead. Initiating conduction by this process will be discussed in conjunction with the triode type of thyristor.

The operation of a thyristor up to this point has been based on the application of source voltage in the foward-biased direction. This is achieved when the negative side of the source is connected to the cathode and the positive side to the anode. Conduction takes place when the breakover voltage is exceeded. Lesser values of V_{BO} do not cause the thyristor to be conductive. If the polarity of the source voltage is reversed, the device cannot be made to go into conduction. Reversing biasing of a thyristor alters the conduction of the three internal junctions, J_1 and J_3 will be reverse biased and J_2 will be forward biased. Essentially, this means that both transistors of the equivalent circuit will have their E–B junctions reverse biased. The C–B junctions will be forward biased. The equivalent transistors are not properly biased for conduction when connected in this manner. As a result, no conduction can be achieved through a thyristor when the V_S polarity is reversed. A thyristor of the *PNPN* type is classified as having unidirectional conductivity. This condition of operation is similar to that of a conventional power diode. A *PNPN* device, however, will respond as a switch only when it is connected in the forward-biased direction.

Shockley Diode

The four-layer *PNPN* thyristor was invented by William Shockley in 1956. Today this thyristor is called a Shockley diode. Its construction is very similar to the device shown in Figure 4–3(A). A Shockley diode can be switched into conduction when its forward breakover voltage is exceeded. It responds as a switch when forward biased.

The *I–V* characteristics and schematic symbol of a Shockley diode are shown in Figure 4–4. Quadrant I of the characteristic shows forward conduction, while quadrant III shows reverse operation. A Shockley diode is not operated in the reverse direction. This part of the characteristic is shown only for maximum value reference purposes. If a Shockley diode is reverse biased, it behaves as a typical reverse-biased *PN* junction. This means that no conduction occurs until the reverse breakdown voltage is exceeded. Ordinarily, this value is described as the peak reverse voltage (PRV). Exceeding the PRV may destroy the diode.

Quadrant I of a Shockley diode's *I–V* characteristics shows operation in the forward conduction direction. This occurs when the anode

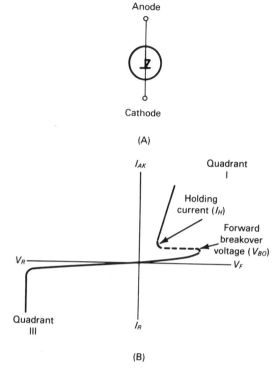

FIGURE 4–4
(A) Shockley diode symbol and (B) I/V characteristic.

Current values less than I_H reduce the alpha of the equivalent transistors in the structure. This action causes the device to switch back to its off state. Switching from on to off occurs at approximately the same rate as the on-switching time.

Shockley Diode Switching

Shockley diodes are primarily used as voltage-switching devices. Figure 4–5 shows an application of the *PNPN* thyristor as a switch for a relaxation oscillator. In this application, the dc source voltage (V_S) is changed into an ac signal. The output has a sawtooth shape that occurs at a predictable frequency. For this circuit to function, the source voltage (V_S) must be greater than the V_{BO} of the diode.

Operation of a Shockley diode as a relaxation oscillator is based on the charging action of a capacitor through a resistor. When voltage from V_S is applied to the circuit, it causes capacitor C_1 to charge through resistor R_1. When the capacitor voltage reaches the forward breakover voltage of the diode, conduction occurs. The diode quickly switches to its low re-

is made positive and the cathode negative. Notice that conduction does not occur immediately. The anode–cathode voltage (V_{AK}) must be increased until the forward breakover voltage (V_{BO}) is reached. At this point, the device switches from its off state to the on state. This switching action takes place very rapidly. A broken line shows this condition on the curve. The internal resistance changes immediately from an infinite value to a very low resistance. The device then responds as a forward-biased diode. A very high current can flow through the device with a low voltage drop. Typical forward voltage (V_F) values are 0.5 to 2.0 V. The device remains in the conductive state as long as I_{AK} exceeds the holding current (I_H).

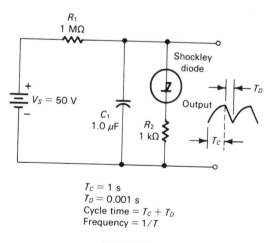

$T_C = 1$ s
$T_D = 0.001$ s
Cycle time $= T_C + T_D$
Frequency $= 1/T$

FIGURE 4–5
Shockley diode relaxation oscillator.

sistant state. The capacitor discharges immediately through the low forward resistance of the diode. When conduction current drops below the holding current, the diode switches back to its off state. Capacitor C_1 begins to charge again through R_1. The process then repeats itself on a continuous basis. Note the shape of the output wave form.

The output voltage of a relaxation oscillator is developed across the capacitor. The developed wave form has the shape of a sawtooth. The charging of C_1 is based on the value of R_1 and C_1. In one time constant, C_1 will charge to 63.2% of the source voltage. Ordinarily, the circuit is designed so that 63.2% of V_S equals the V_{BO} of the Shockley diode. When this voltage is reached, it causes the diode to switch to its on state. C_1 then discharges through the low-resistant diodes and R_2 very quickly. The output wave of Figure 4–5 shows a rather gradual rise in the charging voltage of the capacitor. This is labeled T_C. Discharge of C takes place very quickly. This is labeled T_D. The total time of an operational cycle is $T_C + T_D$. The frequency of the wave can be determined by the formula $F = 1/T$. Relaxation oscillators of this type are commonly used as triggering circuits in power control applications.

SILICON-CONTROLLED RECTIFIERS

The silicon-controlled rectifier (SCR) is undoubtedly the most widely used device in the thyristor family. As described by its name, the SCR is a silicon type of rectifying device whose conduction can be controlled. Construction is very similar to that of a basic *PNPN* device. One additional terminal or electrode called the *gate* is attached to the device. Figure 4–6 shows a junction diagram, crystal struc-

ture, schematic symbol, and the element names of an SCR.

In the two-transistor equivalent of a thyristor, the device had only anode and cathode terminals. Conduction or switching was achieved by exceeding the forward breakover voltage. An increase in V_{BO} caused the combined alpha of the two equivalent transistors to reach 1. Junction J_2 became low resistant and the device switched to its on state. Conduction continued as long as the holding current was maintained. Reducing the value of V_{BO} until it caused a decrease in I_H caused the device to switch back to its off state. Thus, control of this thyristor is achieved by changes in voltage and temperature.

The gate of an SCR permits it to have an additional control capability. The two-transistor equivalent of Figure 4–7 shows the gate attached to the common connection of I_{C1} and I_{B2}. When a V_{BO} that does not cause conduction is applied, the SCR is normally in its off state. The combined alpha of Q_1 and Q_2 does not reach a value of 1. If the gate is momentarily made positive, it causes an immediate increase in I_{C1} and I_{B2}. This is called *gate current (I_G)*. Essentially, I_G increases the alpha level of the two transistors to a value that causes the device to become conductive. Removing I_G does not alter the conduction of the device as long as I_H is maintained.

Gate control of SCR conduction is much

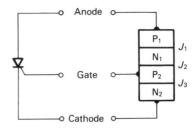

FIGURE 4–6
Crystal structure and schematic symbol of an SCR.

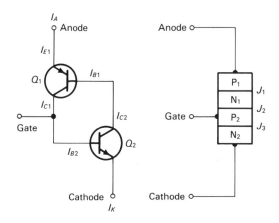

FIGURE 4–7
Two-transistor equivalent and crystal structure of an SCR.

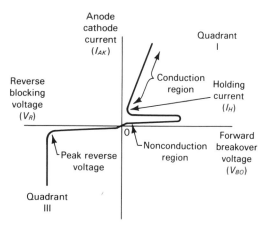

FIGURE 4–8
Voltage–current characteristic of an SCR.

more effective than a change in V_{BO}. A rather small gate voltage (V_G) is needed to produce an I_G. A gate current of only a few milliamperes can be used to control a large value of I_A or I_K. Electronic power control through an SCR is very efficient.

I–V Characteristics of an SCR

The current–voltage (I–V) characteristic of an SCR is shown in Figure 4–8. This device has two conductive states in its operation. Quadrant I shows the forward conduction condition of operation. This characteristic shows how the SCR goes into conduction when the forward breakover voltage (V_{BO}) is exceeded. When conduction occurs, the internal resistance of the device drops to a rather low value like that of most diodes. The total current passing between the cathode and anode must therefore be limited by an external resistor. This resistance may be supplied by the device being controlled or by a separate load resistor. A small change in gate current can then be used to effectively control a large amount of anode–cathode current passing through the SCR.

Quadrant III of the I–V characteristic of an SCR shows the location of the reverse breakdown conduction condition. This is similar to the peak reverse voltage (PRV) of a conventional diode. As a general rule, the SCR will be permanently damaged if operating voltages exceed this value. PRV represents the maximum voltage that can be applied to the device in the reverse-biased direction. PRV ratings of SCRs range from 25 to 2000 V.

For an SCR to be used as a power control device, its forward V_{BO} must be reduced to a smaller value. To achieve this operation, the gate–cathode junction must be momentarily forward biased. When this occurs, gate current (I_G) enters the gate–cathode junction. As a result of this action, current in the N_2P_2 junction increases and enters immediately into the forward-biased N_1P_2 junction. The total I_{AK} passing through the device at this time is unrestricted and must be limited by the external resistance.

Any variation in the cathode–gate current of an SCR causes a corresponding change in V_{BO}. A graph showing some representative gate current values is displayed in Figure 4–9. Only the forward conduction part of this graph is

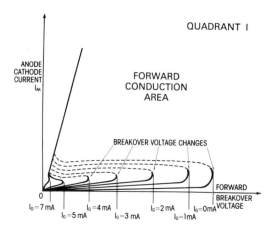

FIGURE 4–9
Representative gate-current characteristics of an SCR.

shown, with an enlargement of the V_{BO} area. Notice that the V_{BO} of an SCR decreases as the gate current increases. At approximately 7 mA of I_G, the SCR goes into conduction instantly. Lesser values of I_G cause the V_{BO} to extend to the right. Conduction time can be delayed because it is dependent on the combination of I_G and V_{BO}.

Electronic Power Control with an SCR

When an SCR is used as an electronic power control device, it primarily responds as a switch. Conduction and nonconduction are the two operational states of an SCR. When the source voltage is below the forward breakover voltage, no conduction will occur. This causes the SCR to be in its off state. To initiate conduction and turn on the device, the V_{BO} must be exceeded or a gate current (I_G) must be applied. When conduction occurs, an SCR becomes low resistant and changes to its on state. If the holding current (I_H) level is maintained, the SCR will latch and remain in conduction.

This condition is representative of the on position of a switch or electrical contactor. In effect, the SCR responds as a bistable or two-state switch.

A very large part of all electronic power control is achieved by static switching. This type of switching is simply a form of on and off control of a load device. The load may be energized by either an ac or dc source. AC static switching is rather easy to accomplish. It is considered to be line voltage commutated. This means that the normal alternation change of the ac line voltage causes an SCR to be turned off. An SCR is not conductive during an alternation that causes the anode–cathode to be reverse biased. AC static switching of an SCR can be achieved up to 30 kHz. DC static switching, by comparison, responds at a much slower rate. This type of switching is controlled by forced commutation. An SCR has a tendency to stay in conduction when it is switched to the on state. To change this condition, the I_H must be reduced to cause it to come out of conduction. In practice, SCR conduction is forced into nonconduction by an outside device or circuit. The recovery time of a dc static switch is relatively slow.

DC Static Switching

The use of an SCR as a static dc switch gives it a definite advantage over all other mechanical switching techniques. Static switching permits the control of a relatively high load current with a very small power source. Since the SCR latches instantly when it is switched to the on state, there is no contact bounce. This method of control tends to eliminate the contact arc problem that is prevalent in mechanical switching.

Figure 4–10 shows an SCR used as a dc static switch. This circuit has a rather large load current controlled by an extremely small

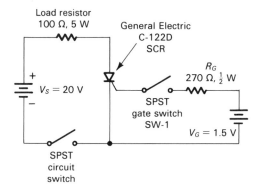

FIGURE 4–10
DC static switch.

gate current. Note that the load is energized by a dc source. The source voltage (V_S) forward biases the SCR. Load current is controlled by turning the SCR on or off.

When the circuit switch of Figure 4–10 is first turned on, the load is not energized. In this case, the V_{BO} of the SCR is greater than the value of the source voltage. When SW-1 is turned on, it energizes the gate circuit. If a suitable amount of I_G flows, the V_{BO} will be lowered. This immediately causes the SCR to become conductive. The load is then energized by V_S. Turning off SW-1 opens the gate circuit. If the holding current (I_H) is maintained, the load continues in its energized state. Switching the load to the off state is achieved by momentarily opening the circuit switch. Turning the circuit switch on again does not energize the load. Conduction can not be restored until the gate is again forward biased by SW-1. In this circuit, only a small value of I_G is needed to control the load current.

The dc static switch of Figure 4–10 requires two switches and an SCR to achieve control. This particular application of the SCR is not a very practical control procedure. The current rating of the circuit switch, for example, must be large enough to accommodate the entire load current. The gate switch can, however, be

rated at an extremely low value. A more practical application of the circuit would permit control of the load from several different locations. A number of gate current switches could be connected in parallel with SW-1. Gate control of this type would permit the SCR to be controlled by a variety of different logic combinations.

A variation of the basic dc static switch is shown in Figure 4–11. This method of control uses one dc source to energize both the gate and the load device. Load control is achieved with two push-button switches. The voltage–current rating of each push button is relatively low. When this type of circuit is used to control large amounts of load current, component cost is very nominal. Turn-off of the load is achieved by lowering conduction current of the SCR below the I_H level. The *off* push button achieves force commutation or turn-off.

Assume now that the SCR of Figure 4–11 is placed into operation by momentarily pushing the start button. This action energizes the gate and causes a suitable value of I_G to flow. An increase in I_G lowers V_{BO} and causes the SCR to become conductive. The load is then energized by the dc source. If a suitable value

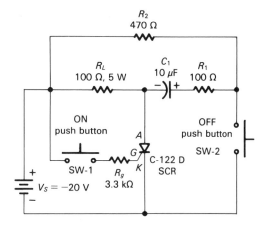

FIGURE 4–11
Push-button-controlled static switch.

of load current flows, conduction is maintained. When the SCR becomes conductive, it also permits capacitor C_1 to charge to the source voltage. The charging path is from the negative side of the source, through the SCR, C_1, R_1, R_2, and to the positive side of the source. The time that it takes C_1 to charge depends on the values of $C_1(R_1 + R_2)$. The polarity of the accumulated charge is shown in the diagram.

To turn off an SCR, the conduction current must drop below the holding current level. For Figure 4–11, this is achieved by depressing the *off* push button. Closing SW-2 places C_1 and R_1 directly across the anode–cathode. The charge on C_1 reverse biases the SCR. This immediately lowers the conduction current and causes it to drop below the holding level. The SCR then returns to its forward blocking state and turns off.

The off-switching operation of an SCR usually occurs very quickly. In the circuit of Figure 4–11, this is based on the time it takes capacitor discharge current to flow in the circuit. In this case, T_D in seconds (s) equals $C_1 \cdot R_1$.

Example 4–2:   Determine the discharge time (T_D) of the SCR circuit in Figure 4–11.

Solution:

Capacitor discharge time = capacitance (C_1) × resistance (R_1)

$$T_D = 10 \ \mu F \times 100 \ \Omega$$
$$= 10 \times 10^{-6} \times 100 \ \Omega$$
$$= 1 \times 10^{-3} \text{ or } 0.001 \text{ s}$$

AC Static Switching

AC static switching is more widely used in power control applications than dc static control. In general, ac switching is very easy to achieve. An SCR, for example, turns off au-

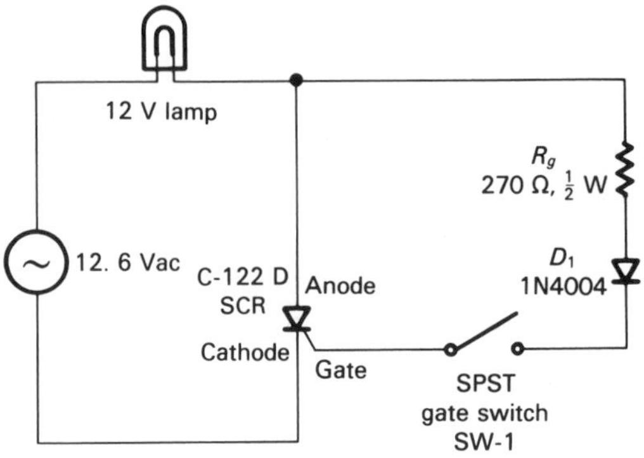

FIGURE 4–12
Static ac switch.

tomatically during one alternation of the ac source voltage. This eliminates the inherent turn-off problem of the dc static switch. A load being controlled by an SCR only receives power for one alternation of the source voltage. The output of an SCR is therefore a rectified version of the ac input.

A simplified SCR ac static switch is shown in Figure 4–12. Connected in this manner, the SCR can only be made conductive when the anode is positive and the cathode negative. This is also dependent on a suitable value of I_G being applied at the same time. I_G is controlled manually by the gate switch (SW-1).

The amount of gate current applied lowers the V_{BO} to cause the SCR to go into conduction. Gate resistor R_g limits I_G to a usable peak value. Diode D_1 permits I_G to flow only when the anode–cathode is forward biased. When the anode–cathode is reverse biased, D_1 prevents this voltage from being applied between

the gate and cathode. With a suitable value of I_G and correct polarity of the anode–cathode voltage, the SCR becomes conductive during one alternation of the ac input and nonconductive during the next alternation. If SW-1 remains in the on position, the SCR is switched on and off during each ac cycle of operation. The load is energized by only one alternation of the input. An ac static switch therefore develops a pulsating dc load current.

An ac static switch is primarily designed to take the place of a mechanical circuit switch. With an SCR static switch, it is possible to control large amounts of load current with a rather small gate current switch. A few milliamperes of gate current can be altered to control several hundreds of amperes of load current. Control of this type is very reliable and efficient, and can be achieved rather inexpensively. The ac static switch does not have contacts that spark and arc with changes in load current. Load control of this type, however, is limited to only on and off or bistable switching operations.

Variable Power Control

An SCR has the capability of altering or varying the amount of power supplied to a load device. Variable power control is a unique alternative to the static switch method of control. Static switching simply permits the load device to be either turned on or off. Variable power control permits the load to receive different values of load current. Motor speed, light intensity, heat, liquid level, and chemical reactions are applications of this type of control. Variable power control is primarily designed to respond to the 60-Hz ac power source.

A simplified version of an SCR variable power control circuit is shown in Figure 4–13. This circuit is designed to alter the conduction of one alternation of ac input. In effect, the load only receives one alternation or half-wave output. Ideally, this represents only 50% of the potential power supplied by the source. Through variable power control, it is possible to alter load current over its entire range of operation.

Operation of the variable power control circuit of Figure 4–13 is based on the charge and discharge of capacitor C_1. This is primarily controlled by the polarity of the ac power source. Wave form A is representative of two complete operational cycles of the ac source. Note that the positive alternation occurs first. This action causes point A of the circuit to be positive and B to be negative. This polarity of V_S forward biases the SCR. If the resistance of R_2 is set to a minimum value, it permits C_1 to charge very quickly through R_L, R_1, and R_2. The load resistance (R_L) and R_1 are usually of a small value. The charge voltage of C_1 therefore builds up to where it forward biases diode D_1. Conduction of D_1 then causes a corresponding gate current. I_G, in this case, triggers the SCR into conduction at the beginning of the positive alternation. Wave form B shows full conduction of the load current for the positive alternation. In effect, this means that the load is receiving the full value of the positive alternation. There is no delay in the turn-on of the load current. This represents the maximum amount of power being supplied to the load. Note that the load current is a half-wave rectified version of the ac input.

The negative alternation of V_S causes the SCR to be reverse biased. This essentially turns off the SCR and prevents the load from receiving any current. Wave form B shows this as the nonconductive time. An interesting condition of operation does occur during this alternation. Remember that C_1 developed a charge voltage during the positive alternation. When point A is negative and B is positive, the polarity reverse biases the SCR and forward biases diode D_2. C_1 then finds a discharge path

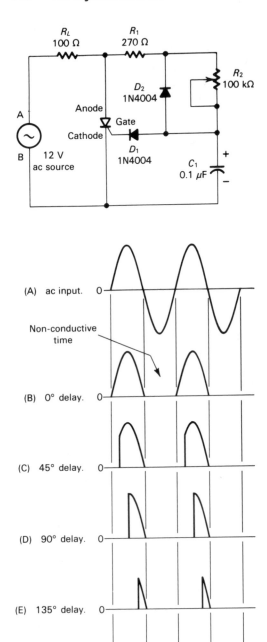

(A)   ac input.   0

Non-conductive time

(B)   0° delay.   0

(C)   45° delay.   0

(D)   90° delay.   0

(E)   135° delay.   0

(F)   180° delay.   0

FIGURE 4–13
Variable SCR power control.

through R_L, R_1, and D_2. This action takes place very quickly because of the low resistance of R_L and R_1. C_1 is then in a ready state to be recharged during the next alternation. D_1 prevents gate current from flowing in the SCR during the negative alternation. The SCR remains in the off state during the entire negative alternation.

Assume now that there is a 25% increase in the value of R_2 over its original setting. This causes a delay in the conduction time of the SCR at the beginning of the positive alternation. Essentially, gate current does not flow immediately, when V_{AK} is first forward biased. The increased value of R_2 delays the time that it takes C_1 to develop a charge voltage. Within a short time, however, the charge voltage of C_1 builds up to where it forward biases D_1. Current flow through D_1 then causes a corresponding gate current. This in turn lowers the V_{BO} of the SCR and triggers it into conduction. Once the SCR is turned on it continues to conduct for the remainder of the alternation. Wave form C shows a 45° delay in conduction of the SCR. This represents a 25% decrease in load current. In a sense, a 25% increase in R_2 delays conduction of the alternation 25% or 45°. This reduces the load current by 25%. Conduction during the positive alternation is based on the value of R_1 and C_1. A change in the value of R_1 alters the charge time of C_1.

A further increase in the resistance R_1 causes an increase in the delay of SCR conduction during the positive alternation. Wave forms D, E, and F of Figure 4–13 show the result of this change. Wave form D shows a 90° delay in conduction of the SCR. Load current flows for only half of the positive alternation. This represents a 50% reduction in power over that of 0° delay. Wave form E shows a 135° delay of the positive alternation. This condition permits the load to receive only 25% of its normal power. If the value of R_2 is great enough, the SCR does not become conductive

during the entire positive alternation. This represents 180° delay of conduction and complete turn-off for the entire operational period. No load current flows for this period of operation. In effect, variable power control permits adjustment of load current from 0° delay (full conduction) to 180° delay or nonconduction.

Half- and Full-wave Power Control

When ac is applied to a single SCR, it can only be made conductive for one alternation of the input. This occurs when the anode–cathode is forward biased. A single SCR can therefore control only half or 50% of the ac input. The output of a single SCR is essentially a half-wave rectified version of the input.

SCRs can be connected in a circuit to achieve full-wave power control. One method of control employs two SCRs; another method applies full-wave rectified input to one SCR. Full-wave power control has nearly twice the output of a half-wave controller. Full-wave SCR controllers are somewhat more complex than the half-wave unit. The amount of power being supplied to a load device and its operational efficiency usually determine if a full-wave controller is needed.

A full-wave controller with SCR is shown in Figure 4–14. This controller has a bridge rectifier that changes the applied ac into a full-wave output. The load (R_L) and SCR are connected in series with the output of the bridge. During the positive alternation of the input, current flow is from point B through diode D_2, the SCR, R_L, diode D_4, and point A. For the negative alternation, current flow is from A through D_1, the SCR, R_L, D_3, and to point B. Both alternations of the input appear as output across R_L. The ac input, however, has been changed to pulsating dc. The gate control circuit alters the gate current of the SCR. An in-

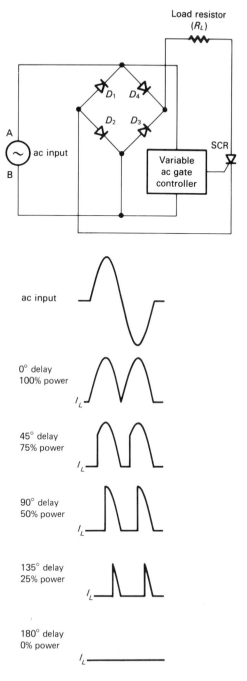

FIGURE 4–14
Full-wave power control with one SCR.

crease in I_G lowers the V_{BO}. Variations in I_G determine the conduction time of the output for each alternation. A maximum value of I_G causes full conduction of each alternation. Reduced I_G values delay the conduction of each alternation.

The output of a full-wave SCR controller has a fluctuating dc value. For the positive alternation, the output starts at zero, rises to its peak value, and then returns to zero. The output of the negative alternation is a duplicate of the positive alternation. Since each output pulse drops to zero upon completion, the SCR is turned off. The next pulse is completely in-

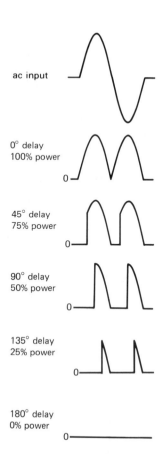

ac input

0° delay
100% power

45° delay
75% power

90° delay
50% power

135° delay
25% power

180° delay
0% power

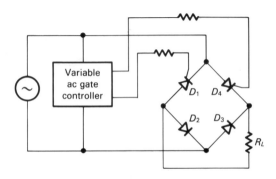

FIGURE 4–15
Full-wave power control.

dependent of the first. Changes in I_G cause a similar response for each output pulse. Decreasing the value of I_G can cause a delay in the conduction of each output pulse from 0° to 180°. This can be used to produce power control from 0% to 100%. Representative output wave forms are shown with the circuit of Figure 4–14 for different power output levels.

Two SCRs are used in the full-wave controller of Figure 4–15. The ac input is applied to a bridge rectifier as in the previous controller. However, two diodes of the bridge are replaced with SCRs. Operation of the bridge is

primarily the same. One diode and one SCR conduct during each alternation. The resulting output current is dependent on the response of these two devices. If conduction is delayed by the SCR, the resulting output reflects this delay. Both alternations of the output respond in the same manner. The ac gate control circuit alters the I_G of each SCR an equal amount. Some representative output wave forms are shown with the circuit for different power output levels. The current-handling capability of the two SCRs is half of the rating of the single SCR full-wave power controller.

SCR Gate Control

The control of gate current in an SCR is an extremely important operational consideration. In static switching applications, the gate is energized with a single value of ac or dc energy. I_G is simply switched on and off to initiate the control operation. Variable gate control is achieved by altering the value of I_G. Variable ac and dc gate control are possible. As a rule, variable gate control is limited to delay times of 90° of an alternation. If conduction does not occur before this part of the alternation, the device does not become conductive. Phase-shifting gate control makes it possible for an SCR to have 0° to 180° delay of its conduction. This type of control permits 50% power control in a half-wave circuit and 100% control of a full-wave unit. Gate control can also be achieved by pulse triggering. Unijunction transistors (UJT) and trigger diodes are commonly used to achieve this operation. Very precise levels of power control can be achieved with pulse triggering. This type of gate control is widely used in electronic power control circuits.

DC Gate Bias

A dc gate bias control circuit is shown in Figure 4–16. The anode–cathode of this SCR is energized by dc and the gate is controlled by dc. This is a dc static switch. When the circuit switch is turned on, it applies dc to the anode–cathode. This forward biases the SCR. As a rule, the dc voltage source is somewhat lower than the V_{BO} of the SCR. No conduction occurs at this point. When the gate switch (SW-1) is turned on, it causes an I_G to flow. This lowers the V_{BO} and the SCR goes into conduction. If a suitable value of I_{AK} flows, latching occurs. The load current is maintained as long as V_S is applied. The gate loses its control over the SCR when it goes into conduction. The

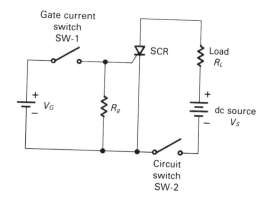

FIGURE 4–16
DC gate bias control.

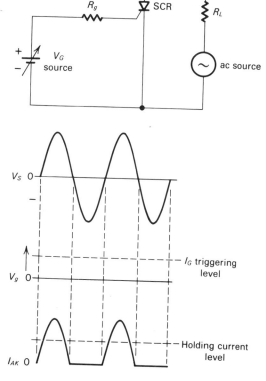

FIGURE 4–17
DC gate control with an ac source.

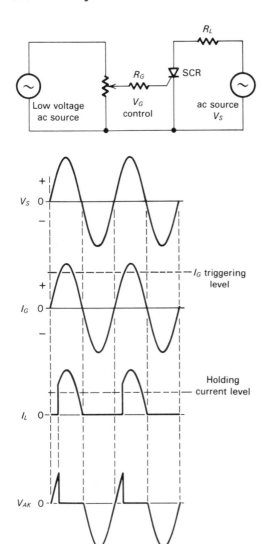

FIGURE 4–18
Gate-biased SCR.

source is shown in Figure 4–17. This method of control has automatic commutation of the conduction current because of the polarity change of each alternation. The gate current of this circuit is variable. Altering the value of V_G permits delay of conduction time of up to 90° of the positive alternation. Notice the representative wave forms in Figure 4–17. The gate resistor (R_g) is used to limit the I_G to a value that will not damage the gate.

DC gate control of an SCR energized with ac is rather easy to achieve. It is rarely used in industry today because of its control limitation. Only 25% of the load current can be controlled by one SCR, and only 50% can be controlled with two of them connected in a full-wave output. AC control therefore seems to be a more practical solution to industrial applications of the SCR.

AC Gate Bias

When the anode–cathode of an SCR is energized, it may be triggered into conduction by applying ac to the gate–cathode elements. Figure 4–18 shows a representative ac gate-biased SCR. Note that the anode–cathode and gate-cathode are both energized by ac. In low-voltage applications, the same ac source may be used to energize both the gate and the anode–cathode. When high ac voltage values are used, an independent low-voltage ac source should supply the gate.

If the ac gate voltage source of an SCR is made variable, its conduction can be altered through a suitable range. A change in the value of V_G simply alters the amplitude of I_G. This essentially changes the I_G triggering point of the gate. See the I_G wave form in Figure 4–18. A small value of V_G increases the delay of conduction. Larger V_G values decrease the delay time. It is essential that the gate source and the anode–cathode voltage have the same phase

gate can be turned off without altering the conduction of load current. This type of gate control provides two-state switching of the load. A problem of dc static switching is commutation of the load after it goes into conduction.

A dc gate bias control circuit with an ac

relationship. An out-of-phase condition does not permit the SCR to be triggered into conduction during either alternation.

When ac gate voltage values are used to trigger an SCR, only 90% of conduction delay can be achieved. This applies only to the positive alternation of the input. If triggering does not occur before 90°, no conduction takes place for the remainder of the alternation. One SCR can therefore achieve only 50% control of one alternation or 25% of the total ac input power. A full-wave SCR circuit can control up to half of each alternation and 50% of the total ac input power applied. The output of the circuit is a varying value or pulsating dc.

Phase Control

Shifting the phase of gate–cathode ac voltage with respect to the anode–cathode voltage can be used to control the conduction of an SCR. In phase-control applications, the shape and amplitude of the gate voltage remain unchanged while its phase is shifted with respect to time. Capacitors and inductors are commonly used to achieve this type of control.

Phase shifting of an ac sine wave usually involves an *LR* or an *LC* component combination. These components are used to alter the current and voltage relationship of the circuit. In an *LR* combination, inductance causes the current to lag behind the voltage by as much as 90°. Altering the resistive component of this combination causes a total circuit impedance *(Z)* change, which in turn produces a phase change. An *RC* network, by comparison, causes the current to lead the voltage by as much as 90°. Adjusting the value of *R* in this type of circuit changes the total impedance, which in turn causes a phase change.

A common way to show the phase relationship of ac current and voltage is to represent these values by lines called *phasors*. The line

length of a phasor is used to show its value, while its direction is used to show phase relationships.

LR Phase Shifters

An LR phase-shifter network is shown in Figure 4–19(A). The ac source voltage *(V)* and component voltages developed across the inductor and resistor are labeled V_L and V_R, respectively. The resistor of this circuit is variable and can be used to alter circuit voltage values. When the resistance of *R* is adjusted so that $V_R = V_L$, phasor diagram Figure 4–19(B) is the result. This diagram shows V_R and V_L to

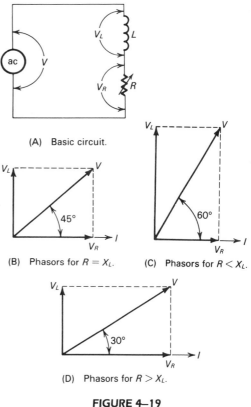

(A) Basic circuit.

(B) Phasors for $R = X_L$.

(C) Phasors for $R < X_L$.

(D) Phasors for $R > X_L$.

FIGURE 4–19
LR **phase shifter.**

be of equal lengths, with the current I in phase with V_R. The inductive component of this circuit causes the voltage to lead the current by 90° as indicated. With respect to V, V_R lags by 45° and V_L leads by an equal amount.

When the value of R is adjusted so that V_R is smaller than V_L, the phasor diagram in Figure 4–19(C) is the result. In this case, V_L still leads V_R by 90°, as indicated by the extension of the R phasor. The length of V_R now becomes much shorter than that of V_L. The phase angle between V and V_R is now, say, 60°, while that of V and V_L is only 30°. The current I continues to be in phase with V_R and lags behind V_L by 90°. When R is adjusted to any value smaller than X_L, the phase angle of V_R with respect to V will be between 45° and 90°.

Adjusting the value of R so that it is made larger than X_L produces the phasor diagram of Figure 4–19(D). In this case, the V_R phasor is much longer than the length of V_L. With respect to V, V_R lags by, say, 30°, and V_L leads by 60°. The series current I continues to remain in phase with V_R but still lags behind V_L

by 90°, as indicated. When R is adjusted to any value larger than X_L, the phase of V_R will be between an in-phase condition, or 0°, and a 45° lag with respect to V.

RC Phase Shifters

Figure 4–20(A) shows a simple RC phase-shifter network connected to an ac source. The resistive component of this network is variable and can be adjusted to a variety of different values. Voltages developed across the resistor and the capacitor are labeled V_R and V_C, respectively. When the resistance of R is adjusted to different values, a phase change of 0° to 90° can be achieved between V and V_C.

When the resistance of R is adjusted so that $V_R = V_C$, the phasor diagram of Figure 4–20(B) is the result. In this case, V_R and V_C are equal in length, with the current being in phase with V_R. An extension of the V_R line is used to show the phase relationship of I. Voltage V_C is shown lagging behind I by 90° in each phasor diagram and will remain unchanged. The V_C to V and V_R to V phase relationships of this network change, however, with each setting of R.

Figure 4–20(C) shows a phasor diagram that is the result of R being larger than X_C. The current I continues to remain in phase with V_R in this diagram. The V_C phasor is much shorter

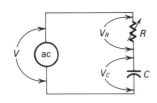

(A) Basic circuit.

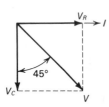

(B) Phasors for $R = X_C$.
     or $V_R = V_C$.

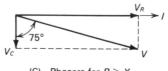

(C) Phasors for $R > X_C$.

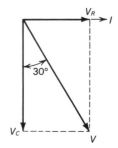

(D) Phasors for $R < X_C$.

FIGURE 4–20
RC phase shifter.

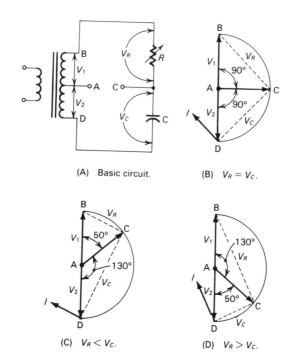

(A) Basic circuit.   (B) $V_R = V_C$.

(C) $V_R < V_C$.   (D) $V_R > V_C$.

FIGURE 4–21
RC bridge phase shifter.

than V_R. This type of diagram shows that, when R is made larger than X_C, the phase relationship of V and V_C is between 45° and 90°.

Figure 4–20(D) shows a phasor diagram that is produced when R is adjusted to a value smaller than X_C. Voltage phasor V_C in this case becomes longer than V_R. The current I continues to remain in phase with V_R. This type of diagram shows that making R smaller than X_C causes the relationship of V and V_C to be between an in-phase condition and a 45° lag.

Single-leg Phase Shifters

The RL and RC circuits just discussed are often described as being a single-leg or series type of phase shifter. Components connected in this type of circuit form a series path for current

when attached to a source. Only 90° of phase shift can be achieved with this type of circuit. In addition to this, the amplitude of the output voltage developed across R, L, or C changes in value with each different phase setting. Single-leg phase-shifter circuits therefore have a rather limited number of electrical system control applications today.

Bridge Phase Shifters

Bridge phase shifters are quite different from the single-leg LR or RC networks just discussed. The bridge network, for example, requires two legs or paths in order to produce phase shifting. A center-tapped transformer is also needed to develop voltages that are of equal amplitude but 180° out of phase. In Figure 4–21(A), these voltages are labeled V_1 and V_2. The three phasor diagrams of Figure 4–21 show these voltage values pointing in opposite directions from the center tap, which is indicated by point A. Phasors V_1 and V_2 represent one leg of the bridge circuit with the output at point A. The alternate leg of the bridge is represented by V_R and V_C. The output for this leg is taken from point C. The combined output of both legs is taken across points AC.

The phasor diagrams of Figure 4–21 show three representative output possibilities of the bridge phase shifter. In Figure 4–21(B), V_R and V_C are equal in value. The output phasor AC is 90° out of phase with both V_1 and V_2. Figures 4–21(C) and (D) show the phase changes that take place when R is adjusted to different values. In Figure 4–21(C), V_R is smaller than V_C. The output phasor AC is 50° out of phase with AB and 130° out of phase with AD. Figure 5–21(D) shows the reverse of Figure 4–21(C). In this case, R is made greater than X_C. Keep in mind that phasor AC can be changed to any value from 0° to 180° with respect to AB or AD. Note also that the lengths

of phasors V_R and V_C change with each different setting of resistor R. The length of phasor AC, however, remains the same regardless of the value of R. This means that the output of a bridge phase shifter has a constant amplitude that can be changed in phase from 0° to 180°.

The current developed in a bridge phase shifter is always in phase with the resistive voltage component of the circuit. In the phasor diagrams of Figure 4–21(B), (C), and (D), the current I is indicated as an extension from point D. It changes position with each setting of R, but continues to remain parallel to phasor BC. The current of an RC phase shifter must also be 90° out of phase with the voltage developed across the capacitor. The 90° phase angle between I and V_C shows this relationship. This condition will remain the same for each setting of R.

The RL bridge circuit of Figure 4–22(A) can be used to achieve phase shifting equally as well as the RC circuit just discussed. The resulting output, phasor diagrams, and circuit construction of an RL shifter are very similar to those of the RC network. Voltages V_R and V_L are the component voltages developed across the variable resistor and inductor. The current I of this circuit is in phase with V_R and is out of phase with V_L. This relationship is shown by the extension of I from the V_R vector at point C.

A half-wave SCR phase shifter circuit is shown in Figure 4–23. The bridge phase-shifter network changes the phase relationship of the gate voltage with respect to the anode–cathode voltage. Conduction of the SCR can be altered from zero to 180° of one alternation. One SCR can therefore achieve 50% control of the applied ac power. Two SCRs in a full-wave controller could achieve 100% control of the applied ac power. The load current of a half-wave or full-wave controller is of a dc value.

Phase control of an SCR is achieved by ap-

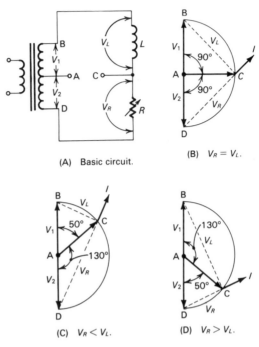

(A) Basic circuit.

(B) $V_R = V_L$.

(C) $V_R < V_L$.

(D) $V_R > V_L$.

FIGURE 4–22
RL bridge phase shifter.

plying two ac signals to the device. The anode–cathode voltage can be from a few volts ac up to several hundred volts. The phase of this signal remains fixed. The gate signal is

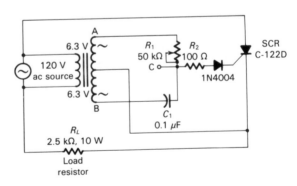

FIGURE 4–23
SCR controlled by a bridge phase shifter.

much smaller than the anode–cathode voltage. The phase of the gate signal is shifted by adjustment of a potentiometer. This action causes the anode–cathode voltage and gate voltage to change from an in-phase condition to a full 180° out-of-phase condition. The forward V_{BO} of the SCR is altered through this condition, which in turn causes a change in conduction time. Figure 4–24 shows six different conduction conditions of an SCR. Note that the gate voltage signal V_G, anode–cathode voltage V_{AK}, and conduction current I_F are all indicated for each condition. For full-wave controls, the output of the second SCR would be added to this display for the negative alternation. The output of a phase-controlled SCR is at a maximum value during full conduction, or zero delay, and at zero when 180° delay is achieved.

Pulse Triggering

A positive pulse of energy can be used to trigger an SCR into conduction instead of a continuous form of ac or dc. Triggering by this method takes advantage of the latching characteristic of an SCR. When conduction is initiated, it can be made continuous for the remainder of the alternation. The duration of the triggering pulse may be extremely short. This method of triggering in general consumes very little energy from the source. The operational efficiency of a pulse-triggered SCR is usually much higher than that of other gate-triggering methods.

To trigger an SCR into conduction, the magnitude of the pulse must be several times greater than the normal I_G triggering level. A

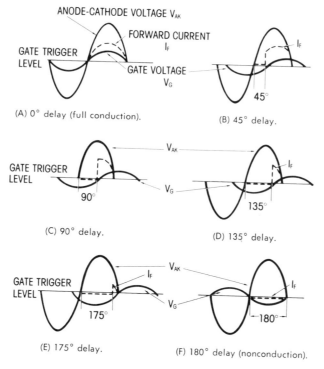

(A) 0° delay (full conduction).

(B) 45° delay.

(C) 90° delay.

(D) 135° delay.

(E) 175° delay.

(F) 180° delay (nonconduction).

FIGURE 4–24
Conduction conditions of an SCR.

high-amplitude voltage pulse discharges into the gate and causes an I_G. For pulses above 20 microseconds (μs) in duration, the triggering level is approximately the same as that of a dc source. Below 20 μs, the magnitude of the pulse should be at least dc gate-triggering level. Pulse widths of less than 1 μs duration will not trigger an SCR into conduction.

The wave forms of a pulse-triggered SCR are shown in Figure 4–25. The anode–cathode voltage (V_{AK}) is ac. The gate current triggering pulse is labeled I_G. The triggering level of I_G is for dc control values. Note that the amplitude of the pulse exceeds the triggering level by a substantial amount. The delay of conduction is based on the position of the pulse with respect to the positive alternation. Load current (I_{AK}) flows during the remainder of the alternation after the gate pulse initiates conduction. By varying the time or position of the pulse, conduction can be altered from zero to 180°.

UNIJUNCTION TRANSISTOR PULSE TRIGGERING

Pulse triggering of an SCR can be accomplished with a unijunction transistor or UJT. This device is commonly described as a voltage-controlled diode. When used to trigger an SCR into conduction, UJTs can be designed to respond to low-level signals from other inputs. The output of photocells, thermocouples, and other transductors can be used to energize the input of a UJT, which in turn will trigger the conduction of an SCR. Through this type of circuitry, it is possible to control a large SCR current with an extremely small input signal.

A unijunction transistor is a three-terminal, single-junction, solid-state device that has unidirectional conductivity. As illustrated in Figure 4–26, a small bar of N-type silicon is mounted on a ceramic base. Leads attached to

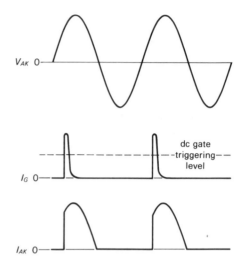

FIGURE 4–25
Wave forms of a pulse-triggered SCR.

the silicon bar are called base 1 (B_1) and base 2 (B_2). The emitter (E) is formed by fusing an aluminum wire to the opposite side of the silicon bar. The emitter is oriented so that it is closer to B_2 than B_1. A PN junction is formed by the emitter and the silicon bar. The arrow of the UJT symbol Points iN, which indicates the the emitter is P and the silicon bar is N material. The arrow of the symbol is slanted to

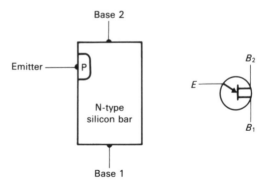

FIGURE 4–26
Unijunction transistor crystal structure and schematic symbol.

distinguish the UJT from the *N*-channel JFET symbol.

An equivalent circuit of the UJT is shown in Figure 4–27. When the E–B_1 junction is reverse biased, R_{B1} and R_{B2} are of practically the same resistive value. Forward biasing of the E–B_1 junction, however, causes the resistance of the junction to change to a rather small value. The E–B_2 junction resistance is not changed by the action of the E–B_1 junction. As a result, E–B_1 responds as a voltage-controlled variable resistor, while E–B_2 remains at a fixed value. The interbase resistance (R_{BB}) is in the range of 4 to 10 kΩ. The interbase voltage (V_{BB}) appears across B_1 and B_2. Emitter voltage (V_E) causes an emitter current (I_E) when E–B_1 is forward biased. No I_E flows when E–B_1 is reverse biased.

The operation of a UJT is quite different from other solid-state devices. When the emitter is reverse biased, B_1–B_2 responds as a simple voltage divider. The resistance of R_{BB} is at its maximum value. Any I_E that flows at this time is due to the leakage current of E–B_1. When the emitter is forward biased, R_{B1} drops to a very small value. A change in E–B_1 voltage therefore causes a significant change in R_{BB}. The current flow between B_1 and B_2 increases, and V_{BB} decreases in value.

A characteristic curve for a typical UJT is shown in Figure 4–28. The vertical part of this characteristic indicates different values of emitter voltage. An increase in the value of V_E causes a sharp vertical rise in the curve. Emitter current is represented by the horizontal part of the graph. Note that the first application of V_E is to the left of a vertical line. This indicates the reverse bias condition of operation. Any current flow that occurs here is due to the leakage of the E–B_1 diode junction. After a very nominal leakage current (I_{EO}), there is a significant increase in I_E, shown by the curve extending to the right. Forward biasing of E–B_1 is shown where the vertical line is crossed. The peak emitter voltage point (V_p) shows where the UJT is triggered into conduction. The peak-point current (I_p) is the minimum I_E needed for triggering. A further increase in I_E causes V_E to drop to the valley voltage (V_v) point. The area between V_p and V_v is called the negative resistance region. An increase in I_E causes a decrease in V_E in this part of the graph. A device that has a negative resistance region is capable of regeneration or oscillation. This part of the characteristic curve is an important operating area for the UJT in pulse trigger generation applications.

The triggering of a UJT is dependent on

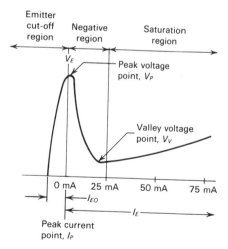

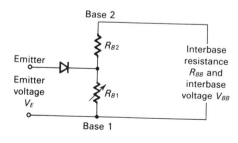

FIGURE 4–27
Equivalent of a UJT.

FIGURE 4–28
Characteristic curve on a UJT.

changes in the conductivity of the $E–B_1$ junction. When the $E–B_1$ junction is forward biased, electrons leave the silicon bar and move into the P material of the emitter. This action causes holes to appear in the silicon bar at the B_1 region. Electrons pulled from the negative side of the source attached to B_1 fill the injected holes. In effect, this causes an increase in the conduction of the $E–B_1$ junction. This region then becomes low resistant. A sudden change in R_{B1} causes a corresponding change in $B_1–B_2$ current. This change in current can be used to trigger the gate of an SCR.

Normal operation of the UJT has B_1 grounded or connected to the negative side of the source voltage and B_2 connected to the positive side. This voltage causes an interbase current to flow between $B_1–B_2$. Internally, V_{BB} divides across the interbase resistance of R_{B1} and R_{B2}. For example, if R_{B1} is 4 kΩ and R_{B2} is 6 kΩ, the voltage across R_{B1} is 0.4 of V_{BB} and R_{B2} is 0.6 of V_{BB}. It is not possible to measure these two voltage values because the junction point of R_{B1} and R_{B2} does not exist. The fractional value of voltage that appears across R_{B1} is called the *intrinsic standoff ratio* (η) or eta. Typical η values are in the range from 0.45 to 0.85 of V_{BB}. This value determines the emitter triggering voltage for a constant V_{BB}. If V_E is less than ηV_{BB}, the emitter junction is reverse biased and only leakage current (I_{EO}) flows. If V_E exceeds ηV_{BB} by a value slightly greater than the voltage drop across the $E–B_1$ diode, triggering occurs. R_{B1} is then reduced to a few ohms, and the interbase current I_{BB} increases.

Figure 4–29 shows a UJT relaxation oscillator that is frequently used to trigger an SCR. In this circuit, two parallel paths are formed by the components. Resistors R_1, R_2, and C form the charge path, while R_3, and the UJT form the discharge path. When the switch is turned on, approximately 4 V appears across R_3 and 6 V across the UJT and R_4. This voltage reverse biases the $E–B$ junction by 6 V.

Resistor R_1 and capacitor C receive energy from the source at the same time that the base path does. Capacitor C begins to develop voltage across it at a rate based on the RC values of R_1 and C. When the charge voltage at C reaches 6 V, it overcomes the reverse biasing of the $E–B_1$ junction. When this occurs, the junction becomes very low resistant and C discharges very quickly. The $E–B_1$ junction immediately becomes reverse biased because of the reduced emitter voltage. The capacitor then recharges and the process is repeated. A sawtooth wave form appears across the capacitor as indicated in Figure 4–29. The discharge voltage across R_3 produces a spiked pulse that shows the discharge time of C. The rise time of the sawtooth wave is adjusted to some extent by different values of R_1. When the charging action of the capacitor is maintained in the first time constant, very accurate pulse generation can be achieved by this circuit.

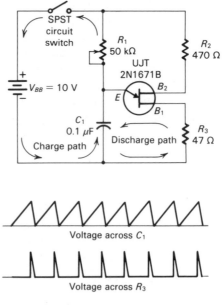

FIGURE 4–29
UJT sawtooth oscillator.

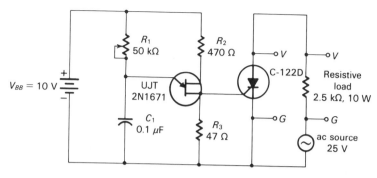

FIGURE 4–30
UJT pulse trigger control circuit.

A UJT pulse trigger control circuit for an SCR is shown in Figure 4–30. Adjustment of the variable resistor (R_1) determines the pulse triggering rate of the SCR. A value change in R_1 alters the RC of the UJT trigger circuit. When the charge voltage of C_1 reaches the V_p value, it discharges through the E–B_1 junction of the UJT and R_3. This current develops a voltage across R_3. The top is positive and the bottom is negative. This forward biases the gate–cathode of the SCR and causes it to be triggered into conduction. The load will only receive current during the positive alternation of the applied ac. A pulse trigger circuit of this type can be used to effectively delay the conduction time of the positive alternation from 0° to 180°.

Synchronized UJT Triggering

A problem with the pulse-triggered SCR circuit of Figure 4–30 is synchronization of the trigger pulse and the ac source voltage. Since the UJT is energized by an independent dc and the SCR by an ac source, it is difficult to get good timing between the two. A variety of circuit possibilities has been developed to correct this problem. One solution is to use an ac

source to develop dc for operation of the UJT. The same ac source is also used to energize the SCR. When the trigger pulse and SCR are both energized by the same source, they will be in continuous synchronization.

One alternative to the triggered synchronization problem is the ramp–pedestal control circuit. A pedestal is used to describe a platform of voltage produced by the ac source during one alternation. A ramp is an ascending incline in this voltage at the top of the pedestal. The ramp and pedestal circuit is frequently used in IC thyristor controllers.

A discrete-component ramp and pedestal control circuit is shown in Figure 4–31(A). The source voltage (V_S) is supplied by the ac power line. The resulting trigger signal developed by the UJT is synchronized with the ac source supplying the SCR.

Operation of the ramp and pedestal circuit is based on alternation changes of the ac source. When the positive alternation of the source occurs, let us assume that point A is positive and B is negative. The zener diode, being reverse biased by this alternation, goes into conduction when the voltage exceeds 20 V. It maintains this voltage at points C-B for the remainder of the alternation. This voltage forward biases D_2 through resistor R_2. Capacitor C_1 then charges through D_2, R_2, and R_1.

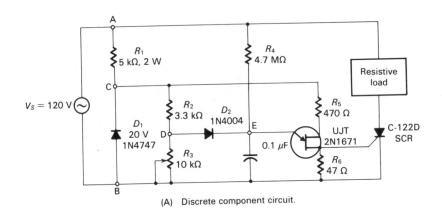

(A) Discrete component circuit.

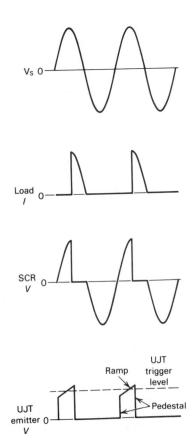

(B) Ramp-pedestal waveforms.

FIGURE 4–31
Ramp–pedestal SCR control circuit.

Resistors R_2 and R_3 determine the bias voltage for D_2. If R_3 is adjusted to the same value as R_2, there is 10 V across each resistor. D_2 is forward biased by 10 V. C_1 continues to charge until the voltage at point E reaches 10 V. This reverse biases D_2 and stops the charging path of C_1 through D_2. C_1, however, continues to charge through its connection to R_4. The high resistance of R_4 slows down the charging rate. This causes the voltage at point E to rise more slowly. The resulting wave form has an inclining ramp riding on the top of the pedestal. Eventually, the charge on C_1 reaches the trigger potential of the UJT. Turning on the UJT causes a gate current that triggers the SCR into conduction. All this occurs during the positive alternation of the ac source.

During the negative alternation, the zener diode is forward biased. Only 0.6 V appears across R_2 and R_3. The charge voltage on C_1 cannot build up to a value to trigger the UJT into conduction. The SCR is also reverse biased by this alternation and will not be conductive. Conduction of the UJT and SCR can only occur during the positive alternation.

The voltage rise across C_1 is shown as the UJT emitter voltage in Figure 4–31(B). Note that the voltage rises very quickly at first. This gives the pedestal effect of the wave form. C_1

is charging through diode D_2 at this time. The ramp part of the wave takes place when C_1 charges through R_4. Triggering of the UJT occurs when the peak of the ramp is reached. Note that this value also triggers the SCR into conduction. If the resistance of R_3 is increased, C_1 charges very quickly to a higher voltage value before D_2 becomes reverse biased. This raises the pedestal level, causing it to reach the UJT triggering level. In effect, the value of R_3 determines the trigger point of the UJT and SCR. When triggering occurs early during the alternation, more power is delivered to the load. Late triggering during the alternation reduces load power.

PUT Pulse Triggering

A programmable unijunction transistor (PUT) is frequently used to generate trigger pulses for SCR control applications. A PUT is actually a thyristor that responds as a UJT that has a variable trigger voltage. This voltage can be adjusted to a desired value by changing two external voltage-divider resistors. The trigger voltage level can therefore be set or programmed to respond to a specific value.

Figure 4–32 shows the crystal structure, schematic symbol, and element names of a

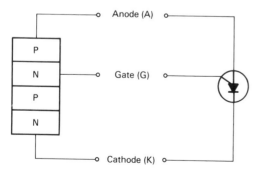

FIGURE 4–32
Programmable unijunction transistor.

PUT. The crystal structure and schematic symbol of the PUT are very similar to the SCR. The gate junction is the primary difference. In a PUT, the gate (G) is connected to the N material nearest to the anode. A PN junction is formed by the anode–gate. Conduction of the device is controlled by the bias voltage of A–G.

The polarity of the bias voltage of a PUT is referenced with respect to the cathode. The cathode is usually connected to the ground or the negative side of the power source. The gate is then made positive relative to the cathode. This is the gate voltage (V_G). The anode voltage (V_A) is also made positive with respect to the cathode. Conduction of the PUT is based on the difference in positive voltage between the gate and anode. When the gate is more positive than the anode, the A–G junction is reverse biased. This condition causes the device to be nonconductive or in its off state. The anode–cathode has infinite resistance and the device responds as an open switch. When the anode becomes more positive than the gate by 0.5 V, it forward biases the A–G junction. This condition causes gate current to flow and the device is triggered into conduction. In the on state, the anode–cathode resistance drops to a very low value. The device then responds as a switch in the on state.

Refer to the PUT circuit and characteristic curve in Figure 4–33. Gate voltage (V_G) is developed by resistors R_1 and R_2 connected across V_{GG}. The anode–cathode voltage (V_{AK}) is supplied by V_S. When V_{AK} is made more positive than V_G, the PUT is triggered into conduction. The characteristic curve shows this by the changing value of V_{AK}. Triggering occurs when V_{AK} reaches the peak voltage point (V_p). The voltage then drops to the valley voltage point (V_v). Conduction current (I_{AK}) is indicated by expansion of the curve to the right. The PUT has a negative resistance region between V_p and V_v. The I_{AK}–V_{AK} charac-

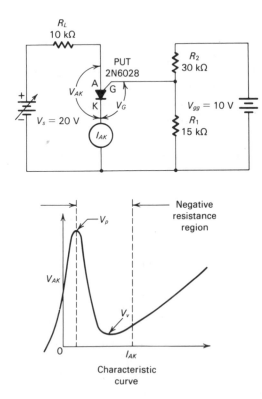

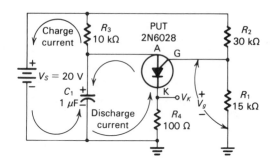

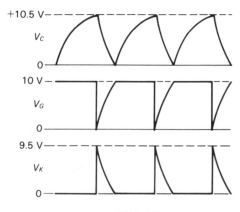

FIGURE 4–33
PUT circuit and characteristic curve.

FIGURE 4–34
PUT relaxation oscillator.

teristic of a PUT is very similar to that of a UJT.

The anode of a PUT responds as the emitter of a UJT. Resistors R_1 and R_2 are similar to the interbase resistance of the UJT. The intrinsic standoff ratio (η) of a PUT is determined by the value of the gate voltage with respect to the anode voltage. V_G can be altered externally by changing the values of R_1 and R_2. This permits the PUT to be programmed or adjusted to different trigger voltage values.

Figure 4–34 shows a PUT relaxation oscillator that can be used to trigger an SCR. In this circuit, two parallel paths are formed by the components and the device. Resistor R_3 and C_1 form the charge path for the capacitor and the anode voltage. The PUT and resistor R_4 form

a discharge path for C. A trigger pulse is developed across R_4 when C_1 discharges through the anode–cathode of the PUT.

When the circuit switch of Figure 4–34 is turned on, it energizes the PUT from the power source V_S. Resistors R_1 and R_2 form a voltage-divider network across the V_{GG} source. In this case, R_1 is 15 kΩ and R_2 is 30 kΩ. The intrinsic standoff ratio (η) is determined as follows:

$$\eta = \frac{R_1}{R_1 + R_2}$$

$$= \frac{15 \text{ k}\Omega}{15 \text{ k}\Omega + 30 \text{ k}\Omega}$$

$$= 0.333$$

The gate voltage (V_G) of the PUT is then determined by $\eta \times V_S$. V_G for this circuit is

$$V_G = \eta \times V_S$$
$$= 0.333 \cdot 20 \text{ V}$$
$$= 6.66 \text{ V}$$

Initially, V_G makes the gate more positive than the anode by 6.66 V. The PUT is in its nonconductive state or off.

After a short period of time, capacitor C_1 begins to charge to the source voltage through R_1. When the charge potential exceeds 6.66 V, it makes the anode more positive than the gate. This condition triggers the PUT into conduction. C_1 then discharges through the low resistance of the PUT and R_4. Discharge takes place very quickly due to the low resistance. The resulting current produces a positive-going voltage pulse across R_4. Triggering the PUT into conduction also causes a drop in the value of V_G. This is due to the low resistance of the forward-biased AG junction. The wave forms of Figure 4–34 show how the relaxation oscillator responds for two operational cycles.

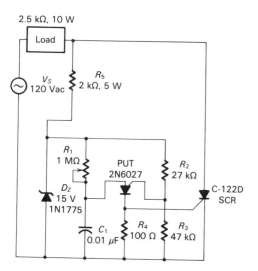

SCR Triggering with a PUT

A programmable unijunction transistor is frequently used to control the conduction of an SCR. The PUT is primarily responsible for generating trigger pulses. These pulses are developed by a relaxation oscillator. The pulses are then applied to the gate of an SCR to initiate the conduction process. Only one pulse is

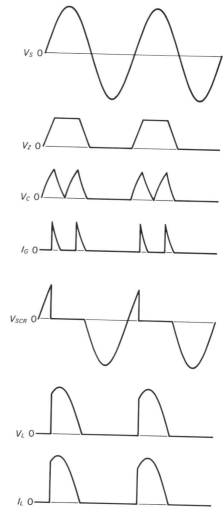

FIGURE 4–35
PUT pulse-triggered SCR power control.

needed during a selected alternation to initiate conduction. A circuit of this type has synchronization of the trigger pulse and the alternation that forward biases the SCR. This is accomplished by energizing the SCR and PUT from the same ac source. Conduction of the SCR only occurs when the anode–cathode is forward biased. Control by synchronized pulse triggering is very precise and has a wide range of adjustment capabilities.

A PUT pulse-triggered SCR power control circuit is shown in Figure 4–35. The outer part of the circuit is controlled by the SCR. Notice the location of the load device, SCR, and ac power source. The center part of the circuit is used to develop trigger pulses that control the conduction of the SCR. The PUT, in this case, is used as a relaxation oscillator. Operation of the oscillator is essentially the same as Figure 4–34.

The PUT is energized by a dc source. A 15-V zener diode is used in this case as a rectifier–regulator. It is energized by the same ac source that supplies the SCR load. A series-dropping resistor connects the ac to the zener diode. During the positive alternation, the zener diode clips the source voltage to a peak value of 15 V. The negative alternation causes forward conduction of the diode and the voltage drops to approximately zero. The dc supply is essentially a pulsating dc of 15 V. See the V_z dc supply and the ac source wave forms. Notice the phase relationship of the ac source and the PUT supply voltage. When the positive alternation and the dc supply pulse occur at the same time, this relationship permits the trigger pulse to have synchronized control of the SCR. The time of the trigger pulse can be changed, however, by altering the resistance of R_1.

The wave forms of Figure 4–35 show how the circuit responds for two complete operational cycles. Note that more than one triggering pulse may be generated by the PUT for a given dc source pulse. The number of pulses produced is based on the time constant of R_1 and C_1. A low-resistance setting causes several pulses to occur. Higher resistance values may permit only one pulse to be generated. The SCR is triggered into conduction by only the first pulse. With a suitable value of holding current, conduction continues for the remainder of the alternation. The SCR is nonconductive during the negative alternation. Refer to the SCR voltage, load current, and load voltage wave forms. V_{SCR} and V_L are primarily the reverse of each other. Conduction causes the amplitude of V_{SCR} to drop to a straight line. Conduction of the load current and voltage is shown as a rise in amplitude. Delay of conduction time is altered by changing the value of R_1.

GATE TURN-OFF THYRISTORS

Gate turn-off thyristors are unique power control devices that can be triggered into conduction or turned off by a gate signal. Characteristically, this type of thyristor responds as an SCR. It has unidirectional current conductivity and responds only in quadrant I of the *I–V* characteristic. Construction is of the *PNPN* type of configuration. This thyristor can be triggered into conduction when the gate is forward biased. Gate current lowers the breakover voltage *(V_{BO})*, and latching is maintained as long as the initial holding current level is exceeded. The unique distinction of this type of device is its gate turn-off feature. The gate can be used to extinguish conduction and turn off the device when it is reverse biased.

The gate turn-off principle of operation is found in two distinct types of thyristors. The silicon-controlled switch (SCS) is a low-power, low-current control device. The gate

turn-off switch (GTO) is used to control larger amounts of power. These devices are primarily used in computer logic circuits, oscillators, and as trigger devices for other thyristors.

Silicon-controlled Switch

The silicon-controlled switch (SCS), like the silicon-controlled rectifier, is a four-layer *PNPN* thyristor. External conduction is made to all four layers of the SCS. It has an anode, cathode, anode–gate, and a cathode–gate. The crystal structure, schematic symbol, and two-transistor equivalent of an SCS are shown in Figure 4–36.

The current–voltage characteristic of an SCS is primarily the same as that of an SCR. Conductivity occurs in quadrant I. This is achieved by making the anode positive and the cathode negative. Quadrant III represents the reverse-biased condition of operation. Oridinarily, the SCS is not designed to operate in this condition. The peak reverse voltage (PRV) rating of the device is represented by quadrant III.

Operation of the SCS is quite different from the SCR. An SCS can be triggered into conduction or turned off by an appropriate signal applied to either gate. A positive voltage or pulse applied to the cathode gate *(G$_C$)* with respect to the cathode causes gate current to flow. This I_{GC} lowers the forward breakover voltage and permits conduction. A negative voltage with respect to the anode forward biases the anode–gate G_A. This reaction causes a corresponding anode–cathode current to flow. I_{GA} then lowers the V_{BO} and causes triggering.

The polarity of the gate triggering voltage is more meaningful if we study the two-transistor equivalent of the SCS in Figure 4–36(C). Note that the cathode–gate is connected to the base of the *NPN* transistor Q_2. It should be obvious that the base of Q_2 must be positive in order to cause forward biasing. When this occurs, some of the output of Q_2 is supplied to the base of Q_1, thus causing regeneration. The entire assembly then becomes conductive. A negative voltage or trigger pulse applied to G_A will also cause forward biasing of the *PNP* transistor Q_1. Some of this output is then returned to the base of Q_2, which causes regeneration and the assembly to be conductive. In effect, a negative voltage forward biases G_A and a positive voltage forward biases G_C. In most SCSs the cathode–gate responds to a lower triggering current than the anode–gate.

An SCS can be turned off or brought out of conduction in three different ways. The most obvious method is a reduction of anode current below the holding current *(I$_H$)* level. This response is the same as that of an SCR. Second, a negative pulse may be applied to the cath-

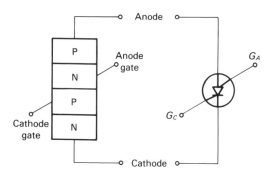

(A) Crystal structure.   (B) Schematic symbol.

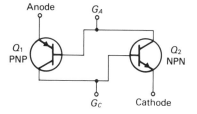

(C) Two-transistor equivalent.

FIGURE 4–36
Silicon-controlled switch.

ode–gate. This would reverse bias the *NPN* transistor (Q_2) of the equivalent circuit. The third method of turn off can be achieved by applying a positive-going pulse to the anode–gate. This condition reverse biases the base of the *PNP* transistor (Q_1). In most SCSs, it takes more gate current to bring the device out of conduction than it takes to trigger it into conduction. The off triggering current must overcome a larger anode–cathode current in order to stop conduction. Ordinarily, this is not a real problem in most SCS applications. Maximum I_{AK} values are usually rather small. Typical I_{AK} values are 100 to 300 mA, with power dissipation ratings of 100 to 500 mW.

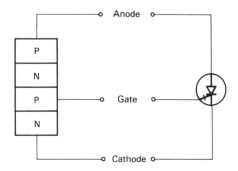

FIGURE 4–37
Gate turn-off thyristor.

Gate Turn-off Switches

The gate turn-off switch (GTO) is a thyristor that is very similar in construction to the SCR. Its operation is different in that conduction can be triggered on or turned off by a single gate. A positive gate pulse causes the device to be conductive. Conduction continues if the holding current is maintained. A negative gate signal turns off a conductive GTO.

The crystal structure and schematic symbol of a GTO are shown in Figure 4–37. The crystal structure is primarily the same as an SCR. The gate of a GTO is, however, normally made thicker than that of an SCR. Reverse biasing of the gate increases the size of the depletion region to a point that it will extinguish conduction. The schematic symbol of a GTO differs from that of an SCR by employing a small line across the gate lead. This denotes the on–off switching function of the gate. Operation other than this is primarily the same as for an SCR. It has unidirectional conductivity and will latch when made conductive.

The most obvious advantage of a GTO over an SCR is its gate turn-off capability. A consequence of this function is an increase in the amount of I_G needed to produce triggering. For an SCR and GTO with similar I_{AK} ratings, an SCR can be triggered with 1 mA while the I_G of the GTO must be 25 mA. The turn-off current of a GTO is significantly greater than the triggering current. GTOs are available that can control up to 3 A with power dissipation of 20 W.

The switching time of a GTO is another important characteristic. The trigger time of a GTO is primarily the same as for an SCR. Typical trigger-time values are 1 μs. The turn-off time of a GTO is, however, approximately the same as its trigger time. An SCR must be turned off by reducing I_{AK} below the holding current level. Typical turn-off values may take from 5 to 30 μs. The rapid on–off characteristic of a GTO permits it to be used in high-speed switching applications.

Figure 4–38 shows a GTO used as a sawtooth generator. When the source voltage is applied, the GTO turns on immediately. The gate is made positive with respect to the cathode by the value of the zener voltage (V_z). Conduction of the GTO permits capacitor C_1 to charge to the source voltage. When the voltage across C_1 reaches V_z, it reverse biases the gate. This action increases the depletion region of the cathode–gate junction. The holding current (I_H) drops in value to turn off the GTO. C_1 then discharges through the combination of

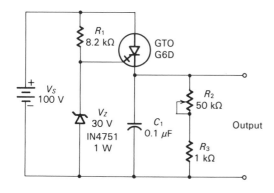

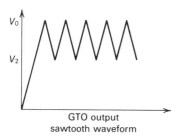

GTO output
sawtooth waveform

FIGURE 4–38
GTO sawtooth generator.

R_2 and R_3. The discharge time is determined by $(R_2 + R_3)\,C_1$. Proper selection of the R and C values will result in a sawtooth wave form. When the value of VC_1 drops below V_z, the GTO will turn on and the process will be repeated.

QUESTIONS

1. What are the primary differences between a bipolar transistor and a thyristor?

2. How does a thyristor go into conduction by exceeding the forward breakover voltage?

3. Explain how a thyristor goes into conduction using the two-transistor equivalent circuit.

4. What must the alpha value of Q_1 and Q_2 of a two-transistor thyristor equivalent be in order to produce conduction?

5. Why does an SCR have unidirectional conductivity?

6. In reference to the I–V characteristics of an SCR, what is:

   a. Forward breakover voltage?

   b. Holding current?

   c. Peak reverse voltage?

7. Explain how the application of gate current to an SCR lowers the forward V_{BO}.

8. Why does a dc static switch require forced commutation when an ac static switch does not?

9. Explain how full-wave dc power control can be achieved using SCRs.

10. What is a problem with dc gate control of an SCR energized by ac?

11. Why does a single-leg RL or RC phase shifter achieve only 90° control?

12. How does an RC bridge phase shifter achieve 180° control?

13. Explain how a UJT is triggered into conduction by an RC circuit.

14. Explain the difference between a UJT and a PUT.

15. Are the PUT triggering circuit of Figure 4–35 and the ac source synchronized? Explain your answer.

16. How would you distinguish between an SCR and an SCS?

17. What is the physical difference in the crystal structure of an SCS and an SCR?

18. In general terms, how much voltage appears across the anode–cathode of an SCR

after it has been triggered into conduction?

PROBLEMS

1. If the alpha of Q_1 is 0.4 and Q_2 is 0.38, and the leakage current is 0.1 μA for Q_1 and Q_2, would this produce conduction of a thyristor?

2. If 150 V is applied to the thyristor of Problem 1, what is a representative internal resistance?

3. What is the time constant *(t)* of a 0.1-μF capacitor and a 100 kΩ resistor used in a relaxation oscillator?

4. The UJT of Figure 4–29 has an η of 0.6. If the E–B_1 diode voltage is 0.6 V, what capacitor voltage *(V_C)* will cause triggering?

5. If R_1 is changed to 20 kΩ and R_2 to 60 kΩ in the PUT circuit of Figure 4–34, what is the new intrinsic standoff ratio?

6. Using the value changes of Problem 5, triggering of the PUT will take place at what voltage value?

7. If 50 V is applied to the *RC* circuit of Problem 5, what voltage will appear across C in two time constants?

8. What is the impedance of R_L of a phase shifter when X_L is 20 Ω and R is 40 Ω?

ACTIVITIES

ACTIVITY 4–1: DC Static SCR Switch Control

Objective: Construct an SCR static switch and evaluate its operation.

Procedure:

1. Construct the SCR switch of Figure 4–10. The load may be a resistor as indicated or a lamp. If a lamp is used for the load, a 12-V lamp must be used with a 12-V source.

2. Turn on the V_S and V_G sources. Close the circuit switch first; then turn on the gate switch. When the SCR has been triggered, it should remain in the on state as long as V_S is supplied. V_G can be removed without altering the conduction of the SCR. To turn off the latched SCR, turn off the gate source; then momentarily turn off the circuit switch.

3. Trigger the SCR into conduction and turn it off several times.

4. Trigger the SCR into conduction. Measure and record the V_{AK}, V_{RL}, and V_G.

5. Turn off the gate switch and repeat step 4. Does this alter the conduction of the SCR?

6. Turn off the SCR and open the gate switch. Then turn on the circuit switch. Measure and record V_{AK} and V_{RL}. Describe the difference between conduction and nonconduction with the measured voltage values.

ACTIVITY 4–2: SCR Push-button Control

Objective: Construction of a push-button-controlled SCR dc switch and evaluation of its operation.

Procedure:

1. Construct the push-button SCR switch of Figure 4–11.

2. Turn on V_S. If the circuit is operating properly, the on push button will trigger the load into conduction and the off push button will turn the load off.

3. Test the operation of the circuit by measuring V_{AK} and V_{RL}.

4. This circuit has forced commutation. The off push button causes C_1 to discharge across the SCR and lower the I_{AK} below the holding current level.

5. Measure the load current and C_1 discharge current when the SCR is turned on and turned off.

ACTIVITY 4–3: AC Static Switch

Objective: Construct an ac static switch with an SCR and evaluate its operation.

Procedure:

1. Construct the SCR ac switch of Figure 4–12.

2. Apply source voltage to the circuit. Turn on the gate switch to energize the circuit. Turning off the gate switch will turn off the load.

3. Test the operation of the circuit several times.

4. Measure and record V_{AK} and V_L for a conductive and a nonconductive operational state.

5. With an oscilloscope, observe the wave form across the lamp and the SCR when the circuit is in the on and off states. Make a sketch of your findings.

6. Why is forced commutation not required in an ac static switch?

ACTIVITY 4–4: Variable AC Power Control

Objective: Construction of a variable power control circuit and evaluation of its operation.

Procedure:

1. Construct the variable SCR power control circuit of Figure 4–13.

2. Energize the circuit and adjust R_2 through its operating range. The dc value of V_{RL} should change from zero to 50% of the rms value of the ac source.

3. Prepare an oscilloscope for operation and connect it across R_L. Adjust R_2 through its range while observing V_{RL}.

4. Make a sketch of the wave form showing maximum, medium, and minimum output values.

ACTIVITY 4–5: SCR Bridge Phase-shifting Control

Objective: To build a bridge phase-shifting control circuit for an SCR and evaluation of its operation.

Procedure:

1. Construct the bridge phase-shifter SCR control circuit of Figure 4–24.

2. Apply power to the circuit and test its operation. It is essential that the 120-V ac source be isolated from ground so that test equipment can be connected to the circuit for evaluation.

3. Connect the oscilloscope common or ground lead to the CT terminal of the transformer. Connect the vertical lead of the oscilloscope alternately to terminal A and B of the transformer. These waves should be of equal amplitude and 180° out of phase. Connect the vertical lead to terminal C and adjust R_1 while observing the phase relationship of the wave form. Describe the wave form change.

4. Connect the oscilloscope across R_L and observe the output wave form for different

settings of R_1. Make a sketch of the output for three different positional settings of R_1. Indicate the amount of delay achieved by the circuit.

5. Connect the oscilloscope across the SCR and compare the V_{AK} wave form with that of V_R. Describe the observed relationship.

6. What percentage of power control can be achieved by this circuit?

ACTIVITY 4–6: Unijunction Transistor Oscillator

Objective: Construction of a UJT sawtooth oscillator circuit and evaluation of its operation.

Procedure:

1. With an ohmmeter, measure the resistance between any two leads of a UJT. If these leads show the same resistance in either direction, they are B_1 and B_2. If the ohmmeter shows low resistance for one polarity and high resistance when the leads are reversed, the positive probe was originally on the emitter and the negative probe on B_1 or B_2. Make the lead diagram of the UJT.

2. Construct the UJT sawtooth oscillator of Figure 4–29. If the circuit is working properly, there will be a small dc voltage across R_3. Measure and record this voltage.

3. Connect an oscilloscope across R_3. This should produce a spiked pulse. Make a sketch of the observed wave form.

4. Adjust potentiometer R_1 through its operating range while observing the influence that this has on the wave form. Describe your findings.

5. Connect the oscilloscope probes across C_1 and observe the wave form. Make a sketch of the observed wave form.

6. This circuit is used in the next activity as a pulse generator to trigger an SCR into conduction.

ACTIVITY 4–7: UJT Pulse Trigger Control of an SCR

Objective: Construction of a UJT pulse circuit that controls the triggering of an SCR.

Procedure:

1. Construct the circuit of Figure 4–30. Apply power to the UJT pulse generator from the V_{BB} source. If the UJT circuit is working, there should be a continuous series of pulses appearing across resistor R_3. Make a sketch of the observed wave form.

2. Energize the SCR with ac. If this part of the circuit is working properly, dc should appear across the load resistor.

3. Connect the oscilloscope across the load resistor at points V and G. Observe the wave form. Adjust the value of R_1 while observing the influence that it has on the load. Describe your findings.

4. Observe the wave forms across the ac source, the load, the SCR, and R_3. Make a sketch showing the relationship of these waves.

5. The trigger control circuit of this activity is considered to be unsynchronized. What does this mean?

ACTIVITY 4–8: Ramp–Pedestal Control of an SCR

Objective: Construction of a ramp–pedestal control circuit for an SCR and evaluation of its operation.

Procedure:

1. Construct the circuit of Figure 4–31. The

circuit will be tested in three parts. The first part deals with the zener-diode voltage source. Part 2 shows the operation of the UJT. The last part deals with the SCR.

2. Apply power to the circuit. If at all possible, the ac source should be isolated from ground to prevent damage to the test equipment.

3. Measure the dc voltage across D_1. This should be 20 V dc. Measure the dc voltage across R_6. This should be a rather small value. If the SCR is operational, there should be dc across the load resistor.

4. Connect an oscilloscope across D_1, R_6, and R_L. Make a sketch of the observed wave forms. Adjust R_3 while observing the influence that this has on the load and UJT trigger pulse. Note that the trigger pulse and the ac source are in synchronism. Compare the zener voltage, trigger pulse, and load voltage.

5. What causes the output to be synchronized with the trigger pulse in this circuit?

ACTIVITY 4–9: PUT Characteristics

Objective: Construction of a PUT circuit to become familiar with its I_{AK}–V_{AK} characteristics.

Procedure:

1. Construct the circuit of Figure 4–33. Turn on V_s and V_{gg}. Adjust V_s to 0 V and monitor I_{AK} and V_{AK}. Increase the value of V_s in 0.5 V increments while monitoring I_{AK}. Record the values of I_{AK} for each value of V_{AK}.

2. Make a V_{AK}–I_{AK} characteristic curve for the PUT. Note the point where I_{AK} drops in value. This is where conduction or breakover occurs.

3. Adjust V_{gg} to 8 V and repeat step 1. What is the new breakover value?

4. Adjust V_{gg} to 12 V and determine the breakover value.

ACTIVITY 4–10: PUT Relaxation Oscillator

Objective: Construction of a PUT relaxation oscillator circuit to explore its operating characteristics.

Procedure:

1. Construct the PUT relaxation oscillator of Figure 4–34.

2. Apply power to the circuit and test its operation. Connect an oscilloscope across resistor R_4. If the circuit is functioning properly, there should be a series of dc pulses at the output.

3. Connect the oscilloscope across C_1 and observe the wave form. Compare this wave form with the one observed across R_4.

4. Connect the oscilloscope across R_1 and observe the wave form. Compare this wave form with that observed across R_4 and C_1.

5. Explain how this circuit responds as a pulse generator.

ACTIVITY 4–11: PUT Pulse Control of an SCR

Objective: Construction of a PUT pulse control circuit for an SCR and examination of its operation.

Procedure:

1. Construct the PUT pulse-triggered SCR control circuit of Figure 4–35. The ac source should be isolated from ground to protect the test equipment.

2. Energize the circuit and measure the volt-

age across D_z. This should be 15 V. If it is, measure the voltage across R_L. A substantial value of V_{R_L} generally indicates satisfactory operation of the SCR.

3. With an oscilloscope, observe the wave forms across the load, the SCR, R_4 for I_G, and C_1 for V_C. Make a sketch of the observed wave forms.

4. Adjust R_1 through its operating range while noting the influence that this operation has on the output of the circuit.

5. Explain how this circuit achieves synchronized control of an SCR.

Alternating current power can be efficiently controlled today with a special device that switches conduction on and off during each alternation. Control of this type is accomplished with a special semiconductor device known as a triac. A *triac* is identified as a three-electrode or triode ac semiconductor switch. Conduction is triggered by a gate signal. A triac is the equivalent of two reverse-parallel-connected SCRs with one common gate. Conduction can be achieved in either direction with an appropriate gate current. AC can be controlled efficiently and accurately with this device.

TRIACs

A *triac* is classified as a bidirectional gate controlled thyristor. Conduction is achieved by selecting an appropriate crystal combination. Selecton depends on the polarity of the source. During one alternation, conduction is through a *PNPN* combination. Conduction for the next alternation is by an *NPNP* combination. The crystal selection process is achieved automatically. *P* and *N* materials are jointly connected to each terminal. Selection is made according to the polarity of a specific alternation.

Figure 5–1 shows the crystal structure, junction diagram, and schematic symbol of a triac. Notice that the crystal structure of this device forms an $N_1P_1N_2P_2$ structure between T_1 and T_2. The gate is commonly connected to P_1 of the P_1N_4 junction. From T_2 to T_1, the crystal structure is $N_3P_2N_2P_1$. The gate of this structure utilizes N_4 of the P_1N_4 junction. This shows that T_1, T_2, and G are in either an *NPNP* or *PNPN* combination depending on the voltage of T_1 and T_2. Selection of the crystal combination is based on the polarity of the applied voltage. When T_1 is negative, N_1 is forward biased and P_1 is reverse biased. Current carriers will flow easily through the forward-

5

Triacs
and Diacs

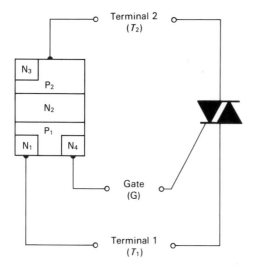

FIGURE 5–1
Junction diagram and schematic symbol of a triac.

biased material and not into the reverse-biased material. This means that the *NPNP* or *PNPN* combination and the appropriate gate voltage for initiating conduction are selected by source voltage polarity. For ac, the polarity changes with each alternation. Thus one structure combination responds for one alternation and the other combination for the second alternation.

I–V Characteristics

When ac is applied to a triac, T_2 is positive and T_1 is negative for one alternation. For the next alternation, T_2 is negative and T_1 is positive. The current–voltage characteristic of a triac must therefore show how it will respond during both alternations of the ac source. Figure 5–2 shows a typical *I–V* characteristic of a triac. Operation in quadrant I occurs when T_2 is positive and T_1 is negative. This represents the forward conduction mode of operation. Quadrant III denotes reverse conduction. T_2 is made negative and T_1 positive for operation in

quadrant III. The breakover voltage in quadrant I or III is usually quite large when the gate current is zero. Ordinarily, a triac is not designed for conduction when the gate is zero.

When gate current is applied to a triac, it lowers the V_{BC}. This action permits conduction to be achieved at a lower voltage. In quadrant I, either a positive or negative gate voltage produces gate current. Positive gate voltage tends to be more sensitive to triggering than negative values. When a suitable value of I_G occurs, the triac is triggered into conduction. I_T flows through T_1, the P_1 material, and the N_2P_2 region, which is forward biased by T_2. This current continues for the remainder of the alternation, when it moves into the holding current region of the *I–V* characteristic.

During the negative alternation of the source, T_1 is positive and T_2 is negative. Quadrant III displays this condition of operation. With no gate current, the reverse V_{BO} is quite large. No conduction occurs unless an extremely high value of V_{BO} is reached. This voltage value, like that of quadrant I, is usually avoided in normal circuit operation. When I_G occurs, it lowers the reverse V_{BO} to a value that can cause conduction. In some triacs either a positive or negative gate voltage may be

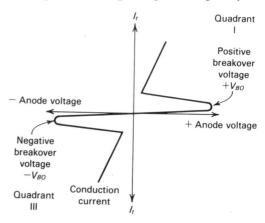

FIGURE 5–2
V/I characteristics of a triac.

Quadrant	Element polarities			Required I_G
I +	T_2 +	T_1 −	G +	5—10 mA
I −	T_2 +	T_1 −	G −	10—20 mA
III −	T_2 −	T_1 +	G −	7—15 mA
III +	T_2 −	T_1 +	G +	> 40 mA

FIGURE 5–3
Trigger modes of a triac.

used to bias the gate. Ordinarily, a positive V_G is avoided in most applications. A negative V_G is therefore used to bias the gate and produce I_G. Conduction is triggered and I_T flows from T_2, through N_3, P_2, N_2, P_1, and T_1. The N_2P_1 junction then sees a significant increase in current when I_G flows in the gate. This current added to that of the N_3P_2 junction lowers the reverse V_{BO} and causes full conduction to occur. The resulting $I–V$ characteristic is thus a mirror image of conduction in quadrant I.

Due to the dual polarity of the gate, T_1 and T_2 of a triac have four possible trigger polarity combinations. The table of Figure 5–3 lists these combinations as trigger modes and representative gate current (I_G) triggering values. Quadrant I operation has T_1 negative and T_2 positive. Note that the positive gate voltage produces an I_G that is smaller than that of the negative voltage I_G. This indicates that the triac is more sensitive to a positive voltage value in quadrant I. Quadrant III operation occurs best when T_1 is positive and T_2 is negative. In this quadrant, the triac is more sensitive to a negative voltage polarity. Ordinarily, the positive V_G mode of operation is avoided in most circuit applications. Some manufacturers recommend that their triacs not be used in this triggering mode. A common practice used in selecting the most sensitive mode of operation is to match the polarity of the gate with the polarity of terminal 2.

Some manufacturers have special function triacs that are designed for operation in the + III operational mode. This device generally has a special number designation or code to denote its unusual sensitivity. General Electric Company lists a standard triac as an SC141B. A device designed for + III operation is numbered SC141B13. The specialized device is usually more expensive than a standard unit.

TRIAC OPERATION

In normal operation, the circuit of a triac must be designed so that it only goes into conduction by action of the gate. The applied source voltage must therefore be of a value that is somewhat less than that normally needed to overcome the operating V_{BO}. This characteristic therefore becomes a critical factor when selecting a triac to do a specific control function. Transient pulses or uncontrolled line voltage spikes must also be limited in order to avoid uncontrolled triggering of a triac. Special bidirectional triggering devices known as diacs are generally used in triac circuits to limit voltage spikes to amplitude levels that will not damage or trigger the gate junction. These devices are discussed on Page 146.

DC Control

DC control of a triac is achieved the same way that it was for an SCR. In general, dc gate control of a triac is not very practical. Conduction can only be delayed for the first 90° of one alternation. After this point of the alternation, conduction will either be on or off for the last 90° depending on the gate current. The resulting output of the two alternations is quite different. Quadrant I and III do not have the same sensitivity to gate current. In quadrant III the gate current must be greater to cause triggering. This, in effect, causes a slightly different triggering level for each alternation. In most

devices, a positive gate voltage in quadrant III will not permit any conduction during the negative alternation. Figure 5–4 shows a dc circuit of this type and some of its representative wave forms.

As a general rule, there is no reason to use dc control to change the operation of a triac. The variable dc source would need to be supplied from a battery or by a rectified power supply and still only produce half-wave dc output. Control of this type is only about 25% effective. AC control of a triac, by comparison, is 100% effective and can be supplied from the same source.

AC Control

With ac control of a triac, it is possible to achieve a 180° delay of the conduction time. For this to be achieved, two distinct ac signals must be applied to the triac. The ac source represents one of these signals. It is applied to terminals 1 and 2 and must not be shifted in phase or altered. The second ac signal is used

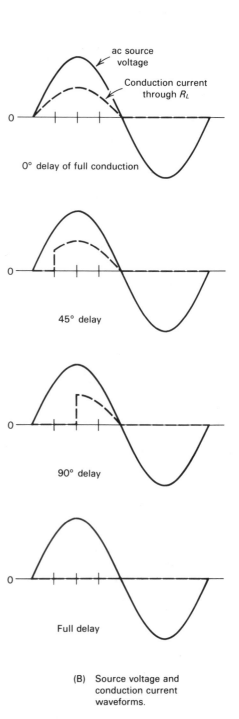

0° delay of full conduction

45° delay

90° delay

Full delay

(B) Source voltage and conduction current waveforms.

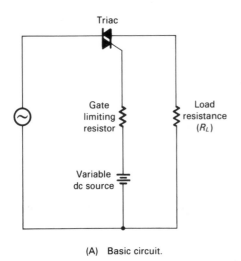

(A) Basic circuit.

FIGURE 5–4
DC control circuit for a triac.

to control the conduction time of a triac by altering $+V_{BO}$ and $-V_{BO}$. This signal is controlled by a phase shifter and can be changed from 0° to 90° or 0° to 180°, depending on its design. This type of control produces a change in the phase relationship that exists between the two signals. The gate control signal of a triac must be made to lag behind the source voltage in order to effectively be used as a control factor.

Figure 5–5 shows two distinct phase control circuits used to alter the conduction time of a triac. The single-leg circuit [Figure 5–5(A)] achieves approximately 90° of conduction time delay. The bridge phase-shifter circuit [Figure 5–5(B)] permits 100% control from full conduction to 180° of delay, or nonconduction. A diac is used in the gate of both circuits. This device permits the gate to be triggered into conduction in either direction when the applied voltage reaches a specific value.

Figure 5–6 shows six different conditions of operation of an ac bridge-controlled triac. In the 0° delay condition of operation, a full sine wave is developed as an output signal. The gate voltage and anode voltage are in phase, which causes immediate conduction, without delay. The power output P, which is determined by multiplying the terminal voltage V_T times the terminal current I_T, is at its maximum output level during this condition of operation.

If the gate voltage applied to a triac is shifted 45° behind V_T, the output current will be delayed. At the 45° point, the gate signal reaches the gate trigger voltage level and causes conduction. Power output in this case is reduced somewhat because I_T occurs for less than the full sine wave.

Delay of conduction time is achieved by the same process for the remaining four conditions of operation. In the 180° delay condition, however, no output is achieved, because I_T is zero. The triac is nonconductive for this condition of

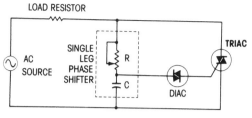

(A) With single-leg phase shifter.

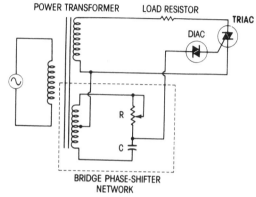

(B) With bridge phase shifter.

FIGURE 5–5
AC phase control of a triac.

operation. By shifting the phase of the gate voltage with respect to terminals 1 and 2, it is possible for a triac to achieve full control of the ac power output. Control of this type is easy to achieve, efficient, and can be done effectively with a minimum of costly components.

Triac Power Control

Triacs are widely used in industry to achieve ac power control. In this application the triac is designed to respond as a switch. Through this switching action, it is possible to control the ac source for a portion of each alternation. If a triac is in conduction for both alternations

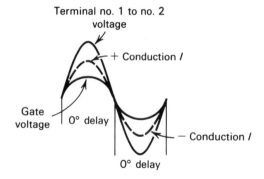

Terminal no. 1 to no. 2 voltage

+ Conduction *I*

Gate voltage

0° delay

− Conduction *I*

0° delay

(A)   0° delay.

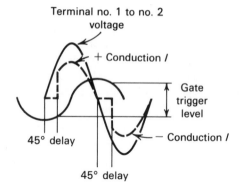

Terminal no. 1 to no. 2 voltage

+ Conduction *I*

Gate trigger level

45° delay

− Conduction *I*

45° delay

(B)   45° delay.

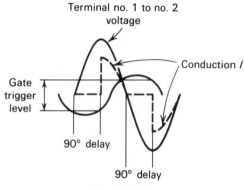

Terminal no. 1 to no. 2 voltage

Conduction *I*

Gate trigger level

90° delay

90° delay

(C)   90° delay.

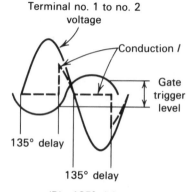

Terminal no. 1 to no. 2 voltage

Conduction *I*

Gate trigger level

135° delay

135° delay

(D)   135° delay.

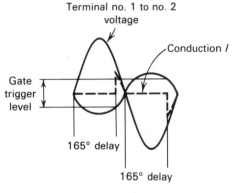

Terminal no. 1 to no. 2 voltage

Conduction *I*

Gate trigger level

165° delay

165° delay

(E)   165° delay.

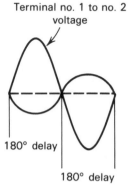

Terminal no. 1 to no. 2 voltage

180° delay

180° delay

(F)   180° delay.

FIGURE 5–6
AC control operationg conditions of a triac.

of the source voltage, 100% of source power is delivered to the load device. Conduction for half of each alternation permits 50% control of the power. When conduction is for one-fourth of each alternation, the load receives only 25% of its normal power. It is possible through this device to control from 0% to 100% of the electrical power being applied to a load device. Electrical power control with this device is very efficient. Very little power is actually consumed by a triac when it is achieving its control function.

Static Switching

The use of a triac as a static switch in ac power control is primarily an on–off operation. Control of this type has a number of advantages over mechanical load switching techniques. A large load current can, for example, be controlled with a very small gate current switch. This type of switching has no control bounce problems. Contact arcing and switch deterioration are reduced to a minimum. Static switching is usually very easy to achieve. Only

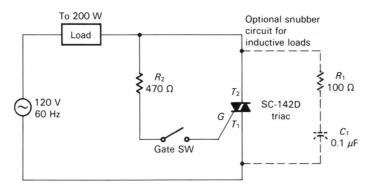

(A)   Static switch.

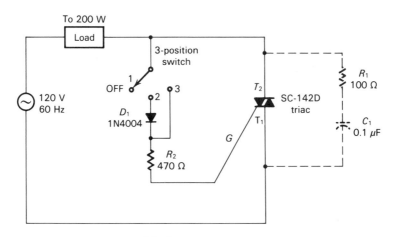

(B)   3-position static switch.

FIGURE 5–7
Triac static switch circuits.

a small number of components are needed to achieve control. In general, static triac switching has no moving parts, is very efficient, and can be achieved at a nominal cost. It is a very important alternative to power control switching.

Two very elementary triac static switch applications are shown in Figure 5–7. Circuit A shows a load being controlled by a triac that is energized into conduction by a small SPST toggle switch. The switching operation could be achieved by a wide variety of small switching elements. Reed switches, thermostats, pressure switches, and light-actuated devices could all be used to initiate the control operation. When the switch is closed, ac is applied to the gate. Resistor R_1 limits the gate current to a reasonable operating value. With ac applied to the gate, current flows during both alternations. During the positive alternation, T_2 and G is positive and T_1 is negative. Gate current and T_2–T_1 voltage occur at the same time. The triac is triggered into conduction without a delay. Conduction continues for the remainder of the alternation. At the zero crossover point, the triac is turned off. The negative alternation then causes T_2 and G to be negative and T_1 to be positive. Conduction is again initiated without a delay. Conduction continues for the remainder of the negative alternation. At the zero crossover point or end of the negative alternation, the triac is again turned off. The process is then repeated for each succeeding alternation. Control is continuous as long as the gate switch is on and T_1–T_2 is energized. Turn-off is achieved by opening the SPST switch.

Figure 5–7(B) is a very simple three-position static switch. In position 1, the gate is open and the power to the load is off. In position 2, gate current flows only during the positive alternation. The triac is triggered into conduction only during the positive alternation. The load is energized for only one alter-

nation or has a half-wave output. Only 50% of the source energy is supplied to the load in this switch position. In position 3, gate current flows for both alternations of the ac source. The load is energized for both alternations and receives full power from the source. The load could be one or more incandescent lamps, a heating element, or a universal motor.

Start–Stop Control

A number of electrical power circuits are controlled by a two push-button switch circuit that has start–stop action. Control of this type is initiated by momentarily pushing the start button. Operation continues after the start button has been released. To turn off the load or reset the circuit, the stop push button is depressed momentarily. The circuit then turns off and resets itself in preparation for the next starting sequence. Power control of this type is largely used in motor operation and light and heating element switching. A triac can be adapted to achieve this type of control.

A simplified start–stop triac control circuit is shown in Figure 5–8. When ac power is initially applied to this circuit, the triac is in its off or nonconductive state. The load does not receive any power from the source. As in an open switch, all the source voltage appears across the triac. Its internal resistance is extremely high. The gate and C_1–R_2 also respond as an open circuit.

To make the circuit operational, the start push button is momentarily depressed. This action closes the circuit path of R_1 and C_1. C_1 charges immediately to the source voltage. This action also causes the gate and T_2 to be off the same polarity. As a result of this condition, gate current flows. The breakover voltage (V_{BO}) of the triac is lowered and it is triggered into conduction. Current then flows through the load for the remainder of the alter-

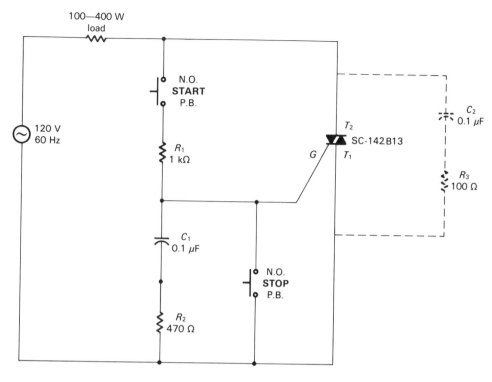

FIGURE 5–8
Simplified start–stop triac control circuit.

nation. The accumulated charge on C_1 reaches its peak value at approximately the same time the alternation changes polarity. Gate current flows for the next alternation due to the remaining charge on C_1. This again lowers the V_{BO} and retriggers the triac. C_1 discharges through the gate and recharges to the peak value of the next alternation. With the triac conductive, the load continues to receive current for this same alternation. The process then repeats itself for each succeeding alternation. The triac remains in conduction as long as power is supplied by the source.

To turn off the circuit, the stop button is depressed momentarily. This action immediately discharges the capacitor and reduces the gate current flow. With no I_G, the triac will not

trigger into conduction during the alternation change. As a result, C_1 is not recharged. The triac then remains in its off state for each succeeding alternation change. Conduction can only be restored by pressing the start button. This circuit is a triac equivalent of an ac electrical contactor used in motor starting operations. Control by this circuit can be achieved with low-current-rated push-button switches.

Triac Commutation

When a triac is used to control an ac load, it must turn on and off very quickly. For a resistive load, the time for turn off occurs when current drops below the holding current level.

Conduction should then take place immediately when the next alternation begins. In an SCR, turn off starts at the end of the forward conduction alternation and continues through the reverse alternation. In most applications of the SCR, this time for commutation is quite adequate.

Triac commutation time can be a problem in many circuit applications. Commutation must occur precisely at the end of the first alternation. Resistive loads can be controlled very effectively without altering the commutation of a triac to any extent. An inductive load such as a motor, transformer, or relay coil can cause an inductive phase shift. Conduction current for one alternation may approach zero a short time after the applied voltage changes to the next alternation. When the conduction current reaches zero and the triac tries to turn off, an increase in voltage may appear across its terminals. The rate of voltage change *(dv)* to time change *(dt)*, or *dv/dt*, is sometimes great enough to trigger the triac during this time. The *dv/dt* of a triac is usually aided by a short-duration reverse or recovery current that flows immediately after the forward current reaches zero. Any current lag caused by an inductive load can interfere with this normally developed recovery current. This usually interferes with the normal commutation action of a triac.

The switching action of a triac can be improved by shunting a series *RC* snubber network across the device. This is generally an optional part of a triac circuit that is dependent on the load. See Figures 5–7 and 5–8. Resistor (R_1) of the network limits the discharge current of the capacitor when the triac conducts. It also dampens the oscillating action or ringing of the inductive load *(L)* and capacitor *(C)*. Typical values of 0.1 μF and 100 Ω reduce the *dv/dt* to 1 V/μs for most inductive loads. Triacs used with an inductive load should have *dv/dt* ratings of at least 2 V/μs.

Triac Triggering

The gate of a triac responds as a nonlinear low-impedance junction similar to that of a forward-biased diode. Triggering of the gate must therefore be achieved by some type of low-impedance source. The gate junction usually requires a rather sizable current to produce triggering. This means that the G–T_1 junction is current sensitive rather than voltage sensitive. Most triacs, for example, require a hundred or more milliamperes of I_G for a few microseconds to be triggered into conduction. Several things can be done to develop this amount of I_G. A capacitor is usually discharged or "dumped" into the gate to initiate the triggering process. As a rule, this necessitates some type of low-power on–off switching device to produce a suitable value of I_G. The device must respond equally well to both alternations of the ac input. Special ac diodes, known as diacs, have been developed for triac triggering.

DIACs

A *diac* is a bidirectional diode that can be triggered into conduction with voltage. The crystal structure of this device is basically the same as an *npn* transistor with no base connection. N_1 and N_2 are identical in nearly all respects so that the two junctions will have matched operating characteristics in either direction. The word diac is derived from the terms *di*ode for *ac*. A diac therefore goes into conduction at precisely the same positive or negative voltage level. A device of this type is *triggered* into conduction by reaching a specific voltage value. For voltage values less than the trigger level, the device is nonconductive.

Figure 5–9 shows the crystal structure and schematic symbol of a diac. Notice that the

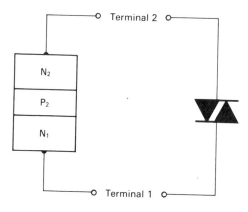

FIGURE 5–9
Crystal structure and schematic symbol of a diac.

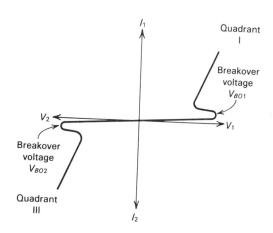

FIGURE 5–10
Current–voltage characteristics of a diac.

two leads are labeled terminals 1 and 2 instead of the conventional anode–cathode designations. When T_1 is negative and T_2 positive, the N_1–P junction is forward biased and N_2–P is reverse biased. When the breakover voltage of N_2–P is reached, the entire structure is triggered into conduction. This is the equivalent of reaching the zener voltage of a zener diode. Reversing the polarity of the source voltage causes T_1 to be positive and T_2 negative. The N_2–P junction is now forward biased, with the N_1–P junction being reverse biased. When the breakover voltage in this direction is reached, the structure again becomes conductive. Ordinarily, the breakover voltage is symmetrical in either direction.

The current–voltage characteristic of a diac is shown in Figure 5–10. Notice that the breakover voltage and resulting current are the same in quadrants I and III. When T_1 is made positive and T_2 negative, this device does not conduct until the forward breakover voltage V_{BO} is reached. For a general Electric type ST-2 diac, triggering occurs at 28 V $\pm$ 10%. Reversing the polarity of T_1 and T_2 causes an identical triggering action as shown in quadrant III.

After the breakover voltage of a diac has been reached, current conduction occurs very quickly. A resistor placed in series with the device limits the conduction current to a safe operating level in either direction. The voltage across a diac also decreases quite readily as it increases in conduction. This conduction is known as the *negative-resistance characteristic* of the diac. The pronounced curve that takes place after V_{BO} is reached shows this characteristic in both quadrants.

Silicon Bilateral Switch

A silicon bilateral switch or SBS is an ac trigger device. Conduction occurs in either direction at a specific breakover voltage. The SBS responds as a diac but is quite different in construction and operation. SBSs are primarily used as trigger devices for the triac. AC applied to the device produces equal-valued positive and negative gate pulses. Symmetrical conduction occurs in either direction when an internal zener voltage is exceeded. The breakover voltage of an SBS can be altered, however, by applying a negative voltage to the

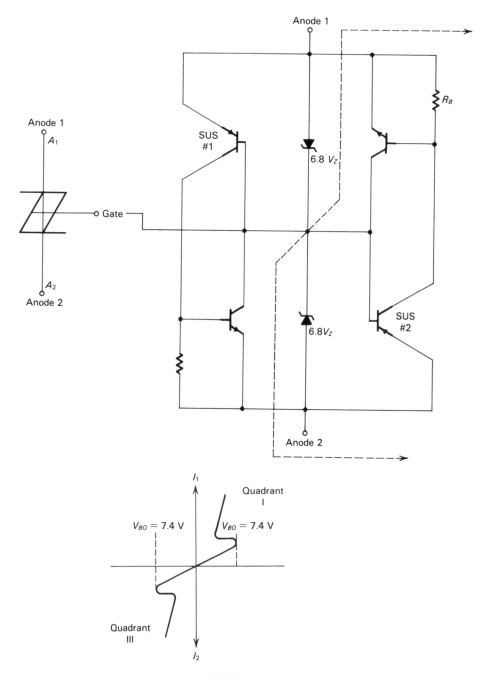

FIGURE 5–11
Schematic symbol, equivalent circuit, and *V/I*
characteristics of an SBS.

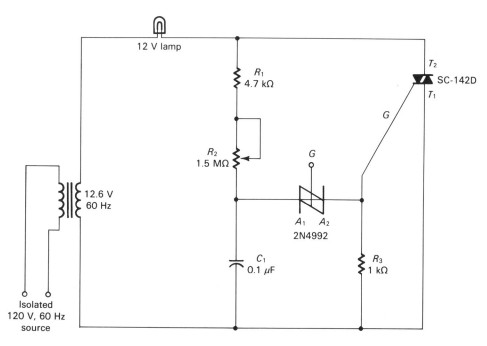

FIGURE 5–12
Triac phase-control circuit with an SBS.

gate with respect to the positive lead polarity.

A schematic symbol, equivalent circuit, and current voltage characteristic of an SBS are shown in Figure 5–11. The terminals are labeled A_1, A_2, and gate *(G)*. The equivalent circuit responds as two identical, silicon unilateral switches connected in inverse parallel. A zener diode in each SUS determines the breakover voltage. With the gate open, triggering occurs at 7.4 V in either direction. This is determined by the zener voltage of D_1 or D_2 (6.8 V_z), plus 0.6 V of transistor voltage. By externally connecting smaller-valued zener diodes to the gate, it is possible to alter the breakover voltage to a lower value. The current–voltage characteristic of Figure 5–13 shows the symmetrical characteristic of a 2N4992 SBS.

A full-range triac phase control circuit using an SBS is shown in Figure 5–12. Control of the gate voltage phase angle with respect to the

source voltage is achieved by R_2. When the charge voltage of capacitor C_1 exceeds the breakover voltage of the SBS, gate current triggers the triac. Triggering occurs equally during each alternation. Because of the small difference in SBS switching voltage, triggering is within 5° of full alternation. This type of control circuit is adjustable from zero delay to a full 180° delay for each alternation. The SBS permits very precise control of a triac over its full operating range.

Diac–Triac Power Control

An elementary full-wave ac power control circuit employing a diac and a triac is shown in Figure 5–13. The diac is used in an *RC* relaxation circuit to trigger the triac into conduction. Operation is based on the polarity of the

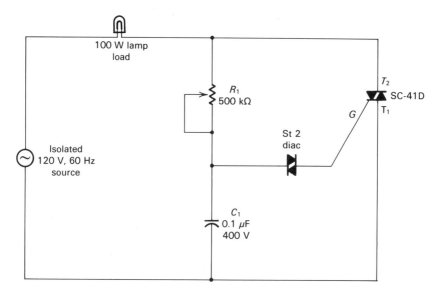

FIGURE 5–13
Elementary full-wave triac power control
circuit.

applied ac source. The circuit is connected so that T_2 and the gate of the triac are of the same polarity. The gate is connected to capacitor C_1 through the diac. Gate current is developed when the capacitor voltage builds up to a value that will trigger the breakover voltage of the diac. Discharging C_1 causes gate current. The polarity of the charge on C_1 is determined by the alternation of the source.

Assume now that the positive alternation of the source occurs first. This will make point A positive and B negative. Capacitor C_1 begins to charge to the voltage source through R_1. At the same time, T_2 is made positive and T_1 negative. When the charge voltage on the capacitor exceeds the breakover voltage of the diac, C_1 discharges. The component values of C_1, R_1, and the ac source determine the amount of gate current and the duration of the discharge pulse. Typical values of I_G are 50 mA or more for approximately 30 μs. The polarity of the charge on the top plate of C_1 is positive for this

alternation. The discharge of C_1 causes current to flow from the bottom plate of C_1, to T_1, through the gate, the diac, and to the top plate of C_1. This discharge current or I_G triggers the triac into conduction. Current then flows into the load during this alternation. Delay of the conduction time is controlled by the resistance value of R_1. A low-resistance setting causes zero or no delay, whereas a high-resistance setting may cause delay for some value up to the end of the alternation.

For the negative alternation of the source, A is negative and B is positive. Capacitor C_1 again charges to its source voltage through R_1. In this case, the charge polarity is reversed because of the alternation change in the source. At the same moment, T_2 is made negative and T_1 is positive. When V_C exceeds the breakover voltage of the diac, C_1 discharges. Discharge current flows from the top plate of C_1, through the diac, the gate, T_1, and returns to the lower plate of C_1. This I_G triggers the triac into con-

duction during the negative alternation. Current flows through the triac and into the lamp from the source. Delay of conduction time is again based on the value setting of R_1. Control of this alternation is nearly the same as that of the positive alternation.

Diac–Triac Hysteresis

The basic diac–triac circuit of Figure 5–13 has a rather undesirable characteristic at low output currents. As the resistance of R_1 is slowly decreased, it would be natural to assume that small conduction angles could be achieved. This would permit the lamp brightness level to be smoothly adjusted from zero to its maximum brightness level. This cannot be achieved, however, with the basic diac–triac circuit. The lamp, for example, cannot be gradually turned on from a zero level. It has a tendency to suddenly glow at a rather moderate intensity level as you attempt to increase light intensity from zero. This is primarily due to an erratic charge buildup on the capacitor before the disc breakover voltage is reached. This condition is called *hysteresis*. It causes the

lamp or load to "snap on" instead of gradually going into conduction. Once conduction occurs, the intensity of the lamp can be adjusted to a wide range of values.

Refer to the wave-form diagram of the diac–triac in Figure 5–14. This wave form was obtained from the circuit of Figure 5–13. Assume that the resistance of R_1 is slowly decreased from its maximum resistance value. The charge voltage on C_1 increases until the diac breakover voltage is reached and it triggers the triac into conduction. Point A1 shows this trigger point on the wave form. The resulting conduction angle is labeled $\theta1$. Ideally, conduction for the next alternation should occur at point A2. Unfortunately, however, triggering does not occur at this point. Triggering at point A1 depletes a large amount of the charge on capacitor C_1. The capacitor voltage therefore does not follow the normal symmetrical sine wave as indicated by the dashed line. This means that the diac now triggers at point B rather than point A2.

Point B of the diac–triac wave form corresponds to the same diac triggering voltage needed at point A2. Triggering at point B, however, occurs sooner than point A2. This

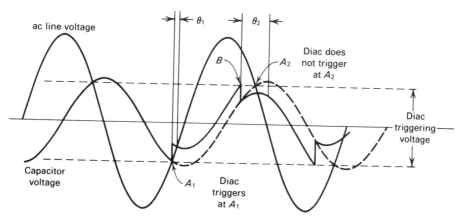

FIGURE 5–14
Triac–diac wave forms.

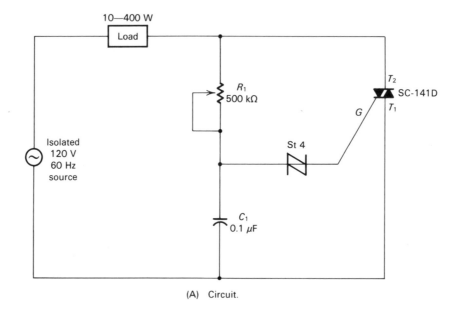

(A) Circuit.

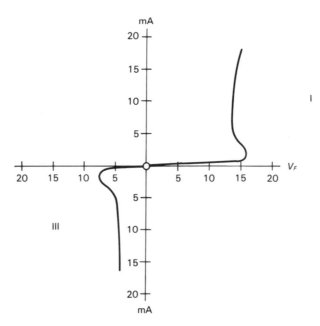

(B) *I-V* characteristics of an asymmetrical diac.

FIGURE 5–15
Triac with asymmetrical diac.

causes conduction of the triac to occur at an earlier time. The conduction angle ($\theta2$) is therefore significantly greater than $\theta1$. All subsequent triggering of the triac will maintain the conduction angle of $\theta2$ at the same place. This will cause the lamp to snap on rather than being adjusted to low conduction levels. Once the lamp is on, it can then be adjusted to lower operating levels by changing the value of R_1. The adjustment procedure of the circuit is somewhat of a nuisance in normal circumstances.

The hysteresis or snap-on effect of the basic diac–triac circuit can be reduced by using a special asymmetrical diac. Figure 5–15 shows an improved version of the basic diac–triac circuit. The ST-4 is an asymmetrical silicon bilateral switch. The current–voltage characteristic of an ST-4 is also shown. Note that the breakover voltage is greater in quadrant I than in quadrant III. This difference in breakover voltage permits triggering of the diac at point A2 rather than at point B of the wave form of Figure 5–14. In effect, a higher breakover voltage is needed to cause conduction at point A2. Triggering at point A2 reduces the conduction angle $\theta2$ to approximately the same time as $\theta1$. Essentially, this means that an asymmetrical diac can be used to reduce the hysteresis effect of a triac. The control demands of the circuit usually dictate the employment of an asymmetrical diac over a symmetrical diac.

Triac Phase Control

Phase control of a triac can be achieved by using an *RC* or *RL* network to alter the gate signal with respect to the T_1 and T_2 voltage. Control of this type is the same as that used to alter the conduction of an SCR. A single-leg *RC* or *RL* phase shifter will control up to 90° of each alternation. A bridge phase shifter will permit approximately 180° control of each alternation.

In triac phase control applications, additional delay of conduction usually occurs because of the diac in the gate circuit. Time is needed for the diac to reach its breakover voltage, which is approximately 30 V. As a result, *RC* or *RL* phase shifting with a diac only permits a total phase shift of 30° to 150° of each alternation. This, of course, reduces the effectiveness of a phase-shifter control circuit to some extent.

IC Phase Control

Up to this point the control of a triac has been fairly simple and straightforward. However, component count can be quite high and circuit construction can be rather complex when high performance and control accuracy are desired. To simplify circuit design while maintaining high performance, a number of manufacturers have developed integrated-circuit phase control units. This type of assembly performs the phase-shifting function and is externally connected to a triac. The chip is generally energized from the source being controlled. It normally has a bridge power supply that provides synchronization of the gate signal and ac source. The gate signal is a negative ramp that rides on a pedestal. The ramp part of the wave starts at a peak and drops to a lower level. This is opposite to that of the positive-going ramp of the UJT ramp–pedestal trigger circuit used to control an SCR. The level of the pedestal is adjusted externally and the ramp is developed internally. The chip also has ambient temperature compensation, inductive load logic control, and feedback regulation. Only a few external components are needed to make the phase-shifter unit operational. Figure 5–16 shows a functional block diagram and circuit diagram of a General Electric PA436 phase control IC.

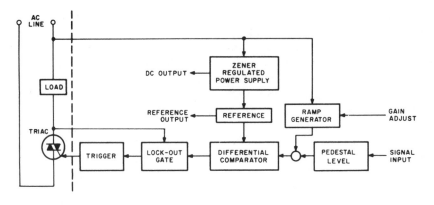

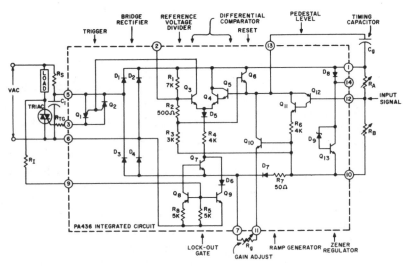

FIGURE 5-16
Block diagram and circuit diagram of a PA436
phase control IC. (Courtesy of General Electric
Co.)

Triac Power Controllers _____

Triac power controllers are now available through a number of different manufacturers. This type of assembly has an entire triac, diac, and phase control circuit built on a single IC chip. The unit has either three or four leads and is housed in a tab mounting enclosure or a block assembly. Figure 5–17 shows the inter-

nal construction of a TO-220 tab mount power pack. Packaging of the device is primarily based on its power dissipation rating. This particular unit has a power capacity of up to 3000 watts.

Applications of the triac power controller include lamp dimmers, heater controls, air conditioners, fans, blowers, conveyer drive mechanisms, and mixers. These units are de-

signed to control either resistive or inductive loads. The inductive load controller has a built-in snubber network connected across the triac. The resistive load unit does not employ a snubber network. Both variations of the controller have radio-frequency interference suppression circuitry. These units are capable of full-wave power control and have a low level of hysteresis.

Figure 5–18 shows some circuit application possibilities for the triac phase controller. Standard connection for the triac phase controller with a resistive load is shown in part A. Only the load, controller phase-shifting potentiometer, and ac source are needed to complete this circuit. Figure 5–18(B) shows a switched phase control resistance. Position 1 has full output or 100% of the power supplied to the load. Positions 2 through 5 supply 75%, 50%, 25%, and 0%, respectively, of the source to the load. Push buttons are generally used to achieve this type of load control. Figure 5–18(C) shows a shunt feedback control system. When R_S is a negative coefficient resistance device such as a thermistor or light-dependent resistor, output of this circuit is a function of temperature or light intensity. In a sense, feedback is established and maintains a specific output level to the load.

ZERO VOLTAGE SWITCHING

Zero voltage switching is an extremely important form of power control that has been developed through the use of triacs. A triac is simply turned on for a number of cycles and then off for a number of cycles. The resulting power output is based on the average number of cycles supplied to the load in a given period of time. Figure 5–19 shows an example of zero voltage switching achieved by a triac. Note how the number of sine waves occurring in a given period of time changes between full power and zero power levels. Only complete sine waves are produced in the output. The void places represent nonconduction of the triac. Power output is based on the average time that the sine wave occurs.

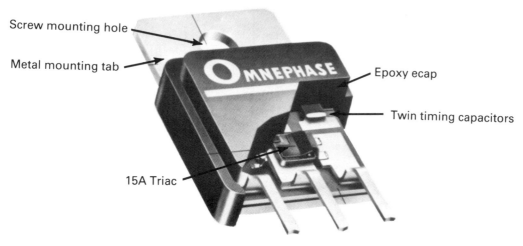

Screw mounting hole

Metal mounting tab

Epoxy ecap

Twin timing capacitors

15A Triac

FIGURE 5–17
Triac power controller. (Courtesy of Omnetics)

The switching action of a triac makes it possible to control the number of cycles occurring within a given period of time. Obviously, control of this type is largely used to control the 60-Hz power line frequency. One cycle of ac occurs every 16,667 μs. A triac, however, is capable of switching operations in the mi-

crosecond range. Average power can then be controlled by altering the number of cycles that occur in a given period of time.

Figure 5–20 shows a functional block diagram of the zero voltage switching (ZVS) method of electronic power control. The diagram shows two inputs connected to an on–off

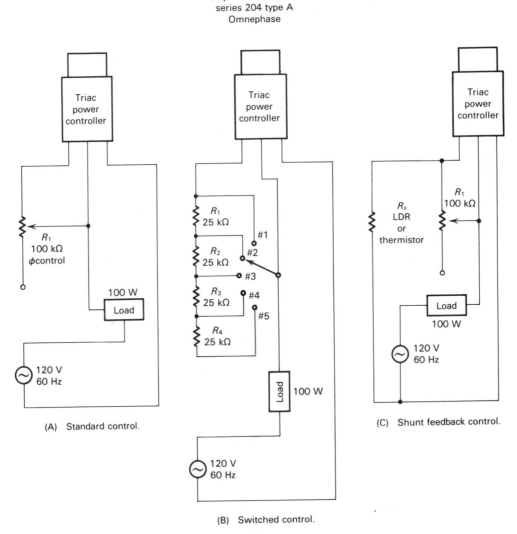

ac phase controllers
series 204 type A
Omnephase

(A) Standard control.

(B) Switched control.

(C) Shunt feedback control.

FIGURE 5–18
Triac phase controller applications.

sensing amplifier. One input is the zero voltage crossing detector. This part of the IC determines when the ac source voltage is at the zero crossing point. The second input is the dc logic or power control circuit. When the two input

or command signals are both zero or low, they energize the on–off difference sensing amplifier. The output of this amplifier enables the gate drive circuit. The triac is then triggered into conduction. If either of the two input cir-

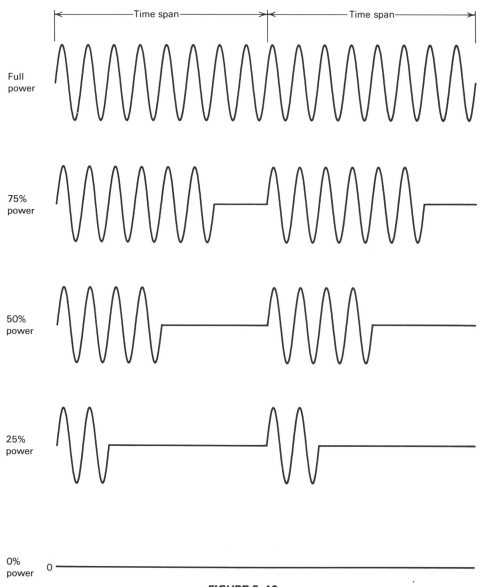

FIGURE 5–19
Zero voltage switching wave forms.

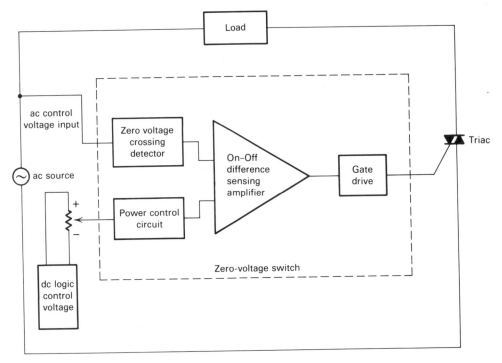

FIGURE 5–20
Functional block diagram of a zero voltage
switch.

cuits is not zero, the sensing amplifier detects this condition and disables the gate drive circuit. The triac at that point becomes nonconductive.

The width of a pulse or the time that the power control circuit is low determines the number of cycles developed by the triac. Turn-on occurs at zero or nearly zero and continues for the remainder of the alternation. For triac operation, conduction is for both alternations without any alternation of the conduction time. Conduction continues for succeeding cycles as long as the gate current is enabled. If the power control input changes polarity, the triac will be disabled. Output is based on the coin-

cidence of the two input signals at the zero or low input level.

At one time, zero voltage switching was accomplished by discrete component circuits. Today this function is achieved by one integrated circuit. The RCA CA3058 is a representative monolithic zero voltage switch IC. Internally, this IC has a zero voltage threshold detector, a difference on–off sensing amplifier, and a triac gate driving circuit. DC operating voltages for the IC are derived from a limiter power supply that operates directly from the ac power line being controlled.

An example of a zero voltage switch IC and a triac are shown in Figure 5–21. The output

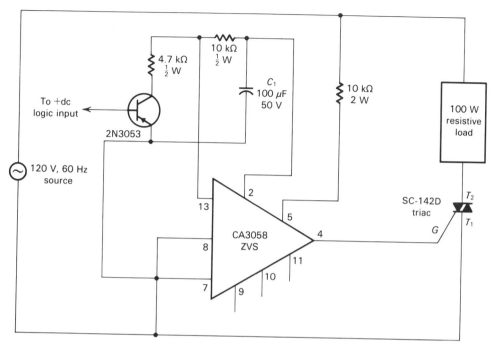

FIGURE 5–21
Zero voltage switch circuit.

of the ZVS is directly connected to the gate of the triac. When the dc logic level input is high or of a positive value, the gate signal makes the triac nonconductive. A low-level input produces gate pulses that trigger the triac into conduction. The duration of the voltage, either high or low, determines the number of operational cycles supplied to the load device.

Zero-voltage switching is best suited for resistive loads. It is primarily used to control power to heating elements. The element is switched on and off at different power levels according to the demands of the heating system. The operational time of a heating element is relatively long. Once heated, the element continues to produce heat even when the power is turned off for a short period of time. Successive on and off operational periods per-

mit efficient use of electrical power for long spans of time.

AC SOLID-STATE RELAYS

A rather new and important application of the triac is the ac solid-state relay. This application is designed to replace the older electromatic relay. The solid-state relay or SSR has no moving parts, has electrical isolation between input and output, and is compatible with IC circuitry. It is also resistant to mechanical shock and vibration, has a fast response time, and does not have contact bounce problems. The triac serves as the ac switching element of a solid-state relay.

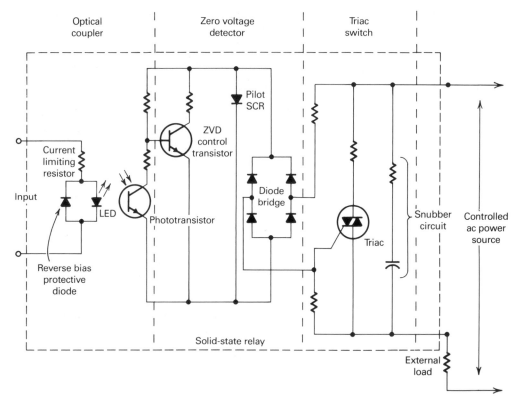

FIGURE 5–22
AC solid-state relay.

A simplified schematic of a representative SSR is shown in Figure 5–22. The circuit is divided into three basic elements: an optical coupler, a zero voltage detector, and a triac switch. The optical coupler isolates the input from the output. Zero voltage switching is used to turn on the switching element at an appropriate time during the ac cycle. The triac serves as an output switching element. The ac source being controlled supplies energy to the circuit to make it operational. Actuation of the triac is achieved when low-voltage dc is applied to the input.

Assume now that ac is supplied to the SSR from an outside source that is being controlled by the device. The circuit components are energized, but no control is achieved initially. When low-voltage dc is applied to the input, it causes the light-emitting diode to be illuminated. The resulting light is applied to the base of a phototransistor and causes it to be conductive. This in turn forward biases the zero voltage detection transistor, which triggers the gate of the pilot SCR near the zero crossover point. This action then triggers the gate of the triac, permitting it to conduct ac through the load. Removal of the dc input disables the ac source from the load. The entire switching operation takes place very quickly and does not involve any moving parts.

QUESTIONS

1. Explain how a triac achieves conduction in either direction.

2. Why is dc gate control of a triac not very practical?

3. Why does static or ac amplitude control only achieve 90° delay of an alternation?

4. Why is it possible to achieve 100% control of ac power to a load with a triac?

5. Why is the commutation time of a triac more critical than that of an SCR when controlling ac?

6. What causes a diac to be triggered into conduction?

7. What is an SBS and how does it respond when ac is applied?

8. Explain how the construction of a triac permits selective conduction and control during each alternation.

9. How is a diac RC relaxation oscillator circuit used to trigger a triac into conduction?

10. What causes hysteresis in a diac–triac control circuit?

11. What is meant by the $+V_{BO}$ and $-V_{BO}$ of a triac? How can it be altered to achieve better control?

12. How is a triac used in zero voltage switching to achieve power control?

13. How is a triac used to achieve control in an ac solid-state relay?

14. What are the possible trigger polarity combinations of a triac? Which of the combinations are best suited for general control use?

ACTIVITIES

ACTIVITY 5–1: Triac Testing and Lead Identification

Objective: To test a triac with a VOM and identify the leads.

Procedure:

1. Prepare a VOM or VTVM to measure resistance on the $R \times 1$ range. The polarity of the leads must be known. We will assume that the meter has straight polarity. As a rule, a digital VOM or FET VOM will not work very well for this test procedure because of the low current capability of the ohmmeter.

2. Randomly select two leads of the triac. Measure resistance between these two leads. If a resistance reading is obtained, reverse the polarity of the ohmmeter. T_1 and G will show low resistance in either direction of the ohmmeter polarity. If a resistance is not obtained, switch to the remaining lead. When a resistance reading is found between two leads, the third or remaining lead is T_2. Now connect the positive ohmmeter lead to T_2 and the negative lead to one of the remaining two leads. This should produce an infinite resistance indication. We will assume that the two leads are T_1 and T_2, with the remaining lead the gate. If this assumption is correct, it will permit the triac to be triggered.

3. With T_{2+} and T_{1-}, momentarily connect the assumed gate lead to T_2. If the assumption is correct, the triac will trigger and hold conduction even after the gate has been removed from T_2. Reverse the polarity of the ohmmeter leads connected to T_1 and T_2. Trigger the triac again by touching the gate momentarily to T_2. A good triac

will trigger equally as well in the reverse polarity. If this test does not produce triggering, we assumed the wrong identity of T_1 and G. Reverse the assumed gate and T_1 leads and repeat the test procedure. If the triac cannot be triggered in the new direction, it must be faulty.

4. Repeat the test procedure on several different triacs.

5. Make a sketch of the lead assignments for each triac that is to be used in the following activities.

ACTIVITY 5–2: Static Switch Circuitry

Objective: To build a static triac switch and test its operational characteristics.

Procedure:

1. Construct the ac static switch of Figure 5–7(A).

2. If at all possible, use an isolation transformer or an isolated ac source for the supply.

3. Low-voltage ac, such as 6.3, 12.6, or 24 V, may be used in place of 120 V. The value of the load should be changed accordingly.

4. If a small universal motor of less than ¼ hp is available, it can be used as a load device for the circuit. The optional snubber circuit should be used with an inductive load.

ACTIVITY 5–3: Three-position Static Switching

Objective: To construct a three-position ac static switch and test its operation.

Procedure:

1. Construct the three-position ac static switch of Figure 5–7(B).

2. If at all possible, use an isolated ac source. Low-voltage ac can also be used to accomplish the same operation. The load must be altered accordingly.

3. If a lamp is used for the load, the switch position will alter the intensity of the lamp. Apply power to the circuit and test the operation of the load for various switch positions. Explain how the circuit varies power to the load.

4. If at all possible, measure ac load current and voltage for each switch position. Calculate the power developed by the load.

5. If a small universal motor is available, see how it responds for the three switch positions. The snubber circuit should be used with an inductive load.

ACTIVITY 5–4: Triac Phase Control

Objective: To construct a low-voltage triac phase control circuit and test its operation.

Procedure:

1. Construct the low-voltage triac phase control circuit of Figure 5–12.

2. Note that the source for this circuit is an isolated 12.6 V. It is imperative that an isolated source be used for this activity to prevent cross-grounding of the test equipment.

3. Turn on the power source and test the operation of the circuit. Adjust R_2 through its range while observing the response of the load. The intensity of the lamp should change with different position settings of the potentiometer. Explain how the load responds.

4. Connect the leads of an oscilloscope across the load. Adjust the position setting of the potentiometer while observing the response on the oscilloscope. Explain how the wave form changes for different potentiometer settings.

5. Connect oscilloscope leads across R_3 and observe the wave forms for three distinct brightness level settings of the potentiometer. Make a sketch of the wave forms.

6. Make a synchronized wave-form sketch of the waves across the load, the triac, and R_3 for three distinct range settings of the potentiometer.

ACTIVITY 5–5: Phase Control with a Diac–Triac

Objective: Construction of a diac–triac phase control circuit and observation of its operating characteristics.

Procedure:

1. Construct the full-wave triac–diac phase control circuit of Figure 5–13.

2. It is essential that the ac source be isolated from ground before attempting to measure any circuit values.

3. Apply ac power to the circuit and adjust potentiometer R_1 while observing the intensity of the load lamp. Describe the influence that this adjustment has on the lamp.

4. With an oscilloscope, observe the wave forms across the lamp. Make a sketch of the observed waves for three position settings of the potentiometer. The lamp should be dim, medium intensity, and full brightness.

5. Using the load lamp wave forms as a reference, make a sketch of the waves observed across the triac and the diac for the same three intensity range adjustments.

6. Measure the load voltage and current for each intensity setting of the lamp. Calculate the power developed by the lamp for each setting.

ACTIVITY 5–6: Phase Control of a Triac with an Asymmetrical Diac

Objective: Construct an asymmetrical diac–triac phase control circuit and test its operation.

Procedure:

1. Construct the asymmetrical diac–triac phase control circuit of Figure 5–15.

2. It is essential that the ac source be isolated from ground in order to safely make the following measurements.

3. Adjust potentiometer R_1 to produce three distinct power output range settings of high, medium, and low.

4. Measure and record the ac voltage and current values for each power output range. Calculate the power output developed by the load for each range setting.

5. Prepare an oscilloscope for operation. Connect the oscilloscope across the load, the triac, and the ST-4 diac while observing the response of these devices for the three power output range settings. Make a sketch of your findings.

6. Using the wave forms obtained from Figure 5–13, do you notice any difference in the wave forms of this activity?

ACTIVITY 5–7: Phase Controllers

Objective: Build a circuit utilizing a phase controller so its operation can be observed.

Procedure:

1. Conduct the standard phase control circuit of Figure 5–18(A).

2. It is important to use an isolated ac source in this activity.

3. Turn on the ac source and adjust the phase control R_1 through its operating range. Depending on the load used, set the phase control to the lowest power output position. If the load is a lamp, this is the lowest level of brightness. If a resistive load is used, the load current and voltage must be measured to find the power output.

4. Connect an oscilloscope across the load and observe the output wave. Make a sketch of the observed wave form.

5. Using the same procedure, set the output to the medium power range.

6. Adjust the output to its maximum level. Make a sketch of the observed wave form. Indicate the power developed by the load.

7. Turn off the ac source and modify the circuit to conform with the switch control circuit of Figure 5–18(B). Test the operation of the circuit, evaluating the output and wave forms.

8. Disconnect the ac source and modify the switched control circuit to conform with the shunt feedback control circuit of Figure 5–18(C). The R_s element may be a light-dependent resistor such as the Radio Shack 276–116 or a thermister such as the Fenwal JA35J1.

9. Adjust the potentiometer to a test level near the middle of its range. Measure the power developed by the load. Record your findings.

10. If an LDR is used, shine an intense light source on the window of the cell. Mea-sure and record the power output to the load for this response. Block the light source from the cell while observing the power output.

11. If a thermister is used for R_s, set the po-tentiometer to its middle position. Mea-sure and record the power supplied to the load. Apply heat from an outside source to the thermister while observing the re-sponse it has on the load. Measure and record the power output of the circuit while it is influenced by the heat. How does this compare with the power devel-oped initially?

ACTIVITY 5–8: Zero Voltage Switching

Objective: Construct a ZVS power control circuit and test its operation.

Procedure:

1. Construct the zero voltage switching circuit of Figure 5–21.

2. Use an isolated ac source to supply power to the circuit.

3. Prepare an oscilloscope for operation and connect it across the load.

4. Apply power to the circuit. Adjust the logic control to the high speed or 100% position. This should produce maximum power to the load. Adjust the oscilloscope so that it displays about 10 complete sine waves.

5. Adjust the logic control to 75%, 50%, 25%, and 0% positions while observing the response of the oscilloscope for each set-ting. Describe your findings.

6. If your oscilloscope has dual trace input ca-pabilities, observe the logic input wave form and the output wave forms at the same time. What is the relationship of the logic input and load frequency?

An industrial electronic system is primarily responsible for controlling or regulating the value of different physical quantities. Each manufacturing operation may require a different type of control. As a rule, the system may be designed to achieve this operation automatically. Variable quantities must be sensed or detected before the control function can be implemented. In an industrial electronic system, sensing is achieved by a transducer. A *transducer* is a device that converts one form of energy or physical quantity into something new or more useful. A large majority of these devices change nonelectrical quantities into electrical values. Electrical transducers are the basis of this discussion.

TRANSDUCER TYPES

One function of a transducer is to detect or convert physical changes into an electrical quantity or value. The physical change is generally called a *measurand*. A measurand represents a value change, physical quantity, or some form of energy being measured or sensed by the system. Such things as the temperature of a vat of milk, the pressure of gas in a container, or the rate that fluid flows through a pipe are examples of measurands. It should be noted that a measurand does not necessarily represent a form of energy. Some measurands may be quantitative values. The number of items appearing at a given point in a system is not representative of a form of energy.

Transducers are divided into two distinct areas of concern. These are defined as active and passive devices. Active transducers are those devices that generate voltage due to some form of physical change. Passive transducers respond to a measurand by altering some physical property. Resistance, capacitance, and inductance are representative elec-

6

Electronic Transducers

trical properties. A passive transducer must be energized by an external source in order for it to function.

ACTIVE TRANSDUCERS

Active transducers are described as those elements that generate voltage due to a change in energy or force. These transducers usually serve as the energy source of an electrical signal. When the signal is generated, it is then processed or conditioned for some control operation. Active transducer signals are generally considered to be independent of the primary energy source.

Active transducers are categorized according to the type of energy transformation process involved in their operation. Six transformation processes can be used to generate transducer voltage. These methods are electrostatic, electrochemical, electromechanical, photovoltaic, piezoelectric, and thermoelectric. The electrostatic and electrochemical methods of energy transformation are not very commonly used as energy transducers. Electromechanical, photovoltaic, piezoelectric, and thermoelectric energy transformation processes are widely used today in industrial applications.

Electromechanical Transducers

The fundamental principle of an electromechanical transducer is the operational basis of an electric generator. In this regard, voltage is induced in a conductor placed in a magnetic field if there is relative motion between the conductor and the field. The conductor can pass through the field or the field can move across the conductor. Motion is the key factor of electromagnetic induction.

In the 1880s, Michael Faraday, an English scientist, developed an electromagnetic generator. He found that a conductor formed into a disc had voltage induced into it when rotated through a magnetic field. Electromagnetic transducers respond to this basic principle. A permanent magnetic field cutting across a conductor causes voltage to be induced in the conductor. Figure 6–1 shows the principle of electromagnetic transduction.

An alternative to the stationary coil moving field induction principle of Figure 6–1 is shown in Figure 6–2(A). In this mode of operation the field is stationary and the conductor is moving. Motion of the conductor produces a rather constant level of induced voltage as the conductor passes through the field. In Figure 6–2(B), the conductor is rotated through the field. This causes alternating current volt-

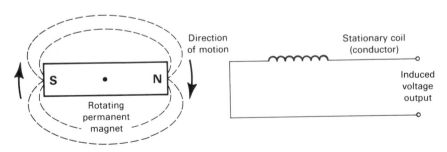

FIGURE 6–1
Principle of electromagnetic induction.

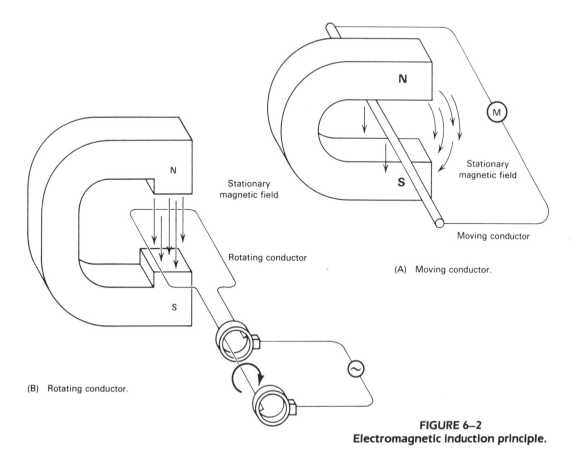

Stationary magnetic field

N

S

Stationary magnetic field

Moving conductor

(A)   Moving conductor.

N

S

Stationary magnetic field

Rotating conductor

(B)   Rotating conductor.

FIGURE 6–2
Electromagnetic induction principle.

age to be induced into the conductor. The induced voltage *(V)* is dependent on the density of the magnetic flux *(B)* of the magnet, the length of the conductor *(L),* and the speed of conductor motion *(S).* This is expressed by the formula

Induced voltage = flux density × conductor length × conductor speed

$$V = BLS$$

A transducer that responds to the electromagnetic principle is the motion sensor. This transducer is used in industrial electronic systems to detect moving objects. Speed detectors, motion failure alarms, and noncontacting tachometers are applications of this type of sensor. Figure 6–3 shows a number of typical mounting installations of motion sensors used in mining, pulp processing, chemical mixing, loading, and food processing.

Figure 6–4 shows a typical transducer and preamplifier assembly. The unit is cast in

epoxy, which makes it impervious to water and dust and immune to most chemicals. The back end of the probe houses a preamplifier.

The entire assembly is energized by 25 V dc from two No. 18 AWG wires. When the permanent magnet field of the probe is broken

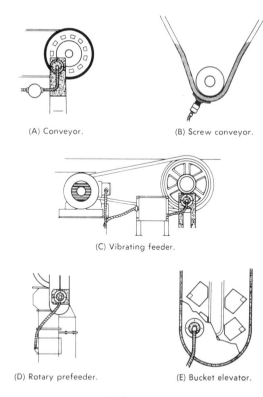

(A) Conveyor.

(B) Screw conveyor.

(C) Vibrating feeder.

(D) Rotary prefeeder.

(E) Bucket elevator.

FIGURE 6–3
**Motion sensor applications. (Courtesy of
Miltronics Corp.)**

or changed by a moving object, a pulse is generated in the helix coil. This pulse is detected by a sensitive preamplifier. The output of the preamplifier is applied directly to an operational amplifier that develops a current pulse in the two connecting wires. The pulse is immune to extraneous field voltage noise, which permits long runs of up to 5000 feet (ft) of wire. The sensitivity of the probe is such that accurate detection can occur from 2 to 4 inches (in.) from the moving object. The sensing capability of this device ranges from 4 to 6000 pulses per minute. Conveyor belt systems, vibrator screens, rotary feeders, screw drive assemblies, and bucket elevators are typical process control applications.

Hall-effect Transducers

The Hall-effect principle is the operational basis of an active transducer that responds or detects changes in magnetic field strength. An output voltage is generated in response to a change in magnetic field strength. This voltage appears at the sides of a current-carrying conductor that is subjected to a magnetic field. The generated voltage is proportional to the applied magnetic field strength at a constant conductor excitation current.

The Hall-effect principle has been known for a number of years. Edward H. Hall discovered this effect in 1879 at Johns Hopkins University. He found that, when a magnet was placed perpendicular to one face of a current-carrying conductor, a voltage appeared at the

(A) Photograph.

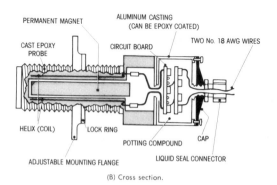

PERMANENT MAGNET

ALUMINUM CASTING
(CAN BE EPOXY COATED)

CAST EPOXY
PROBE

CIRCUIT BOARD

TWO No. 18 AWG WIRES

HELIX (COIL)

LOCK RING

ADJUSTABLE MOUNTING FLANGE

POTTING COMPOUND

CAP

LIQUID SEAL CONNECTOR

(B) Cross section.

FIGURE 6–4
**Motion sensor probe. (Courtesy of Miltronics
Corp.)**

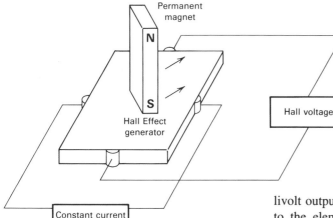

Permanent
magnet

Hall Effect
generator

Hall voltage

Constant current
source

FIGURE 6–5
Hall-effect principle.

opposite sides of the conductor. The generated voltage is proportional to the current flowing through the conductor and the flux density of the magnetic field. Today this principle is utilized to generate Hall voltages across a semiconductor material.

The basic operating principle of a Hall-effect transducer is shown in Figure 6–5. This transducer is essentially a strip of semiconductor material. In practice, the strip is called a *Hall generator*. A constant control current is passed through the strip from an external source. When a magnet is brought near the surface of the strip, a small voltage appears at the sides of the conductor. The magnetic field must be directed at a right angle to the surface of the strip. The generated voltage appears at contacts attached to each side of the strip. When the magnet is moved or repositioned, the generated voltage changes accordingly. One manufacturer makes a Hall sensor that is approximately 0.040 in.^{2}. A microscopic view of the strip is shown in Figure 6–6.

Figure 6–7 shows a block representation of a Hall generator and its *B–V* characteristic curve. Notice the linear relationship between magnetic flux density *B* and the generated mil-

livolt output. When a magnet is brought closer to the element, the output voltage increases. Nearly 10 mV is generated from a magnetic field of 150 gauss. Moving a magnet closer to the element increases the output voltage in a linear manner.

Applications of the Hall sensor are similar to those of other electromagnetic devices. The sensor must be physically mounted in a specific position or location. It must then be energized by a constant current source. A magnet or magnetic field change is then used to generate the output voltage. Output voltage is gen-

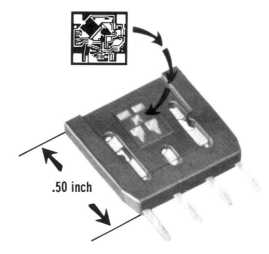

.50 inch

FIGURE 6–6
Microscopic view of a Hall generator chip.
(Courtesy of Microswitch/Honeywell)

(A)

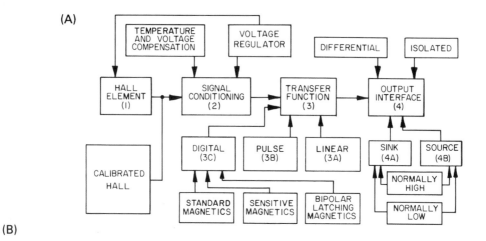

(B)

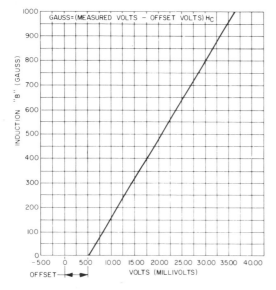

FIGURE 6–7
**(A) Hall effect block diagram and (B) flux
density/millivolt characteristics. (Courtesy of
Microswitch/Honeywell)**

erated with the field in a fixed position or in response to a moving field. The millivolt output signal is usually conditioned or amplified before it can be used to achieve a control function. Some manufacturers have the Hall generator, signal conditioner, and output amplifier all built on a single IC chip. The output can be of a linear voltage value or a digital signal, depending on the design of the chip. Figure 6–8 shows a Hall transducer chip and a solid-state keyboard switch with which it is used. The chip in this case is extremely small and located near the center of the switch assembly. When the plunger of the switch is depressed, it causes the position of the magnet or shunt member to be relocated. This action causes a pronounced difference in the output voltage between the depressed and nondepressed

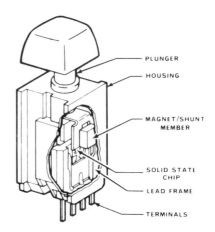

FIGURE 6–8
**Hall-effect solid-state keyboard switch.
(Courtesy of Microswitch/Honeywell)**

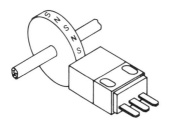

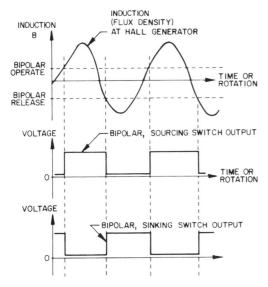

FIGURE 6–9
Speed-sensing Hall transducer principle.
(Courtesy of Microswitch/Honeywell)

switch position. The output, in this case, is two state, or voltage and no voltage.

Figure 6–9 shows an application of the Hall transducer as a speed-sensing device. This transducer has a ring magnet attached to the rotational member. As the ring magnet rotates, it generates an output wave form that is frequency dependent on rotational speed. The generated frequency can be counted and used to indicate rotational speed in rpms. The output or frequency of the sensor is an electrical signal that varies directly with shaft speed. The amplitude of the signal does not change with frequency.

Photovoltaic Transducers

A photovoltaic transducer converts light energy directly into electrical energy. Light energy applied to this device causes voltage to appear across its terminals. An increase in the intensity of light causes a corresponding increase in voltage. These transducers have been used for a number of years to energize satellites and spacecraft. Light from the sun, or solar energy, is converted directly into electrical power. Because of these applications, the photovoltaic cell is often described as a solar cell or sun battery.

Photovoltaic cells are classified as active transducers because of their voltage-generating properties. Industrial applications of this device have increased rather significantly in recent years. Photovoltaic cells are now widely used in the photographic industry. Exposure-sensing devices and aperture control for automatic electronic flash units are very popular. Infrared sound transmission and remote-control signal production are applications in the communication electronics field. The transmission of light energy between different systems for coupling purposes is another use. Photovoltaic cells are also used to sense light signals that are transmitted through fiber-optic cables. In the future, these devices will probably find wider acceptance as direct power conversion devices.

A photovoltaic cell is essentially a bipolar junction device made from semiconductor materials. A number of different materials have been used in the construction of this cell. Today, selenium and silicon seem to be preferred over nearly all other materials. Silicon is more widely used than selenium for industrial transducers. The response to different wavelengths of light energy usually dictates the material being used. Selenium tends to respond to wavelengths similar to the human eye. The conversion efficiency of light to voltage, how-

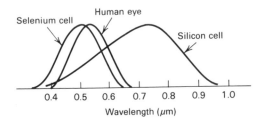

FIGURE 6–10
Spectral response of silicon, selenium, and the human eye.

ever, is less than 3% for selenium. Silicon cells are more efficient. Typical light-to-voltage conversion efficiency ratings are 8% to 12% for silicon. The spectral response of silicon peaks at wavelengths in the infrared region. However, it does develop an output when exposed to ultraviolet, visible, or infrared light energy. Figure 6–10 shows the spectral response of silicon and selenium cells compared with the response of the human eye.

The construction of a silicon cell is illustrated in Figure 6–11. Note that a thin layer of N-type silicon is deposited on a metal plate. A P-type layer is then placed on the N-type layer forming an NP junction. Electrical contacts are attached to the metal plate, and a thin ring or strip of conductive material is deposited over the P layer. A transparent window covers the P layer. Light energy or radiation is applied to the cell through the window.

Operation of a photovoltaic cell is based on changes in the depletion region of the PN junction. The depletion region is essentially an area near the PN junction that is void of current carriers. With no light applied to the window, the depletion region remains void of current carriers. No voltage appears at the two output terminals. With light applied, discrete bundles of energy called *photons* enter the window area. These bundles of energy are absorbed by the PN junction at various depths depending on the wavelength of the light energy. A particular photon can impart some of its energy to specific atoms. If sufficient energy is transferred to an atom, it causes valence electrons to be released. These electrons become free to respond as current carriers. An atom, having lost an electron, then takes on a positive charge and responds as a hole. Thus photons of light energy can cause electron–hole pairs to be formed in the depletion region of the PN junction.

With light applied to a photovoltaic cell, free electrons and holes are generated in the depletion region of the PN junction. Electrons and holes that appear outside the depletion region may also be drawn into it by light energy. This action causes large numbers of free electrons in the depletion region to move from the P material to the N material. At the same time, new holes appear in the P region because of the exiting electrons. This shifting of holes and

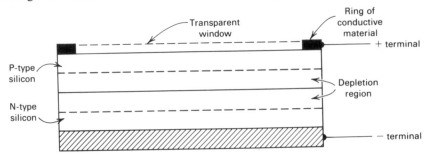

FIGURE 6–11
Silicon photovoltaic cell construction.

electrons causes a small voltage to appear across the *PN* junction. If an external resistance is connected across the terminal leads of the cell, this internal voltage causes a small current to flow through the resistance. Current flow is from the *N* material through the external resistance to the *P* material. In a sense, light causes the *N* and *P* material of the cell to respond as the negative and positive terminals of a power source. The voltage developed is directly dependent on the intensity of light. A single silicon photovoltaic cell can produce an output of 0.45 V at 2000 footcandles (fc).

Piezoelectric Transducers

Piezoelectric transducers respond to a unique property of certain crystal materials that generates a voltage when pressure is applied. In effect, a force exists between the individual at-

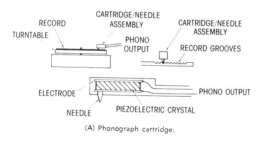

(A) Phonograph cartridge.

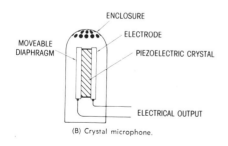

(B) Crystal microphone.

FIGURE 6–12
Piezoelectric transducers.

oms of the material. This force is based on the interconnected electron orbits of each atom and the repulsion of charged nuclei. Elements and compounds have atomic structures that form unique geometric patterns. These structures provide stability and equilibrium between individual atoms. These atoms tend to vibrate, and their electrons follow a unique interlacing orbit. They are arranged in a pattern and maintain the same relative position.

In certain crystals the structure formation tends to resist change caused by heat, electricity, and pressure. Substances such as tourmaline, Rochelle salt, and quartz are naturally pressure sensitive. They have a tendency to release electrons when the crystal structure is compressed along specific lines and axes. These materials are classified as *piezoelectric*. Subjected to surface pressure, such crystals vibrate at a specific frequency and produce a stable voltage for long periods of time. A variety of materials that do not have natural piezoelectric properties can be transformed into quasi-piezoelectric crystals. These materials must be subjected to a strong direct current during the formation process. This action causes the atoms to be polarized. Ceramic materials such as barium titanate, lead zirconate, and lead titanate can be fabricated to have piezoelectric properties. Ceramic transducers are made in a variety of shapes to conform with the application.

A common application of the piezoelectric principle is the phonograph cartridge. Figure 6–12(A) shows a representative phonograph cartidge–stylus assembly. The cartridge houses a piezoelectric crystal that vibrates according to variations in the groove of a phonograph record. The stylus rides in a record groove, which transmits pressure to the surface of the crystal. The crystal then develops an electrical potential across its surface due to the mechanical vibrations. The voltage developed is amplified by the sound system. As a result, me-

chanical energy is converted to electrical energy by a piezoelectric transducer.

It is also possible to convert sound energy to electrical energy with piezoelectric transducers. This is commonly done with crystal microphones in which sound waves cause vibration of a piezoelectric crystal. An electrical potential is then developed across the crystal and is amplified by the sound system. Figure 6–12(B) shows a simplification of the crystal microphone.

A stainless-steel pressure transducer that employs a silicon crystal is shown in Figure 6–13. This transducer incorporates a diffused silicon semiconductor crystal attached to a stainless steel diaphragm. This configuration provides excellent sensitivity to pressure variations that cause strain to the silicon crystal. Signal voltage developed by the crystal is amplified by a hybrid IC that is built into the sensor. The amplifier assembly is energized by 10 V dc. The primary crystal voltage signal is then amplified and conditioned for output by the linear IC. Typical outputs are 50 or 100 mV depending on operating range and excitation voltage. This transducer senses pressure values from 0 to 5 or 0 to 300 pounds per square inch (psi) in both gauge and absolute ranges.

FIGURE 6–13
Pressure transducer. (Courtesy of AMETEK)

Thermocouples

Thermocouples are active transducers that convert temperature into voltage. Thermocouples are widely used in industrial applications today. This transducer dates back to 1821 when Thomas Seeback, a German physicist, joined two dissimilar wires together and found that heat applied to the junction caused current to flow in a closed circuit formed by the wires. This phenomenon is called the *Seeback effect*.

Figure 6–14 shows an example of a thermocouple connected in a closed-loop circuit configuration. Heat applied to junction T_1 causes electrons to flow from the copper wire to the iron wire. The resulting current flow is directly dependent on the temperature of T_1. Electron flow is indicated by arrows.

If the closed-loop thermocouple circuit of Figure 6–14 is opened at junction T_2, a voltage appears across the two terminals. Figure 6–15 shows a thermocouple connected to produce a voltage output. Heat is applied to junction T_1, with the output voltage appearing across T_2. The T_2 junction is generally called the *cold* or *reference* junction. The fused-metal junction (T_1) is called the *hot* or *measuring* junction.

A variety of different thermocouple structures is available for industrial applications. Open-wire thermocouples are made of two dissimilar metal wires joined at a common point. Metal combinations of iron–constantan, copper–constantan, and platinum–rhodium are very widely used. The output voltage of a thermocouple is in the millivolt range. Various wire combinations are used to respond to different ranges of temperature. Open-wire thermocouples have the quickest response time to changes in temperature. Thermocouples are also housed in metal enclosures and heavy metal cases called *thermowells*. Encased thermocouples are protected from the environment. As a rule, the response time of an enclosed device is much slower than the open-

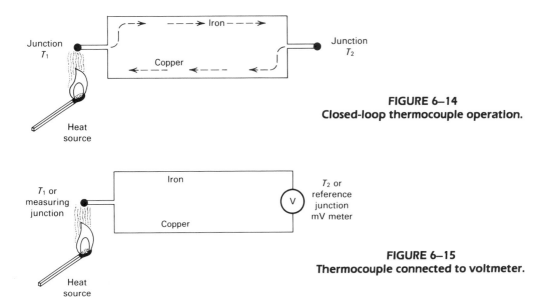

FIGURE 6–14
Closed-loop thermocouple operation.

FIGURE 6–15
Thermocouple connected to voltmeter.

wire type of structure. The application of a thermocouple usually dictates the type of enclosure needed for the device.

PASSIVE TRANSDUCERS

A rather large number of the transducers used in industrial electronic systems are of the passive type. These transducers require an external power source in order to be functional. Operation is based on the control of voltage or current from a power source. Electrical properties such as resistance, inductance, and capacitance are altered by the transducer. Control is achieved by changing the value of one or more of these properties.

Passive transducers are often described by the electrical property being controlled. In this regard, we have light-dependent resistors, thermistors, resistance temperature detectors, capacitance–pressure transducers, and linear variable differential transformers. The electrical property being altered and the method of

changing this property are important concepts in transducer operational theory.

Resistive Transducers

Resistive transducers convert a measurand into a change of resistance. Resistance is then used to vary the current or voltage of a power source. Current flows from the source through the transducer. Variations in resistance are then transposed into variable current values. A control signal is initiated by this procedure. The system then responds to the control signal.

The resistance of a transducer is determined by the same four factors that influence the resistance of an electrical conductor. These are based on the material, length, cross-sectional area, and temperature. Resistance can be altered by changing one or more of these factors. The primary difference in most transducers is in the method of initiating a resistance change.

The material from which a resistive transducer is constructed is extremely important. Each material that is used has a resistivity fac-

tor. Copper, for example, has a resistivity of 10.37 Ω/ft of length, with a cross-sectional area of 1 mil. This is referred to as a *mil-foot* of copper. By comparison, silver has a resistivity of 9.9 Ω/mil-foot, gold has 14 Ω/mil-foot, and tungsten is rated at 33 Ω/mil-foot. This factor represents the ability of a material to oppose or resist current flow.

Most electrical conductor materials produce a linear change in resistance. Semiconductor materials, by comparison, have a nonlinear characteristic. The material selected for transducer use has a great deal to do with the accuracy of its response. Linear characteristics are more accurate and predictable over a wider range of operation. Nonlinear material characteristics are generally used over limited or narrow spans of the operating range.

The length of a conductor or semiconductor is directly related to its resistance. An increase in conductor length causes a corresponding increase in resistance. Reducing the length lowers the resistance of a conductor. This resistance factor can be changed very effectively with sliding contacts or brushes. Conductor length is widely used to alter resistance values because of the ease with which it can be changed.

The cross-sectional area of a conductor is inversely related to its resistance. A small-diameter conductor has a rather high resistance compared with a large-diameter conductor. This resistance factor is not commonly used in transducer design. As a rule, it is rather difficult to change the cross-sectional area and cause it to return to the original resistance value.

The temperature of a conductor has two distinct ways of influencing the resistance of a transducer. Most metals have a positive temperature coefficient with respect to resistance. This means that the resistance is directly related to temperature. An increase in temperature causes an increase in resistance, whereas a decrease in temperature reduces resistance. Materials such as carbon, germanium, and silicon have a negative temperature coefficient. An increase in temperature causes a corresponding decrease in resistance. A decrease in temperature increases the resistance of the conductor. The material used in the design of a transducer has a great deal to do with its response to temperature. Temperature changes are widely used to influence the resistance of a transducer.

Strain Transducers

The measurement of strain in solid objects is a very common industrial process control application. Strain transducers are used to sense changes in flow, pressure, weight, and acceleration. Pressure values from over a million pounds per square inch to those produced by a living biological organism have been sensed by strain transducers. This type of transducer responds to changes in pressure that cause an object to become slightly deformed. Object deformation due to the force of outside pressure causes *stress*. The amount of object deformation produced is called *strain*. In effect, these transducers respond to pressure changes that cause stress by indicating the resulting strain. Strain is a measure of object length as a percentage of its original length.

Metal Strain Gauges

Metal strain gauges are passive resistance transducers. Figure 6–16 shows foil and wire strain gauge patterns. These transducers are cemented to the surface of a solid object that is subjected to some external force. The design of the gauge is such that its conductor offers a nominal resistance. Typical values range from 60 to 1000 Ω. The conductor may be made of fine wire 0.001 in. in diameter or a comparable-

sized strip of metal foil mounted into an insulating strip. The conductor has a high elasticity so that its dimensions can be changed. When the object is subjected to a strain, the wire is stretched. Thus the cross-sectional area of the wire is reduced and its length is increased. The resistance of a conductor can be expressed mathematically as

$$R = \frac{\rho l}{A}$$

where

R = resistance of the conductor

ρ = resistive constant of the conductor

l = length of the conductor

A = cross-sectional area of the conductor

Therefore, as the wire of the strain gauge is stretched, its resistance increases because of the change in cross-sectional area and length.

Metal strain gauges are usually designed to

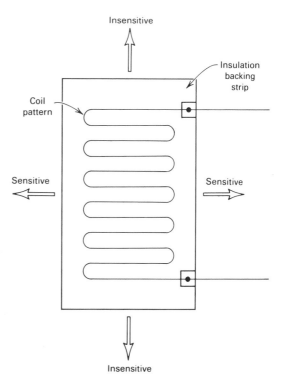

FIGURE 6–17
Sensitivity pattern of a strain gauge.

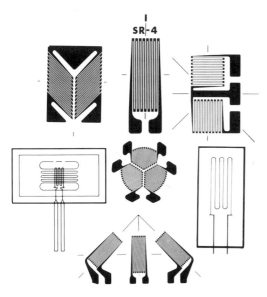

FIGURE 6–16
Foil and wire strain gauge patterns. (Courtesy of BLH Electronics)

have unidirectional sensitivity. This means that they will respond to strain in only one direction. Figure 6–17 shows the sensitivity pattern of a representative strain gauge. Note that folding the material back and forth from one side to the other causes a rather significant change in conductor length. This decreases the cross-sectional area and increases the length, which causes an increase in resistance. Strain applied transversely tends to unfold the pattern rather than cause it to stretch. This produces very little if any change in resistance. Gauges of this type are generally mounted on a paper or plastic backing strip. The strip is then bonded to the surface being sensed. Strain gauges of this type have resistance values of 60, 120, 240, 350, 500, and 1000 Ω.

The relationship between strain and the resistance change of a strain gauge is called the *gauge factor*, or GF. Gauge factor is defined as

$$GF = \frac{\Delta R/R}{\text{strain}}$$

where $\Delta R/R$ is the fractional change in resistance due to strain, and strain is a measure of gauge length change, or $\Delta l/l$. $\Delta l/l$ is the fractional change in gauge length. For metal strain gauges the GF is typically 2. Special alloys of carbon and silicon have a GF rating of 10 or more. High GF values are desirable because they indicate a greater resistance change for a given strain change.

Example 6–1:   A strain gauge has a GF of 2.03 and a nominal resistance of 350 Ω. If a strain of 1450 μm/m is applied, what is the change of resistance (ΔR)?

Solution: The GF formula must be transposed to

$$\Delta R = (GF)(\text{strain})(R)$$

Since strain is expressed as $\Delta l/l$, then the amount of strain is 1450 μ/m or 1.45×10 m. Substituting values in the transposed formula shows

$$\Delta R = GF \times \text{strain} \times R$$
$$= 2.03 \times 1.45 \times 10^{-3} \times 350 \ \Omega$$
$$= 1.03 \ \Omega$$

The total change in the gauge is

$$350 \ \Omega + 1.03 \ \Omega = 351.03 \ \Omega$$

Semiconductor Strain Gauges

Solid-state device design and advances in semiconductor technology have made the semiconductor strain gauge a reality today.

This type of strain gauge has a number of advantages and some disadvantages over the conventional metal conductor transducer. In a semiconductor gauge, the resistivity of the material changes along with the physical dimensions. This is primarily due to changes in electron–hole mobility when strain is applied to a crystal structure. The net result is a larger gauge factor.

The gauge factor of a semiconductor strain gauge is determined by the formula

$$GF = \frac{\Delta R/R}{\text{strain}}$$

Typical gauge factors are somewhere between 50 and 200. A strain gauge has a positive resistant coefficient with respect to strain. An increase in strain therefore causes an increase in resistance. Representative GFs are 25 to 100 times greater than that of a metal conductor strain gauge. It is important to note that semiconductor gauges have a nonlinear resistance–strain characteristic. This means that the GF is not very constant over a wide range of strain. For example, the GF may be 150 with no strain and drop nonlinearly to 50 when 5000 μm/m of strain is applied. To use this type of gauge to measure strain, a GF curve or value table must be employed to determine strain from resistance.

The construction of a semiconductor strain gauge is rather simple compared with that of a metal foil or wire conductor device. Figure 6–18 shows several different construction configurations. In effect, the gauge is a thin bar of doped silicon bonded to a backing strip. Leads are attached to each end of the silicon bar. The entire unit is quite small and rather fragile. Short-span gauges have an active length of 0.63 to 0.12 in.; long-span devices are 0.09 to 0.5 in. Short gauges have a nominal resistance of 120 to 1000 Ω; long gauges are 1000 to 5000 Ω with a GF of 135 to 180. Semiconductor strain gauges are commonly used in bridge circuits to detect output values. Semiconductor

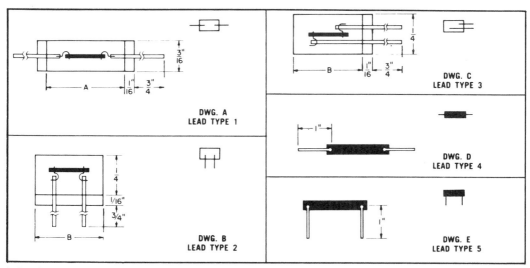

1. Total Filament Length Gage Length + .030'' min.
2. BACKED GAGES
   A = Filament Length + 1 4''
   B = Filament Length + 3 16''

Minimum Trim Width	Minimum Trim Length
Type 1 .05''	Type 1 = Fil. Length + .15''
Type 2 .10''	Type 2 = Fil. Length + .03''
Type 3 .15''	Type 3 = Fil. Length + .09''

3. Backed gages are provided with nickel-plated, copper leadout ribbons 7 8'' long.

4. Unbacked gages are provided with gold lead-out wire 1'' long.

5. All intermediate gold leads are welded to ribbon leads.

FIGURE 6–18
Semiconductor strain gauges. (Courtesy of BLH Electronics)

gauges are primarily classified as piezoresistive elements.

Potentiometric Transducers

Potentiometric transducers are resistive devices that convert a measurand change into a voltage ratio change. Positional changes of a movable contact or wiper arm on a resistive element alter the voltage across its terminals. Figure 6–19 shows a potentiometric transducer element. A measurand causes a force to act on the movable wiper arm. The wiper arm makes contact along the resistance with respect to the amount of force from the measurand. As the wiper arm moves, an output voltage is developed between the arm and one outside lead of the potentiometer. The output of a potentiom-

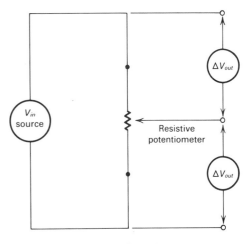

FIGURE 6–19
Potentiometer transducer.

eter may be linear, trigonometric, logarithmic, or exponential.

The output voltage of a potentiometer transducer is predictable with respect to a resistance ratio between the wiper arm and the end terminals. Mathematically, this is determined by the voltage-divider rule. The basic formula for this rule is

$$V_{out} = V_{in} \frac{R_2}{R_{1X} + R_2} \quad \text{or} \quad V_{in} \frac{R_1}{R_1 + R_2}$$

If the output voltage is taken from the wiper arm and the bottom lead (R_2), the first expression is used. The second expression is used when the output voltage is taken from the top lead (R_1) and the wiper arm. The voltage ratio is reversed depending on the outside lead selected. Potentiometers are used with measurands that respond to some type of physical displacement.

Inductive Transducers

Inductive transducers are used to change a measurand value into a variation in self-inductance. These tranducers employ an electrical conductor that is wound in a coil structure. When the coil is energized, it produces a magnetic field. The strength of the magnetic field depends on the physical makeup of the coil and the permeability of its core. Inductance is determined by a reaction of the coil to magnetic field changes.

The inductance of a coil or inductor may be altered by two primary factors. Essentially, these are determined by the number of coil turns and the core material. The structure of the coil can be modified with respect to its diameter, length, or closeness of the respective turns. As a rule, these factors are rather difficult to alter after the coil has been constructed. The core may be air or a variety of metals. The value of an inductor can be altered rather eas-

ily by changes in the core material or its physical position. Figure 6–20 shows some of the ways of altering the inductance of a transducer by changing the core.

The inductance of a coil is determined by its reaction to magnetic field changes. When a coil is energized, a magnetic field expands around each conductor. This property causes a counterelectromotive force (cemf) to be induced in the coil. This countervoltage has a tendency to oppose the source voltage. As a result, there is a reduction in current when a coil is first energized.

When current passes through a coil, a magnetic field expands around each turn or coil. Turning off the energizing source causes the magnetic field to collapse and return to the coil. This collapsing magnetic field also causes a cemf to be induced in the coil. The effect of this voltage causes a continuation of current flow for a short time after the source has been removed.

When low-frequency ac is used to energize an inductor, the inductive reactance is low and its only opposition is the ohmatic resistance of the wire. At high frequencies, the X_L increases and power losses from eddy current and hysteresis increases, which causes the Q to be decreased. In this regard, the Q of a coil is often identified as a ratio of reactive power to resistive power. This is expressed by the formula

$$Q = \frac{PX_L}{P_R}$$

where

Q = the quality or merit factor of a coil

PX_L = reactive power

P_R = resistive power

When an inductor is energized by ac, the resulting magnetic field is in a constant state of change. The field expands and collapses during each alternation. This condition causes the cur-

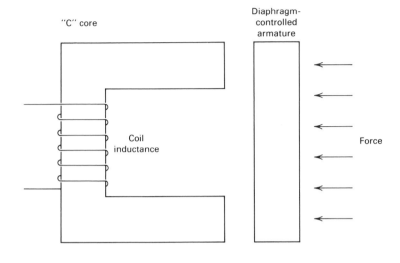

FIGURE 6–20
Inductive transducers.

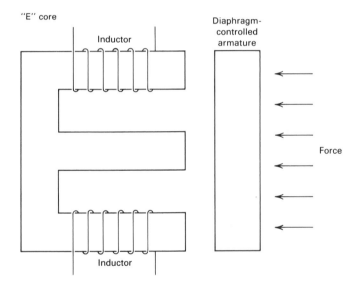

rent to continually lag behind the voltage. In a pure inductance, the current may lag behind the voltage by as much as 90°. In a functional inductive circuit, the phase angle may range from 0° to 90° depending on the resistance of the coil. The phase difference caused by inductance is an important circuit operating condition.

An inductive transducer is primarily designed to produce an electrical signal that is controlled by the value of its inductance. As a rule, this type of transducer has a stationary coil and a movable core, as shown in Figure 6–21. The movable core can be connected to some physical variable whose movement is to be sensed. As the core changes position within

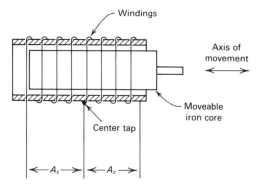

FIGURE 6–21
Movable-core inductive transducer.

Linear Variable Differential Transformer

An often-used variation of the inductive transducer is the linear variable-differential transformer (LVDT). The operational principle of an LVDT is illustrated in Figure 6–22. A movable metal core is placed within an enclosure that has three windings wrapped around it. The center winding (primary) is connected to an ac source. The two outer windings have voltage induced from the primary winding. When the movable core is placed in the center of the enclosure, the voltages induced in the two outer windings are equal. Any movement of the core in either direction causes one induced voltage to increase and the other induced voltage to decrease. It is possible to measure the difference in voltages induced into the two outer windings in terms of the amount of movement of the core. The variation in flux linkage due to the movement of the metal core is responsible for the change in induced voltages. Thus linear movement or a physical quantity can be con-

the stationary coil, the inductance of the coil varies. The current flow through the coil varies inversely with the inductive reactance of the coil, since $X_L = 2 \pi fl$ and $I = V/X_L$. An ammeter connected in series with the ac line can be calibrated to indicate the position of the core, thus using its relative position to produce an electrical variation.

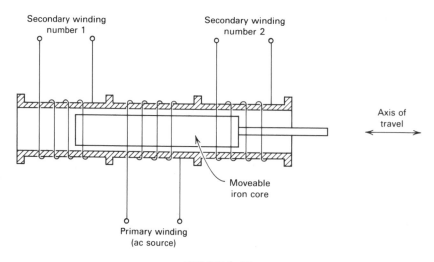

FIGURE 6–22
Linear variable-differential transformer (LVDT).

verted to an electrical response by this type of inductive transducer.

An LVDT dimension gauge is shown in Figure 6–23. This transducer is designed to quickly check the work dimensions of an object. If the size of the object does not meet specifications, an electrical signal is generated. An off-specification object placed between test points causes the armature core to move. The LVDT then produces an output voltage whose magnitude and polarity show how much difference there is in the size of the object. Center-line dimensional differences from −0.100 to +0.100 in. can be detected. The primary winding of the LVDT is energized by 4.2 V at 3 kHz.

LVDTs are frequently used in load cells to determine weight. Figure 6–24 shows the operating principle of a load cell. When a force

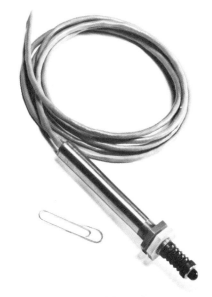

FIGURE 6–23.
LVDT dimension gauge.

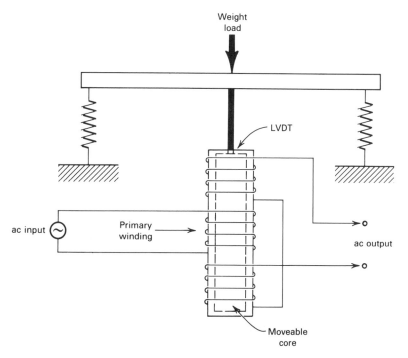

FIGURE 6–24
Operating principle of LVDT load cell.

is applied to the top platform, the parallel flexure plates deflect against the opposing spring in proportion to the applied force. The armature of an LVDT is rigidly connected to the mounting plate, while its coil is attached to the stationary mounting plate. The core of the LVDT detects movement of the top platform and generates a signal voltage that is proportional to the applied force. The transducer in this case changes the downward force of a weight into an electrical signal. Load cells of this type have a measuring range of 5 to 1000 pounds (lb).

Capacitive Transducers

Capacitive transducers convert measurand values into a change in capacitance. A capacitor is described as two or more metal conductors separated by a dielectric or insulating material. A capacitive transducer takes on the same general construction as that of a capacitor. Leads attached to the conductor plates serve as connection points to the device. Force developed by a measurand alters the value of the capacitor. This change in capacitance can then be used to alter the electrical properties of a circuit. When a capacitive transducer is energized, a change in capacitance causes a change in capacitive reactance. Capacitive reactance (X_C), which is measured in ohms, alters the current flow of an ac circuit.

In a capacitive transducer, a force of some type initiated by a measurand change is used to change the capacitance of the device. The factors that affect the capacitance of a transducer are of prime importance. Capacitance depends on the area of the plates, the distance they are separated, and the dielectric constant of the material. The formula for calculating the value of a parallel plate capacitor is

$$C = \frac{kA}{D}$$

where

C = capacitance in farads

k = dielectric constant

A = area of either plate

D = distance between plates

This formula indicates that capacitance can be altered by changing the type of dielectric material, the area of the plates facing one another, or the distance between the plates. All three of these factors can be used to change the value of a capacitor in a transducer. Figure 6–25 shows how these factors can be altered to change the value of a capacitor.

The dielectric constant of a capacitor is determined by material from which the dielectric is made. Representative dielectrics are air, paper, mica, ceramics, and glass. Air has a dielectric constant of 1; constants for other materials are a vacuum (1), paper (2), mica (3), glass (8), and ceramics (100). A wide range of dielectric materials is used in capacitive transducers.

Another important consideration of a capacitive transducer is expressed by the equation

$$Q = CV$$

where

Q = quantity of charge in coulombs

C = capacitance of the capacitor

V = voltage applied

This equation shows that the charge on a capacitor is made by repelling electrons from one plate, thus making it positive (+), and attracting electrons from the other plate, making it negative (−). In effect, this causes a difference in potential to appear across the dielectric material that is equal to the applied voltage. To discharge a capacitor or neutralize the charge, a conductor must be connected between the two plates. This action permits electrons to

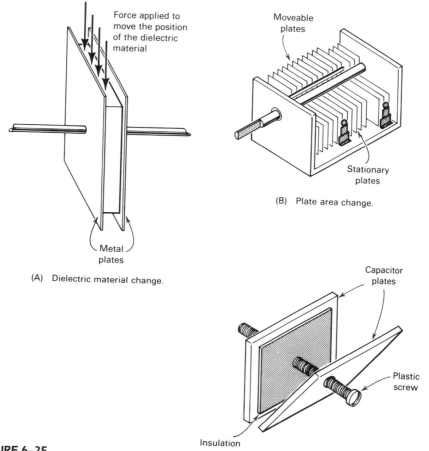

(A)   Dielectric material change.

(B)   Plate area change.

FIGURE 6–25
Capacitance changing.

(C)   Distance between plates change.

move back to the valence rings of their origin and become stabilized.

THERMORESISTIVE TRANSDUCERS

One factor that alters the resistance of a conductor is temperature. Resistance can then be used to alter the current in an electrical circuit or to develop a changing voltage that can be amplified to a level that permits control. Thermoresistive transducers are passive devices. Operational energy must be supplied to the device by an external source. Either ac or dc energy can be used as a source for this transducer.

Operationally, the transducer is placed in contact with a device or in an environment whose temperature is being sensed. The transducer then takes on the temperature of the device being evaluated or that of the environmental area. This in turn causes a change in transducer resistance that can be used as an indication of the temperature being sensed. As a

rule, it takes time for the transducer to reach its new thermal equilibrium. The size of the resistive element, the material involved in its construction, and the type of enclosure all influence the response time.

A variety of different thermal-resistive transducers are presently used in industrial systems. These devices are usually classified according to the material used in their construction. The resistance temperature detector (RTD) is one major group of devices in this classification. RTDs generally have pure metals in their construction. Platinum, nickel, and copper are presently used in these devices. Thermistors are included in the second group of devices. Thermistors are made of oxidized materials such as nickel, manganese, cobalt, copper, and other metals. Semiconductors form the third group of transducers. These devices are constructed from thin slices of a doped semiconductor material. Semiconductor temperature detectors may be constructed as diodes, transistors, or integrated circuits. Each group or division of thermoresistive transducers has a number of unique features that are used in selecting a device for a specific application.

Resistance–Temperature Detectors

Resistance–temperature detector (RTD) operation is based on the principle that metal resistance increases with temperature. An RTD therefore has a positive temperature coefficient. An increase in temperature causes a corresponding increase in resistance. Platinum is a metal that is commonly used in the construction of an RTD. It has reasonably high resistivity, a high melting point, and a relatively large coefficient of resistance. The resistance of this metal varies linearly for a rather wide range of temperature. Figure 6–26 shows a resistance

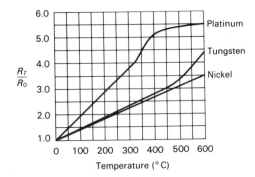

R_0 = Wire resistance at 0°C
R_T = Wire resistance at measured temperature

FIGURE 6–26
Resistance–temperature characteristic for common RTD materials.

versus temperature characteristic for some common RTD materials. Note the linearity of platinum compared with the other materials.

An RTD is made of a wire cut to a length that produces a predetermined resistance at 0° C. The wire is then coiled within a tube or wound on a glass mandrel. The assembly is placed in a metal capsule that is filled with an insulating material. The temperature-sensing part of the probe is from 0.5 to 2.5 in. long. The probe may be placed in a larger housing called a *thermowell*. Construction of this type protects the probe from outside contamination. Figure 6–27 shows some representative coil-type probe assemblies.

A new type of RTD probe construction utilizes metal film resistor technology. Platinum, for example, is deposited on a small ceramic substrate. It is then etched to a prescribed resistance value by a laser-beam trimming system. The completed assembly is then sealed in an enclosure. Figure 6–28 shows an example of the film type of RTD. The construction cost of this device is significantly less than that of the coil device. Film RTDs generally have a faster response time than other devices.

The circuitry of a simple RTD thermometer

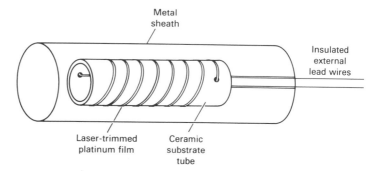

Metal
sheath

Insulated
external
lead wires

Laser-trimmed
platinum film

Ceramic
substrate
tube

FIGURE 6–27
RTD probe assembly.

FIGURE 6–28
Thin-film resistance–temperature detector
(TFD). (Courtesy of Hy-Cal Engineering)

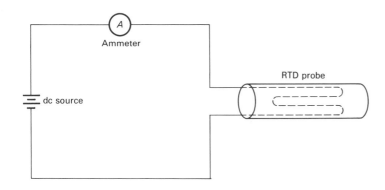

A

Ammeter

dc source

RTD probe

FIGURE 6–29
RTD thermometer.

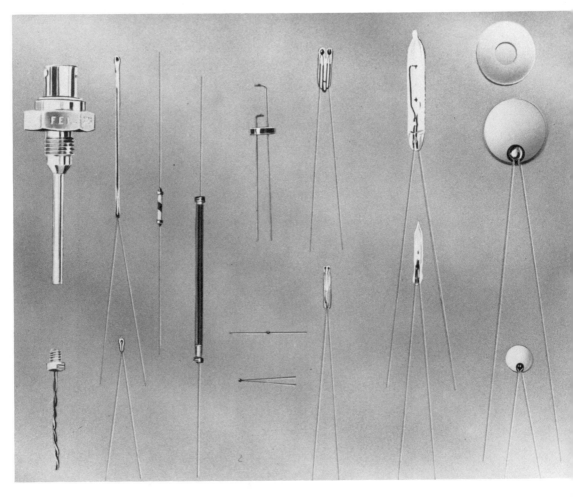

FIGURE 6–30
Thermistor packages. (Courtesy of Fenwal,
Inc.)

is shown in Figure 6–29. If a constant dc potential is applied to the resistive element, a constant current is indicated on the ammeter. However, if the resistive element is heated, its resistance increases. The increase in resistance causes the current reading to decrease. Due to the small-diameter metal element used, resistance thermometers respond rather rapidly to changes in temperature. They can also be used with bridge circuitry for making precise comparative measurements of temperature.

Thermistors

A thermistor is a thermoresistive transducer that senses temperature through changes in resistance. Thermistors are made from complex

metal oxides. They respond as an RTD, except they have a negative temperature coefficient and a nonlinear resistance–temperature relationship. An increase in temperature causes a decrease in resistance. Figure 6–30 shows some of the common package styles for thermistors.

Oxidized metals behave electrically as semiconductors. At low temperature values, valence electrons are bound to each atom or molecule with sufficient strength so that they do not enter into the conduction process. This type of material responds as a good insulator when there is no thermal energy or at 0 kelvin (K). When the thermal activity of the material increases, valence electrons gain sufficient energy and go into conduction. These electrons are free to take part in current flow that passes through the material. With an increase in temperature, more electrons become available for conduction. The material therefore becomes more conductive or less resistive as the temperature increases.

The resistance–temperature characteristic of a thermistor is shown in Figure 6–31. Note that the curve is nonlinear over its span. The resistance varies exponentially. This means that the temperature sensitivity of a thermistor is quite high. As much as 5% resistance change per degree Celsius can be achieved with a typical device. As a rule, thermistors have reasonably good linearity over a narrow span of the temperature range. Selection of a thermistor is generally made for operation over a narrow span of its operating range.

Thermistors are manufactured in a wide range of resistance characteristics and temperature coefficients. The use of thermistors as temperature-sensing elements for industrial applications has increased in recent years. They can be used with calibrated meters for direct measurement of temperature. They can also be used with comparative bridge circuitry for making temperature measurements. When a thermistor is used in a comparative bridge circuit, a change in temperature upsets the balance of the bridge. The bridge is then rebalanced, with the difference in resistance for rebalancing calibrated to indicate temperature.

Semiconductor Temperature Sensors

Semiconductor temperature transducers are now available that sense temperature changes in the very low cryogenic region. These sensors have a resistance–temperature characteristic very similar to that of a thermistor. This characteristic is primarily dependent on the material used in the construction of the sensor. Germanium has a negative temperature characteristic. These sensors are used to detect temperature in the range of 1 to 35 K. (The kelvin temperature scale is used in scientific work. Absolute zero, for example, is 0 kelvin, $-273.15°$ C or $-459.67°$ F.)

Gallium arsenide (GaAs) crystals are also used in the construction of semiconductor temperature sensors. This material has a usable sensing range of 1 to 300 K. The resistance–temperature characteristic of this detector is fairly linear for decreasing temperatures com-

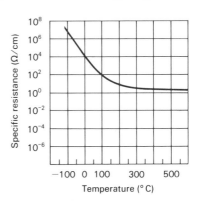

FIGURE 6–31
Resistance–temperature characteristic of a representative thermistor material.

pared with germanium. The resistivity of GaAs is much greater than germanium.

Silicon crystals doped with phosphorus are now available as semiconductor temperature sensors. These sensors respond well in the medium temperature range, as well as in the low cryogenic range. Electrical conduction takes place in a diffused layer near the surface of the crystal. The resistance–temperature characteristic of this material is unique when compared with other materials. Above $-50°$ C the temperature coefficient is positive and has a fairly linear slope. Below $-50°$ C it has a sharp angle negative temperature coefficient. Different doping techniques are now being used to alter this characteristic.

The development and use of semiconductor materials in temperature sensors is primarily responsible for the innovation of an integrated-circuit temperature sensor. An IC can develop a voltage or current output that is directly proportional to temperature. This type of sensor has excellant linearity over its operating range. Presently, these sensors can respond to temperatures up to $+300°$ F. The linearity exceeds that of an RTD over this range. The sensitivity of an IC sensor is 1 μA/$°$ C or 10 mV/$°$ C. Figure 6–32 shows the voltage and current modes of operation for an IC temperature sensor.

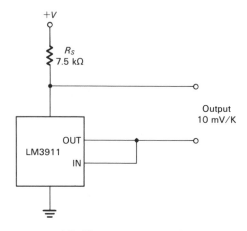

(A) IC temperature sensor in voltage operational mode.

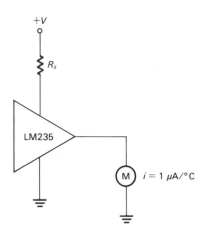

(B) IC temperature sensor in current operational mode.

FIGURE 6–32
Operational modes of IC temperature sensors.

PHOTOCONDUCTIVE TRANSDUCERS

A transducer that changes light intensity to electrical conductivity is classified as a photoconductive device. Conductance or conductivity is the reciprocal of resistance. Conductivity is a measure of the ease with which current carriers pass through a material. Because of the relationship between conductance and resistance, these transducers are usually described as photoresistive cells or light-dependent resistors. Photoresistive cells are passive devices that are energized by an electrical source. Either ac or dc can be used as an energy source.

Photoconductive or photoresistive cells are essentially semiconductor devices. Light-sensitive materials such as cadmium sulfide

(CdS), cadmium selenide (CdSe), and cadmium telluride (CdTe) are used in the construction of these devices. The material used in device construction determines how it will respond to different levels of light and different wavelengths of radiant energy. CdS cells have a response very similar to that of the human eye. They respond best to yellow-green light, which has a wavelength of 5500 angstroms (Å). CdS cells are more sensitive to red or 7000 Å, while CdTe is best suited for infrared light of 8000 Å.

Cadmium sulfide cells are currently used in more applications than the other materials. This popularity is primarily related to its high sensitivity. The resistance of a CdS crystal in the dark may be from 10,000 to 100,000 times greater than its resistance when exposed to an intense light. The sensitivity of the material is improved by increasing its surface area. Most CdS cells are constructed with a geometric pattern of the material on a glass substrate. Figure 6–33 shows a pattern designed to have maximum surface area coverage. This wafer is then hermetically sealed in a glass or metal housing. A glass or plastic window covers the CdS

pattern area. Light energy passing through the window causes the material to change resistance.

Operation of a photoconductive cell is based on the response of its material to light energy. When discrete bundles of light energy, called *photons,* strike the light-sensitive material, it causes valence electrons to break their atomic bonding. These electrons are then free to take part in the conduction process. For each free electron produced, there is a corresponding hole established in the covalent bonded structure. When conduction takes place, electrons move in one direction and holes appear to move in the reverse direction. Conduction is based on the number of current carriers moving in the material. High levels of conduction cause the material to be low resistant. Reduced conduction causes an increase in material resistance. When the level of light intensity is reduced, electrons fall out of conduction and recombine with holes. The intensity level of light and its wavelength control the conductivity of the material.

A variety of industrial transducers is classified as photoconductive or photoresistive de-

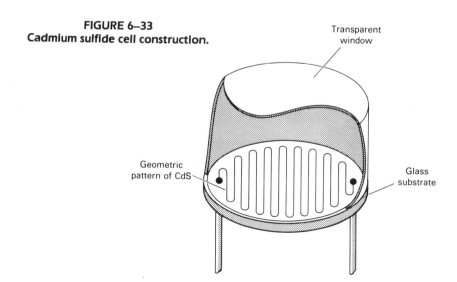

FIGURE 6–33
Cadmium sulfide cell construction.

Transparent
window

Geometric
pattern of CdS

Glass
substrate

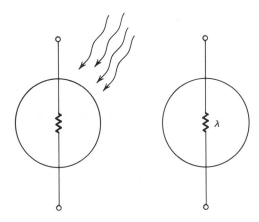

FIGURE 6–34
Schematic symbols of a CdS cell.

vices. The schematic symbol of a CdS cell or light-dependent resistor (LDR) is shown in Figure 6–34. This transducer is represented by two different symbols. The symbol with arrows shows light energy being directed to the resistive material. The alternate symbol shows a resistor with the Greek letter lambda (λ). Lambda is a common designation for wavelength. This symbol shows that the resistor responds to light wavelengths. When these transducers are connected in a circuit, as indicated, an increase in light intensity causes a reduction in resistance. This causes a corresponding increase in device current and a reduction in voltage across the LDR. In a sense, this type of transducer responds as a variable resistor that is controlled by light intensity.

Photodiodes

Photodiodes are also classified as photoconductive devices. This type of transducer has light-sensitive P and N materials in its construction. A PN junction is formed by the two materials. Normally, a photodiode is connected in the reverse-biased mode of opera-

tion. Without light, there is an extremely high reverse resistance. Any conduction current that flows is called *dark current*. As a rule, dark current is due to the thermal generation of current carriers. Only a few nanoamperes (nA) of dark current occur in a reverse-biased photodiode at low light levels.

When a photodiode is illuminated, radiant energy causes the valence electrons of the P and N materials to go into conduction. In effect, this causes electrons and holes to be returned to the current carrier depletion region near the reverse-biased PN junction. The return of current carriers increases conductivity and lowers junction resistance. A photodiode will change its conductivity with light intensity only when the junction is reverse biased. Forward biasing the same PN junction causes conductivity that does not change with light intensity. Photodiodes are energized in a circuit with reverse-biased dc.

PIN Photodiodes

A rather recent innovation in photodiode construction is the *PIN* device. As shown in Figure 6–35, a regular photodiode has a PN junction in its construction. Light applied to the junction causes current carriers to return to the depletion region. This type of diode has a rather significant junction capacitance (C_j). This capacitance tends to slow down the response of the diode to change in light intensity.

A *PIN* diode, as shown in Figure 6–35(B), has a layer of undoped semiconductor material placed between the PN junction. The letter I denotes this intrinsic or undoped semiconductor material. The added I layer physically increases the width of the depletion region of the PN junction. This type of construction lowers the junction capacitance of the device. A *PIN* diode therefore has lower C_j and a faster re-

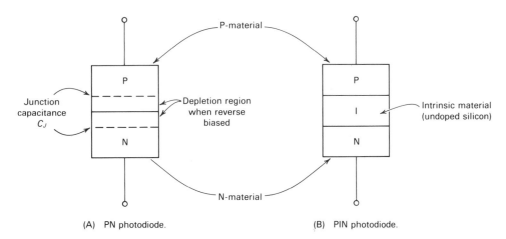

(A)   PN photodiode.

(B)   PIN photodiode.

FIGURE 6–35
Comparison of *PN* and *PIN* photodiodes.

sponse to changes in light intensity. As a rule, this type of construction also reduces the dark current of the device to a much lower value.

Phototransistors

The phototransistor is a conductivity device that has two *PN* junctions in its construction, which is similar to that of a conventional bipolar transistor. The collector–base junction is reverse biased, and the emitter–base is forward biased. The collector–base junction therefore responds as a photodiode. Light energy applied to this part of the device generates current carriers in the base region. This photocurrent controls the emitter–collector current. Essentially, a small change in base current is used to control a larger collector current. A phototransistor is therefore capable of amplification. This makes the phototransistor more sensitive to changes in light intensity than the photodiode.

A cross-sectional view of a phototransistor is shown in Figure 6–36. In this structure, light energy must be directed toward the base area. The entire assembly is housed in an enclosure that has a lens or window centered over the base region. Many devices of this type have the base lead omitted. A *floating base* device has only emitter and collector lead connections. Base current is generated by light energy and controls current flow between the emitter and collector. With an external base lead, the phototransistor has additional control over the collector current. A three-lead phototransistor can also be used as a photodiode by disconnecting the emitter and using only the base–collector leads. Figure 6–37 shows schematic symbols for the floating-base and three-lead phototransistors.

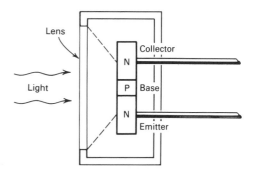

FIGURE 6–36
Cross-sectional view of a phototransistor.

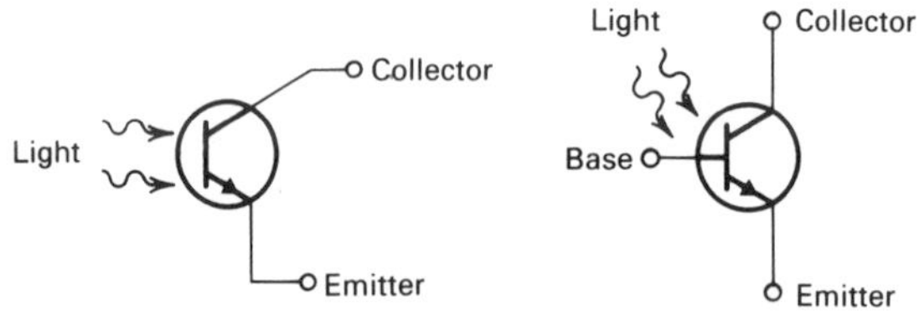

(A) Floating base phototransistor.

(B) Three lead phototransistor.

FIGURE 6–37
Schematic symbols of a phototransistor.

Photo-Darlington transistors are now available through a number of manufacturers. This type of transducer is composed of two directly coupled phototransducers on a single structure. It is characterized as having high input impedance, lower output impedance, and high sensitivity. The response time of a photo-Darlington connected transistor is slower than the phototransistor and photodiode.

HUMIDITY TRANSDUCERS

Humidity is a measure of the moisture content or vapor level of air. Many industrial processes depend on precise control of humidity and continuous assessment of its level during manufacturing. The term *absolute humidity* is used to describe the actual amount of water present in a specific volume of air. *Relative humidity* (RH) is a ratio of the absolute humidity to the maximum amount of water vapor that air can hold. These two conditions are dependent on several factors. The most important is temperature. Warm air, for example, has the ability to hold more moisture than cold air. Temperature is a significant item in humidity transducers.

Humidity can be sensed in a variety of ways. One very common method employs the use of a psychrometer. This method of sensing responds to temperature changes as a means of determining humidity levels. The hygrometer principle is an alternate method of humidity sensing. Hygrometers respond to a material whose properties change when moisture is adsorbed. *Adsorption* is the process by which a gas or soluble substance is retained on a solid material. The level of retained moisture is used to cause a change in an electrical value.

Psychrometric Humidity Sensing

The psychrometric principle determines relative humidity through the temperature measurement of two sensing elements (see Figure 6–38). One element, called the *dry bulb*, measures ambient temperature. The other element, called the *wet bulb*, is covered with a cloth wick. The wick is saturated with distilled water. Air circulating over the moist wick causes its temperature to be cooler than that of the ambient air sensor. Wet-bulb temperature is an indication of the evaporation capabilities of the air. Temperature is sensed by an RTD or a thermistor in electronic psychrometers.

A very dry atmosphere or one with a low relative humidity causes the moist wick of the wet-bulb sensor to evaporate very rapidly. This causes a very large difference in wet-bulb and dry-bulb temperature values. A large differ-

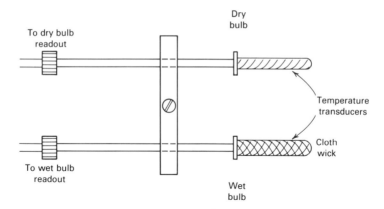

FIGURE 6–38
Psychrometric sensing element.

ence in temperature indicates a rather low level of relative humidity. Higher humidity levels are indicated by a smaller difference in the two temperature values. At 100% RH, the dry-bulb and wet-bulb temperatures are equal. This shows that the air is saturated with moisture and cannot accept any more. The wick of the wet-bulb sensor does not effectively evaporate, thus causing it to have the same temperature as the dry-bulb sensor.

Relative humidity is usually determined by plotting dry-bulb (DB) and wet-bulb (WB) temperatures on a psychrometric chart. A representative psychrometric chart is shown in Figure 6–39. Assume that a psychrometer shows a dry-bulb temperature of 90° F and a wet-bulb value of 75° F. Locate these two values on the chart. The 90° F DB value is projected vertically to the 75° F WB line. Relative humidity is read on a line that passes through the intersection of these two grid lines. In this example, the RH is 50%. A psychrometric table may be attached to an instrument that reads the temperature values. In some instruments the chart data may be stored in memory. Temperature values are applied to the memory unit, and relative humidity values are displayed on a digital display.

Electronic Hygrometers

Hygrometers are used to produce an output that is directly indicative of humidity. Earlier hygrometers were mechanical elements that produced some physical change in their dimensions with the adsorption and desorption of moisture. Human hair, animal membrane, and some inorganic materials were used as sensing elements. Electronic hygrometers are quite different. An electronic sensor or transducer responds to moisture by producing a change in an electrical property. Impedance sensors are commonly used to achieve this operation. Figure 6–40 shows a representative relative humidity probe of the impedance type. In this case, the probe is a resistive element. Changes in humidity cause a change in resistance, which also causes a change in impedance.

Relative humidity probes of the impedance type are made of a special insulating material that is interleaved with a gridlike structure. The grid is then coated with a hygroscopic material such as lithium chloride. Hygroscopic materials have the inherent ability to adsorb and release moisture. As the relative humidity of air increases, the sensor's resistance or impedance decreases. The change in imped-

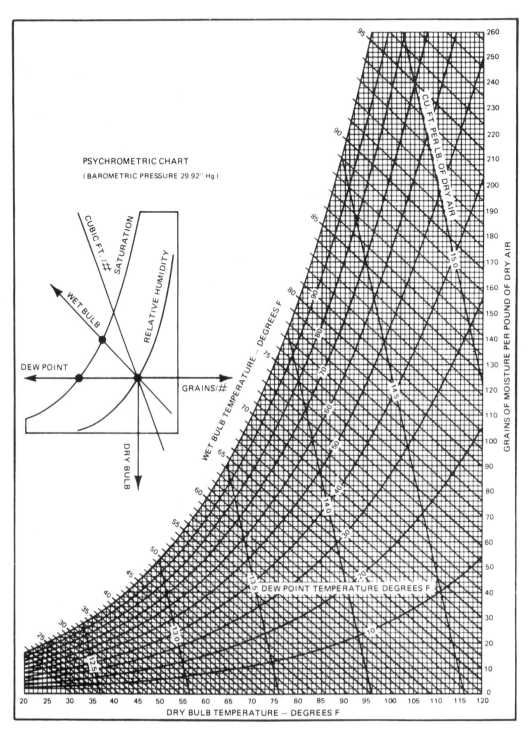

PSYCHROMETRIC CHART
(BAROMETRIC PRESSURE 29.92" Hg)

SATURATION

CUBIC FT. / #

WET BULB

RELATIVE HUMIDITY

DEW POINT

GRAINS/#

DRY BULB

WET BULB TEMPERATURE — DEGREES F

CU. FT. PER LB. OF DRY AIR

GRAINS OF MOISTURE PER POUND OF DRY AIR

DEW POINT TEMPERATURE DEGREES F.

DRY BULB TEMPERATURE — DEGREES F

ance can then be sensed by a Wheatstone bridge. Changes in bridge current serve as an ac signal source that is representative of the relative humidity sensed by the probe.

Aluminum oxide is another hygroscopic material used in the construction of impedance hygrometer probes. Aluminum oxide elements exhibit a change in resistance as well as capacitance. Impedance in this type of sensor is the combined opposition to ac produced by resistance and capacitive reactance (X_C). The sensing element is constructed of an aluminum strip that has been anodized so that a thin film of aluminum oxide is formed on its surface. Multiple fibrous pores exist in the oxide film. The oxided area is then coated with a very thin film of gold. The gold film serves as one electrode, with the internal aluminum substrate serving as the other electrode. The oxide layer serves as a dielectric or insulating material. Subjecting the sensor to the atmosphere causes water vapor to diffuse through the gold film into the oxide layer. A high level of moisture causes the impedance of the oxide film to decrease in value. Lesser moisture content levels cause the film to be of a higher impedance. In effect, the moisture content of the air is transposed into an impedance value. This is detected by an impedance bridge that is calibrated to read the percentage of relative humidity.

PRESSURE TRANSDUCERS

Nearly all products manufactured by industry today are the end result of a process that involves some form of pressure. The conditions, ranges, and materials for which pressure is used call for a variety of different transducers. A majority of these devices respond to pressure by causing some type of displacement or physical change. Most of these transducers are of the pressure-to-position type. A column of mercury or water, for example, changes its position when subjected to pressure. Elastic deformation elements in a similar manner change their shape when pressure is applied. As a rule, these elements are nonelectrical. It is possible, however, to adapt certain pressure transducers to produce an electrical property change. Pressure-to-position transducers generally serve as the primary element for this type of sensor. The physical change produced by pressure is then used to alter such things as resistance, capacitance, or inductance. These transducers are widely used in automatic process control applications.

Pressure Principles

Pressure is defined as the force per unit area that a gas or liquid exerts on its surroundings. Pressure is expressed in pounds per square inch (psi) in the English system or newtons per square meter (N/m^2) in the metric system. The name pascal (Pa) has been assigned as the

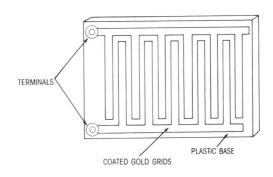

FIGURE 6–40
Impedance sensor for humidity.

basic unit of pressure in the metric system. One pascal equals one newton per square meter, or 1 PA = 1 N/m^2. The pascal is a rather small indication of pressure. One pascal, for example, equals 1.45×10^{-4} psi. Typical industrial pressure values are usually expressed as kilopascals (kPa).

We find pressure expressed or described in a variety of ways. These expressions are rather important because they describe the pressure response of the transducer.

Absolute pressure is the difference between zero pressure (which exisits only in a perfect vacuum) and some known pressure. It is derived by adding the pressure of a gauge to the barometric pressure. Barometric pressure is considered to be 14.7 psi at sea level. A pressure gauge reading 10 psi would actually be indicating an absolute pressure of 24.7 psi.

Ambient pressure is the immediate pressure surrounding or adjacent to a functioning device. This may not necessarily be atmospheric pressure.

Atmospheric pressure is caused by the weight of air. At sea level, atmospheric pressure is arbitrarily considered to be 14.7 psi. The designation psia denotes absolute pressure.

Barometric pressure is the actual pressure in a given locale. This pressure value is subject to change with different weather conditions.

Differential pressure is the value difference between a referenced pressure and a measured pressure. Differential pressure is expressed as psid.

Dynamic pressure is the result of gas or liquid being in motion. As fluid or gas flows through a pipe or tube, it encounters a certain amount of opposition due to friction. Dynamic pressure is the result of fluid being forced against the resistance of surface areas of a system.

Gauge pressure is the actual reading of a nonabsolute pressure gauge that does not com-

pensate for changes in barometric pressure. The term psig denotes gauge pressure.

Head pressure is the result of gravitational forces on liquids. Head is measured in terms of liquid depth with respect to a free surface and a zero reference.

Negative pressure has its zero point at atmospheric pressure and its maximum point at zero absolute pressure. This pressure designation is also described as a vacuum.

Static pressure is the force produced by a stationary or nonmoving fluid.

Pressure-sensing Elements

A majority of the pressure-sensing transducers used in industry today are of the mechanical element type. This type of transducer responds to pressure by changing its physical position or shape. The primary principle of operation is called *elastic deformation*. A number of different elastic elements are now available. Figure 6–41 shows eight representative elements. Pressure applied internally causes the element to change its shape or dimensions.

The diaphragm element of Figure 6–41(A) is essentially a thin circular plate fastened continuously around its edge. When pressure is applied to the inlet port, it causes linear expansion of the flexible diaphragm. The corrugated diaphragm of Figure 6–41(B) and the capsule element of Figure 6–41(C) respond in the same manner. The capsule consists of two annular corrugated diaphragms formed into shells of an opposite curvature that are sealed together. The amount of physical change produced by these three elements is rather limited. As a rule, they are not used as frequently in transducers as other elements.

The bellows element of Figure 6–41(D) is made from thin-walled tubing formed with deep convolutions and sealed at one end. Pressure applied to the inlet causes linear displace-

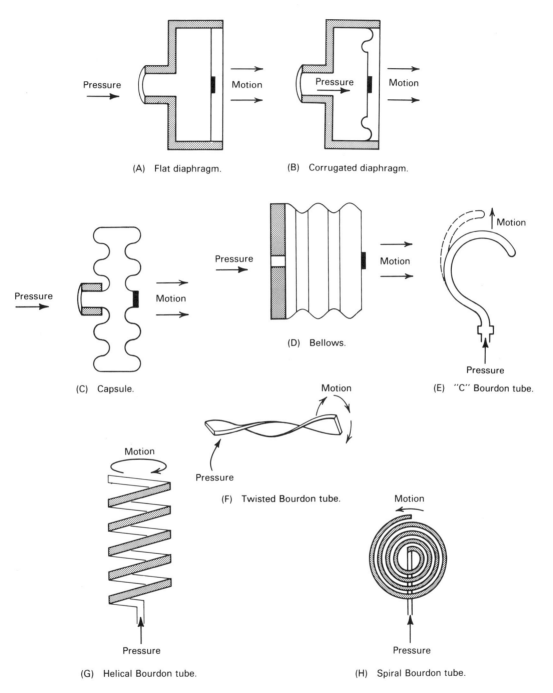

(A) Flat diaphragm.

(B) Corrugated diaphragm.

(C) Capsule.

(D) Bellows.

(E) "C" Bourdon tube.

(F) Twisted Bourdon tube.

(G) Helical Bourdon tube.

(H) Spiral Bourdon tube.

FIGURE 6–41
Representative pressure elements.

199

ment axially. The number of convolutions can vary from 10 to over 20, depending on the pressure range and desired displacement. The bellows element is primarily used for response to low pressure values.

A Bourdon tube is used in the construction of the elements shown in Figures 6–41(E) through (H). The Bourdon tube is a curved or twisted tube with an oval or elliptical cross section that is sealed at the tip end. When pressure is applied to its inlet, the tube tends to straighten. Physical change or displacement is produced by the straightening action. The C-shaped Bourdon tube of Figure 6–41(E) has an angle of curvature between 180° and 270°. The tip end moves outward with increasing pressure. The helical Bourdon tube of Figure 6–41(G) tends to unwind when pressure is applied to its inlet. Tubes of this type amplify tip movement according to the number of turns.

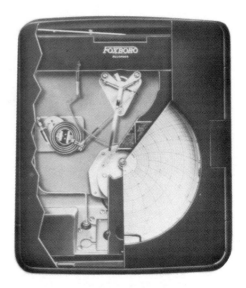

FIGURE 6–43
Cutaway view of a typical pressure recorder.
(Courtesy of Foxboro Co.)

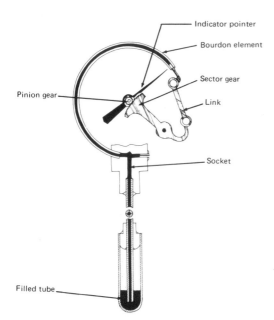

FIGURE 6–42
Components of a Bourdon-tube pressure gauge.

The twisted Bourdon tube of Figure 6–41(F) has from two to five twists along its length. Pressure applied to the inlet causes the tube to straighten throughout its length.

The mechanical action of a pressure-sensing element is generally used to do some form of work. An indicating hand, for example, can be deflected to register different pressure values. Pressure gauges employ the sensing element to move an indicating hand. Figure 6–42 shows the components of a pressure gauge that responds to the mechanical action of a Bourdon element. Gauges of this type can be purchased to measure pressure in a number of ranges from 15 to 1000 psi or 103.425 to 6895 kPa.

A cutaway view of a typical pressure-indicating recorder with a spiral Bourdon element is shown in Figure 6–43. Pressure from 14 to 4000 psi or 96.53 to 27,580 kPa can be measured and recorded on this type of indicator. Instruments of this type have direct reading ca-

pabilities. This means that the output is taken directly from the pressure-sensing element. Instruments of this type are generally mounted at a fixed location while they are in operation.

Pressure-to-electrical Sensors

Most pressure-to-position sensing elements respond to pressure by producing a mechanical output. A pressure-to-electrical transducer generally employs the mechanical action of a sensing element as a pressure summing device. The mechanical output is then used to change an electrical property. Resistance, capacitance, and inductance can be altered to produce an electrical output. The electrical element generally responds as a passive transducer. The resulting output can be ac or dc energy according to the electrical property being altered.

Resistance Pressure Transducers

Resistance pressure transducers are somewhat different from other electrical pressure transducers. A transducer of this type generally responds to the physical stress of a resistive element such as the strain gauge. The strain gauge is attached to the pressure-sensing element. Pressure applied to a diaphragm, for example, causes linear deformation. A strain gauge attached to this element causes a corresponding change in resistance. The resistance of this transducer generally serves as one arm in a Wheatstone bridge. Pressure is transposed into resistance as a result of this application.

Figure 6–44 shows a strain-gauge absolute pressure transducer with a sensing diaphragm. Pressure applied to the inlet port causes deflection of the diaphragm. This action is trans-

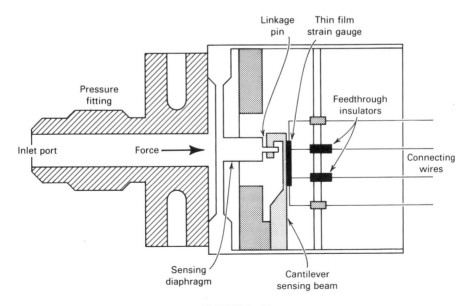

FIGURE 6–44
Strain-gauge absolute pressure transducer.

ferred through a push-rod or linkage pin to a cantilever beam. The beam is designed to provide some mechanical amplification of the deflection action. A thin-film strain gauge is attached to the back side of the sensing beam. In this case, the bridge components and an operational amplifier are housed in the back compartment of the transducer. Operational energy is supplied through an electrical connector on the right side of the housing. Transducers of this type are capable of sensing pressure values below 700 kPa.

Potentiometric Electrical Transducers

Potentiometric electrical transducers were the first pressure-to-electrical transducers to be developed. Through the years a large variety of designs has been produced. The electrical output of this element varies between 0% and 100% of the applied excitation voltage. As a general rule, the high-level output of this device does not need amplification in most applications.

Figure 6–45 shows a representative potentiometric pressure transducer and its internal layout. The pressure element of this sensor is

a helical Bourdon tube. The tip end of the tube is attached to a rotary support that rides on ball bearings. The wiper arm of the potentiometer is attached to the support and slides over the exposed resistance element wire. Pressure applied to the inlet port causes the helical tube to unwind or twist. This mechanical action is transposed into a resistance value change. The entire cavity of the assembly is generally filled with silicon oil to reduce vibration. Pressure is applied to the bottom of the element through a metal fitting. Electrical connection is made to the potentiometer at the top of the element.

Capacitive Pressure Transducers

A capacitive transducer contains two or more conductive plates housed in a container. Pressure admitted to one end of the container causes one plate of a capacitor to move. The other plate remains in a stationary position. A diaphragm or a bellows is frequently used to alter the position of the movable plate. Capacitance is then determined by the position of the movable plate with respect to the stationary plate. A change in capacitance is generally used to vary the frequency of an oscillator or

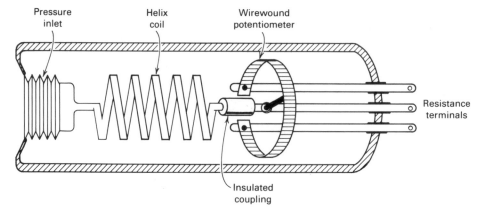

FIGURE 6–45
Potentiometric pressure transducer.

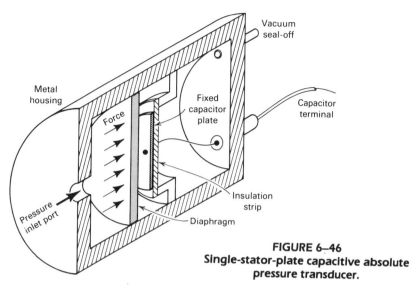

FIGURE 6–46
Single-stator-plate capacitive absolute pressure transducer.

to alter the capacitive reactance (X_c) of an ac circuit.

Figure 6–46 shows a single-stator-plate capacitive absolute pressure transducer. The pressure-sensing element is a diaphragm. Pressure applied to the inlet causes the diaphragm to move toward the fixed or stationary capaci-

tor plate. Full-scale deflection of the diaphragm is approximately 0.1 mm. A lead connected to the stator plate serves as one terminal. The entire housing serves as the other plate. Positional change of the diaphragm causes a corresponding change in capacitance. The stationary plate of this unit is insulated

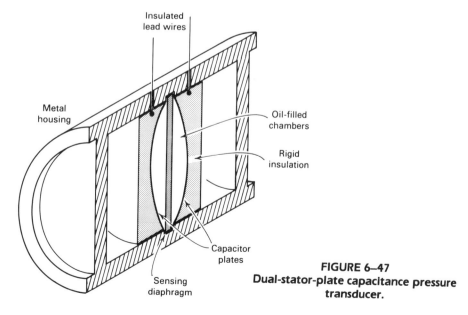

FIGURE 6–47
Dual-stator-plate capacitance pressure transducer.

from the metal housing. The internal cavity area is evacuated and sealed, which permits the unit to respond as an absolute-pressure transducer.

Dual-stator-plate capacitance pressure transducers are also available today. Figure 6–47 shows the construction of this transducer. The diaphragm serves as a common movable plate for two independent stator plates. Pressure applied to either side of the diaphragm causes it to deflect. Deflection to the right causes the capacitance of the right plate to increase and the capacitance of the left plate to decrease. Deflection to the left reverses the capacitance values. This type of unit has an isolating diaphragm on each side and a transfer fluid to isolate the sensing cavity from the applied pressure. A capacitive transducer of this type can be used in differential pressure measurements. The diaphragm deflects in the direction of the greatest pressure value. Equal-valued pressures cause the same capacitance on each side of the diaphragm. A dual-stator capacitive transducer has the advantage of capacitance multiplication over the single-stator capacitance unit.

Inductive Pressure Transducers

Inductive pressure transducers are divided into two major types or groups. One type utilizes two inductors in a bridge configuration. The pressure-sensing element is a diaphragm or a bellows. The second group employs a linear variable differential transformer (LVDT). The core of the LVDT is altered by a capsule, bellows, or Bourdon tube.

The inductance-bridge pressure transducer has a magnetically permeable member that alters the inductance of two coils. Figure 6–48 shows a cross-sectional view of this transducer. The pressure-sensing element of this device is a diaphragm. It is made of a magnetically permeable material. The difference in pressure between P_1 and P_2 causes deflection of the diaphragm. Deflection to the right increases the inductance of coil L_1 while decreasing the inductance of L_2. Diaphragm movement to the left increases the inductance of L_2 and decreases L_1. The position of the diaphragm changes the reluctance of the core material of the respective coils.

An LVDT inductive pressure transducer has a three-coil assembly and a moving core. One coil serves as the primary winding, and two coils serve as secondary windings that are differentially connected. All three coils are wound on a hollow mandrel in which a core of magnetic material moves axially. The core is actuated by a Bourdon tube or a capsule sensing element. Displacement of the core from its center or null position decreases the coupling between the primary winding and one secondary coil while increasing it to the other secondary coil. The secondary voltage at one coil increases while the voltage of the other secondary coil decreases.

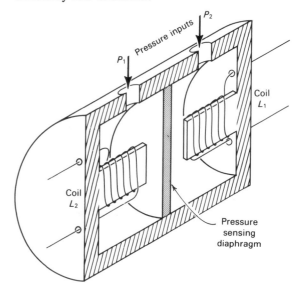

FIGURE 6–48
Inductance-bridge pressure transducer.

"C" type Bourdon tube

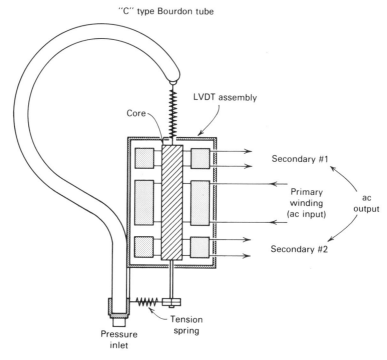

Core

LVDT assembly

Secondary #1

Primary
winding
(ac input)

ac
output

Secondary #2

Tension
spring

Pressure
inlet

FIGURE 6–49
Pressure-actuated LVDT Inductive transducer.

Figure 6–49 shows an LVDT inductive transducer that is actuated by a Bourdon tube. The C Bourdon tube moves the core in and out of the LVDT mounting block according to the applied pressure. Inductive transducers of this type are used to respond to pressure up to 3.5 MPa or 500 psi. Nearly any of the elastic deformation elements could serve as the pressure-sensing elements in this type of transducer.

FLOW TRANSDUCERS

Flow is a manufacturing process that deals with the movement of a substance through the system. The substance can be solid materials,

solids suspended in liquid, gases, or liquids. Flow can be through an open trench, on a conveyor belt, or in a closed pipe or tube. Measurement and control are the primary concerns of flow. Flow transducers are used to sense these two conditions of operation.

A variety of flow transducers is available today. In general, these devices are designed to measure flow rate or total flow. *Flow rate* is an indication of the amount of substance that moves past a given point at a particular instant. *Totalized flow* is an indication of the accumulated flow that occurs during a specific period of time. Flow rate is expressed as volume per unit of time or mass per unit of time. Cubic meters per second (m^3/s) is a common expression of volumetric flow rate. Mass flow rate is expressed in kilograms per second (Kg/s). To-

talized flow is measured in cubic feet (ft^3), cubic meters (m^3), or gallons (gal).

Solid-flow Transducers

Solid material flow measurement is commonly achieved when the material is carried by a conveyor belt. Flow is indicated as the mass or weight per unit of time that is being transported by the conveyor system. To make a measurement of this type, it is necessary to weigh a quantity of material on a fixed length of the conveyor belt. The speed at which the

mally responds to the droop of the conveyor belt at the point of measurement. Solid-flow transducers are nearly always weight-measuring devices.

Liquid-flow Transducers

The measurement of liquid flow appears in nearly every facet of industry today. The conditions under which flow occurs and the different materials that flow through a system are responsible for the development of a very large number of flow transducers. Liquid flow, in fact, can be measured in more ways today than any other manufacturing process. The diversity of this instrumentation can be simplified to

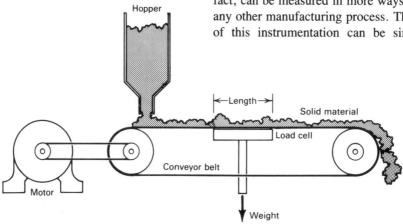

FIGURE 6–50
Solid-flow conveyor measuring system.

conveyor is moving is an important factor in this determination.

Figure 6–50 shows a system where solid material is drawn from a hopper and transported by a conveyor belt. The flow transducer is a weighing platform placed under a length of the conveyor. Flow in this case is a weight measurement with respect to time. Resistance can be changed by weight applied to the platform. Load cells and strain gauges are typical transducer elements. A linear variable differential transformer can also be used to sense the weight change. This type of transducer nor-

some extent by grouping it according to the principle of operation. This includes such things as head flowmeters, variable-area instruments, magnetic flow instruments, and ultrasonic flowmeters.

Head Flowmeters

The head pressure metering principle is used rather extensively in a number of industrial flowmeters. This type of instrument or transducer takes advantage of the fact that a change

in pressure occurs when liquids or gases are forced to flow through a restriction placed in the flow path. The resulting difference in pressure or head is ultimately used to indicate different values of flow. In practice, pressure is measured before and after the restriction. The pressure differential is then changed into an indication of flow rate.

Figure 6–51 shows three very common head flowmeters. A cross-sectional view of the orifice-plate transducer is shown in Figure 6–51(A). This element simply has a hole in a metal plate. Fluid passing through the restriction forms a unique flow contour. When the velocity of the flow stream increases, pressure on the downstream side of the restriction decreases. The rate of flow can then be translated into different pressure values.

Figure 6–51(B) shows a venturi-tube flowmeter. Operation is similar to that of the orifice-plate instrument. This type of device is primarily designed for slurry measurements or liquids that contain solids in suspension. Construction is designed so that the tube has no sudden changes in contour, projections, or sharp corners in the flow path. The pressure differential is measured at one-half of the pipe diameter upstream and at the center of the throat area.

A flow nozzle instrument is shown in Figure 6–51(C). This element has a unique bell-shaped flare on the flow approach section, which is followed by a cylindrical throat section. Differential pressure taps are located one pipe diameter in front of the approach and one-half diameter on the downstream section. Construction of the nozzle reduces erosion and clogging problems in the flow stream. Applications of this instrument are in the measurement of high-velocity fluid flow streams.

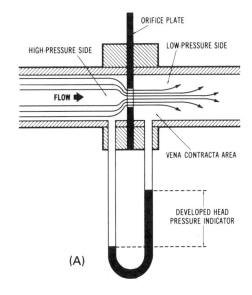

(A)

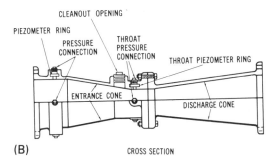

(B)

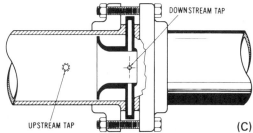

(C)

FIGURE 6–51
Head flow meters: (A) orifice-plate
transducer; (B) venturi-tube flow transducer;
(C) flow-nozzle transducer.

Variable-area Flowmeters _____

Variable-area flowmeter operation is based on the movement of a float in a tapered tube. Flow entering the bottom of the tapered tube lifts the float. Flow rate is indicated on a calibrated scale according to float position. The density of the float must be substantially greater than the flowing substance being measured. This means that buoyancy alone will not lift the float. A suitable value of flow is needed to cause movement of the float.

A variety of variable-area flowmeters is available for industrial use. Rotameters, orifice meters, and piston instruments are three general meter classifications. A rotameter has a tapered metering tube and a float that moves in the tube. Orifice flowmeters employ a tapered float assembly and a fixed-diameter orifice. Piston flowmeters employ a sleeve or cylinder that is held in a cast body and fitted with a piston. Orifices cut into the sleeve are uncovered by the piston as it moves. Flow is based on piston movement and the number of orifices uncovered. These transducers all respond to flow by producing some type of physical movement or positional change of a float. In general, this transducer is a nonelectrical device.

Magnetic Flowmeters _____

A magnetic flowmeter is a transducer that changes the volumetric flow of a conductive substance into voltage. This instrument is generally used to measure fluids that are somewhat difficult to handle. Corrosive acids, sewage, detergents, food pulp, beer, and liquid foods are substances measured with this instrument. A partial cutaway view of a magnetic flowmeter is shown in Figure 6–52. Flow passes vertically through the meter tube in this unit.

A simplification of the operational principle

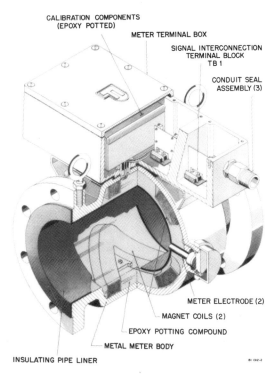

FIGURE 6–52
Partial cutaway view of a magnetic flowmeter. (Courtesy of Fischer & Porter Co.)

of a magnetic flowmeter is shown in Figure 6–53. An electromagnetic field represented by arrows and the letter B is produced by two field coils. This field is perpendicular to the axis of the flow-metering tube. Flow velocity is represented by the letter V and is in the direction of the arrows. The letter D denotes the inside diameter of the flow tube. When the velocity of flow (V) passes through the electromagnetic field (B), it causes voltage (E_s) to be induced into the fluid. The fluid, in a sense, responds as a moving conductor. The induced voltage is perpendicular to the direction of flow and the electromagnetic field. This voltage is a summation of the incremental voltage developed by each molecule of the flow substance. Electrodes on each side of the flow tube measure

the induced voltage. This voltage is a linear expression of flow velocity.

Ultrasonic Flowmeter

One of the most unusual flowmeters in operation today is the ultrasonic instrument. This instrument employs transducers that respond to the propagation of electromagnetic waves in liquid. Essentially, electrical energy is converted into mechanical vibrations that are transmitted into a liquid as a pulsed wave. When the pulsed wave is directed downstream with the flow, its frequency adds to that of the flowing stream. When the wave is then directed upsteam, its frequency decreases by the speed of the flow. Alternately transmitting waves up and downstream causes a change in frequency. Frequency difference is then equated to flow rate of a specific value. A representative clamp-on ultrasonic flowmeter is shown in Figure 6–54.

A simplification of the ultrasonic flowme-

tering principle is shown in Figure 6–55. In this case, two opposing transducers are inserted into a flow tube at a 45° angle. This angle has been found to produce an optimum propagational pattern through most liquids. In practice, ultrasonic pulses of 1.25 MHz are radiated alternately between the two transducers. One transducer serves as the transmitter and the other as a receiver for one pulse of energy. The process reverses for the next pulse. An electrical signal is developed alternately by the two transducers.

The transducer of an ultrasonic flowmeter is generally a piezoelectric crystal. When no electrical voltage is applied to a crystal, its molecules or domains are aligned in a random manner. The net charge between its two surfaces is zero. With voltage applied, molecules of the crystal align themselves in a specific order according to the polarity of the applied energy. This action causes a shock wave or vibration to be generated in the crystal. These vibrations occur at a continuous rate. AC applied to a crystal causes it to vibrate and gen-

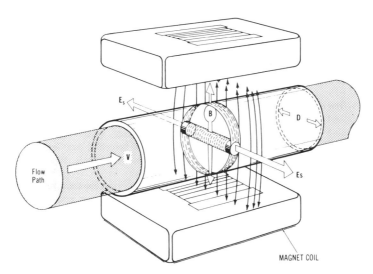

FIGURE 6–53
Simplification of the magnetic flowmeter
principle. (Courtesy of Fischer & Porter Co.)

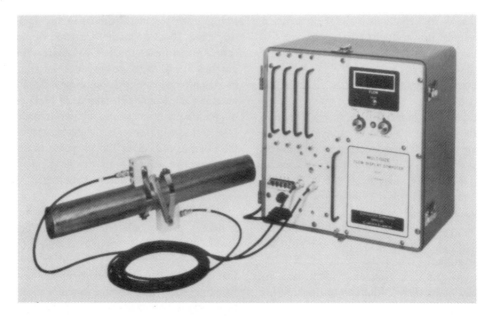

FIGURE 6–54
**Clamp-on type of flow indicator. (Courtesy of
Controlotron Corp.)**

erate mechanical waves. These waves radiate away from the surface of the crystal.

When a crystal responds as a receiver, it changes pressure variations into an ac voltage. Waves radiated from the transmitting crystal cause pressure changes in the liquid. These pressure variations in turn cause the molecules or domains of the receiving crystal to be rearranged. This action causes a sympathetic vibration to take place in the receiving crystal.

The vibrations cause a voltage to be generated by the crystal. This crystal generates ac according to the frequency of the received vibrations. In an ultrasonic flowmeter, the two crystals alternately respond as a transmitter and a receiver.

LEVEL DETERMINATION

Level sensors are used to determine the content or volume of a container. Liquids, solids suspended in liquid, powdered material, and granular-solid levels are measured in open or closed tanks, hoppers, and ducts. The level may be of a continuous value or measured at a discrete point. The level of gasoline in the tank of an automobile is, for example, measured continuously. Point level sensors determine the presence or absence of material at a specific

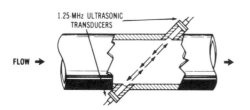

FIGURE 6–55
**Simplification of the ultrasonic flowmetering
principle.**

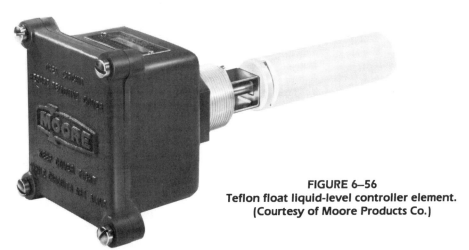

FIGURE 6–56
Teflon float liquid-level controller element.
(Courtesy of Moore Products Co.)

level. This type of sensor is used to fill a container to a specific level and then stop the filling operation. The work function of the system usually dictates the type of sensor employed.

Level sensing can be achieved in a variety of ways. In general, a great deal of this sensing involves some type of mechanical response. Pressure, buoyant force, float mechanisms, and sight glass tubes are examples of mechanical response. Electrical and electronic transducers are also used to detect changes in level. In some applications, a mechanical response is used to alter the operation of a passive electrical device. The response of the sensor can be mechanical, electrical, or mechanical–electrical. The selection of a specific sensor is determined by the material involved, accuracy, range of measurement, construction techniques, and temperature.

Float Level Sensors

One of the oldest and most widely used level sensors responds to the buoyant-force principle. Buoyant force, which was discovered around 250 B.C., is called the Archimedes' principle. A body placed in water is buoyed up by a force that is equal to the weight of the liquid that it displaces. The body in this case

is called a *float*. A float is considered to be a liquid-level to mechanical motion transducer.

Figure 6–56 shows a point level sensor with a Teflon float mounted on a short float arm. A change in buoyant force of less than 1 ounce or 28.35 grams applied to the float arm causes actuation of a microswitch. This particular level sensor will operate in liquids having a minimum specific gravity of 0.5.

A "unifloat" liquid level controller of the magnetic-float type is shown in Figure 6–57. The sensor of this device is a single magnetic float that travels up and down the length of a guide tube. The length of the guide tube can be adjusted to conform to the depth of any tank or container. A number of reed switches are placed at desired levels in the guide. As the magnetic float moves to a specific level, it actuates a reed switch. Level sensors of this type respond to different points depending on the number of reed switches used. The level of a rather wide range of applications can be detected with this type of sensor.

Displacer Level Sensors

A displacer level sensor responds to the Archimedes' principle in a slightly different way. The displacer, for example, has force applied

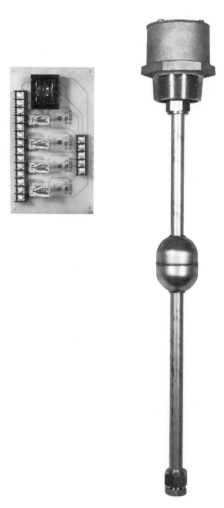

FIGURE 6–57
Magnetically actuated liquid-level sensor.
(Courtesy of B/W Controls, Inc.)

bly to be loaded by the weight of the displacer. The indicator shows level to be at a low value.

When the level of liquid in the container rises, it reverses the buoyant force and weight force. Figure 6–58(B) shows how the displacer responds to this condition. The buoyant force of the displacer increases while the displacer weight force decreases. This change in level causes the spring assembly to have reduced loading. As a result, the indicator shows less deflection. This indicates that the level is at high value.

A displacer sensor can be used directly as a level indicator or harnessed to change an electrical signal. Positional changes of the displacer element can be used to alter a potentiometer or an LVDT. Level in this case will have an electrical signal output instead of the physical change of an indicating hand.

Pressure-sensitive Level Transducers

A very important characteristic of level is its relationship to pressure. Liquid level is directly related to the pressure developed at the bottom of a container. As the level of a liquid in-

to it that is equal to the weight of the liquid displaced by the element. Sensors of this type employ an element that is submerged in the liquid.

Figure 6–58 shows an illustration of the displacer principle. When liquid is at a low level [Figure 6–58(A)], the buoyant force (F_B) is quite small and the displacer weight force (F_W) is large. This condition causes the spring assem-

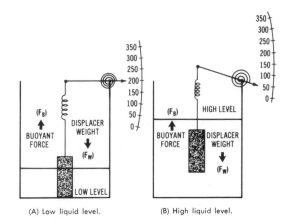

(A) Low liquid level.   (B) High liquid level.

FIGURE 6–58
Displacer operating principle.

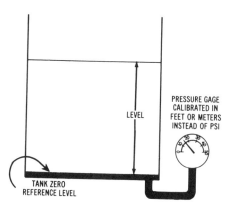

FIGURE 6–59
Level-measuring system using tank pressure.

creases, it exerts more pressure at the bottom of a container. Devices that respond to this principle are called hydrostatic-head transducers. Level is determined by dividing pressure by the density of the liquid involved. In some applications a pressure gauge is simply calibrated in feet or meters instead of psi. Figure 6–59 shows a simplification of the pressure-level sensor.

The mechanical action of a pressure-sensing element can be used to actuate an electrical device. Bellows, diaphragm elements, and Bourdon tubes are commonly used as the pressure sensor. The electrical element can be a strain gauge, potentiometer, or LVDT. Transducers of this type change level values into pressure, which is then converted into an electrical signal.

One very common point level sensor utilizes a pressure switch to energize a filling pump to control level. The pressure switch is actuated by an air trap in a diaphragm chamber. Figure 6–60 shows a pressure switch that is used as a level control element. Changes in air pressure on the lower side of the unit move a diaphragm that actuates a microswitch. Pressure switches of this type are generally purchased to respond to a specific actuating pressure. In some cases the actuating pressure can

be adjusted to a limited extent. Both liquid and solid material levels can be used to actuate pressure switches.

Weight Level Sensors

Another rather important method of level determination is based on changes in weight. An increase or decrease in level can be directly equated to a change in weight. The tank or vessel may be weighed mechanically or electrically to determine level. An important consideration that must be taken into account when weight is used to determine level is that particle size of the material must be uniform and the moisture content must be constant. A change in weight must be attributed entirely to changes in level in order for this method to be meaningful.

Small container filling applications are gen-

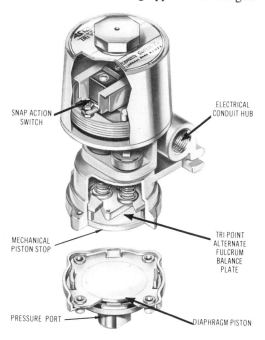

FIGURE 6–60
Pressure-actuated switch. (Courtesy of Automatic Switch Co.)

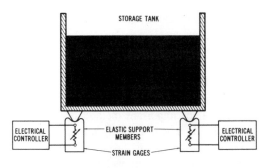

FIGURE 6-61
Strain gauges attached to elastic support
members of a large storage tank.

erally of the weight level control type. The
container being filled is automatically placed
on a mechanical or electronic scales. When a
specific weight is achieved, it indicates that the
container is filled to a predetermined level.
The container is moved to the next operation
and the next container is positioned for the filling operation. Automatic level control is an
important industrial process.

Large containers and in some cases storage
tanks may be filled to a desired level by the
weight process. Level control can be applied
to both liquid and uniformly shaped solid ma-

terials. Electrical strain gauges, resistance load
cells, and LVDTs can be used to sense the
weight of a container. Figure 6-61 shows a
strain gauge attached to the elastic support
members of a storage tank. Weight changes, in
this case, are transposed into resistance. Voltage or current is then controlled by a change
in resistance. Strain gauges and resistive load
cells are normally used to sense weight in large
containers. LVDTs are generally used to detect
weight changes in small container level control
operations.

Capacitance Level Sensors

A capacitor is defined as two or more electrical
conductors separated by a dielectric or insulating material. If a probe is made of two metal
conductors that form a capacitor, it can be
used to detect changes in liquid level. The liquid serves as a dielectric material. Level
changes in liquid cause a change in probe capacitance. The liquid must be nonconductive
or have a low dielectric constant.

Figure 6-62 shows a cross-sectional view of
a capacitor probe used to determine the level
of a liquid with a low dielectric constant. Liquid entering the bottom of the probe causes an
increase in probe capacitance. The change in
capacitance is due to the dielectric constant of
the liquid being greater than air. A probe of
this type exposed to air would have a normal
capacitance of 10 picofarads (pF). Air has a
dielectric constant of 1.0. When the same
probe is immersed in a liquid that has a dielectric constant of 2.0, its capacitance changes to
a higher value. A probe of this type could increase to a value of 200 pF. Immersing the
probe only halfway reduces the capacitance by
one-half of its value. Capacitance can therefore
be equated to linear changes in liquid level.
Capacitance probes are generally energized by
an ac signal frequency of 500 kHz to 1.5 MHz.
A change in capacitance can be transposed

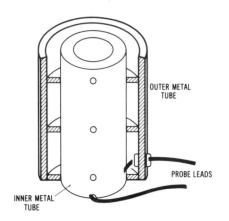

FIGURE 6-62
Cutaway view of a capacitor level sensing
probe.

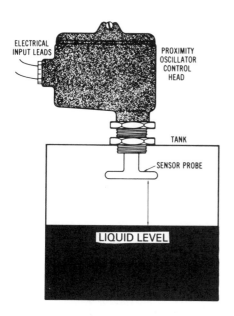

FIGURE 6–63
Proximity capacitance detector.

Ultrasonic Level Sensing

Ultrasonic level determination systems utilize a form of energy that is beyond the human range of hearing. This system combines the effects of acoustics and electricity. *Acoustics* refers to the science of vibrations passing through liquids, gases, and solids. The electrical function of the system deals with the generation of high-frequency electrical energy. Ultrasonic vibrations are generated by an electronic oscillator.

Ultrasonic level sensing is based on the damped sensor principle or the density change principle. A damped sensor is primarily used to detect or locate a discrete point level. Normally, this sensor controls an automatic filling operation. The density change principle generally applies to continuous level monitoring operations. This principle responds to ultrasonic waves being transmitted through materials of the same density. When a wave reaches a pronounced change in density, it is reflected. Technically, this is called *echo ranging*. Radar

into an ac voltage value. Voltage can then be referred to feet or meters of liquid level.

When the level of a highly conductive liquid is being sensed, there is change in probe design. A single insulated conductor serves as one plate of the capacitor while the metal serves as the other conductor. Level changes in the conductive liquid still cause a change in capacitance. The capacitance changes value in a linear manner.

Some capacitance sensing probes determine level without actually touching the liquid. An installation of this type employs a proximity probe. Figure 6–63 shows a representative proximity probe. Level changes between the sensor probe and liquid surface produce a change in capacitance. Changes in capacitance value usually alter the frequency of an oscillator. Counters are then used to register frequency values that are ultimately expressed as level indications in feet or meters. Installations of this type express level on a digital display.

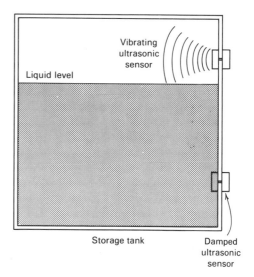

FIGURE 6–64
Mounted ultrasonic sensors.

and sonar respond to this principle of operation.

Figure 6–64 shows a simplification of the operating principle of a damped level sensor. Two sensors are located on the side of the storage tank. These sensors respond as ultrasonic wave sources. High-frequency ac applied to each piezoelectric crystal causes vibration and the emission of waves. The upper sensor is surrounded by gas or vapor from the liquid being sensed. The density of this gas is usually quite low. As a result, the piezoelectric crystal vibrates with a minimum of opposition. This loading effect on the ac source is minimal and very little energy is needed to generate waves. Generation continues as long as the density surrounding the crystal remains the same.

When the level of material in a storage tank rises to or above the position of an ultrasonic sensor, it causes the waves to be damped. The lower sensor of Figure 6–64 shows this response. The density of the liquid in this case is much greater than air or vapor. In effect, the crystal places a heavier load on the ac energy source. Typically, the source voltage drops in value with a corresponding increase in current. Electrically, these value changes can be used to energize a pump or actuate an alarm. This condition change can be used to indicate that a particular level has been reached. In effect, this type of sensor is in either a damped or undamped operational state. These two states can be equated to on or off conditions of operation. Level is determined by the status of the sensors' output.

The density change principle deals with the transmission of ultrasonic waves through materials of the same density. When an emitted wave reaches a pronounced change in density, it is reflected away from the interface. The density change in this case is the difference in gas or vapor and the level of material being sensed. The reflected signal is called an *echo*. It is sensed by an ultrasonic receiver. Level is

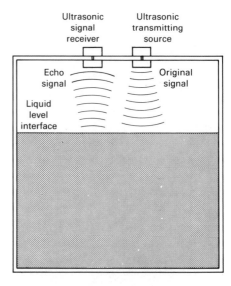

FIGURE 6–65
Echo-ranging level sensing.

determined by the time it takes an emitted wave to travel from its source to the material surface and back to the receiver. Figure 6–65 shows a simplification of an echo-ranging level sensor that responds to the density change principle.

Radiation Level Sensing

Nuclear radiation is now used in noncontact level sensing systems. This type of system utilizes transducers that react to the emission of gamma rays from a radioactive source. The system employs a radiation source, a transducer, and an output control signal. Figure 6–66 shows three representative radiation level determination systems.

The source of radiation may be mounted outside a tank at a single point, in an external strip source, or inside thick-wall tanks. The material level determines the attenuation of radiation from the source. There is no direct electrical connection between the source and

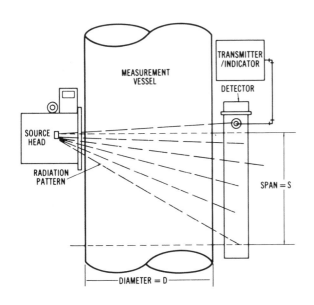

(A) A point-source level determination system.

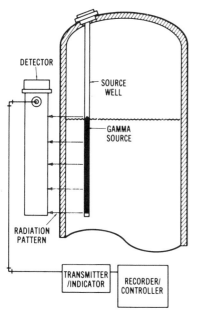

(B) An inserted-strip level determination system.

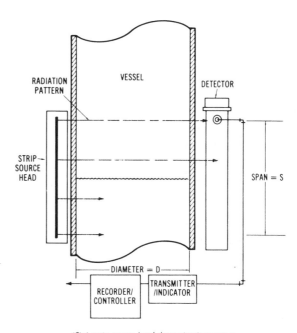

(C) A strip-source level determination system.

FIGURE 6–66
Representative radiation level determination
system installation. (Courtesy of Texas
Nuclear Div., Ramsey Engineering)

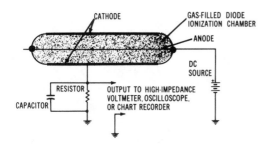

FIGURE 6–67
Gaseous-diode ionization chamber.

the detector. If the source is placed at the bottom of the tank and the sensor at the top, the detected signal increases when the material drops to a low level. The output signal can be used to actuate a filling operation.

Strip-type radiation sources mounted on the side of a tank permit continuous or analog level monitoring. In an installation of this type, variations in level cover different parts of the radiation source. At low levels, very little of the source is covered, which causes the sensor to have a high output. At high tank levels, less radiation reaches the sensor. Making the radiation source strip longer than the control range desired makes sensor output linear.

The sensor or transducer of a radiation level system is a Geiger–Mueller tube, an ion chamber, or a scintillation counter. The ion chamber of Figure 6–67 is used rather extensively today in level sensors. Radiation applied to the gas-filled diode chamber produces positive ions and electrons. Electrons move toward the positive anode and ions move toward the negative cathode. This causes current to flow in the respective electrodes of the diode. Externally, this current flows through a resistor. An output voltage developed across the resistor is indicative of the level of radiation sensed by the detector. The detector is a passive device that is energized by an external dc source.

Level control by nuclear radiation has nu-

merous applications in process tanks, reactors, bins, pipes, silos, hoppers, and other vessels. Its ability to operate at high temperatures, with a low level of radiation, and high reliability make it particularly useful for level sensing of liquids, slurries, and solids.

SPEED SENSING

A common type of industrial measurement is the measurement of speed. Usually, speed is measured as a rotary movement because of the nature of industrial equipment, which has shafts, gears, pulleys, and the like. Several different principles can be used to determine speed. One method, referred to as a dc tachometer system, is illustrated in Figure 6–68. This tachometer is connected directly to a rotating machine or piece of equipment. The operational principle of this transducer is that, as the shaft of the small permanent-magnet dc generator rotates faster, the voltage output increases in proportion to the speed of rotation. Voltage output increases can then be translated into speed changes and indicated on a calibrated tachometer scale.

Electronic tachometers, such as the photoelectric tachometer shown in Figure 6–69, are now used extensively owing to their increased

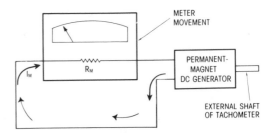

FIGURE 6–68
Direct-current tachometer.

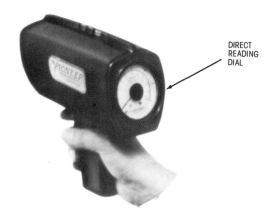

DIRECT
READING
DIAL

FIGURE 6–69
Photoelectric tachometer. (Courtesy of
Pioneer Electric & Research Corp.)

precision and ease of usage. In the photoelectric tachometer, movement is measured by providing a reflective material on the surface of the equipment or machine subject to measurement. The tachometer has a light source that is interrupted by the passage of the reflective material. A photoresistive cell converts the changes of light energy into electrical impulses. The electrical impulses control the movement of an indicator calibrated in revolutions per minute (r/min or rpm), or the pulse rate of a digital counter that provides a direct numerical readout of revolutions per minute.

Stroboscopic tachometers are also used in industry. This type of tachometer creates an illusion of motionlessness when the flash rate of its light source is the same as the speed of movement of the object being measured. The stroboscopic tachometer is basically a light source with electronic circuits to turn it on and off at a predetermined rate. A dial calibrated in revolutions per minute is adjusted until the flash rate equals the speed of movement of the measured object. At this time, an illusion of motionlessness of the object exists. The dial position indicates the speed of movement.

VIBRATION TRANSDUCERS

Vibration is a factor that is frequently monitored and controlled when machinery is in operation. As a rule, vibration is an unwanted machine parameter. Abnormal amounts of vibration generally indicate an improper operating condition. Bearing damage, broken components, improper mounting, and loose-fitting connections can cause unusual amounts of vibration to be generated. Transducers that monitor vibration are extremely important machinery maintenance tools.

Vibration has three parameters or conditions that can be monitored when it is being analyzed. These are acceleration, displacement, and velocity. Acceleration is monitored in g's or gravity units. A g is the accleration produced by the force of the earth's gravity. A standard g is 9.80665 m/s^2 or 386.087 in./s^2. Displacement is the actual distance that an object moves from its equilibrium or resting position. Displacement is measured in peak-to-peak inches. Velocity is measured in peak inches or centimeters per second. Vibration is

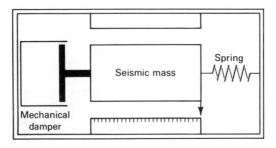

(A) No acceleration applied.

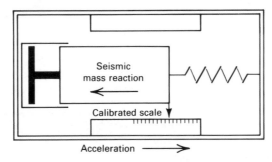

Acceleration ⟶

(B)   Acceleration applied.

FIGURE 6–70
Spring mass accelerator.

related to all three of these factors. Evaluation may take into account the response of all three factors or only one depending on the need.

Acceleration transducers or accelerometers respond to vibration that acts on a small mass of material that is restrained by a spring assembly. Figure 6–70 shows a simplified spring mass acceleration transducer. When acceleration is applied, the mass moves in a direction that is opposite to that of the accelerating force. Reduced acceleration returns the mass toward its original position. Acceleration is a measure of mass displacement in centimeters multiplied by the weight of the mass in grams times a spring tension constant. Electrically, an accelerometer can produce a change in capacitance, resistance, inductance, or piezoelectric crystal pressure.

Displacement transducers respond to vibration by sensing the amount of physical change or movement that takes place when a machine is in operation. In general, a sensing shaft or probe is mechanically connected to or placed at the point where displacement is to be measured. The remainder of the sensor must be immune to the vibration being sensed. The probe then moves according to the displacement produced by the machine under test. Displacement of the probe can be used to change resistance, capacitance, inductance, or the core of an LVDT. Most displacement transducers are passive electrical devices. Figure 6–71 shows a vibration meter being used to test a piece of industrial equipment.

Velocity of vibration is a measure of displacement that occurs with respect to time. As

a rule, velocity can be measured with transducers that respond to acceleration. Typically, the seismic mass principle is used in the operation of these devices. The transducer is usually mounted or attached directly to the machine being evaluated. In this case, vibration is measured relative to a fixed point or position in space. The seismic mass may be a piece of permanent magnetic material. Vibration determines the rate of back and forth movement of the magnet. A coil surrounding the magnet will have an induced voltage that is dependent on the rate of vibration. The frequency of the induced voltage is indicative of vibration velocity. The output of the transducer is ac voltage. Transducers of this type are classified as active devices.

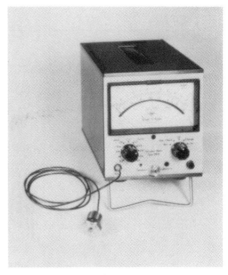

(A) A commercial vibration meter.

(B) Vibration meter with transducer attached to electric motor.

FIGURE 6–71
Vibration meter. (Courtesy of Bruel & KJaer Instruments, Inc.)

QUESTIONS

1. Explain the primary difference between an active and a passive transducer.

2. How is the electromechanical principle utilized in a transducer?

3. Explain how a signal voltage is generated by the Hall effect.

4. How is voltage generated by a photovoltaic cell?

5. Explain how voltage is generated by the piezoelectric transducer.

6. How are thermocouples used to sense a change in temperature?

7. How does the material, length, cross-sectional area, and temperature of a conductor alter its resistance?

8. What does the gauge factor (GF) of a strain gauge represent?

9. What electrical properties of a coil are altered by an inductive transducer?

10. What is an LVDT, and how is it used as a transducer?

11. What electrical properties of a capacitor are altered by a capacitive transducer?

12. Explain the functional differences between an RTD and a thermistor.

13. How does the resistance of a cadmium sulfide cell change with light intensity?

14. Explain how dry-bulb and wet-bulb temperatures can be used to determine relative humidity.

15. What is an elastic deformation element and how is it used to determine pressure?

16. Explain how the head principle can be used to determine liquid flow.

17. Explain how ultrasonics can be used to determine level.

18. How is speed determined by a photoelectric tachometer?

19. Vibration can be monitored by observing changes in acceleration, displacement, and velocity. Explain how vibration can be determined by any of these parameters.

ACTIVITIES

ACTIVITY 6–1: Electromagnetic Transducers

Objective: Contruction of an electromagnetic transducer and observation of its characteristics.

Procedure:

1. Wind an air core coil of 100 turns of no. 18 enameled wire on a 1-in.-diameter hollow tube.

2. Connect the coil in series with a 10-kΩ resistor. Connect a voltmeter across the resistor.

3. Move a permanent magnet around the outside of the coil. Measure and record the amount of voltage developed in the coil. Note that the magnet must be moving in order to have voltage induced into the coil.

4. Place a 1-in. steel rod in the center of the coil and repeat step 3. Does the coil respond differently?

5. What factors determine the inductance of the coil in this activity? How do they influence the induced voltage.?

6. What type of voltage is generated by the coil?

ACTIVITY 6–2: Photovoltaic Cell Transducer

Objective: Construct a photovoltaic cell circuit and observe the voltage–light intensity characteristics.

Procedure:

1. Connect a photovoltaic cell in series with a 10-kΩ resistor. Connect a voltmeter across the resistor.

2. Measure and record the voltage developed by the cell in normal room light. Notice that the cell has a definite polarity.

3. Increase the light intensity while observing the voltage. What influence does light intensity have on the developed voltage?

4. Test the cell with respect to different wavelengths of light energy. Use incandescent light, fluorescent light, and sunlight. Which light develops the greatest voltage?

5. If a light meter is available, position the cell next to the light meter and vary the intensity level of light from zero to 100 footcandles. Measure and record the voltage developed for different levels of light.

6. Plot a voltage–light intensity level graph for the photovoltaic cell.

ACTIVITY 6–3: Piezoelectric Transducer

Objective: To connect a piezoelectric transducer to an indicator and observe the generated output.

Procedure:

1. Connect the output of a crystal phonograph cartridge to an ac voltmeter.

2. Carefully rub your finger across the stylus while observing the output. What are some representative voltage values?

3. Disconnect the voltmeter and connect an oscilloscope across the output. Carefully rub your finger across the stylus while observing the output. Rub the stylus with a file or rough-textured surface. How does this alter the output?

4. Replace the phonograph cartridge with a crystal microphone.

5. Connect an ac voltmeter across the output and speak or whistle into the microphone. Measure and record the developed voltage.

6. Connect an oscilloscope across the output and repeat step 5. Describe the output wave form.

7. What are the pressure-producing factors of the transducers used in this activity?

ACTIVITY 6–4: Thermocouple Transducers

Objective: Construction of a thermocouple circuit that will permit the measurement of its output voltage with respect to temperature.

Procedure:

1. Connect a millivoltmeter across the output of a type J (iron–constantan) thermocouple. The thermocouple has a definite polarity that must be observed.

2. As a general rule, very little voltage is produced by ambient temperature. Measure and record the output voltage developed by room temperature.

3. Grasp the tip end of the thermocouple with your fingers and see if there is any indication of voltage being developed. Measure and record the output voltage.

4. Connect an electrical heat cone to the ac power source. Place the thermocouple within ¼-in. of the outside of the cone. Avoid touching the thermocouple to the heating element.

5. Measure and record the voltage developed by the thermocouple.

6. Carefully move the thermocouple away from the heat source. Notice how long it takes for the output to change value. Place the thermocouple near the cone again while observing the change in output.

7. Describe the temperature, voltage, and response time characteristics of the thermocouple used in this activity.

ACTIVITY 6–5: Capacitive Displacement Transducers

Objective: Construction of a capacitive transducer circuit and evaluation of its operational characteristics.

Procedure:

1. Connect a 20–150 pF variable capacitor, signal generator, and a 10-kΩ resistor in series. Adjust the output of the signal generator to 3 V at 100 kHz.

2. Adjust the capacitor so that the plates are fully closed or meshed. Measure and record the voltage across the resistor.

3. Assume that some form of physical displacement causes the capacitor plates to become fully open or unmeshed. Measure and record the voltage across the resistor when this condition occurs.

4. Describe the effect of a displacement change on the voltage measured across the resistance.

5. Measure and record the voltage across the capacitor for different position settings of the capacitor.

6. For a given capacitor value, measure V_C, V_R, and the source voltage. Does $V_C + V_R = V_S$? How do you account for this?

ACTIVITY 6–6: RTD Transducers

Objective: To examine the operating characteristics of an RTD in a circuit application.

Procedure:

1. Connect an RTD in series with a precision 100-Ω resistor, a milliammeter, and a 1-V dc source. An Omegafilm RTD, type 100 P 30 is recommended for this activity.

2. Apply power to the circuit. Measure and record the current for ambient temperature.

3. Place the RTD in a small container of crushed ice. Measure and record the current of the circuit at the calibration point. Ideally, the current should be 5 mA. How closely does your circuit conform to this value? Adjust the value of the source or change the value of the series resistor to calibrate the circuit as closely as possible.

4. The alpha of the RTD used in this activity is 0.00385. This represents the percentage of change in resistance for each degree Celsius change.

5. Remove the RTD from the ice and grasp the probe end of the unit with your fingers. After 3 minutes the circuit current should be stabilized. Record the new current value. Using the new current value, determine the resistance change in the circuit. With this value, determine the resistance of the RTD and the temperature of your hand.

6. Using the same procedure, determine the temperature of the surface of a 100-W lamp that has been energized for 5 minutes.

7. Measure other warm surfaces and record your findings. Avoid measuring temperatures in excess of 600°C.

8. Describe the characteristics of an RTD and explain how it is used to find temperature.

ACTIVITY 6–7: Thermistor Transducers

Objective: Construction of a thermistor circuit that can be used to measure temperature and analyze its characteristics.

Procedure:

1. Connect a precision 1-kΩ resistor in series with a thermistor, a milliammeter, and a 0.5-V dc source. A Fenwal KA31J1 thermistor is recommended for this activity.

2. Apply power to the circuit. Measure and record the circuit current with the thermistor at room temperature. Calculate the resistance of the thermistor.

3. Place the thermister in a container of warm water. Measure and record the circuit temperature. Calculate the resistance of the thermistor.

4. How does an increase in temperature alter the resistance of the thermistor?

5. Place the thermistor in a container of boiling water. Measure the circuit current. Calculate the resistance of the thermistor.

6. Place the thermistor in a container of crushed ice. Measure and record the circuit current. Calculate the thermistor resistance.

7. Plot a graph showing the relationship of thermistor resistance and temperature. Describe the characteristics of a thermistor with respect to resistance and temperature.

ACTIVITY 6–8: Light-dependent Resistor Transducers

Objective: To observe the resistance–light characteristics of an LDR and see how it responds in a circuit.

Procedure:

1. Connect an ohmmeter across the two out-put leads of a representative LDR. A Clairex CL5M2L is recommended.

2. Darken the cell and record the resistance.

3. Measure and record the resistance of the cell at normal room light.

4. Measure and record the resistance of the cell when exposed to light from a 100-W incandescent lamp. Expose the cell to fluorescent light and sunlight. How does it respond to different levels of light?

5. Connect the LDR in series with a 1-kΩ resistor and a 10-V dc source.

6. Apply power to the circuit and measure the voltage across the LDR and the resistor. Change the level of light and measure the voltages again. How does the LDR cause a change in circuit behavior?

ACTIVITY 6–9: Photodiode Transducers

Objective: Construct a photodiode circuit and analyze its operation with respect to variations in light intensity.

Procedure:

1. With an ohmmeter, measure the forward and reverse resistance of a photodiode to determine the anode and cathode of the device. A Texas Instrument TIXL80 or equivalent should be used in this activity.

2. Connect the photodiode in series with a 10-kΩ resistor, a microammeter, and a variable dc source. The diode must be connected in the reverse-biased direction in order to respond as a photoelectric transducer.

3. Apply power to the circuit, and carefully increase the source voltage. Under normal circumstances, there should not be an indication of current at this time. If there is a

current indication, it generally indicates the diode is connected in the forward-biased direction.

4. Increase the voltage to 2 V and apply light energy to the photodiode. This should cause a corresponding increase in current. Try different voltages and see how the cell responds. Do not exceed 10 V.

5. Set the source voltage to 5 V and measure the voltage across the diode and the resistor. Change the light level and measure the voltage again.

6. Describe how the photodiode responds to different light levels with respect to voltage and current.

Industrial timing systems are an indispensible part of all automatic process control operations today. These systems are designed to provide the necessary time needed to perform a number of different fabrication operations. This function ranges from a simple delay to some rather complex event timing that is used to establish a number of sequential steps. With increased emphasis on automatic process control, timing becomes an essential part of industrial electronics.

INTRODUCTION

Timing systems follow the same general format outlined in other industrial electronic systems. This includes an energy source, transmission path, control, load, and indicators. As a general rule, all parts of the system must function properly in order for it to be operational.

The *energy source* of a timing system normally uses either ac or dc electricity. This electrical energy is commonly derived from the ac power line or through a chemical cell or battery. Some dc sources are developed by rectifying the ac line voltage into a usable form of dc. At one time mechanical energy was an important source for timing systems. Mechanical timers had a clock spring or a weight-driven pendulum. Potential energy, stored in the position of weights or in a taut spring, was released to energize timing systems. In industry today, however, a large part of all timing systems are energized by electrical energy.

The *transmission path* of a timing system is essentially electrical conductors. Copper wire and printed-circuit-board conduction strips are used exclusively for this system function.

In industry today, timing systems are generally used as control elements for other electrical devices. In this regard, the *control* func-

7

Industrial Timing Systems

tion ranges from a simple on–off operation to rather elaborate sequencing operations that produce a number of changes. The control function of a timing system is often divided into classifications dealing with different timing functions. This includes delay, interval, repeat-cycle units, and the reset function.

The *load* of a timing system refers to a single part or number of parts that are actuated by the control element. It ranges from a relay or contactor coil to a variety of solenoid-driven devices that move cams, gears, clutches, or motors. This action of the load is then used to control larger amounts of energy applied to other devices.

The *composite load* of a timing system refers to those things that consume energy from the primary energy source. In a relay type of system, this would include all the energy transformed into heat by the relay coil and the conductors of the transmission path. Timing system loads may also include lighting devices, motors, heating elements, or solenoids that are actuated by direct switching action of the timing control device.

The *indicator* of a timing system is an optional component as in other systems. Clock dials, lamps, and numerical display units are often used as indicators. These may be permanently attached to the system or connected temporarily to it to make operational tests. Clock dials are normally attached to timers to indicate appropriate operational setting positions.

TIMERS

The word *timer* undoubtedly is more commonly used in industrial applications than the term *timing system*. Timers, in a strict sense, are often considered complete operating systems in a self-contained unit. They may be en-

ergized by an outside source and ultimately be used to control the operation of a device outside the enclosure. Timers are typically small in physical size and are often permanently attached to the machine they are controlling. We will use the terms timer and timing system interchangeably in this discussion. Keep in mind, however, that timers may be classified as either separate systems or as the control element of a much larger electrical power system. As a general rule, the end result of the system is fundamentally the same regardless of the terminology used.

TIMER FUNCTIONS

Industrial applications of the timer are so numerous today that it is rather difficult to place them in meaningful classifications. One category places all timers in classifications related to the type of functional control achieved. This includes timers that delay a starting cycle, control intervals, and repeat operational cycles, and those that reset themselves after a cycle has been completed. Some timers have the capability of achieving two or more of these functions after some minor modifications are made. Others may be designed to achieve only one specific function. The function of a timer is an important concept that will be expanded on.

Delay Timers

In machine tool operations and a variety of electronic circuit applications, delay timers are used to alter the starting time of a load device or controlled circuit. When the timer is initially energized, it sees an adjustable time setting value and delays the turn-on operation according to this setting. It eventually closes the

FIGURE 7–1
Solid-state delay timer. (Courtesy of Industrial Solid State Controls)

power switch, which energizes the system load. Many delay timers are designed to de-energize their own circuitry after the control cycle has been completed.

Figure 7–1 shows a typical delay timer of the solid-state type. This unit features six adjustable time ranges with a locking potentiometer and an LED indicating control. Initially, the unit is adjusted to a specific delay time setting. When electrical energy is applied, the load device or output circuits remain off until the delay time has elapsed. By switching action, the load then turns on and latches in the on position. Through this action, the timer remains actuated without consuming a great deal of electrical energy from the source.

Interval Timers

Interval timers are used in applications where the load is turned on at the start of an operational cycle and kept on for a specific time period. At the end of this interval, the load is turned off automatically. Industrial applica-

tions of this timer are found in heating units, photographic light source control, mixing valves, and automatic machine tool operations.

Interval timers can be adjusted to a range of different settings. The type of adjustment needed to change the interval varies a great deal with different timer mechanisms. In some applications a number of different intervals and control possibilities can be achieved by ganging two or more timers together.

Figure 7–2 shows a solid-state interval timer with memory. To operate this timer, the digit dials are adjusted to a desired interval. When energized, the unit counts the interval and registers it on the display. When the interval is reached, the load turns off and the display returns to zero. The same interval can be repeated by actuating the unit again.

Repeat-cycle Timers

Repeat-cycle timers are designed to perform their operating cycle continually until the operation is stopped. Timers of this type can be

FIGURE 7–2
Solid-state interval timer with memory. (Courtesy of Automatic Timing & Controls Co.)

FIGURE 7–3
Motor-driven repeat-cycle timer. (Courtesy of Haydon Switch & Instrument, Inc.)

stopped by an automatic overriding program, by a safety interlock, or through manual switch action. Some type of resetting operation must take place after the timer has been stopped. Both manual and automatic resetting devices are available today.

A large number of repeat-cycle timers used in industrial timer applications today are of the motor-driven type. A synchronous ac motor is commonly used to drive a camshaft or a rotating dial. Contacts are opened or closed according to cam action or by switch-tripping tabs attached to the dial. A specific cam or tab can be used to turn on a switch and an alternate one can be used to turn it off. Several sets of tabs or cams can be attached to the drive mechanism of these timers.

Figure 7–3 shows a typical motor-driven repeat-cycle timer that makes and breaks switching operations as long as the motor is energized. The motor-driven cam of the device has notches or cutouts that change the snap-action switch arm at certain locations. Each switch-arm position change causes the switch to alter its condition. Cycle changes can range from 10 seconds to 24 hours by changing the cam notches.

The rotational speed of a repeat-cycle timer is determined by the gear ratio of the drive mechanism and the operating speed of the motor. When 60 Hz of ac is used to energize the drive motor, power line accuracies can be achieved for long periods of time. Timers of this type are typically found in electrical energy saving applications in industry today.

Reset Timers

Reset timers represent a variation of the cycling timer operation just discussed. This type of timer typically employs a motor-driven gear assembly that is actuated by a clutch mechanism. As a result, the cycle starts and goes through an interval. At a certain time, the clutch mechanism is tripped. This action disengages the drive motor from the gear mechanism and permits it to return to the starting position by spring action. Upon its return to the starting point, this timer may turn off, go into an idling condition, or repeat the cycle again automatically. The cycle may be repeated by manually depressing a push button without making a new dial setting. The clutch mechanism is a unique part of this timer.

Figure 7–4 shows a typical reset timer of the motor-driven type. Timers of this type are

FIGURE 7–4
Motor-driven interval of delay reset timer. (Courtesy of Automatic Timing & Controls Co.)

designed to energize the load at a preset interval. Interval setting is achieved by turning the pointer to the desired time interval. The cycle then starts when the center push button is depressed. When the time interval is reached, the load is turned off and the push-button pointer returns to the starting position. The cycle is repeated again by simply depressing the push button.

Timer Classifications

A broad range of techniques is used to achieve industrial timing. This includes thermal changes, electromechanical action, electrochemical changes, electronic signals, mechanical action, and digital operations. For convenience, these techniques are first placed into groups that respond to either analog or digital changes. *Digital* timers are designed to count pulses generated by an electronic clock circuit. *Analog* timers, by comparison, respond to physical quantities or changes. Practically all timers are of the analog type today. Digital timers are relatively new to the industrial electronics field.

Expansion of the analog classification finds the general terms thermal, electromechanical, electrochemical, electronic, and mechanical in common use. Division of these terms leads to some specific kinds of timers. The block diagram of Figure 7–5 shows the relationship of these timer classifications.

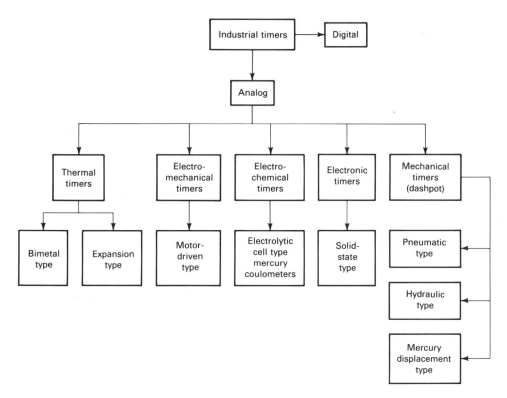

FIGURE 7–5
Block diagram of timer classifications.

THERMAL TIMERS

Thermal energy has been used in industrial applications about as long as any of the other basic principles of timing. A fundamental principle that metal expands when heated and contracts when cooled is used in the timing element. Each type of metal has unique linear expansion characteristics. When dissimilar metal strips are connected together, they tend to bend or flex when heat is applied. As a result of this action, the bending property of a bimetal strip is used to force electrical contacts together. A majority of thermal timers respond to an applied heat source and contract naturally by heat reduction.

Bimetal-strip Timers

Figure 7–6(A) shows a delay type of thermal timer that has been used in industrial applications for a number of years. The electrical part of the timer in Figure 7–6(B) employs two self-supporting metal strips with electrical contacts. When electrical energy is applied to the heating element, it causes the bimetal strip to bend or flex. The side of the strip near the heating element expands faster than the contact side. As a result, the bending action causes the contacts to be forced together after a short delay period.

Bimetal timers can be obtained in a variety of different styles and types. The glass-enclosed type of Figure 7–6(A) is designed for a fixed delay time. The delay ranges from 2 to 180 seconds (s). Timers of this type must be replaced periodically, which accounts for the plug-in type of structure. Gaseous tubes and vacuum-tube circuits frequently use thermal delay timers of this type to permit proper warm-up periods before source voltage is applied to the electrodes.

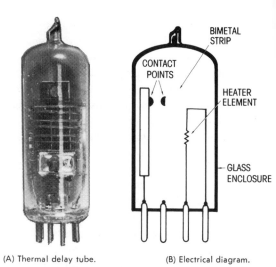

(A) Thermal delay tube.   (B) Electrical diagram.

FIGURE 7–6
Thermal delay timer. (Courtesy of Amperite Co., Inc.)

A dual-bimetal-strip timer is shown in Figure 7–7. Timers of this type are designed to correct contact point position that occurs with ambient temperature changes. In this construction, any change in temperature alters both supports an equal amount. As a result, the contacts maintain a constant gap with normal temperature changes. This means that the delay action stays fairly consistent over a wide range of temperature changes. The time accuracy of

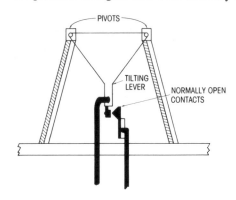

FIGURE 7–7
Dual bimetal-strip time delay unit.

this device is more consistent than that of the timer in Figure 7–6(A).

The operation of a dual-bimetal-strip timing element is similar to that of the single-element type. Heat is applied to only one strip when the element is energized. After a period the heated strip bends outward due to its expansion. The alternate strip does not change shape significantly. As a result of this action, the normally open contacts are forced to close, thus completing the delay action.

Thermal Expansion Timers

The expansion type of timer shown in Figure 7–8 is a very common industrial device. Its operating principle is also based on the expansion characteristic of metal. In this device, metal is made to expand instead of bend or warp. The end result of this device is, however, the same as that of the bimetal-strip timer.

An expansion timer is energized by an external source. Either an ac or dc source of energy can be applied to the heating element. After a short period, the wide upright piece of metal tends to expand. The amount of expansion that takes place before the contacts are closed is based on the position setting of the tension compression adjustment screw. A variable degree of time delay is therefore permitted with this device. Delay ranges from 1 to 3 min are possible with the timer of Figure 7–8. In general, delay timers have a rather limited range of delay capabilities.

A Thermal Timer Application

Thermal timers usually suffer from a rather serious problem when they are used independently as control devices. The heating element, for example, must be constantly energized in order to continue contact conduction after the delay action takes place. For long-duration operating cycles after delay, a great deal of heat would be needed to keep this device operational. For applications other than short operational periods, thermal timers are frequently used in latching relay circuits.

The circuit of a thermal delay–relay timer unit is shown in Figure 7–9. In this circuit, when the operational switch is turned on, 6.3 V ac is applied to the heating element of the ther-

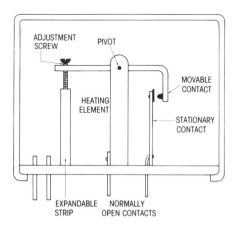

FIGURE 7–8
Expansion-type timer.

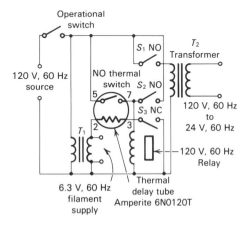

FIGURE 7–9
Thermal delay timer circuit.

mal delay unit. After a short delay period, the contacts come together and activate the relay coil. The normally closed (NC) relay contacts break and the two normally open (NO) contacts make connection. Note that the NC contacts are placed in series with the heating element. As a result of this action, the heater element source is disconnected. The S_2 NO contacts are now closed, however, which bypasses the contacts of the delay unit. This creates a latching condition that holds the relay coil actuated until the operational switch is turned off. Control energy to the load device is completed through the S_1 NO contacts by the same relay action.

Through the action of a delay–relay circuit, the heater source is removed after the load has been actuated. The operational efficiency of this circuit is improved, and electrical energy waste is reduced to a very low level. As a general rule, the operational life of a thermal delay unit is increased when it is used in a circuit of this type.

ELECTROMECHANICAL TIMERS

Electromechanical timers are used in a very large number of all industrial timer applications today. Primarily, this classification of timers refers to those devices driven by a motor mechanism. Since 60 Hz of ac is readily available at most industrial sites, it typically serves as the energy source for these timers. The drive mechanism is usually actuated by an inexpensive synchronous motor. These low-cost timing devices are commonly used to achieve delay, interval, repeat cycle, and reset functions with power-line-frequency accuracy. As a general rule, the life expectancy of this kind of timer is quite good. The operational life of electromechanical timers ranges from 100,000 to 10 million cycle completions.

Practically all motor-driven timers conform to the basic system structure outlined previously. This refers to the energy source, transmission path, control, load device, and indicator. Specifically, the primary energy source is ac electricity to drive a small synchronous motor. Electromagnetic energy developed by the motor is then used mechanically to turn a gear train or transmission. Control of this energy can then be achieved by a gear mechanism, clutch assembly, or spring. The end result of the system sees mechanical energy being applied to a drive mechanism that actuates switches or an electrical relay coil. Calibrated dials with time pointers are also attached to the actuator drive mechanism to achieve the indicator function. Each timer in a strict sense can be classified as a unique system or as a control element for a larger system.

Motor-driven Delay Timers

Motor-driven delay timers are used in industrial applications where a specific amount of time is needed before a load device is energized. Timers of this type are used to provide warm-up time for some electrical components or to ensure proper sequencing steps in production-line assembly applications.

Figure 7–10(A) shows a schematic diagram of a motor-driven delay timer. When the operational switch is turned on, power is applied directly to the drive motor through the normally closed (NC) relay contacts. This energizes the motor and causes rotation until it strikes an actuator mechanism that trips the relay switch. Actuation of the relay armature automatically closes the normally open (NO) contacts and opens the NC contacts. Through this same action, the load device is energized electrically. With the NO contacts now closed, the relay and load continue to operate. Through this same relay action, the drive motor energy is removed by opening the NC con-

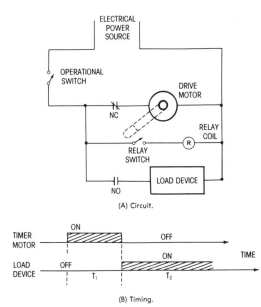

(A) Circuit.

(B) Timing.

FIGURE 7–10
**Motor-driven delay timer. (Courtesy of
Haydon Switch & Instrument, Inc.)**

tacts. As a result of this action, the timer remains in this operating state until the electrical power source is turned off by the operational switch.

The bar graph of Figure 7–10(B) shows the operational sequence of the timer motor and load device. Note that the motor is in operation only during T_1 and off during T_2. The load responds in reverse order to this action.

Motor-driven Interval Timers

Motor-driven interval timers are commonly used in industrial applications where the load is turned on immediately and left on for a certain interval of time. After this interval, the load is automatically turned off. It then remains in the off state until the timer is reset and started again. Figures 7–11 through 7–14

show some application diagrams of the interval timer.

Push-button Interval with Stop Feature

In Figure 7–11, the start button of the interval timer needs to be depressed to start the operational cycle. When this occurs, the load is energized immediately for a set time period. Depressing the stop button de-energizes the operation before it completes the cycle if the need arises.

When the NO start button is depressed, it completes the energy path from the source to

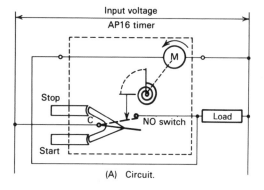

(A)   Circuit.

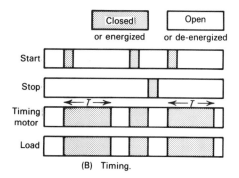

(B)   Timing.

FIGURE 7–11
**Interval timer with push-button stop.
(Courtesy of Haydon Switch & Instrument, Inc.)**

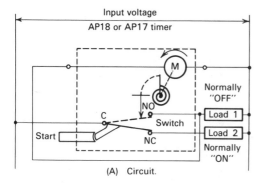

(A) Circuit.

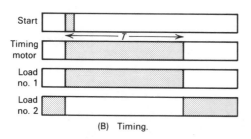

(B) Timing.

FIGURE 7–12
Interval time with push-button on and off interval. (Courtesy of Haydon Switch & Instrument, Inc.)

the load and timing motor. With the motor in operation, its drive mechanism turns the switch-tripping arm. After an elapsed time, the switch-tripping arm actuates the timing switch, which turns the motor and load off. This action de-energizes the entire unit. To start the cycle again in the same sequence, the timer must be reset to its starting position.

Push-button Interval ON or Interval OFF

Figure 7–12 shows an interval timer that causes an *on* or *off* load control condition to be initiated automatically by push-button action. Depressing the start button actuates the motor and energizes load 1. This same action causes

load 2 to change from its normally on state to an off condition. After an elapsed time interval, the switch-tripping arm changes the SPDT switch back to its original starting position before actuation. Load 2 is, therefore, on again and load 1 is off. The timing motor must be reset to ready itself for the next operational cycle.

Limiting Control with Memory

The primary function of the timer of Figure 7–13 is to limit the time that a load is energized. Exceeding a prescribed time setting causes this device to interrupt both the load and timer motor. Through this action, the timer cannot be

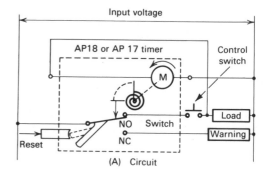

(A) Circuit

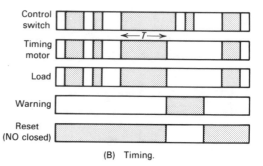

(B) Timing.

FIGURE 7–13
Limiting control interval timer with (reset) memory. (Courtesy of Haydon Switch & Instrument, Inc.)

recycled until the reset button or memory switch is pressed.

When this timer is in the reset state, the load and timer motor are both turned off as indicated. Depressing the control push button starts the operation cycle by turning on both the load and the motor. Holding the push button closed for a time longer than the set time interval causes the switch-tripping arm to change the SPDT reset switch. This de-energizes the load and timer and actuates the warning light. When this occurs, the timing motor will not reset upon release of the control swtich until it is reset manually. Holding the control push button in for a time less than the prescribed time interval will not actuate the tripping switch. As a result, the motor resets to its original starting point when the push button is released. Through this action, the timer cannot be turned on again until its timing cycle is reset.

Hand-set Interval Timer

With a hand-set interval timer (Figure 7–14), the load and motor are energized immediately when the timing dial is manually turned to a set-time position. The motor operates for this set-time period until its timing switch drops into a notch on the cam drive wheel. When this occurs, the SPDT switch turns the motor and load off. To initiate another operating cycle, the calibrated dial is adjusted to a new time interval manually.

Motor-driven Cycle Timers

Motor-driven cycle timers play a very important role in squence control operations in industry today. Primarily, this type of timer is used to control one or more different on and off operations on a continual basis. Figure 7–15 shows three different circuit possibilities of

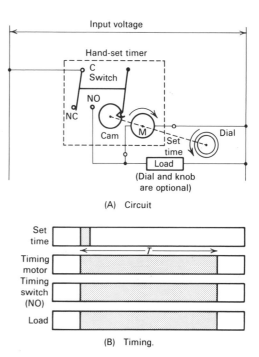

(A) Circuit

(B) Timing.

FIGURE 7–14
Hand-set interval timer. (Courtesy of Haydon Switch & Instrument, Inc.)

multiple-load control applications. Each switch of this timer is controlled by a separate cam that can be adjusted to any position according to the needs of the system.

Special switch-actuating arms that ride on the cam of a motor-driven timer are used to trigger the switch when a physical change in cam diameter occurs. See the cam and switch assembly in Figure 7–16. The screws on the cams are tightened in place when the cam is adjusted to a desired position.

Continuous On–Off Repeat Cycle Timers

Figure 7–17(A) shows a schematic diagram of a repeat cycle timer of the continuous on–off type. In this circuit, when the contact switch is

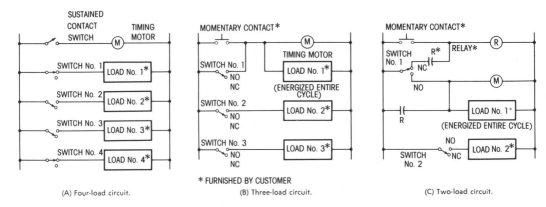

(A) Four-load circuit.   (B) Three-load circuit.   (C) Two-load circuit.

* FURNISHED BY CUSTOMER

FIGURE 7–15
Typical circuit applications of motor-driven
on–off cycle timers. (Courtesy of Haydon
Switch & Instrument, Inc.)

turned on, the timing motor is energized. The motor shaft, in turn, drives cams 1 and 2. The position of the cams of this motor can be altered to fit the needs of a specific application. With respect to time, the cams trip snap-action timing switches in accordance with the operating sequence set into each cam position. The

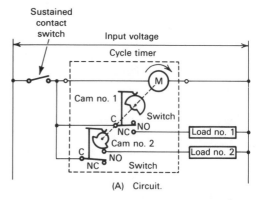

(A)   Circuit.

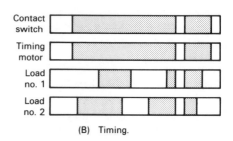

(B)   Timing.

FIGURE 7–16
Cam-switch arm of a motor-driven timer.
(Courtesy of Automatic Timing & Controls
Co.)

FIGURE 7–17
Continuous on–off repeat-cycle timer.
(Courtesy of Haydon Switch & Instrument,
Inc.)

complete operational time of the cycle is determined by the speed of the motor.

For loads that are to be energized more than 47% of the duty cycle, cam 1 should be used. For those to be energized less than 47% of the duty cycle, cam 2 should be used. The entire unit may also be wired so that the loads cannot be actuated unless the contact switch is in the on position.

Single-revolution Cycle Timers

The single-revolution cycle timer of Figure 7–18 completes one operating cycle and then

turns off automatically. Operation is achieved by switch contacts that are actuated by a rotating cam. The cam is driven by a timing motor. The entire unit is housed in a dust-free container. External terminals are provided for the ac line and load switching.

To start the operation, the momentary contact switch must be depressed. This action energizes the timing motor. The motor must rotate the cam until the contact lifts out of the notch. The cam must be set for the smallest notch possible. Typically, 2% to 3% of the total cycle time is involved in this state. Notch lift-out latches the motor on and energizes the load device. At this time, the momentary contact switch can be released. The motor remains on and the load is energized as long as the contact mechanism is out of the notch. The cycle continues until the notch in the cam is again reached at the end of one revolution. At this time, the relay and load are both turned off. The cycle can again be initiated by manually depressing the momentary contact button.

Motor-driven Reset Cycle Timers

Reset cycle timers are motor-driven devices equipped with a mechanism that causes the timer to return to its original starting position automatically after the time interval setting has been reached. Devices of this type are by far the most versatile of all motor-driven timers. They are very reliable, have a long life expectancy, and can repeat operations with exceptional accuracy.

The clutch of a reset timer is primarily responsible for permitting the reset action of this device. Internal clutches are primarily used on short-operation timers, whereas external clutches are used for long-duration reset operations.

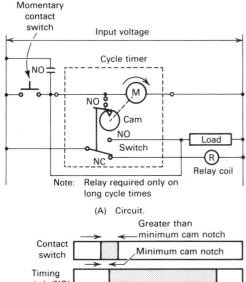

FIGURE 7–18
Single-revolution cycle timer. (Courtesy of Haydon Switch & Instrument, Inc.)

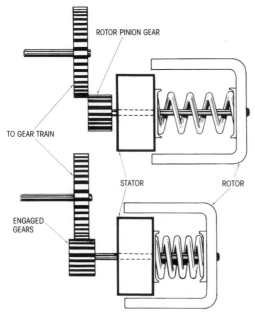

FIGURE 7–19
Interval clutch of a reset timer.

Reset Timer Clutch Mechanisms

A unique feature of the reset type of timer is its internal or built-in clutch mechanism. When a synchronous drive motor is energized, it is designed to pull the rotor into its stator poles (Figure 7–19). As a result of this action, the timer gear train is engaged with the motor drive gear. Electromechanical energy from the drive motor is then transferred to the gear train. Through this action, the entire gear train assembly is driven by the motor.

When a set time period has elapsed in the operation of a reset timer, the stator winding is de-energized by a switch-tripping mechanism attached to the gear train assembly. This in turn causes the stator field to lose its hold on the rotor, which ultimately causes it to pull away from the gear train. As a result of this

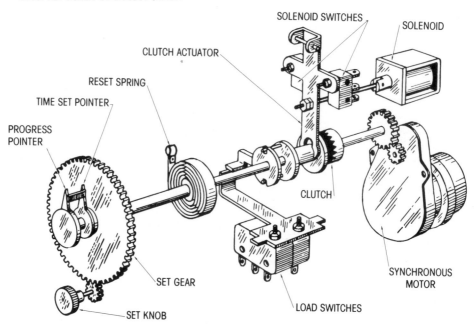

FIGURE 7–20
External clutch assembly for a reset timer.

action, the gear train loses its driving power. A spiral spring attached to the gear train shaft then causes it to reset or return to its original starting position.

When rather long operational times are required of reset timers, an external clutch mechanism similar to the one shown in Figure 7–20 is used. In this case, the clutch is engaged by an independent solenoid. When actuated, the solenoid pulls the clutch jaws together. Rotary motion from the motor is then applied to the entire drive assembly. This action ultimately causes the reset spring coil to wind into a taut condition.

When the solenoid of Figure 7–20 is de-energized, it opens the clutch jaws. This action immediately disengages the motor from the gear train assembly. The reset spring then releases its potential energy, which causes the gear train assembly to return to its original position automatically.

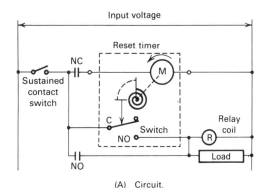

(A)   Circuit.

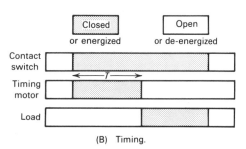

(B)   Timing.

Reset Timer Applications

Reset timers have a number of specific applications in industry today. Most of these applications are a direct result of the timer's versatility. Five rather significant applications include delay on energization, interval on momentary make, interval on energization, delay on break, and cycle on energization. Figures 7–21 through 7–25 show representative schematic diagrams of these applications.

Delay on Energization.   Figure 7–21(A) shows a schematic diagram of a reset timer used to delay the energization of a load device. When the contact switch is turned on, it energizes the timing motor through the NC contacts of the relay. The load device is not energized at this time. After the time interval period set in the timer has elapsed, the switch arm changes the switch to the NO position.

(C) Reset timer with external holding relay.

FIGURE 7–21
Delay-on energization reset timer: (A) circuit; (B) timing; (C) reset timer with external holding relay. (Courtesy of Haydon Switch & Instrument, Inc.)

This completes the energy path from the source to the relay and the load. The relay and load are both actuated.

Through relay actuation, the NC contacts open and the NO contacts close. The timer motor then becomes de-energized and stops rotating. The clutch is released and the timer resets itself to the starting position. The closed NO contacts latch the relay and load device into an operational state.

Opening the contact switch causes the relay and load device to be de-energized. The operational cycle can then be repeated again by simply closing the contact switch. Figure 7–21(C) shows a reset timer with an external holding relay.

Interval on Momentary Make. In this application of the reset timer, the load and the relay are all energized immediately when the momentary contact switch is pressed (Figure 7–22). Actuation of the relay causes the NO

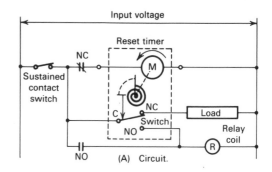

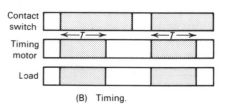

(A) Circuit.

Contact switch
Timing motor
Load

(B) Timing.

FIGURE 7–23
Reset timer with an interval-on organization. (Courtesy of Haydon Switch & Instrument, Inc.)

contacts to close and latch the relay, motor, and load into an operational state.

After an interval of operation, the motor mechanism trips the SPDT switch. This action in turn opens the NC switch contacts and de-energizes the relay coil. The closed NO contacts of the relay are likewise opened by this same action. As a result of this, the relay, load, and motor are all turned off. The motor immediately resets itself to the original interval starting point. The entire unit is again ready for the sequence to be repeated on momentary closure of the contact switch.

Interval on Energization. The interval on energization application of a reset timer is shown in Figure 7–23. This application is very similar to the interval on momentary make application just discussed. The entire operation of this timer is, however, based on the condition of the sustained contact switch. When it is

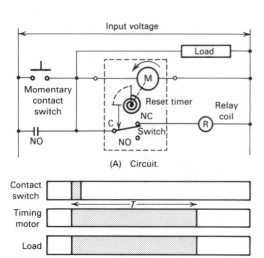

(A) Circuit.

Contact switch
Timing motor
Load

(B) Timing.

FIGURE 7–22
Reset timer with an interval-on momentary make. (Courtesy of Haydon Switch & Instrument, Inc.)

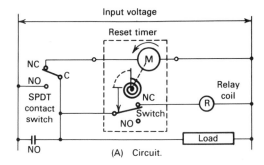

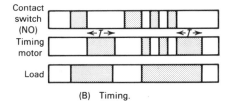

FIGURE 7–24
**Delay-on break reset timer. (Courtesy of
Haydon Switch & Instrument, Inc.)**

turned on initially, the load and timing motor
are both energized through the NC relay contacts and the timing switch. After an interval
of operation, the timer motor trips the SPDT
switch. This immediately energizes the relay,
which is then latched by the now closed NO
contacts. This same action also shuts off the
load and timing motor because of the opened
NC contacts. The motor quickly resets itself to
the operational starting point. The relay then
switches off and the timer is ready to repeat
the next operational sequence.

When the sustained contact switch is
opened, it de-energizes the entire timer assembly and load. If the timer has been in operation
for a partial interval, it can be reset to the starting position. The sustained contact switch
must be rated to handle the combined load and
timer assembly.

Delay on Break. Figure 7–24 shows the
circuit diagram of a delay on break application

of the reset timer. In this application the load
and relay are energized immediately when the
SPDT contact switch is placed in the NO position. At this time, the NO relay contacts are
also closed, which latches the relay and load
both into an operating condition.

Breaking the SPDT contact switch by
switching it to the NC position does not alter
the operating condition of the timer. In this
switch position the timer motor is now energized along with the load and relay coil.

After the motor has been in operation for a
certain interval, it trips the timer switch. This
action opens the relay coil, which in turn
causes the closed NO contacts to return to the
NO condition. This same action turns off the
load and timer motor. The timer immediately
resets itself to the original time set position,
which prepares it for the next sequence.

Assume now that the cycle just described is
to be repeated again with a slight modification.
In this case the contact switch is placed in the
NO position as described. It is then switched
to the NC position, which actuates the motor.
If by chance the SPDT contact switch is re-
closed to the NO position, the motor will stop
without completing its delay interval. It will,
as before, reset itself to the original starting
point and prepare for the next break sequence.

Cycle on Energization. The cycle on
energization application of a reset timer is
shown in Figure 7–25. In this diagram, note
that two timers and two loads are controlled by
one relay with two sets of contacts. Initially,
load 1 is on and load 2 is off. The loads
change states for a period and then return to
the original state. This operational cycle permits repeated load switching after a timed delay period.

To start the operational cycle, the sustained
contact switch is placed in the on position.
This immediately energizes load 1 and the motor of reset timer 1. After operating through

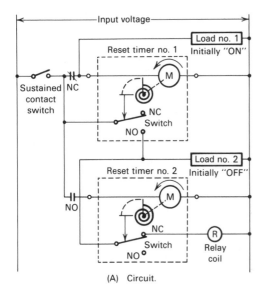

(A)   Circuit.

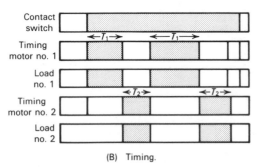

(B)   Timing.

FIGURE 7–25
**Cycle on energization reset timer. (Courtesy
of Haydon Switch & Instrument, Inc.)**

the delay interval set into it, timer motor 1 trips its switch. This action turns on load 2, the relay, and the motor of reset timer 2. Actuation of the relay also causes the NC contacts to break and the NO points to make. With open NC contacts, load 1 and motor 1 are both turned off. Motor 1 resets immediately, which prepares it for the next sequence.

With relay actuated, the NO contacts complete the energy path to the motor of reset timer 2. This latches timer motor 2, load 2, and the relay all in the on state. After operating through the delay time set into it, timer motor 2 trips its switch to the NO position. This action then opens the relay latch, which turns off load 2, motor 2, and the relay coil. Motor 2 immediately resets itself for the next operational sequence.

With the NC relay contacts closed and the NO contacts open, the cycle is back to its original condition of operation. The cycle repeats itself as long as the sustained contact switch is closed.

ELECTRONIC TIMERS

A wide range of electronic devices has been used through the years as industrial timing devices. Initially, vacuum tubes served as trigger devices for relays. In some low-current load control applications, direct control was achieved by the device without a relay. High-current load applications often included vacuum-tube triggering of gaseous-tube thyratrons. Many of these timers are still being used in industrial applications today.

Solid-state devices were then added to the list of electronic timers. In the past few years, many different timing applications have been achieved by these devices. Bipolar transistors, FETs, and UJTs are a part of this classification. These devices may be used to drive a relay or, by triggering an SCR or a triac, they can achieve direct control of the load device.

Solid-state timing offers a number of unique advantages over the earlier vacuum- and gaseous-tube units. A solid-state timer, for example, consumes very little energy in the operation of its devices. Vacuum tubes and gaseous devices, in contrast, usually require heater voltage to be made operational. Solid-state timing can be achieved without moving parts. This improves device reliability and op-

erational life expectancy. Solid-state timing may have electrical isolation between the input and output. This reduces safety hazards and removes any potential breakdown problems. In general, solid-state timing is physically smaller, less fragile, and has a substantially longer operational life span.

The most recent trend in electronic timer design is to include integrated circuits in the construction of timers. Both linear amplifiers and digital counting timers are included in this category. A number of advantages, such as long time delay and accuracy, are the result of the addition of ICs to the timer family.

Our discussion of electronic timers will primarily center around solid-state circuits and IC applications. Vacuum- and gaseous-tube time control principles, in general, can be applied equally as well to the same circuits. At the present time, solid-state timers play a much larger role in industrial control applications than their vacuum- or gaseous-tube counterparts.

ELECTRONIC TIMER CLASSIFICATIONS

The term *electronic timer* is a rather broad classification used today to describe a number of devices employing electronic components. To make this classification a little more workable, we have divided these timers into two major groups according to the type of timing element employed. These are resistor–capacitor or *RC* elements and digital timers. The *RC* element produces time delay by the charge or discharge action of a capacitor through a resistor. Digital timers, by comparison, employ oscillators or pulse generators that switch on and off at a precise *RC* rate. These pulses are ultimately counted and used to trigger the load device into operation. The end result is basically

the same for both units. Timing accuracy, repeat accuracy, and setability are the major differences between these two major groups.

Further classification of the electronic timer is directed toward the triggering element. This component detects changes produced by the timing element and processes them for application to the load control element. The triggering element can be a bipolar transistor, FET, UJT, or operational amplifier. In general, this component amplifies or changes the signal from the timer element in such a way that the load control element can be actuated by it.

Final division of our electronic timer classification refers to the load control switching element. In this regard, timers achieve either direct switching control of the load device or actuate it by relay action. In both cases the end result is the same. There are, however, some specific differences in the two methods of control. This includes such things as repeatability time, actuating speed, isolation between input and load, and operational life expectancy.

Repeatability refers to the rate or number of times that the load can be switched on and off in a given period. Direct device switching has an excellent repeatability factor while relay switching is inherently very slow. *Actuating speed* refers to the time it takes for the load to be energized after the control signal has been applied. Repeatability and actuating speed are primarily influenced by the same factors.

Isolation is an expression of the breakdown voltage that separates the input and load. Relay isolation can be very high because of the physical distance separating the actuating coil and the load. Direct switching often has a lower isolation breakdown factor. This has been improved rather significantly, however, with the inclusion of optoelectronic isolation devices.

The *operational life expectancy* of the switching element is certainly a distinguishing characteristic. Relay switching is generally limited by moving contacts, pivot points, and

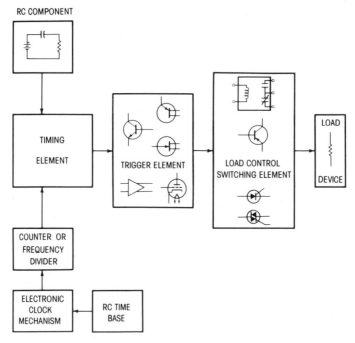

FIGURE 7–26
Block diagram of the basic elements of an electronic timer.

spring tension. Direct actuation does not involve any moving parts. This is obviously more desirable than the moving parts of a relay. The functional application of the timer usually dictates these features when it is selected to do a specific job.

Figure 7–26 shows a block diagram of the three basic elements of an electronic timer. Some of the possible components used by each element are represented by schematic symbols.

RC Timing Elements _____

For a number of years the timing elements of industrial timers have been of the resistor–capacitor or *RC* type. In this component network, when dc voltage is applied, the capaci-

tor gradually builds up a charge potential or voltage. In general, this is described as the *RC time constant*. The formula $T = R \times C$ refers to the time in seconds that it takes a capacitor to build up to 63% of the full charge potential of the applied source.

In electronic *RC* timing elements, the voltage buildup of a capacitor is used to trigger an active device into conduction. Transistors, UJTs, and ICs are commonly used to sense this voltage level change. Ultimately, the sensing device triggers the control element, which actuates the load device.

An *RC* timing element has two major factors that can be used in timing applications. These factors are the charge and discharge of the capacitor voltage. If the charging condition is used as the timing factor, it is usually lim-

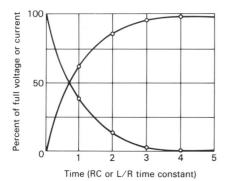

FIGURE 7–27
Universal *RC* time constant curve.

ited to one time constant. The universal *RC* time curve is fairly linear during this charging time. Figure 7–27 shows a universal *RC* time constant curve. Notice the nearly linear characteristic of T_1. From this point on, the curve is nonlinear due to its exponential characteristic. *RC* timing applications are generally restricted to the first time constant because the values can be accurately predicted.

The discharge action of the *RC* network must also be taken into account in a timer element. In one *RC* time constant, the capacitor discharges 63% of its full charge potential. This means that the charge voltage drops down to 37% of its charge in one time constant. This part of a universal *RC* time curve is also linear. Time element accuracy is primarily based on operation on the linear part of the *RC* curve.

A large number of electronic timers are designed to respond to the discharge condition of an *RC* network. The capacitor must therefore charge very quickly and discharge gradually. Large fixed capacitors and variable resistors are typically employed to make timing elements adjustable. Ranges from a few milliseconds to approximately two hours are possible today. A large number of all industrial timer applications seem to operate in a range of approximately 10 min or less.

If the discharge action of a capacitor is used to determine timing action, then the charging cycle is also very important. In this case, the charging action determines the reset interval. This is the smallest time interval that is needed to repeat a cycle after its completion. Ranges from 1 to 30 ms are typical in industrial tim-

FIGURE 7–28
Adjustable solid-state timer. (Courtesy of Industrial Solid State Controls)

ers. As a rule, long delay times tend to lengthen the reset time period.

The solid-state timer of Figure 7–28 uses capacitor discharge time to achieve delay of energization at the start of its cycle. The adjustable time delay control alters the value of a resistor in the *RC* network. The accuracy of this timer is restricted to operation on the linear part of the universal *RC* time curve. Beyond this point, nonlinearity occurs very quickly and the timing action loses its accuracy.

A rather recent trend in solid-state timing is to extend the linear portion of the *RC* time constant well into the normal nonlinear area. This is achieved in a number of ways. Switching devices can be used to turn the source voltage on and off for short periods. As a result, the charge or discharge action is delayed beyond its normal time period. In addition, it can be extended by distorting in a direction that offsets the normal distortion. Through these methods and others, it is possible to extend the *RC* curve to achieve 30 min or more of delay very accurately. Standard component values can be readily employed to achieve this circuitry. This obviously reduces production cost for longer-time-delay units. Figure 7–29 shows an extended *RC* curve used in some solid-state timers today.

Digital Timing Elements

A rather large number of digital timers of the solid-state type are finding their way into industrial applications today. These devices may employ *RC* circuits, but the resulting timing action achieved is quite different. Digital timing elements, for example, employ a time-base generator and a counting circuit for frequency division. The output of this element is then applied to the trigger device, which is then used to control the switching device and ultimately actuate the load.

Time-base Generators

The time-base generator of a timing element in a strict sense is a source of electrical energy. This source produces an output signal that is counted for interval timing or divided electronically for delay applications.

The time-base generator of a digital timer is the heart of the timing element. Its accuracy and stability are extremely important. High-frequency signals tend to produce a short time base, which helps to develop precise and accurate timing conditions. Generators that de-

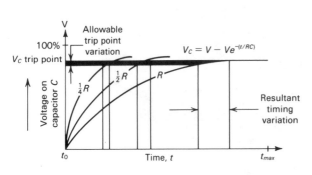
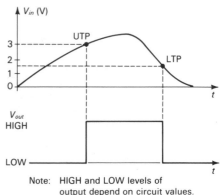

FIGURE 7–29
Extended *RC* curve using solid-state timers.

velop time increments of 1 ms are very common in industrial digital timers. The reset time for this type of unit is often less than 20 ms.

Power-line frequencies of 60 Hz can also be used as a source for the time-base generator. Time measurements down to 10 ms can be achieved with this type of signal. Timing accuracy can be held to within 0.005% of the real operating time through this type of source.

Schmitt Trigger

When power-line frequencies are used as a source for a time-base generator, they must first be applied to a shaping circuit. A Schmitt trigger is primarily used to achieve this function. Essentially, a sine wave of 60 Hz is applied to the circuit and a 60-Hz square wave appears in the output.

Figure 7–30 shows a schematic diagram of a bipolar transistor Schmitt trigger circuit. When the applied ac sine-wave signal exceeds a certain input value level, it causes transistor Q_1 to be conductive. The V_{CE} voltage across Q_1 drops quickly in value because of the increased current. This in turn lowers the bias voltage to Q_2, which causes it to be nonconductive. As a result, the collector current through R_3 stops and the output voltage rises to the value of V_{CC}.

Signal values less than those that exceed the input conduction level cause Q_1 to be nonconductive. As a result, the internal resistance of Q_1 approaches infinity. The V_{CE} of Q_1 therefore rises in value. It usually approximates the value of $+V_{CC}$. This immediately forward biases Q_2 into full conduction. The collector current Q_2 then rises very quickly. The V_{CE} of Q_2 immediately drops to a value very near zero. The output is essentially zero when the input signal is less than the input conduction level.

A Schmitt trigger is often called a *squaring*

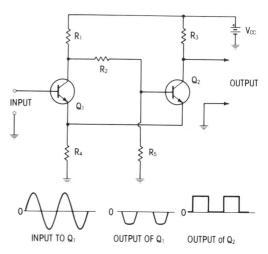

FIGURE 7–30
Basic Schmitt trigger.

circuit. Its output, as in this case, has a square or rectangular shape. The output pulse repetition rate (or PRR) of a Schmitt trigger corresponds directly to the frequency of the input signal. The accuracy of the output is based entirely on the input frequency. Digital timers that use Schmitt trigger circuits typically have a repeat accuracy of ±0.5% for 60-Hz, power-line frequency.

Today, Schmitt triggers are available on a single IC chip. This type of device has two threshold points or trigger values. When the input signal exceeds the upper threshold point (UTP), the circuit goes to its high-level output value. When the input signal falls to the lower threshold point (LTP), the output switches back to its low-level value. The *threshold point* corresponds to the voltage value that causes conduction or nonconduction of the bi-

FIGURE 7–31
Schmitt trigger symbols and trigger levels.

polar transistor circuit. Figure 7–31 shows the symbol of a Schmitt trigger IC and its UTP and LTP. Note that UTP and LTP occur at different value levels.

Astable Multivibrator Generators

Astable multivibrators are commonly used as time-base generators for timing frequencies other than 60 Hz. An astable multivibrator is basically a wave-form generator that is self-starting and operates continuously for long periods of time. The shape of the wave form and its frequency are primarily determined by an *RC* network applied to each transistor. A basic two-transistor astable multivibrator is shown in Figure 7–32.

Generation of a square or rectangular wave is achieved by connecting two amplifying devices so that the output of each device is connected to the input of the other. The pulse repetition rate (PRR) of this circuit is dependent on the different *R* and *C* values connected to each amplifier. When the component values of each amplifier are the same, the on and off pulse widths are equal. When corresponding sizes differ in value, the pulse width of the output wave has a rectangular shape. Generators of this type are often called *multivibrators*. Some multivibrators produce a consistent output wave form that is not controlled or trig-

gered into operation by an outside source. The terms *astable* and *free-running* are both used to describe this type of multivibrator.

The operation of an astable multivibrator depends on the saturation and cutoff conditions of a transistor. When V_{CC} of Figure 7–32 is first applied to the circuit, one transistor starts to conduct before the other. An extremely minute difference in component values causes this to occur. In this circuit, assume that Q_1 goes into conduction first. When this occurs, the I_c of Q_1 rises quickly and the voltage across R_{L1} increases in value. Transistor Q_1 then becomes extremely low resistant, which provides an easy charge path for C_1 through R_{B2}. The charging current of C_1 passing through R_{B2} causes the base of Q_2 to swing negative. As a result, Q_2 is driven into cutoff immediately. At this same time, C_2 begins charging through the emitter–base (E–B) junction of Q_1 and R_{L2}. As a result of this charging action, the base current of Q_1 is increased, causing it to go into saturation. The process continues according to the time constant of R_{B2} and C_1. When this charging current drops off, the base of Q_2 comes out of reverse biasing and Q_2 goes into conduction. This in turn causes Q_2 to become low resistant, which completes a charge path for C_2 through R_{B1} and Q_2. Charge current through R_{B1} causes it to immediately drive Q_1 to cut off. Capacitor C_1 now begins to charge through the E–B junction of Q_2 and R_{L1}. This adds to the base current of Q_2, which drives it into saturation. From this point on, the operation cycle is repeated, with Q_1 and Q_2 alternately changing conduction states.

The output of a multivibrator can be taken across either one of the two transistors. The shape of the wave form is primarily based on the time constant of $R_{B2}C_1$ and $R_{B1}C_2$. A symmetrical square-wave output occurs when these values are equal, and a rectangular output results when they are unequal. Free-running

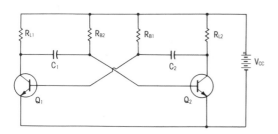

FIGURE 7–32
Two-transistor astable multivibrator.

multivibrators are self-starting and can be designed to produce a rather high level of accuracy.

Digital Counters

Counters are a very important part of the digital timing element. After pulses have been generated by an astable multivibrator or shaped by a Schmitt trigger, they must be counted in order to achieve time delay. A counter, essentially, is an electronic circuit that achieves frequency division in various steps.

Figure 7–33 shows a block diagram of a digital timer counting unit. The input for this counter is a time-base generator. Note that the frequency of the generator is 1000 Hz. Each pulse takes $1/1000$ s to achieve its period of operation. After the first division process, the frequency is 10 Hz. The second division process changes the frequency to 0.1 Hz. The third division step changes the frequency to 0.001 Hz. Since frequency equals the reciprocal of time, or $f = 1/T$, we can transpose this formula into the time formula $T = 1/f$.

The output of the frequency-divider circuit of Figure 7–32 is 0.001 Hz. By changing this frequency into a period of time, we can simply say that time equals 1/0.001 or 1000 s. Essentially, this means that an output pulse from the

divider circuit occurs every 1000 s when a signal with a 1000-Hz time base is applied. Through repeated steps of frequency division, it is possible to achieve extremely long time delay capabilities very accurately.

Bistable Multivibrator

One of the most common circuits used to achieve frequency division in digital timers is the bistable multivibrator, or flip-flop. Compared with the astable multivibrator, which constantly changes states, the flip-flop has two stable states. It turns on and remains in one state. When an appropriate triggering pulse is applied, it then changes to the alternate state. A bistable multivibrator is therefore designed to have two stable states and must be triggered to change states.

Figure 7–34 shows a typical two-transistor bistable flip-flop. The two transistors of this circuit are directly connected by resistors R_{B2} and R_{B1}. Any state change in the conduction of Q_1 or Q_2 takes place instantly. Note also that the dc source forward biases the E–B junctions through R_{L1}–R_{B2} and R_{L2}–R_{B1}. Each collector is also reverse biased by its respective R_L resistor. As a general rule, corresponding resistors and transistors are of a similar value in all respects.

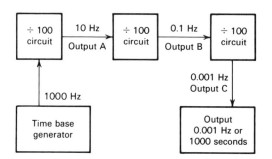

FIGURE 7–33
Frequency-division time delay.

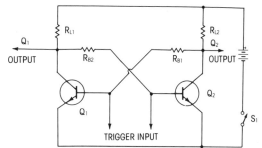

FIGURE 7–34
Bistable multivibrator circuit.

When the operational switch, S_1, is turned on, it supplies dc energy to the entire circuit. Due to the similarity of corresponding component values, conduction occurs randomly. In this case, assume that conduction of Q_2 occurs first. When this takes place, the collector current passing through R_{L2} rises very quickly. The voltage drop across this resistor causes the collector of Q_2 to immediately become less positive than V_{CC}. This less positive or essentially negative-going voltage is then applied to the base of Q_1 by resistor R_{B1}. As a result, this voltage drives Q_1 into its nonconducting state. The process continues until Q_2 is fully conductive or saturated and Q_1 is cut off. This represents the first stable state of operation. The collector voltage of Q_2, which is used as its output, ultimately drops to approximately 0.2 V. Voltages of this value are considered to be at the low or zero output level. The collector of Q_1 by comparison rises to the full value of V_{CC}. This voltage level represents the high or 1 output level of the flip-flop.

As long as V_{CC} energy is applied to the multivibrator just described, it remains in its stable state. To initiate a change in state, a trigger pulse or voltage level change must be applied to the base of either Q_1 or Q_2. A momentary positive pulse to the base of Q_1 or a negative pulse to the base of Q_2 causes a state change. A reverse of this polarity does not cause triggering of the flip-flop.

Assume now that the flip-flop of Figure 7–34 is in the set or stable condition just described. This means that Q_2 is conducting and Q_1 is off. If a momentary positive pulse is applied to the base of Q_1, it is triggered into conduction immediately. As a result, collector current through R_{L1} produces a voltage drop, which in turn causes the collector to become less positive, or negative going. This voltage is then transferred to the base of Q_2 by resistor R_{B2}, which immediately drives Q_2 into cutoff. The collector voltage of Q_2 rises immediately

to $+V_{CC}$, which is then returned to the base of Q_1 through resistor R_{B1}. This in turn adds to the conduction of Q_1, which causes it to latch into a stable condition. This condition remains until the next trigger pulse arrives.

T Flip-flops

When a basic bistable flip-flop is equipped with a trigger steering circuit, it is called a *T flip-flop*. This type of circuit has the capability of changing states automatically when each trigger pulse is applied. If the output of this circuit is removed from a single transistor, it has the capability of dividing by 2. Figure 7–35 shows a diagram of the divide-by-2 function of a negative triggering flip-flop. The negative trigger pulse is steered or directed to the base of the conducting transistor each time a state change is initiated.

Figure 7–35(B) shows a schematic diagram of a T flip-flop. When switch S_1 is turned on, it energizes the entire circuit. Assume that Q_1 is on or conducting and Q_2 is off initially. The diodes X_1 and X_2 are used to steer the trigger pulse to the *on* transistor. With Q_1 on, its collector voltage is at 0.6 V or the low level. Transistor Q_2, by comparison, is off and its collector voltage is at $+V_{CC}$ or at the high level. The anode of diode X_2 is positive and the anode of X_1 is negative because of their connection to the respective transistors. A small positive voltage from V_{CC} is also applied to the cathodes of X_1 and X_2 by resistor R_1. As a result of this condition, both diodes are reverse biased. The flip-flop is now in a stable state.

When a short-duration negative-going trigger pulse arrives at the input, it passes through C. If the voltage level of the pulse is of sufficient magnitude to overcome the positive voltage across R_1, it causes X_2 to be forward biased. Diode X_1 continues to be reverse

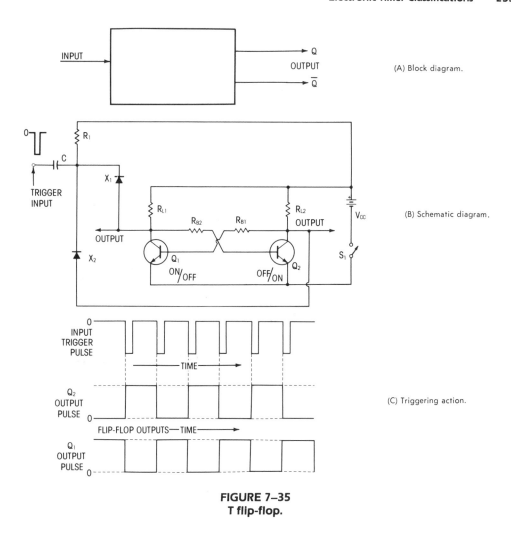

(A) Block diagram.

(B) Schematic diagram.

(C) Triggering action.

FIGURE 7–35
T flip-flop.

biased because of its anode voltage. As a result, the pulse is steered through X_2, to the collector of Q_2, and through R_{B1} to the base of Q_1. A negative-going pulse of this magnitude immediately drives the base of Q_1 into a reverse-biased state. This causes nonconduction of Q_1, which in turn drives Q_2 into the on state. One trigger pulse therefore initiates the first state change of the flip-flop.

The alternate state of Q_1 off and Q_2 on is now in effect. In this condition of operation, the anode of X_2 is now negative and X_1 is pos-

itive. Nothing occurs at this time because both diodes remain nonconducting due to the positive voltage across R_1. When the next trigger pulse arrives, however, it causes X_1 to conduct because of the polarity of its anode. Diode X_2 in this state is reverse biased and nonconductive. The trigger pulse is now steered through X_1, to the collector of Q_1, through R_{B2}, and to the base of Q_2. This negative-going pulse immediately causes Q_2 to change its state, which in turn causes Q_1 to turn on again. The two transistors are now back in the same state be-

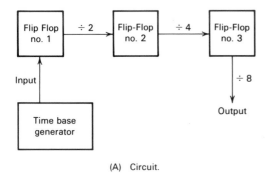

(A) Circuit.

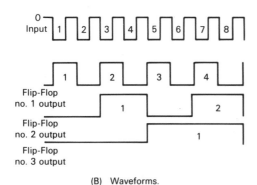

(B) Waveforms.

FIGURE 7–36
Flip-flop frequency divider.

Trigger Element

The trigger element of an electronic timer is simply an active device that responds to the output of the timing element. Solid-state devices such as bipolar transistors, FETs, and UJTs are commonly used to achieve this operation. In addition, a number of operational amplifiers, or op-amps, are also being used to achieve this function in solid-state timers.

Essentially, the trigger element of an electronic timer is responsible for amplifying the timing element signal. In many cases, this signal may be quite small and not capable of driving the load control switching element into conduction directly. The trigger element is therefore considered as a basic signal amplifier. The role of this amplifier is simply that of increasing the amplitude of a small signal applied to its input. The signal sensitivity of the load control switching element usually determines the level of amplification to be performed by the trigger element.

Load Control Element

The load control element of an electronic timer ranges from a simple electromechanical relay operated system to a direct load energizing solid-state device. Relays, as a general rule, are used to control heavy current load devices. This type of control element necessitates a certain amount of pull-in time to actuate the relay armature after coil voltage has been applied. A certain amount of drop-out time is also required for the relay contacts to return to their normal position when the coil voltage is removed.

Solid-state load switching elements, by comparison, are used to turn on or off the load device without moving parts. Transistors, triacs, and SCRs are components commonly used to achieve this function. Basically, when

fore the first pulse was applied. The process is therefore ready to be repeated with each succeeding trigger pulse. Since two trigger pulses are needed to produce one complete pulse or state change from a transistor [see Figure 7–35(C)], the divide-by-2 function can be readily achieved by the T flip-flop.

To achieve division by greater than 2, several T flip-flops are simply cascaded together. Since each flip-flop has a divide-by-2 factor, the total output of this circuit is considered as a power of 2. Figure 7–36 shows a block diagram of cascaded T flip-flops that achieve division by a factor of 8. This process could be continued to achieve larger division factors by simply adding more flip-flops in cascade.

the trigger signal is applied to the load control device, it energizes the load. When the trigger signal is not present, the load device is not energized.

Transistor-relay Load Control

The transistor-relay load control circuit of Figure 7–37 is an interval timer of the momentary-on type. The timing element of this circuit includes C, R_1, R_2, and the emitter–base resistance of the transistor. The transistor is considered as the trigger element of this timer. The load device, which is an incandescent lamp, is controlled electromagnetically by the relay load switching element.

When switch S_1 is turned on to start the interval, it energizes the transistor, the relay coil, and the RC components of the circuit. The lamp is therefore energized through the NO contacts when the relay is actuated. This particular timer responds to the charging action of the capacitor.

When the V_{CC} source is turned on initially, it causes C to charge through R_1 and R_2 and the transistor E–B junction. These component values are selected so that the initial charging

current is great enough to trigger the transistor into conduction. After a certain interval of time, the charging current of C decays in value. This causes a corresponding reduction in transistor base current. Ultimately, the base current drops in value until the transistor becomes nonconductive. As a result of this action, the transistor collector current drops below the relay armature holding current level. This in turn causes relay to drop out and turn off the lamp.

When the reset push button is closed momentarily, it provides a discharge path for the charged capacitor. Releasing the button causes the capacitor to charge again, thus repeating the interval. Adjustment of the timing interval is achieved by altering the value of resistor R_2. The on time of the circuit is usually limited to only a few seconds action.

SCR Load Control Switching

Figure 7–38 shows an extremely simple yet very accurate solid-state delay timer circuit. The switching element of this circuit is the

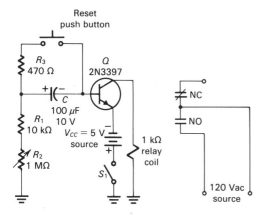

FIGURE 7–37
Transistor timer (momentary-on type).

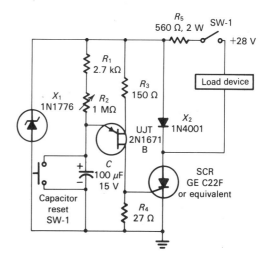

FIGURE 7–38
Solid-state delay timer.

SCR. The UJT is used as a trigger element that develops its signal from the $(R_1 + R_2)C$ timing element. The entire circuit is designed to energize the load device without the use of moving parts.

Resistor R_5 and the zener diode are used in this circuit to develop a stable dc source for operation of the UJT. When operational switch S_1 is turned on initially, the SCR is in its off state. The load is also de-energized at this time. Capacitor C, however, begins to develop a charge voltage through R_1 and R_2. When the charge voltage of C ultimately reaches the peak-point trigger voltage of the UJT, it goes into conduction. This action causes a current through R_4, which triggers the SCR into conduction. If a sufficient amount of holding current passes through the SCR when it energizes the load device, it remains latched in the on state. The amount of delay time developed by this circuit is altered by the setting of R_2. After the load has been energized, it remains in this state as long as electrical energy is supplied by the source.

To reset the delay time of this circuit, the operational switch must be momentarily turned off. This action switches the SCR into its off state, which in turn de-energizes the load device. To be assured of the proper delay time setting of R_2, the capacitor reset button should also be pressed momentarily to discharge C. When the circuit is turned on by S_1, the delay sequence is repeated by the RC network, trigger device, and the SCR switching element. The operating current and voltage of this circuit are primarily determined by the selection of the SCR.

IC Electronic Timing Systems ———

Special integrated-circuit chips are now available that have the capability of producing a variety of timing functions. This development

has opened the way for a number of new and unusual approaches to electronic timing. Through this device, timing operations can now be achieved with a minimum of components. The 555 IC series was one of the first developments in this area. It was first introduced by Signetics Corporation. Several variations of the basic timer are now available through other manufacturers. Figure 7–39 shows a functional block diagram of the timer chip.

The operation of a SE/NE 555 timer is directly dependent on its internal functions. The three resistors, for example, serve as an internal voltage divider for the source voltage. One-third of the source appears across each resistor. Connections made at the $\frac{1}{3}$ and $\frac{2}{3}V_{CC}$ points serve as reference voltages for the two comparators. A comparator is an op-amp that changes states when one of its inputs exceeds the reference voltage. Comparator 2 is referenced at $+\frac{1}{3}V_{CC}$. If a trigger voltage applied to the negative input of this comparator drops below $+\frac{1}{3}V_{CC}$, it causes a state change. Comparator 1 is referenced at $+\frac{2}{3}V_{CC}$. If voltage at the threshold terminal exceeds this reference voltage, the comparator goes through a state change. Note that the output of each comparator is connected to an input of the flip-flop.

The flip-flop of the SE/NE 555 timer is a bistable multivibrator. It changes states according to the voltage value of its input. If the voltage value of the threshold terminal rises in excess of $+\frac{2}{3}V_{CC}$, it causes the flip-flop to change its state. A decrease in trigger voltage below $+\frac{1}{3}V_{CC}$ also causes comparator 2 to change its state. This means that the output of the flip-flop is controlled by the voltage values of the two comparators. A state change occurs when the trigger input drops below $+\frac{1}{3}V_{CC}$ or when the threshold rises above $+\frac{2}{3}V_{CC}$.

Note that the flip-flop output of the SE/NE 555 is used to drive the discharge transistor and the output stage. A high or positive flip-

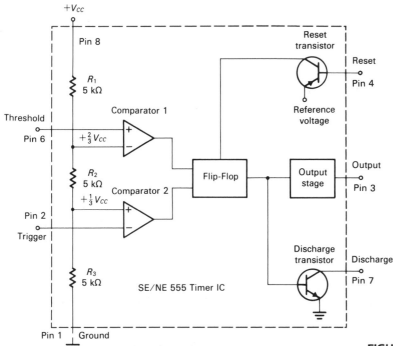

FIGURE 7–39
Functional block diagram of an SE/NE 555 IC.

flop output is used to turn on both the discharge transistor and the output stage. This condition causes the discharge transistor to be conductive and causes it to respond as a low-resistant short to ground. The output stage responds in the same manner. A reversal of this action takes place when the flip-flop output changes to a low or zero state. The discharge transistor then responds as an open circuit or becomes infinite. The output state swings to its high or positive V_{CC} state. In effect, the operational state of the output and discharge transistor is based on voltage applied to the trigger or threshold input terminals.

555 Timer Operation

The 555 timer series has two fundamental modes or methods of operation. Practically all timing applications are in some way a variation of these operational modes. One very important application deals with the generation of digital time-base wave forms. Used in this manner, the 555 responds as an astable multivibrator. Only two resistors and one capacitor are needed to make an astable multivibrator. The other mode of operation is as a monostable multivibrator. In its simplest form, a monostable multivibrator can be made with one resistor and one capacitor. Monostable operation permits the 555 IC to be used in delay and interval applications.

Astable Multivibrator Mode of Operation

Figure 7–40 shows an SE/NE 555 IC timer connected as an astable multivibrator. In this time-base generator, pins 8 and 4 are con-

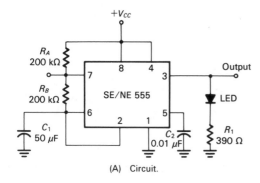

(A) Circuit.

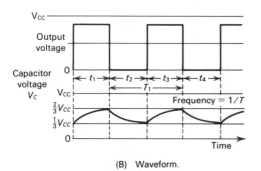

(B) Waveform.

FIGURE 7–40
Astable multivibrator using an SE/NE 555.

When C begins to discharge through R_B, the voltage drops to one-third of the value of V_{CC}. This is represented by the time that the output drops to a low value, or t_2. In seconds, t_2 is $0.693 R_B C$.

The output frequency of an astable multivibrator is represented by the total time required to charge and discharge C. The combined period of $t_1 + t_2$, $t_2 + t_3$, or $t_3 + t_4$ is represented by a capital letter such as T. The frequency of a total operational cycle is therefore a function of time. In practice, the formula $f = 1/T$ shows this relationship. For a multivibrator, the following formula is used:

$$\text{Frequency in hertz} = \frac{1.44}{(R_A + 2R_B)C}$$

The resistance ratio of R_A and R_B of an IC multivibrator is quite critical. If R_B is more than half the value of R_A, the circuit will not operate. Essentially, this would not permit pin 2 to drop in value from $\frac{2}{3}V_{CC}$ to $\frac{1}{3}V_{CC}$. This would not allow the IC to retrigger itself, which prepares it for the next time period. IC manufacturers usually supply design data information of this type that can be used to select proper resistor–capacitor ratios for a desired operating frequency.

Monostable Multivibrator Mode of Operation

Not all timing applications require a continuous repetitive wave such as that developed by the free-running or astable multivibrator. Many timing situations call for operations that last for a specified length of time. The monostable multivibrator permits the 555 timer series to be used for these applications. Figure 7–41(A) shows the 555 IC connected in a monostable circuit configuration. Note that only one resistor (R_A) and one capacitor (C) are needed in a monostable circuit.

nected to the dc energy source of somewhere between 5 to 15 V dc. When pins 2 and 6 are connected, the 555 triggers itself and operates as a free-running multivibrator. The external capacitor (C) charges through both resistors R_A and R_B and discharges through R_B and the internal parts of the IC. The duty cycle, which is total cycle time divided by the on time, is precisely set by the ratio of these two resistors.

In actual circuit operation, the capacitor charges from one-third to two-thirds of the V_{CC} voltage. It then discharges through R_B and the IC to a value $\frac{1}{3}V_{CC}$. As shown by the waveform graph of Figure 7–40(B), as C starts to charge, the output goes to a high value. It remains at this level for the time period t_1. In seconds, this represents 0.693 of $(R_A + R_B)C$.

A monostable multivibrator is primarily designed to generate a single output pulse in response to an input trigger pulse. The duration of the output pulse depends entirely on the time constant of C and R_A. When a negative-going pulse is applied to the trigger input (pin 2), it causes the output (pin 3) to go high or to $+V_{CC}$. The trigger pulse causes comparator 2 to drop below its referenced value of $+\frac{1}{3}V_{CC}$. This action causes the flip-flop to go to its low state. A negative voltage to the discharge transistor causes it to become infinite. This removes the short to ground for capacitor C. The voltage across C begins to rise in value according to the time constant of R_A and C. When the voltage of C exceeds $+\frac{2}{3}V_{CC}$, it causes comparator 1 to change states. This in turn causes the discharge transistor to again become conductive. C then discharges very quickly to ground through pin 7. The output stage follows this action and drops to its low or ground state. In effect, the output stage follows the change in the trigger input level. Figure 7–41(B) compares the trigger input and output wave forms.

The duration of the trigger pulse of a multivibrator can be either longer or shorter than the generated output pulse. The resulting width of the output pulse is based on the values of R_A and C. The time (T) of the output is based on the formula

$$\text{Time (high)} = 1.1 \times R_A \cdot C$$

This means that the time duration of the output can be altered according to the application. A short-duration input pulse can therefore be used to produce a rather long duration output pulse. Because of this, monostable multivibrators of this type are often called *pulse stretchers*. The monostable mode of operation is also used to produce delay and interval timing operations. Note that the starting of a monostable multivibrator is based on the application of a trigger pulse.

ELECTROCHEMICAL TIMERS

An unusual alternative for industrial timing applications is achieved by electrochemical action. This method of timing uses specially designed electrochemical devices called

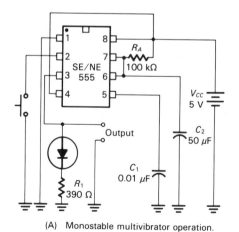

(A) Monostable multivibrator operation.

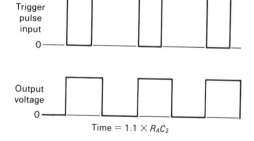

(B) Trigger-output waveforms.

FIGURE 7–41
Monostable multivibrator operational mode.

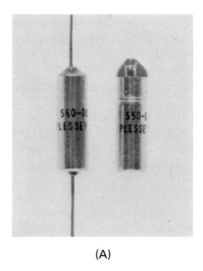

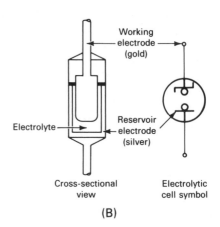

(A)   (B)

FIGURE 7–42
Electrolytic cell for timing units:
(A) electrolytic cell (Courtesy of Plessey
Electro-Products); (B) construction and
symbol.

electrolytic timing cells and mercury coulometers. In these devices, a form of electroplating takes place that is based on the amount of current passing through the cell. During the plating process, ions and electrons serve as the current carriers. The resistance of the cell and the voltage developed across it are quite small during this operational time. As the cell nears completion of the plating process, its internal resistance and voltage rise rather abruptly. This change in voltage can then be applied to a trigger element, and in some cases it may be applied directly to the load switching element.

Figure 7–42 shows an electrolytic timing cell, a cross-section view of its interior, and the electrical symbol. Typically, the working electrode of this cell is made of gold, and the reservoir electrode holding the electrolyte solution is silver. The electrolyte solution transfers current carriers between the two electrodes.

Charging an Electrolytic Cell

For an electrolytic cell to be used as a timer, it must first be charged or set. This operation is achieved by connecting the negative side of a dc energy source to the working electrode and the positive terminal to the reservoir electrode [see Figure 7–43(A)]. The resulting charging current must be carefully measured by a milliampere meter for a desired period. During this charging time, electrons flow from the gold electrode into the electrolyte solution and on to the silver electrode. At the same time, silver ions are pulled away from the silver electrode and forced into the electrolyte. These ions ultimately travel through the electrolyte and are deposited on the gold electrode. Essentially, for each electron leaving the gold electrode, a silver ion is deposited in its place. The supply of ions moving into the electrolyte from

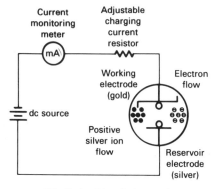

(A) Plating (charging) operation.

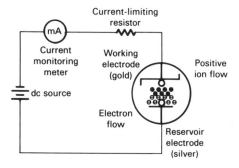

(B) Deplating (clearing) operation.

FIGURE 7–43
Electrolytic cell plating and deplating
operation.

the silver electrode makes it an excellent electrical conductor. The internal resistance of the cell is typically less than 100 Ω during this process.

Deplating an Electrolytic Cell

After an electrolytic timing cell has been charged or plated, it is ready to be cleared or deplated. In this operation the electron and ion flows are simply reversed by switching the polarity of the energy source. The time that it

takes this cell to be deplated is based on the amount of silver deposited on the working electrode and the current carriers flowing through it.

Figure 7–43(B) shows a diagram of the clearing or deplating operation of an electrolytic cell. In this operation, the silver deposited on the gold electrode is removed and returned to the silver electrode. Electrons therefore flow from the reservoir electrode to the working electrode, while silver ions move from the gold electrode back to the silver electrode. The process is continuous until all the silver is stripped from the gold electrode.

When an electrolytic cell is completely deplated, its internal resistance rises very quickly. The electrolyte in this case becomes a rather poor conductor because of the loss of silver ions. Its resistance rises very quickly to something in excess of 1 MΩ. At this same time, the voltage across the cell increases to something in excess of 1 V.

Figure 7–44 shows the plating and deplating

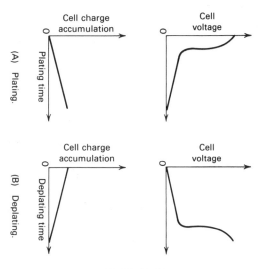

FIGURE 7–44
Plating and deplating graphs of an
electrolytic cell.

action of an electrolytic cell in graph form. Note that the accumulated charge on the cell has an ideal linear rise time and fall time. The voltage developed across the cell is not linear at all, and it is high at the beginning of its charging cycle and low when completed. The deplating action of the cell also causes a complete reversal of this condition. The abrupt rise in voltage at the end of the deplating operation makes it ideal as a triggering signal for an electronic timer.

Electrolytic Cell Timers

Electrolytic cell timers are commonly used in industrial applications today as data accumulation devices, for operational time measurements, in delay and repeat cycle timing circuits, and to monitor changing physical values. In these applications the electrolytic cell is primarily used as either an accumulator or as a timing element. In both applications the principle of operation is basically the same. The cell must first be charged or plated. The process is then reversed and can be used to generate a timing signal or record conduction times for a prolonged period.

Electrolytic Cell Timing Elements

As a timing element, the electrolytic cell must first be charged or plated to be of value. The circuit of Figure 7–45 shows an application of the electrolytic cell as a delay timer. Initially, the SPDT switch is placed in the set or charge position. The charging current indicated by the meter and the charging time must be accurately recorded.

Placing the SPDT switch in the clear position causes the cell to respond as a timing element. After a predictable delay period, the plating action stops. The voltage across the cell rises to $+1$ V. This in turn forward biases Q_1, which causes an emitter current through R_3. Voltage developed across the resistor is then used to trigger the SCR into conduction. The SCR latches into conduction, which causes the load to remain on until the circuit is de-energized. This type of circuit is very accurate and can be used to produce several hours of delay if needed.

An electrolytic cell can be plated or charged at one rate for a certain period and deplated at a slower rate by adjustment of R_1. A number of circuit designs and modifications are possi-

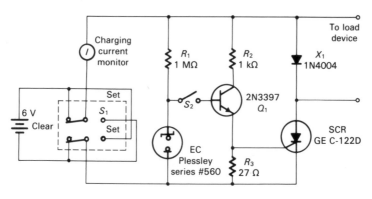

FIGURE 7–45
Electrolytic cell timer for long delay operations.

ble with a basic timer of this type. For low-current loads, the SCR may be omitted with the load substituted as either R_2 or R_3. In addition, separate setting or charging circuits are often used to establish proper plating time values. Charged cells may also be plugged into the timer or connected into it by switching action.

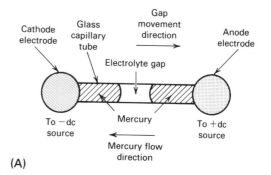

(A)

Electrolytic Cell Accumulators

The accumulator function of an electrolytic cell represents an important industrial application in data collecting. In this situation, the cell is connected in the charging or plating state when a machine or sensing device is placed into operation. The total amount of plating that takes place is the product of time and current. This device is then used to record equipment running time or to tabulate data changes that take place over a long period. Time may be recorded in seconds, minutes, or hours, according to the application.

After the cell has been in operation for a long recording time, it is cleared by attaching it to a dc energy source for deplating. The deplating current–time is then recorded and used to indicate the accumulated operational time of its original source. The usage time of rental equipment, fraud detection equipment, and maintenance record information can be developed by this device.

(B)

FIGURE 7–46
Mercury coulometer: (A) construction;
(B) typical time elapsed indicator (Courtesy of
Curtis Instruments, Inc.).

Elapsed Time Indicators

A very common elapsed time indicator used in industrial equipment today is the mercury coulometer. This device is similar in operation to that of the electrolytic cell. In this case, mercury is transferred from one electrode to the alternate electrode by current carriers passing through an electrolyte solution. The electrolyte

solution is used to separate the two columns of mercury. When the cell is in operation, it causes mercury to be removed from one column and deposited in the second column as a function of current and time. A graduated scale attached to the cell is then used to display elapsed time. Standard scales of 1000, 2000, 5000, and 10,000 hours are very common today.

Figure 7–46(A) is a drawing of a mercury

coulometer. This device is fabricated from a short length of glass capillary tube. Two columns of mercury in the tube are separated by a small amount of electrolyte solution. Electrodes are inserted into mercury at each end of the tube and sealed to the glass.

When dc energy is attached to the coulometer electrodes, it causes mercury to be transferred through the electrolyte solution from anode to cathode. Electrons move from the cathode to the anode, while mercury ions flow from anode to cathode. This action corresponds to the plating operation of the electrolytic cell. In this device, however, the electrolyte solution shifts position as the mercury columns change in length. The electrolyte gap moves in a direction opposite to that of the mercury flow.

When a constant-current dc source is attached to the coulometer through a precision resistor, it causes a very accurate transfer of mercury. The position of the electrolyte gap is then used to denote the elapsed time needed to cause this change in the mercury column length. Figure 7–46(B) shows a typical industrial mercury coulometer. Devices of this type

are attached to machines and equipment to indicate equipment utilization, calibration scheduling, and mean-time-to-failure recording and for preventive maintenance references.

Time-elapsed indicators of the coulometer type may be used to their full time range then reversed. Reversible scales are often used to permit this type of change. A device with an elapsed time scale of 10,000 hours is completed when 0.32 μA flows from a 5-V dc source.

MECHANICAL ACTION TIMERS

Many industrial timers use mechanical energy as a means to achieve different timing operations. Devices placed in this category are more conveniently called *dashpot timers* because of their operation. The resulting action of such a device is based on the amount of time that it takes fluid or air to pass through a small opening or orifice. The physical size of the orifice can either be fixed or adjustable according to

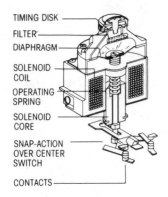

TIMING DISK
FILTER
DIAPHRAGM
SOLENOID COIL
OPERATING SPRING
SOLENOID CORE
SNAP-ACTION OVER CENTER SWITCH
CONTACTS

(A) De-energized condition.

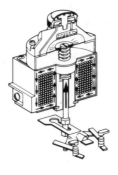

(B) Beginning of energized condition.

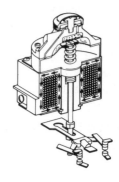

(C) Completed stroke of solenoid core.

FIGURE 7–47
Operational steps of a delay-on pneumatic dashpot timer. (Courtesy of Amerace Corp.)

its design. Through this type of construction, many timing possibilities are available for industrial applications.

Three classes of dashpot timers are commonly used in industry today: pneumatic devices, hydraulic-action units, and mercury-displacement timers. These classifications are based primarily on the material being processed by the timer.

Pneumatic Timers

The operational cycle of a pneumatic timer is primarily based on the amount of time it takes air to be forced through a small hole or orifice in an enclosed container. Timers of this type are used to achieve delay or interval timing operations.

Figure 7–47 shows the basic operation of a delay-on pneumatic dashpot timer in three steps. In Figure 7–47(A), the timer is in its normal de-energized condition. Note the position of the solenoid core in the center of the electrical coil and the diaphragm at the top of the coil.

When the pneumatic timer is energized, the solenoid core moves up into the coil as shown in Figure 7–47(B). When this occurs, the core applies pressure on the diaphragm. This forces the diaphragm to move into the top chamber. Air trapped in the chamber is gradually expelled through the needle valve timing disk. As a result of this action, the solenoid core cannot complete its stroke until the diaphragm resistance is reduced by the expelled air. The amount of delay that occurs, in this case, can be altered by adjusting the needle valve orifice control screw.

Figure 7–47(C) shows that the air expelled from the chamber enables the solenoid core to complete its upward stroke. This action also causes the snap-action switch to transfer its force to the lower contacts. As a result, the

electrical contacts are closed after a delay period. De-energizing the coil causes the solenoid core to pull back by spring action. This in turn transfers its force to the snap-action switch, thus causing it to open the contacts.

A pneumatic interval timer could be achieved with a slight modification of the unit just described. First replace the needle valve with a check valve. This lets air escape from the chamber quickly when the solenoid is energized. Then the snap-action switch immediately turns on. De-energizing the solenoid, however, does not permit it to drop out of the chamber, if it is attached to the diaphragm. In this case, a partial vacuum at the top of the chamber would not release the diaphragm. A needle valve attached to the chamber can be used to restrict the amount of outside air admitted to the top of the chamber. This eventually releases the diaphragm so that it can complete its switching action.

Pneumatic timers in general are very reliable and have a very long operational life expectancy. Their accuracy ranges from $\pm 5\%$ to 10% of their set time. Nearly all units have a variable time setting capability that is usually adjusted by trial and error. A few rather expensive units are equipped with a calibrated time setting dial. As a rule, pneumatic timers are rather small and compact and can be operated in ranges up to 60 min or more.

Hydraulic-action Timers

Hydraulic-action timers as a general rule are similar in appearance and operation to the pneumatic unit just discussed. Silicone fluids, however, are used in hydraulic dashpots to achieve the appropriate delay action. These units retain fluid in an enclosed area where it is used each time the device is actuated. Silicone fluid is commonly used because of its wide temperature range of constant viscos-

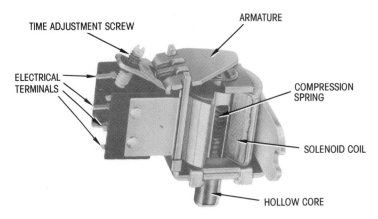

FIGURE 7–48
Hydraulic dashpot timer. (Courtesy of
Heinemann Electric Co.)

ity. This fluid remains consistent from 34.4° to 49°C.

Figure 7–48 shows a dashpot timer of the silicone-fluid hydraulic type. When the solenoid coil is energized electrically, it pulls the hollow core into the center of the coil. Fluid in the hollow core is forced to pass through a small orifice or hole in the top of the core. A one-way check valve at the bottom of the hollow core prevents the fluid from escaping through the bottom.

After a certain period, the fluid is expelled through the small orifice. This permits the hollow core to ultimately complete its upward stroke. At the top of its stroke, the core strikes the pole piece. This closes an air gap in the core, which in turn increases its electromagnetic field strength. The armature is then attracted to the core, which actuates the switch contacts.

When the coil of a hydraulic timer is deenergized, it releases the hollow core. Fluid is forced into the hollow area of the core through the check valve during its downward motion. As an end result, the fluid is acted on when the unit is energized again.

Hydraulic action timers are usually designed

for a specific delay time. This is normally set at the factory during their manufacture. The range of delay or interval time for this device is typically from 0.25 to 120 s. These timers ordinarily require a short release time to prepare for the next timing operation. Generally,

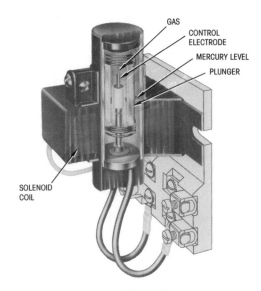

FIGURE 7–49
Cutaway view of a mercury plunger timer.
(Courtesy of Watlow Corp.)

release time is 10% to 20% of the delay time. Timers of this type are very reliable and have a long operational life expectancy.

Mercury-displacement Timers

Mercury-displacement timers represent a very important classification of mechanical action timers. These devices depend on the displacement of a pool of mercury that ultimately makes connection between two electrodes. The electrical contacts are hermetically sealed, thus making them ideal for high-current switching in hazardous environments. Figure 7–49 shows a cutaway view of the internal construction of a mercury-displacement device.

Delayed-make Displacement Timers

The operation of a mercury-displacement timer of the delayed-make type is shown in Figure 7–50. In the de-energized step [Figure 7–50(A)], the plunger (P) of this unit is floating in a container of mercury (M). A space (S) at the top of the unit is filled with an inert gas. The entire cylinder is placed in the center of an electrical coil.

When electrical energy is applied to the coil (C) of Figure 7–50(B), it pulls the floating plunger into its center. Mercury displaced by this action enters the thimble (T) through an orifice (O). Inert gas trapped at the top of the thimble prevents the mercury from rising immediately. Eventually, this gas escapes through a porous ceramic plug (CP) that permits the mercury to rise and fill the thimble.

When mercury entering the thimble rises to an appropriate level [Figure 7–50(C)], it makes a mercury-to-mercury contact between the center electrode (E) and the cylinder electrode (EE). The amount of delay produced by

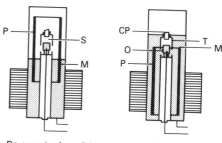

(A) De-energized condition.   (B) Energized condition.

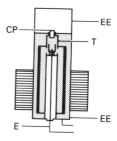

(C) Condition with contact.

FIGURE 7–50
Operation of a delay-on make mercury displacement timer. (Courtesy of Watlow Corp.)

this action is primarily determined by the porosity of the ceramic plug. Timers of this type are manufactured with a fixed delay value.

Slow-break Displacement Timer

A mercury-displacement timer of the normally open, slow-break type is shown in Figure 7–51. In the de-energized condition [Figure 7–51(A)], the plunger (P) is floating in mercury. The electrical contacts are normally open, or off, in this operational state.

The energized condition [Figure 7–51(B)] shows the plunger pulled into the center of the

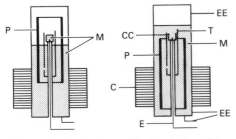

(A) De-energized condition.   (B) Energized condition.

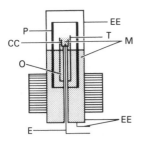

(C) Slow-break condition.

FIGURE 7–51
Operation of normally open slow-break
mercury displacement timer. (Courtesy of
Watlow Corp.)

coil. When this occurs, mercury is displaced to a level where it flows into the top of the thimble (T) and fills the ceramic cup (CC). This action establishes a mercury-to-mercury contact between electrodes E and EE. The contacts remain thus as long as the coil is energized.

When the coil of the timer is de-energized [Figure 7–51(C)], the plunger rises immediately to its original position. Mercury remaining inside of the thimble must now flow through orifice (O) to reach the outside level. When it falls below the lip of the ceramic cup, electrical contacts E and EE become open. The physical size of the orifice is used to regulate

the delay time of the connection break. Timers of this type are designed with a fixed delay period. Typical delay values range from seconds up to a maximum of 20 min.

QUESTIONS

1. What is meant by the term *analog timing action?*

2. Compare analog and digital timers.

3. Explain how each of the following timer functions can be used to achieve control:

   a. Delay

   b. Interval

   c. Repeat cycle

   d. Reset cycle

4. What is an astable multivibrator? How does it achieve timing control?

5. How does the operation of a solid-state timer compare with the operation of a relay timer?

6. Explain how a T flip-flop is triggered. How does it achieve frequency division?

7. How is a UJT used as a trigger element in an electronic timer?

8. How is the electroplating process used to achieve time control?

9. Briefly compare the operation of three types of mechanical timers.

10. How are motors used to achieve timing delay, intervals, recycling, and resetting functions?

11. Prepare a comparison of the five basic timer classifications, pointing out unique characteristics, general operational proce-

dures, advantages, limitations, and time ranges.

12. Explain how an RC network is used to achieve control.

PROBLEMS

1. A 1-MΩ resistor ($\pm 5\%$) and a 0.1-μF capacitor of $\pm 5\%$ tolerance are connected. What is the time constant of this unit and what is its operational range?

2. If 100 V dc is applied to a 1.5-MΩ resistor and a 0.1-μF capacitor, what voltage will occur across the capacitor in one and five time constants?

3. A 10-μF capacitor has accumulated a 100-V dc charge. In one time constant, what will the discharge voltage be? In two time constants? In five time constants?

4. Digital timers that operate from the 60-Hz power line have a $\pm 0.5\%$ accuracy. What does this mean?

5. The output of a 555 IC timer changes from one-third to two-thirds of V_{CC} in one time constant. In seconds this represents 0.693 of $(R_A + R_B)C$. If $R_A = 1$ MΩ, $R_B = 110$ kΩ and $C = 1.5$ μF, what is the charging interval?

6. What is the charging time interval of the RC network of Figure 7–38, assuming the maximum value for R_2?

7. If an electrolytic cell is charged at a rate of 10 mA for 10 hours, how long in hours will it take the cell to be deplated when discharged at a rate of 10 μA per hour?

8. What is the frequency of an IC timer in the astable mode that has an R_A of 200 kΩ, an R_B of 200 kΩ, and a 50-μF capacitor (C)?

ACTIVITIES

ACTIVITY 7–1: Thermal Timers

Objective: To build a thermal timer, study its operation, and see how it can be used to achieve control.

Procedure:

1. With a thermal timer, such as an Amperite 6NO120T, determine the pin connections for the heater and the contacts. Identify the heater voltage, type of switching, and actuation time.

2. Make a sketch of a wiring diagram that will control the actuation of a 7-W, 120-V lamp. Have the instructor approve the circuit.

3. Build the control circuit and test its operation.

4. Construct the thermal delay timer circuit of Figure 7–9.

5. Apply power to the circuit and test its performance. The output of T_2 can be attached to any type of load device. T_2 can be any value depending on the function of the load.

ACTIVITY 7–2: Motor-driven Timers

Objective: To study the operation of a motor-driven timer by connecting it in an operational circuit to achieve control.

Procedure:

1. Refer to the manufacturer's data sheet of the particular timer used in this activity. An Automatic Timing & Controls Co. 324C series or a General Time Corporation RJ series can be used for the activity.

2. Using a single cam, design a circuit that will permit repeat cycle control of a load. The load should cycle on and off as long as the motor of the timer is energized. Have your circuit approved by the instructor.

3. Construct the timer and evaluate its operation.

4. Explain how the timer achieves its control function.

5. If a two-cam motor-driven timer is available, design a stop-cycle timer. One cam should be used to control the load, with the second cam controlling operation of the timer motor. The timing motor should be wired in series with the stop cam and in parallel with an external NO push button. When the push button is closed for at least 1% of the operational cycle, the stop cam should maintain the motor in operation for one cycle and then stop.

6. Have your timer circuit approved by the instructor.

7. Construct your timing circuit and evaluate its operation.

8. Explain the operation of your timing circuit.

ACTIVITY 7–3: Reset Timers

Objective: To become familiar with the operation and physical construction of a reset timer.

Procedure:

1. Study the manufacturer's data sheet of the reset timer being used for this activity.

2. Design a timer circuit that will achieve the delay-on energization function of Figure 7–21. Have the circuit approved by the instructor.

3. Construct the reset timer and evaluate its operation.

4. Design a reset timer with an interval-on momentary make as shown in Figure 7–22. Have the instructor approve the circuit.

5. Construct the timer and evaluate its operation.

6. Explain the operation of a reset timer.

ACTIVITY 7–4: Solid-state Transistor Timer

Objective: To construct a transistor interval timer with discrete components and evaluate its operation.

Procedure:

1. Construct the transistor timer of Figure 7–37.

2. To test the operation of this timer, turn on switch S_1. If the circuit is functioning properly, the load should turn on immediately and remain on for a period of time based on the setting of R_2. Pressing the reset button will repeat the operational cycle.

3. Turn off the circuit and press the push button. Connect a voltmeter across the base–emitter of the transistor. Observe how V_{BE} changes value during an operational cycle. Record the value of V_{BE}. Change the positional setting of R_2 and repeat the operational cycle. What influence does this have on the value of V_{BE}?

4. Explain how the circuit achieves interval timing.

ACTIVITY 7–5: Solid-state Delay Timer

Objective: To construct a solid-state delay timer with discrete components and evaluate its operation with respect to circuit voltage and current value changes.

Procedure:

1. Construct the solid-state delay timer of Figure 7–38.

2. If the circuit is correctly wired, turning on switch SW-1 will start an operational cycle. The load device will be in an off state initially. After a period of time, the load will turn on. To reset the operational cycle, turn off SW-1 and push the capacitor reset button. Then turn on SW-1 and the delay function will be repeated.

3. Test the operation of the timer circuit.

4. Prepare a voltmeter for operation. Connect it across C and observe the change in emitter voltage V_E during an operational cycle. Place the voltmeter across R_4 and observe the voltage change across it for an operational cycle. This represents the gate voltage V_G and determines the gate current of the SCR. Describe the relationship of V_E and V_G in the operation of this circuit.

ACTIVITY 7–6: Astable Multivibrators

Objective: To construct an astable multivibrator, evaluate its operation, and make calculations for its timing cycle.

Procedure:

1. Construct the astable multivibrator of Figure 7–40.

2. Test the operation of the timer. If the circuit is functioning properly, the LED should blink on and off at a specific rate.

3. Calculate the charge time (t_c) of the capacitor and record its value.

4. Calculate the discharge time (t_d) of the capacitor and record its value.

5. Calculate the operational time (T) and frequency (f) of an operational cycle.

6. Turn off the power source and exchange the 50-μF capacitor with a 0.01-μF capacitor.

7. Prepare an oscilloscope for operation and connect it across the trigger input (pin 2) and ground. Make a sketch of the observed wave form.

8. Connect the oscilloscope across the output (pin 3) and observe the wave form. Make a sketch of the observed wave form.

9. Calculate the values of t_c, t_d and f for the modified astable multivibrator.

ACTIVITY 7–7: Monostable Multivibrators

Objective: Construct a monostable multivibrator, evaluate its operation, and trigger it into a state change.

Procedure:

1. Construct the monostable multivibrator of Figure 7–41. Initially, the circuit should be in the high state. This should cause the LED to be illuminated.

2. Depress the trigger push button and the LED should change operational states. After a short time period, the LED should return to its original state.

3. Test the operation of the circuit by triggering it into different states.

4. Turn off the source and exchange C_2 for a 0.1-μF capacitor.

5. Connect a square-wave generator or trigger-pulse generator to the trigger input (pin 2). Remove the bush button or use it to actuate circuit operation by holding it down.

6. Adjust the generator to produce a very slow change in the LED output. Describe your observations.

7. Prepare the generator for a high-speed trig-

ger pulse signal. Connect an oscilloscope to the output and observe the wave form. Move the oscilloscope to the trigger input and observe the wave form. Describe your findings.

ACTIVITY 7–8: Electrolytic Cells

Objective: To construct an electrolytic cell circuit and evaluate its operation.

Procedure:

1. Construct the electrolytic cell timer of Figure 7–45.

2. The cell must be charged or set before operation can be achieved. To prepare the circuit for charging, switch S_2 should be off and resistor R_1 set to the middle of its range. Turn switch S_1 to the set position and adjust R_1 to produce 50 μA of charge current. Accurately time the current flow for 1 min; then switch S_1 to the clear position.

3. Turn on switch S_2. The circuit should be off until the charge time has expired; then a voltage will be generated by the E-cell. This voltage will forward bias Q_1, which will in turn trigger the gate of the SCR. The load will be energized.

4. Test the operation of the circuit. The set time and clear time in this case should be equal.

5. If the circuit functions properly, repeat the charging operation for a time of 2 min. Before clearing the E-cell, adjust R_1 to a different value. Then clear the cell and record the actuation time.

6. Repeat the first step again. Measure and record the base trigger voltage and the gate trigger voltage.

ACTIVITY 7–9: Mechanical-action Timers

Objective: Construction of a mechanical-action timer circuit that will achieve control and evaluation of the timer.

Procedure:

1. Prepare an ohmmeter to measure resistance and connect it to two of the electrical contacts of the timer. The timer recommended for this activity is an Eagle Signal 86-0-A00021. It should contain a SPOT switch.

2. If the two leads contain the hinge point of the switch, the meter will indicate resistance. Determine the hinge point of the switch. The switch should make contact between two terminals in the out position and break the contacts in the depressed position. Make a skektch of the switch contacts for the two conditions of the timer.

3. Design a mechanical time delay circuit in which a 120-V, 60-Hz load is actuated after a 30-s delay.

4. Have your circuit approved by the instructor; then test it for operation.

5. Alter the circuit so that the timer will operate for a 30-s interval before turning off. Have the circuit approved by the instructor; then test its operation.

6. Explain how the timer of this device can be altered. What is the operational range of this timer?

Optoelectronic systems are designed to respond to light signals or to transfer information from one point to another by light energy. These systems are unique in that they employ a number of rather specialized light transducers. There must be a source of light energy and a device that will detect light. Changes in light are then used to actuate the final control element of the system. On and off control and partial variations in the load can be achieved through an optoelectronic system.

Optoelectronic systems can be placed in the same basic format that has been used to describe other systems. There must be an energy source, transmission path, control, load, and possibly one or more indicators. These parts are the operational basis of nearly any functioning system. Figure 8–1 shows the elementary components of an optoelectronic system.

An optoelectronic system has a number of specific features that distinguish it from other systems. The primary energy source of an optoelectronic system, for example, is responsible for producing light energy. The transmission path is usually air. In addition to this, some systems may use optical fibers as a transmission path. Control is achieved by detecting changes in light energy. The load device will then respond in some way to changes initiated by light energy.

THE NATURE OF LIGHT

Optoelectronic devices are light-sensitive devices that rely on the characteristics of light in order to function. Light is a visible form of radiation that is actually a narrow band of frequencies along the vast electromagnetic spectrum. The electromagnetic spectrum, shown in Figure 8–2, includes bands of frequencies for radio, television, radar, infrared radiation, visible light, ultraviolet light, x-rays, gamma

8

Optoelectronic Systems

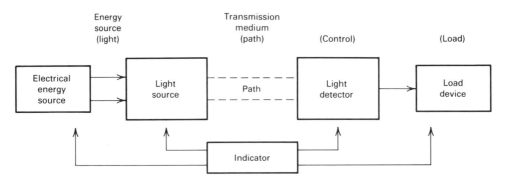

FIGURE 8–1
Components of an optoelectronic system.

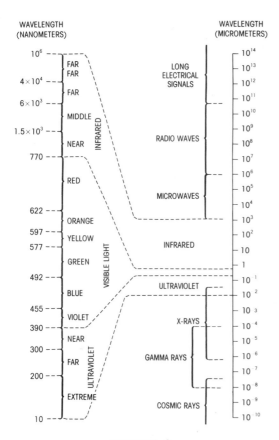

FIGURE 8–2
Electromagnetic spectrum.

rays, and various other frequencies. Radiation, such as light, heat, radio waves, and x-rays, differ only with respect to their frequencies or wavelengths.

The human eye responds to electromagnetic waves in the visible light band of frequencies. Each color of light has a different frequency or wavelength. In order of increasing frequency, or decreasing wavelength, colors range as follows: red, orange, yellow, green, blue, and violet. The wavelengths of visible light are in the range of 4×10^{-7} meters (m) for violet to 7.7×10^{-7} m for red. Wavelength can also be expressed as 0.4 to 0.77 micrometers (μM) or 400 to 770 nanometers (nm). A micrometer is 0.000,001 or 1×10^{-6} m, while a nanometer is 0.000,000,001 or 1×10^{-9} m. In practice, light wavelengths are more commonly expressed in angstrom units (Å). An angstrom is one-tenth of a nanometer or 0.000,000,0001 (1×10^{-10}) m. Visible light would therefore be described as 4000 to 7700 Å.

The response of the human eye to visible light exhibits a frequency selective characteristic, such as shown in Figure 8–3. The greatest sensitivity is near 5500 Å, and the poorest sensitivity is around 4000 Å on the lower wavelengths and 7700 Å on the higher wave-

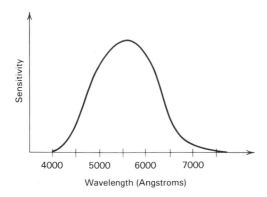

FIGURE 8–3
Response of the human eye.

lengths. Our eyes perceive various degrees of brightness due to their response to the wavelengths of light. The normal human eye cannot see a wavelength of less than 4000 Å or more than 7700 Å (400 to 770 nm).

When dealing with light, there are several characteristic terms that should be understood. The unit of luminous intensity is a standard light source called a *candela* (cd). The intensity of light is therefore expressed in candelas. The amount of light falling on a unit surface all points of which are a unit distance from a uniform point source of 1 cd is 1 *lumen* (lm). The illumination of a surface is the number of lumens falling on it per unit area. The unit of illumination is the *lux* (lx) or lumens per square meter.

We see only light that is reflected. Reflected light is measured in candelas per square meter of surface. A term called the *reflection factor* is the percent of light reflected from a surface expressed as a decimal. Therefore, the light reflected from a surface is equal to the illumination of the surface times the reflection factor.

OPTOELECTRONIC SYSTEM CLASSIFICATIONS

The method used to couple light energy from the source to the detector is often used to distinguish one optoelectronic system from another. Two rather general classifications are now made in industry. These are commonly described as interruptible systems and noninterruptible systems.

Interruptible Systems

Interruptible systems at the present time are by far the most common of all optoelectronic applications. Systems of this type have a very obvious source of electromagnetic radiation and a detector or receiver. A system with an independent source and detector is shown in Figure 8–4. Electromagnetic energy emitted from the source travels through space or air to

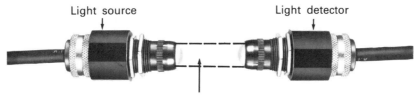

FIGURE 8–4
Photoelectric system with independent source and detector. (Courtesy of Automatic Timing Controls)

the receiver. Systems of this type are used in industry to achieve a number of different control operations. Response time is generally considered to be very fast. Actuation is accomplished by breaking or interrupting the radiation path between the source and detector.

Interruptible systems are designed to detect the presence or absence of light in the transmission path. In this type of system the light source and detector are usually positioned so that they will respond to changes in the transmission path. Counting, automatic door control, motion or product movement, and object position adjustments are made by this type of system. A large number of these systems are in use today.

Noninterruptible Systems

Noninterruptible systems are designed to respond to a constant flow of light through a slightly unusual medium. This type of system can be used to detect changes in light intensity, respond to variations in object colors, and transmit data. The end result of the system could be film exposure, the slicing of an object by a laser beam, or circuit isolation. Operation is not necessarily based on the breaking of a light beam. Data transmission, for example, is achieved by turning the light source on and off according to some predetermined coded signal. Electrical isolation between different circuit components can be achieved by interconnecting them through a light beam. Communication signals can be transmitted by light between different locations through fiberoptic cables. A number of unique developments have occurred in this area of optoelectronics. As a rule, noninterruptible systems represent some of the most innovative developments in the optoelectronics field.

There is very little difference between the general operation of an interruptible and a non-interruptible system. A source of radiant energy and a receiver or detector are usually needed in both system types. The end result of the system or the resulting work produced by its load is used to distinguish one system from the other. In general, the most significant advances in optoelectronics have occurred in noninterruptible system applications.

OPTOELECTRONIC SYSTEM FUNCTIONS

An optoelectronic system has two rather important operational conditions that are used to distinguish it from other systems. The source, for example, must generate some form of radiant energy. Normally, this energy is in or near the visible portion of the frequency spectrum. Second, the system must have a detector or receiver of radiant energy. A variety of devices may be used to detect this energy. The design of the system and its application have a great deal to do with the selection of its energy source and detector. System operation is primarily dependent on the function of these two components.

Radiation Sources

A variety of radiation sources are now used in optoelectronic systems. Light-emitting diodes, tungsten lamps, neon lamps, fluorescent lamps, and xenon tubes are some of the more common sources of electromagnetic radiation. As a rule, these sources radiate energy in the visible part of the electromagnetic spectrum. Some light-emitting diodes (LEDS), however, are purposely designed to radiate only infrared energy. Emitters that generate infrared wavelengths or energy outside of the visible part of the spectrum are said to be radiometric. In a

sense, all optoelectronic sources can be classified as *radiometric*. If the radiation source produces some form of visible light, however, it may be described as *photometric*. Optoelectronic specifications may be stated in either radiometric or photometric terms. Radiometric terms are usually preceded by the word *radiant*. Common expressions are radiant flux, radiant intensity, and radiant incidence. Photometric terms are preceeded by the word *luminous*. Luminous flux, luminous intensity, and luminous incidence are typical photometric expressions.

Photometric sources are frequently classified by the amount or range of visible light emitted. In this regard, sources are described as being panchromatic, heterochromatic, or monochromatic. The term *chromatic* in these expressions refers to a specific color or various colors of the spectrum. An incandescent lamp is an example of a panchromatic source. Its radiation extends over a very large portion of the optical spectrum. A wide range of visible color can be produced by an incandescent source.

Heterochromatic sources are different be-cause they produce a very limited number of different colors. Mercury arc lamps, for example, produce colors that are predominantly red or orange. Specifically, this particular source generates light in the range of 6500 Å.

A monochromatic source radiates energy of only one specific wavelength or a very narrow part of the spectrum. A sodium-vapor lamp, for example, radiates energy at 5000 Å. Neon lamps emit energy at 5500 Å. Figure 8–5 shows the spectral response of several different light sources. Notice the chromatic differences in these sources.

Incandescent Lamp Sources

Incandescent lamps are frequently used as the radiation source of an interruptible system. This type of source is readily available, is very reliable, and has a consistent level of operation. Tungsten filament lamps are widely used in industrial applications. The radiation output of this source peaks at approximately 10,000 Å (see Figure 8–5). It also radiates electromagnetic energy in the visible light region.

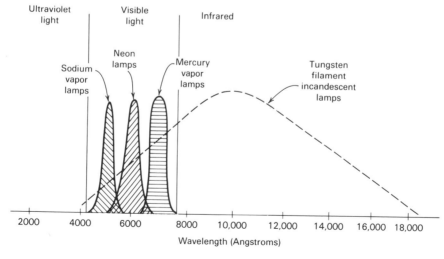

FIGURE 8–5
Spectral response of radiation sources.

The incandescent lamps of an interruptible system are generally operated at the lowest voltage value that is consistent with good performance. Low-voltage operation extends the life span of the lamp. The operating life of a lamp is equal to the twelfth power of the ratio of the rated voltage to the operating voltage. Lamp life in an optoelectronic system ranges from 5000 hours (h) to something in excess of 50,000 h depending on the lamp and its operating voltage.

Many optoelectronic radiation sources employ modulated light signals. A modulated light beam is one that is interrupted or pulsed on and off several times per second. The modulation rate ranges from 100 pulses per second (pps) to several thousand.

Modulation can be accomplished mechanically or electrically. Mechanical pulsing is normally achieved by a slotted rotating disk. The disk is rotated by a motor. Light passes through each slot and is blocked by the remainder of the disk. In a sense, the light beam is turned on and off according to the rotational speed of the disk. Modulation of this type can be very high in accordance with motor speed and the number of slots in the disk. Figure 8–6 shows an example of a rotating disk modulation source.

Electrical switching of an incandescent lamp is usually achieved by an SCR or a triac. The lamp is simply made to be conductive or turned off at a constant rate. As a rule, electrical modulation of an incandescent lamp can only be achieved at a rather slow rate. There is, for example, a time factor involved in this operation. When electrical power is applied initially, it takes a short time for the lamp to produce filament heat and ultimately light. When the power is removed, there is a short time delay before the filament cools off and stops emission. Modulation by switching is generally limited to a few hundred pulses per minute. Modulation of the light source is only used where the effects of strong ambient light are objectionable to normal system operation.

Light-emitting Diode Sources

A semiconductor optoelectronic device that is used rather extensively as a light source today is the light-emitting diode (LED) or solid-state lamp (SSL). An LED is shown in Figure 8–7).

In general, the LED is small and lightweight. This makes it very desirable for use with digital circuitry and other miniaturized applications. The *pn* junctions of an LED are commonly made of gallium arsenide phosphide (GaAsP) and gallium phosphide (GaP). A light-emitting diode has fast response time and presents a low impedance that is compatible with solid-state circuitry.

An LED is operated in a forward-biased condition. The semiconductors used in its fabrication have the property of producing electromagnetic radiation when a forward-biased po-

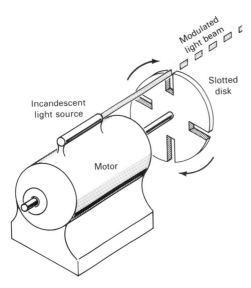

FIGURE 8–6
Rotating disk modulation source.

tential is applied. Thus electrical energy causes the radiation of visible light energy. The spectral response of LEDs varies according to the type of semiconductor materials used in their design. LEDs are made to produce a number of different colors. Typical LED spectral response curves are shown in Figure 8–8. Compare these curves and their peak response to the color response curve shown in Figure 8–5. This comparison will show that the wavelength of radiated energy from an LED is well beyond the visible light range. Therefore, phosphors are added to produce the desired color effects. LEDs are very sensitive to temperature changes. Any change in temperature will cause the spectral response of an LED to shift its wavelength.

A unique feature of the LED as a light source is its rapid switching time. Compared with an incandescent lamp, the LED can be switched on and off very rapidly. Switching

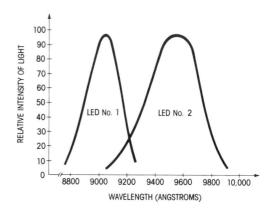

FIGURE 8–8
LED spectral response curves.

rates of several thousand hertz (Hz) can be achieved today. The LED does not have a significant delay time for its switching action. No heat is required by an LED to produce light. Radiation occurs when a *pn* junction is forward biased. Light is produced when holes and electrons recombine at the surface of the junction. Modulation of an LED source is commonly achieved by a high-speed switching device. Electronic switching is widely used for this type of modulation today.

Radiation Detection

Interruptible optoelectronic systems are generally classified according to the method of light detection. The mode or method of detection selected for a particular installation is often determined by the amount of contamination in the air. Any buildup of foreign matter on a lens or in the air has a great deal to do with the response of the system. Three distinct modes of detection are used in interruptible systems today. These are described as through beam, reflex, and proximity modes of detection. Each detector is unique and has a set of characteristics that distinguishes it from the others. These characteristics have a great deal

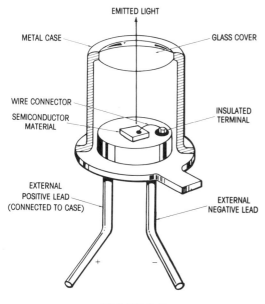

FIGURE 8–7
Light-emitting diode.

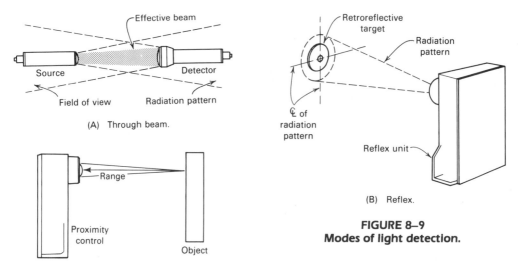

(A)   Through beam.

(C)   Proximity.

(B)   Reflex.

FIGURE 8–9
Modes of light detection.

to do with the installation of a particular system. Figure 8–9 shows a simplification of the three detection modes.

Through-beam detection is probably the most common of all detection modes. This type of system has the light source and the de-tector both mounted in independent units. The source sends out a light signal from its location. The detector then responds to this signal at some remote location. Object detection occurs when the light beam is broken. The light source and detector both require electrical energy for operation.

Figure 8–10 shows some representative

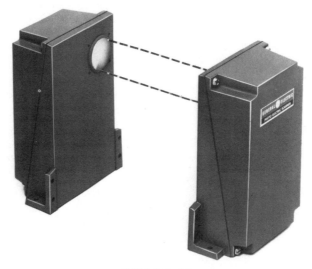

FIGURE 8–10
Through-beam optoelectronic system.
(Courtesy of General Electric Co.)

through-beam detector systems designed for heavy-duty installations. These units are all equipped with an incandescent light source. The detector employs either a phototransistor or a photo IC. A 10- to 30-V dc source is needed to energize the detector. An output current of 200 mA can be developed by the detector. Maximum switching time is 100 μs. The range of operation is from 0 to 65 m. The output of two or more detectors may be connected directly in parallel, which permits AND/OR logic functions.

A variation of the incandescent light source uses a modulated infrared LED source of light. The LED in this case is energized by a 2.4-kHz square-wave source. Operating ranges of this system may be extended to 650 m or 2132 ft. This type of system is usually immune to normal room light. It is used in installations where ambient light may interfere with normal operation. The detector of this system must respond to infrared radiation.

Reflex detection has the light source and detector unit both mounted in the same assembly. The source can be either an incandescent light or a modulated LED. Operation is primarily based on the reflection of an emitted light beam back to the detector. A light beam sent out by the source strikes a retroreflective target and reflects back to the detector. A retroreflective target reflects or turns back radiant waves of energy so that the reflected waves are parallel to the original wave. Retroreflective surfaces are generally less sensitive to misalignment than plane-surfaced mirrors. Detection then occurs when an object crosses between the light beam and the target. This type of system only requires electrical power to one unit.

Figure 8–11 shows a self-contained, long-range reflex detector with a solid-state (LED) light source. This particular system is designed for operation in high-ambient-light locations. The operational range is 0 to 60 ft with a 3-in. retroreflective target. The light source is con-

FIGURE 8–11
Self-contained reflex detector system.
(Courtesy of Sick Optik Electronik)

trolled by high-frequency ac. The entire system is designed to respond to light in or near the infrared (IR) part of the spectrum. This normally makes the unit immune to room light.

A block diagram of the reflex detector system is shown in Figure 8–12. Note that only one lens is needed for this assembly. A special beam-splitting mirror permits light emission and detection on the same axis. Alignment is generally not critical because the retroreflective target returns light to the detector even when it is tilted 15° at the rated operating range. The detector in this unit is a silicon photovoltaic cell. Amplification of the detected signal is achieved by high-speed silicon transistors. The output of this system has a number of different options. It can be on–off solid-state switching, relay control, or one-shot pulser switching, or it can have a time-delay feature. Different plug-in modules for this particular system are available for each of the output options.

Proximity detection is achieved with a com-

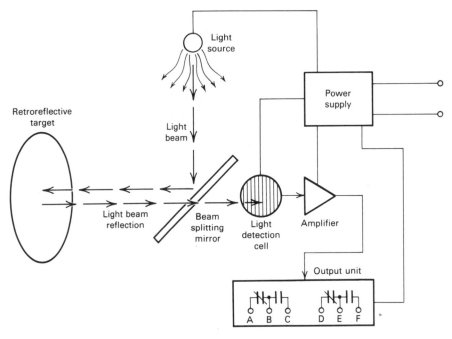

FIGURE 8–12
Block diagram of a reflex detector system.

bined light source and detector in a single unit. The specific difference in proximity and reflex detection is the light source and its operating range. The light source and detector usually respond to visible light. The object being detected simply reflects the light signal back to the detector. Electrical energy is only supplied to the combined source–detector unit.

Figure 8–13 shows a representative proximity detector unit. Systems of this type usually employ a visible light LED source. The source is normally energized by a high-frequency square wave. Frequencies of 2.5 kHz are widely used. This particular wave is generated by an oscillator that is built into the supply unit.

The operational range of a proximity detector system is rather limited when compared with other methods of detection. Operation is primarily based on the material surface being

detected. Smooth glossy surfaces obviously produce more reflection than rough-textured surfaces. The maximum range of detection is approximately 24 in. or 600 mm. System response is also influenced a great deal by the condition of the air. Most installations of this type are found in clean-environment areas.

OPTOELECTRONIC SYSTEM DESIGN CONSIDERATIONS

In the design of an optoelectronic system for a specific application, a number of considerations must be taken into account. These include such things as component matching characteristics, the transmission medium selection, and a variety of optical factors. The operation of the system is directly dependent on these

FIGURE 8–13
Proximity detector. (Courtesy of Sick Optik Electronik)

improved. Figure 8–14(B) shows a characteristic where the devices are approximately 25% compatible. Matching is indicated by the shaded region where the two curves overlap. Matching in this case is very effective around 5750 Å.

Unity component matching is shown in Fig-

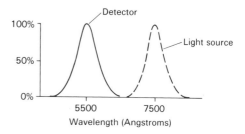

(A)   Component mismatch.

considerations, and as a rule, they should not be altered or changed after a system has been designed for a specific application.

Component Matching

Component matching of an optoelectronic system is an important system design consideration. In this regard, matching refers to the spectral response of the light source and the detector. These two parts must have compatible characteristics in order for the system to be effective. A graphic indication of the component matching characteristic is shown in Figure 8–14. Part A shows a complete mismatch between the source and the detector. A characteristic of this type shows that the detector will not respond to any of the light source energy. This would be similar to tuning a radio receiver to a frequency at one end of the band for reception of a station at the other end of the band.

When the spectral response of the source and detector overlap, operational efficiency is

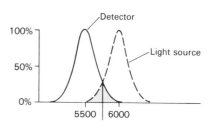

(B)   25% compatible matching.

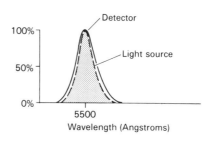

(C)   Unity matching.

FIGURE 8–14
Component-matching characteristics.

ure 8–14(C). This condition occurs when all the source energy falls on the detector. Ideally, this means that the two components are perfectly matched. Their matching factor is based on the product of the two response curves. The matching factor is the shaded region where the two curves overlap.

The matching factor of an optoelectronic system is an extremely important operational characteristic. The table of Figure 8–15 shows representative matching factor relationships for different light sources. Note that the human eye and a light sensitive *PN* silicon crystal are compared. Examination of the table shows that the light-sensitive crystal is a much better detector than the human eye in all examples. The human eye is most sensitive to the sun and the neon lamp. In both cases the light-sensitive detector is a much more efficient detector. Sensitivity, in this case, is not an indication of brightness. It primarily refers to a higher percentage of a specific light wavelength that is detectable by the device. Optoelectronic systems do not necessarily need to respond to light energy that is responsive to the human eye. In practice, many systems employ ultraviolet (UV) or infrared (IR) light instead of visible light.

Light Matching Relationships

Source of Light Energy	Eye	Light sensitive silicon PN device
Sun	0.16	0.5
2,200K tungsten lamp	0.007	0.19
2,600K tungsten lamp	0.02	0.24
3,000K tungsten lamp	0.04	0.3
Neon lamp	0.35	0.7
Light-emitting diode gallium arsenide 9000A	0.0	1.0
Light-emitting diode gallium phosphide 7000A	0.08	0.7

FIGURE 8–15
Light-matching relationship table.

Transmission Medium

The medium through which light energy is transferred from the source to the detector is an extremely important operational consideration. Regardless of the type of system, there is always a time when there must be some transmission of light energy. The medium must first be capable of passing light at a desired frequency with minimal loss or attenuation. In an interruptible system, blocking the light source must also cause a corresponding change in the output. The medium must therefore be capable of responding to both the presence and absence of light in its operation.

Air is a very common transmission medium for most optoelectronic systems. Light travels through air very rapidly. Typical indications of the speed of light are 300,000 kilometers per second or 186,000 miles per second. Light travels in this medium through waves. These waves are of the transverse type. This means that their motion is in a plane that is at right angles to the direction of travel. We believe that light waves travel in a straight line. This condition is called *rectilinear propagation*. Most optoelectronic systems respond to lightwave propagation through air for only a limited distance.

Optical fibers are frequently used today in many systems as a transmission medium. These fibers are made from glass or plastic. The fiber material serves as the actual transmission medium. At present, glass fibers are used more frequently than plastic. Glass is available in diameters from 2 micrometers (μm) to more than 6 mm. Each fiber has a central core that has its outside coated or clad with a reflective surface. The cladding material has a reflective index slightly lower than that of the core. To a light wave, the interface between the core and the cladding material responds as a mirror. Light striking the interface is reflected back into the core. It moves and

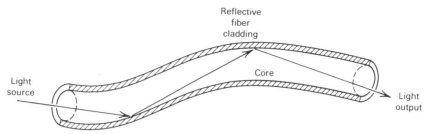

FIGURE 8–16
Cutaway view of a fiber-optic cable.

remains in the core until it strikes the core-cladding interface again. The process is then repeated. As many as 500 or more reflections may occur in 30 centimeters (cm) of the fiber core.

The principle of fiber optics, illustrated in Figure 8–16, utilizes optical fibers made of glass or plastic to transmit light from one point to another. Light may be transmitted in very unconventional ways, such as around corners, in limited space, or over long distances by using the fiber-optics principle. The light will transmit through the fiber-optic material regardless of how it is bent or shaped. The core of the fiber-optic material is designed to be reflective to the light passing through it. Advances in fiber-optic design have made possible low-loss fiber lengths that are used for numerous applications. Optical communications are the most common use of fiber optics.

Optical Coupling Considerations

Optical coupling considerations take into account those things that influence the transmission of light other than the conduction medium. Such things as windows, optical filters, lenses, mirrors, and prisms are included in this design consideration. Each item may be used in a system singly or in combination with others.

Windows are a very common optical coupling consideration. A window is the covering or closure through which light passes from a packaged light source to the outside or from the outside to the inside of a packaged detector. Figure 8–17 shows the windows of a number of discrete optoelectronic devices.

Windows are normally made of glass, plastic, quartz or sapphire. The design of the window has a great deal to do with the wavelength of the light energy radiated by the source or received by the detector. Such things as refraction and diffusion must be taken into account. Light waves passing from one medium into another have a natural tendency to bend. Refraction of this type could cause light to be emitted at an unusual angle or be improperly directed toward the active device. Window selection must take this into account.

Diffusion is primarily dependent on the intended function of the device. In some applications, diffusion is needed to disperse the light source over a large area. In other cases, it is important for light to be developed in a finely concentrated beam. The surface of the window has a great deal to do with its diffusion factor. Smooth, well-polished windows reflect light with a minimum of distortion. Rough-surfaced windows cause light to be scattered or dispersed. Selection of the window surface is a very important system consideration.

Optical filters are purposely placed in a

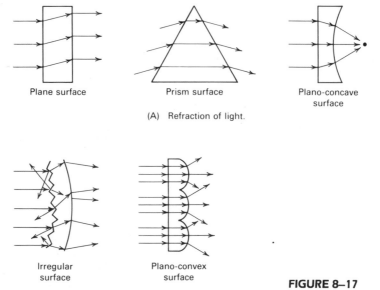

Plane surface Prism surface Plano-concave surface

(A) Refraction of light.

Irregular surface Plano-convex surface

(B) Diffusion of light.

FIGURE 8–17
Optoelectrical window surfaces.

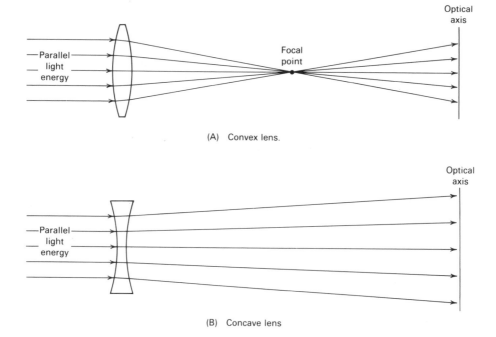

(A) Convex lens.

(B) Concave lens

FIGURE 8–18
Convex and concave lens action.

light path to restrict the passage of specific frequencies. In many applications, only selected bands of frequencies are permitted to pass through the system. Optical filters are designed to pass only desired wavelengths and to block out unwanted frequencies. A red optical filter, for example, passes only the frequencies of light that the system detects as the color red. All other frequencies are attenuated.

A wide range of optical filters is used today in optoelectronic systems. Typically, these filters are made by depositing very thin layers of metal on a base of glass or quartz. The operational frequency of a system usually dictates the need for an optical filter. In most industrial applications, filters are used to reduce or eliminate light that may produce an erroneous indication in the output.

Lenses are primarily used in an optical system as a window. In this regard, they must pass light waves without causing a great deal of attenuation. They are purposely used to focus or send light energy to a specific point or in a particular direction. Directing light waves into a single or common point is called *conver-*

gence. A lens may also be used to cause a light wave to spread out. This function is called *divergence*. The physical structure of the lens determines how it will respond when light energy is applied.

The ability of a lens to modify light energy is primarily dependent on refraction. Figure 8–18 shows how light energy is altered by a lens. Parallel light waves entering a convex lens are bent toward a common point or axis. A convex lens is considered to be positive and causes light to converge at a common point. The concave lens has a negative function and causes a divergence of light energy. Parallel light waves entering this lens are bent away from the axis. The function of an optical system primarily dictates the type of lens being used.

Mirrors are designed to reflect light and in most applications do not pass light energy. They respond by directing light beams in one direction and can cause the beam to either converge or diverge. The structure of the mirrored surface determines its response.

Optoelectronic mirrors generally consist of a thin metal surface deposited on a glass sub-

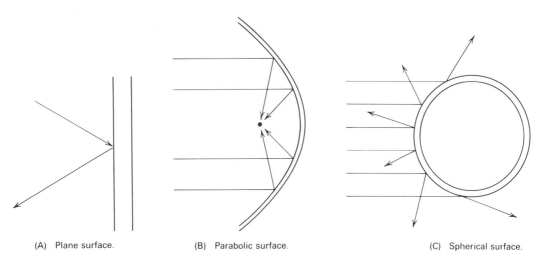

(A) Plane surface.   (B) Parabolic surface.   (C) Spherical surface.

FIGURE 8–19
Three mirror surfaces.

strate. The reflecting properties of the mirror are based on the reflectance of the metal being used. Aluminum is widely used today because it has excellent reflectance throughout the visible and infrared regions of the optical spectrum.

The surface of a mirror is primarily responsible for its response to light energy. Figure 8–19 shows three common mirror surface configurations. Plane mirrors have a smooth flat surface. This type of surface is used to reflect all or part of an optical wave in a new direction. Curved mirrors respond as a lens. A curved parabolic surface reflects light to a common point. This type of mirror permits light to be collected at a distant location and be directed into a narrow beam. A spherical surface causes light to diverge. This type of surface causes light to scatter in many directions.

Prisms respond in an optoelectronic system as a lens. Operation in general is based on the refraction of light. The velocity of a light wave passing through glass depends on its wavelength. For this reason, prisms are used to divide a light beam into its component wavelengths. Figure 8–20 shows how incident light is separated into distinct components.

A system employing a prism could be used to detect a particular color from a common light source. An alarm could be turned on at a remote location if an unusual amount of one color appeared in the output of a specific detector. Systems of this type are frequently used in color-mixing operations in the textile field.

OPTOELECTRONIC DEVICES

Optoelectronic or photoelectric devices are by far the most unique part of a composite light-actuated system. These devices, in general, are classified as being either sources or detectors. A source is responsible for changing electrical energy into some form of radiant energy. Incandescent lamps, LEDs, gaseous or vapor lamps, and lasers are typical sources of radiant energy. These sources may be responsible for the emission of visible light or some form of radiation in another part of the spectrum. The source in a strict sense is a transducer. Electrical energy is changed into radiant energy.

The detector of an optoelectronic system is also classified as a transducer. Detectors are designed to change radiant energy into electrical energy. In effect, detectors are the reverse or have an opposite function to that of the source. A number of detection devices are available today. Detectors are divided into three general categories: (1) photoemissive, (2) photoconductive, and (3) photovoltaic. *Photoemissive devices* emit electrons in the presence of light. Vacuum and gaseous phototubes are typical photoemissive devices. *Photoconductive devices* are designed so that their resistance decreases when light becomes more intense and increases when light intensity decreases. Photodiodes, phototransistors, and photoresistive devices are common examples of photoconductive devices. *Photovoltaic devices* convert light energy into electrical energy. When a photovoltaic device is illuminated, an electrical potential is created by the device. Most optoelectronic detectors fit into one of these categories. However, there is such

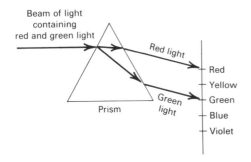

FIGURE 8–20
Incident light separation by a prism.

a diversity of new semiconductor optoelectronic devices used in industry today that it is more desirable to discuss each device individually. The sections that follow will deal with various types of optoelectronic devices and related systems that have applications in industry.

Photoemission

The phototube shown in Figure 8–21 is similar in appearance to a vacuum tube or gaseous tube. This particular type of tube has a cathode that emits electrons when it is struck by light. This effect is called *photoelectric emission*.

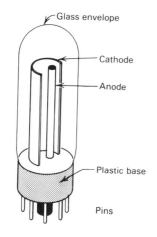

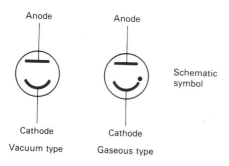

FIGURE 8–21
Photoemissive cell.

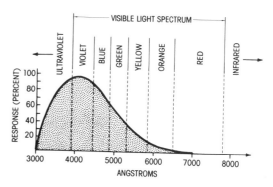

FIGURE 8–22
Spectral response curve for a phototube.

The cathode emits electrons, whose energy depends on the wavelength of the light striking it. A spectral response curve is plotted by the manufacturer for each type of device produced. A representative spectral response curve is shown in Figure 8–22.

Light energy exists in the form of photons, which are discrete bundles of energy. When photoemission takes place in a phototube, photons of light are absorbed by the surface of the cathode. The absorption of this energy causes electrons on the surface of the cathode to gain enough energy to leave the cathode. The energy possessed by the electrons that leave the cathode is based on the frequency of the applied light. Electron emission is based on the intensity and wavelength of light.

A phototube may be connected in a circuit as shown in Figure 8–23. When light of the proper wavelength is focused on the cathode, electrons are emitted and travel to the positively charged anode or plate. A plate current (I_P) will now flow, which causes a voltage drop across the load (R_L). The plate current, caused by various combinations of light and plate voltage, may be determined by using a phototube characteristic curve supplied by the manufacturer. Such a curve is shown in Figure 8–24. Photoemissive tubes may be of the vac-

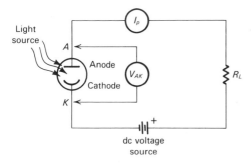

FIGURE 8–23
Phototube circuit action.

uum type or filled with a gas. A gas phototube is usually more sensitive and thus requires less light to produce a given amount of anode current. A phototube circuit may be calibrated in order to measure specific values of light. This permits the tube to be used in instruments such a light-exposure meter.

At one time nearly all industrial control by light was achieved by photoemissive tubes. The unusually high voltage needed to energize a phototube is rather uncharacteristic of most electronic devices today. In general, this type of device has been replaced by solid-state photodiodes. As a rule, circuit control can be achieved more efficiently with lower voltage values. The photoemissive principle is important, however, because it is the basis of photomultiplier tube operation.

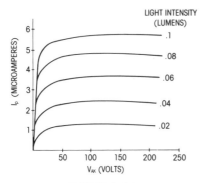

FIGURE 8–24
Phototube characteristic curves.

Multiplier Phototubes

Most phototubes have a very small output when the light intensity is low. The multiplier phototube, shown in Figure 8–25, overcomes this disadvantage. Note the internal construction of this phototube. When photons of light energy strike the cathode, electrons are emitted from its surface. These electrons then strike successive positive plates called *dynodes*. Through the principal secondary emission, a larger number of electrons is produced by each successive dynode. Most multiplier phototubes use from 9 to 14 dynodes to produce a high output at low light levels.

Light that strikes the cathode causes electrons to be emitted and focused toward the second dynode. Each dynode possesses a successively higher positive charge to attract these electrons. The anode has the highest positive potential. Thus a small amount of light can cause enough electrons to be emitted to produce a significant output. Photomultiplier tubes have a fairly high level of signal multiplication, which is extremely important in sensing low levels of light detection.

Photoconductive Devices

The photodiode, shown in Figure 8–26, is a specialized semiconductor diode that is operated in the reverse-biased condition. Thus there is essentially a linear increase in reverse current as light intensity increases. When light of the proper wavelength is focused toward the *pn* junction of the diode, current carriers move across the junction. This causes a current through the external load that is proportional to the amount of light falling on the junction. Note the set of characteristic curves shown in Figure 8–26(C).

The photodiode is usually followed by an amplifying device. If the amplifier is made by

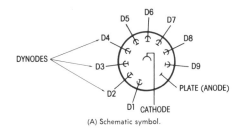

(A) Schematic symbol.

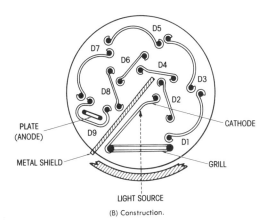

(B) Construction.

(C) Photograph.

FIGURE 8–25
Multiplier phototube. (Courtesy of RCA)

the manufacturer on the same silicon chip, the device is called a *phototransistor*. A phototransistor equivalent circuit and characteristic curve are shown in Figure 8–27. The collector–base junction is reverse biased. When light is focused on the collector–base junction, base current flows. This base current is amplified by the transistor. It is possible to bias the base to affect the sensitivity of the device.

A modification of the basic phototransistor is the Darlington-connected phototransistor shown in Figure 8–28. This device is similar to the basic phototransistor except it has much higher current gain. The additional gain is largely due to a directly coupled transistor configuration built on the same silicon chip. Low light levels can be easily detected by a high-gain Darlington phototransistor. Essentially, light energy is applied to both transistor sections at the same time. This configuration has the advantage of higher input impedance,

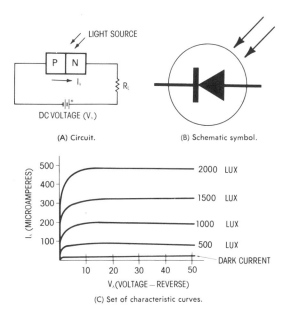

(A) Circuit.

(B) Schematic symbol.

(C) Set of characteristic curves.

FIGURE 8–26
Photodiode circuit and characteristic curves.

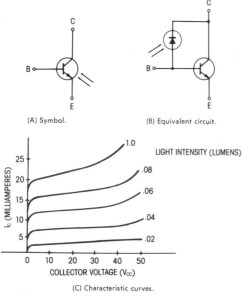

(A) Symbol.   (B) Equivalent circuit.

(C) Characteristic curves.

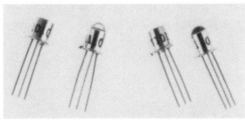

(D) Photograph.

FIGURE 8–27
Phototransistor, equivalent circuit,
characteristic curves, and photograph.
(Courtesy of EG & G Vactec)

other electronic devices. The load may be activated by either the presence or absence of light. The specific function of the load determines when the control circuit must be actuated.

The circuit of Figure 8–29 is a basic photodiode relay control circuit. When light shines on the reverse-biased photodiode, it causes an increase in the current through R_B. The voltage across R_B is such that the top of it is positive with respect to ground. This voltage (V_B) forward biases the base of Q_1. An increase in V_B produces a corresponding increase in I_B. An increase in I_B, in turn, causes an increase in collector current. Since the relay coil is connected in the collector circuit, it will actuate, causing the incandescent light load to be energized. Removal of the light source causes the relay to drop out or change back to its original state. This type of circuit is connected in the forward direction. An increase in light therefore causes an increase in load current.

Another photodiode application is shown in Figure 8–30. The two photodiodes are used to control the input signal of an operational amplifier. The output of the op-amp is used to

lower output impedance, and less current drawn from the source.

There are numerous applications for photodiodes, phototransistors, and Darlington-connected phototransistors. Most of these applications use the light-sensitive device as a control element to activate some type of load. Load activation is normally accomplished through the amplifying action of transistors or

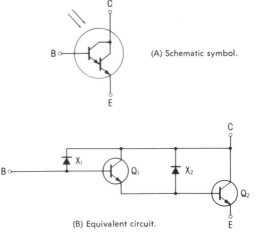

(A) Schematic symbol.

(B) Equivalent circuit.

FIGURE 8–28
Darlington-connected phototransistor.

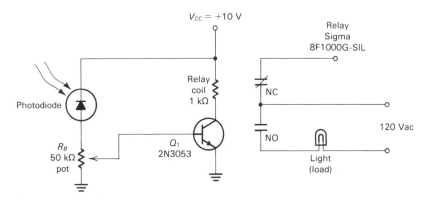

FIGURE 8–29
Photodiode relay control.

position items that are passing along an assembly line. This output is used to drive a servomotor system that controls assembly line movement. The principle of operation for this circuit is that when the photodiodes conduct equally, the op-amp output will cause the assembly line to stop for a predetermined period. This circuit application provides exact positioning control.

A phototransistor is often more desirable to use in control circuitry than the photodiode because of its built-in amplifying capability. The

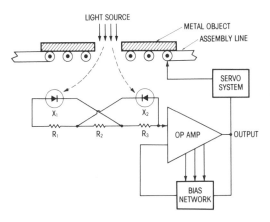

FIGURE 8–30
Photodiode applications.

phototransistor may be used in circuits that are controlled by either the presence or absence of light. Figure 8–31 shows a circuit in which light causes the SCR to turn on. When the phototransistor (Q_1) has no light applied, base current through Q_2 is minimum. However, when light strikes the phototransistor, it becomes conductive and causes Q_2 to go into conduction. When Q_2 conducts, gate current flows into the SCR, causing it to be triggered. Conduction of the SCR causes the light to be energized. Once the load has been energized, it continues to remain in the on state even when the light source has been removed. To reset the SCR, the reset button must be momentarily depressed. This prepares the circuit to accept the next change in light energy.

A phototransistor can be used to energize a load with the absence of light. This type of circuit is frequently used to energize an emergency light source in the event of a power failure. It could also be described as an automatic night light. Figure 8–32 shows a phototransistor driving a power transistor for direct control of a 6-V lamp. Specifically, the circuit is reverse connected. This means that, with light applied, Q_1 is on and Q_2 is cut off. The load or lamp L_1 is off. The circuit remains in this

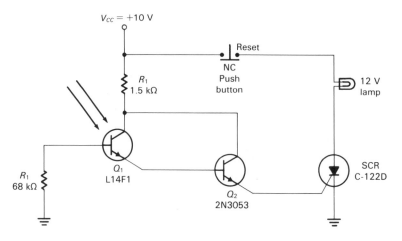

FIGURE 8–31
Phototransistor control circuit.

condition as long as light of a suitable intensity is applied to Q_1.

Assume now that the light intensity applied to Q_1 is suitable enough to cause conduction. This condition causes current carriers (holes and electrons) to return to the depletion region of the reverse-biased E–B junction of Q_1. As a result of this condition, there is an increase in base current (I_B). An increase in I_B causes a corresponding increase in I_C. The collector–emitter voltage of Q_1 then drops to a rather small value. With Q_1 being directly coupled to Q_2, the value of V_{CE} will not provide a suitable I_B for Q_2 to be conductive. As a result, Q_2 is

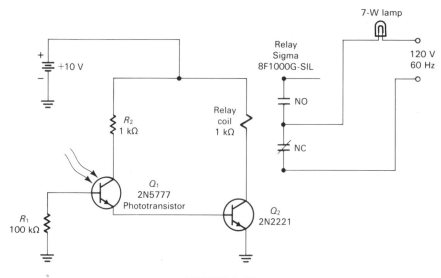

FIGURE 8–32
Phototransistor control circuit.

cut off and no current is supplied to lamp L_1. The lamp is off and will remain in this state.

If the light intensity applied to Q_1 drops below an ambient value based on the value of R_1, the transistor is driven to cutoff. This condition causes the V_{CE} of Q_1 to rise in value. With an increase in V_{CE}, the base current of Q_2 rises. This causes a corresponding increase in I_C, which is then great enough to energize L_1. The lamp continues to be conductive as long as the light intensity of Q_1 remains at a low level. At a low level of light, the lamp is on; a high level of light causes the lamp to be off. The conduction of lamp current, in this case, is based on the current-handling capability of Q_2. All the load current must pass through Q_2. It must therefore have a power dissipation rating that will handle the lamp used in the circuit.

Phototransistors in general are not very widely used today as discrete component con-

trol devices. As a rule, other optoelectronic devices can achieve control equally as well and in many cases much better than a single phototransistor. Phototransistors are, however, very commonly used in optocoupling devices today. This application permits the interfacing of a computer output to a high-current or high-voltage source with excellent isolation. Light energy of radiation is coupled from an LED to a phototransistor without a direct electrical connection between the two devices. This permits electrical signal transfer between equipment without the hazards of a direct electrical connection. A variety of optocoupling devices is available today. This will be discussed in a later section of this chapter.

The Darlington-connected phototransistor may also be used as a discrete component control device. Figure 8–33 shows a photo-Darlington transistor used with a transistor amplifier to control a relay. The Darlington device

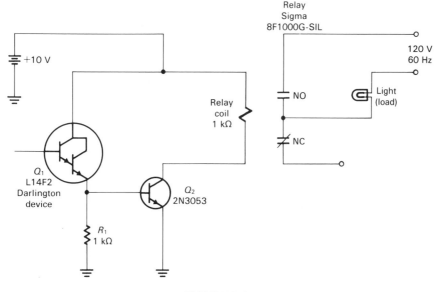

FIGURE 8–33
Darlington-connected phototransistor
application.

is used to control transistor base current. The relay in this circuit activates when the light level drops. Thus the load connected across the normally open (NO) contacts will be energized.

Avalanche Photodiodes

For practically all semiconductor devices that exist today, there is an optoelectronic counterpart. We have already discussed the photodiode and phototransistor, which respond to light variations rather than electrical variations. The avalanche photodiode is a special-purpose optoelectronic device similar to a zener diode. It is designed to operate in the reverse breakdown region. We know from *pn* junction diode characteristics that when electrons drift into the reverse breakdown or avalanche region of operation they become accelerated to a high speed. When an electron strikes another atom, more electrons are dislodged from their parent atoms. This process is cumulative as additional electrons are caused to break away from their atomic structure. The absorption of light energy can produce this cumulative effect of breaking away electrons as current carriers. A small amount of light energy can cause many current carriers to be generated. The avalanche diode is similar in its operation to a vacuum tube photomultiplier tube. Therefore, we have a semiconductor counterpart of the phototube multiplier. Applications of avalanche photodiodes include high-speed detection of light energy and sensitive detectors for modulated light from lasers and light-emitting diodes.

Photo-field-effect Transistors

A photo-field-effect transistor or photo-FET (PFET) with its crystal structure is shown in Figure 8–34. This optoelectronic device is

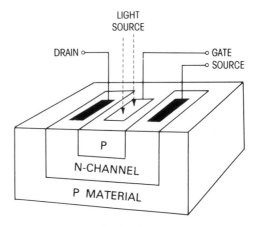

(A) Structure.

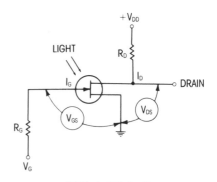

(B) Photo-FET circuit.

**FIGURE 8–34
Photo-FET.**

similar in many ways to a conventional junction field-effect transistor. Its construction has a lens that focuses light on a sensitive photodiode gate. This diode is normally operated in the reverse-biased direction. In the circuit of Figure 8–34(B), when light energy strikes the photodiode gate–channel junction, it changes the value of the reverse-biased voltage appearing across resistor R_G. A very small amount of reverse-biased gate current lowers the value of the gate voltage. A reduction in the reverse-biased gate voltage V_G causes a corresponding increase in drain current through the channel.

A photo-FET is quite different in operation

from that of a conventional JFET. The gate impedance is extremely high when the photodiode junction is dark. An increase in light intensity tends to lower the gate impedance. Some photocurrent must flow in the gate circuit of a PFET. This could be compared with the leakage gate current of a JFET. The gate leakage current of a JFET and the gate photocurrent of a PFET are both temperature dependent. PFETs as a rule do not produce a very significant amount of drain current. The drain current can, however, be controlled by light instead of voltage. Photo-FETs are one of the newest members of the solid-state optoelectronic family.

A PFET used as a light control is shown in Figure 8–35. In this circuit, very little power is consumed in darkness owing to the high impedance of the channel. The output voltage will be at its highest value and the drain current will be extremely low or zero. The gate voltage will have an extremely high reverse-biased voltage. When the gate is exposed to light, there is a corresponding increase in drain current and a reduction in drain voltage. This is reflected in the output voltage that is developed across the source–drain. The power output of this circuit is very small and primarily used to drive another active device. PFET control circuits are not very widely used in industrial circuitry today.

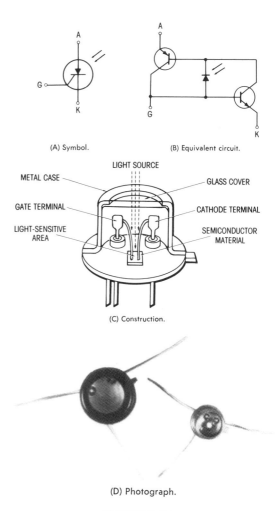

(A) Symbol.   (B) Equivalent circuit.

(C) Construction.

(D) Photograph.

FIGURE 8–36
Light-activated SCR (LASCR).

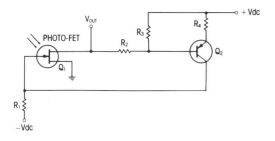

FIGURE 8–35
Photo-FET applications.

Light-activated SCRs

An optoelectronic device that has become a very popular control element is the light-activated silicon-controlled rectifier, or LASCR. The LASCR is shown in Figure 8–36. We know that SCRs are four-layer *pnpn* devices that act as semiconductor switches for handling large amounts of current. The SCR is similar

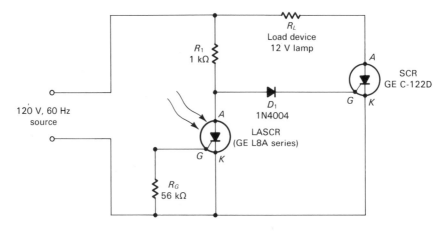

FIGURE 8–37
Reverse-connected LASCR control circuit.

to a latching relay that changes from a high-resistance state to a low-resistance state when a trigger pulse is applied to its gate terminal. The LASCR is a semiconductor optoelectronic switch which has a lens that focuses light on its gate. It is triggered into conduction by light rather than by an electrical trigger pulse. Its power-handling capability far exceeds that of the other semiconductor optoelectronic devices discussed. LASCRs may be used as switching devices in systems for counting, sorting, or similar functions where a circuit must be switched on and off. The LASCR uses a small amount of light energy to control a much larger amount of electrical energy.

An application of the LASCR is shown in Figure 8–37. Here the LASCR serves as a control device that alters the conduction of a conventional SCR. When the conventional SCR goes into conduction, current flows into the load device. In this circuit the LASCR serves as part of a voltage-divider network that controls the ac source voltage to the gate of the SCR. The circuit shown here is described as being reverse connected. With no light applied to the LASCR, current flows through the SCR and the load device. When light is applied, the load becomes nonconductive and switches to

its off state. With the SCR energized by an ac source, it turns off without a reduction in gate current after one alternation.

When no light is applied to the LASCR of Figure 8–37, it functions as a nonconductive device. Essentially, this means that an open condition exists between its anode–cathode terminals. As a result of this, full gate current is applied to the SCR through R_1 and D_1. The SCR becomes fully conductive and the load is energized. This condition continues as long as ac power is supplied to the circuit.

When light is applied to the LASCR, it becomes conductive. Its anode–cathode drops to an extremely low resistant value. In a sense, the LASCR responds as a ''low resistant short'' for the gate current of the SCR. Hence the I_G of the SCR drops in value. With ac energizing the SCR, a reduction in gate current causes the SCR to be nonconductive. The load, which is controlled by the SCR, then becomes inoperative. This means that no light will cause full conduction of the load and light applied to the LASCR will cause the load to be nonconductive. Reverse conduction of this type could be used to detect the absence of an object in a production line.

A LASCR circuit with forward conduction

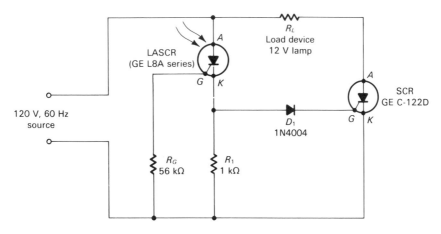

FIGURE 8–38
Forward-connected LASCR control circuit.

is shown in Figure 8–38. In this circuit, the locations of the LASCR and resistor R_1 have been transposed. Conduction of the SCR will not occur unless light is applied to the LASCR. With light applied, the LASCR becomes conductive and I_G flows into D_1 and the gate of the SCR. The load device then becomes conductive or turns on. Without light, the LASCR is nonconductive. No gate current flows into the SCR and the load is in an off state. Forward conduction means that light causes conduction of the load, and no light causes the load to be nonconductive. Forward conduction of this type could be used to detect "log jamming" of a conveyor belt assembly line. A large accumulation of objects at one point in the production line would shut down the conveyor motor drive assembly.

Photovoltaic Cells

The photovoltaic cell, commonly called a *solar cell,* is used to convert light energy into electrical energy. Since this process represents a direct energy conversion, a great deal of research has been conducted in an attempt to convert large amounts of light energy into electrical energy. A common application of the solar cell is for photographic light-exposure meters. The electrical output of the solar cell is proportional to the amount of light falling onto its surface. The output of the solar cell is used to energize a light-intensity meter.

The construction of a photovoltaic cell is shown in Figure 8–39. This selenium cell has a layer of selenium deposited on a metal base, then a layer of cadmium. In the fabrication, one layer of cadmium selenide and another layer of cadmium oxide are produced. A transparent conductive film is placed over the cadmium oxide, and a section of conductive alloy is then placed on the film. External leads are connected to the conductive material around the cadmium oxide layer and the metal base. When light strikes the cadmium oxide layer, electrons are emitted and move toward the external load device. A deficiency of electrons is then created in this region, which is filled by electrons from the cadmium selenide. Electrons from the metal contact then flow into the cadmium selenide. The metal contact plate then becomes positive. Thus light energy causes a difference in potential to exist between the two external terminals.

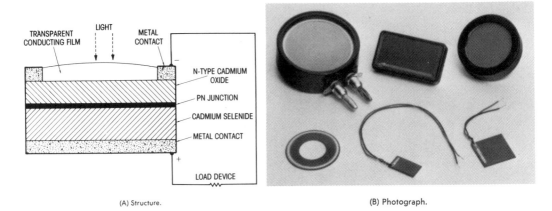

(A) Structure.

(B) Photograph.

FIGURE 8–39
Selenium photovoltaic cells. (Courtesy of EG & G Vactec)

Selenium cells have a very low efficiency for converting light energy into electrical voltage. Typical efficiency ratings are less than 1%. A great deal of light and an extremely large active area are needed to produce electrical energy of any significant value. Selenium photovoltaic cells, however, have a spectral response that is very similar to that of the human eye. In many applications the spectral response is much more significant than a high level of output efficiency.

Silicon photovoltaic cells are used much more readily today than the selenium units. Silicon cells have efficiencies as high as 15%. The more common silicon photovoltaic cell is shown in Figure 8–40. When no light is focused onto the silicon cell, it operates similarly to a conventional *pn* junction diode. When light strikes the cell, a voltage is developed across the external leads. The more intense the light, the greater the potential difference across the cell.

Photovoltaic cells are used for a variety of applications. Although their electrical output is low, they may be used with amplifying devices to develop an output that will drive a relay or

some other load device. One such application is shown in Figure 8–41. In this circuit, the output of the photovoltaic cell is amplified by transistor Q_1 so that, when light strikes the photovoltaic cell, the base current (I_B) of the transistor increases. The increase in I_B is amplified by Q_1, causing a collector current (I_C) that is of sufficient value to cause the relay to activate. The load connected across the relay terminals could be turned either off or on by the presence of light on the photovoltaic cell.

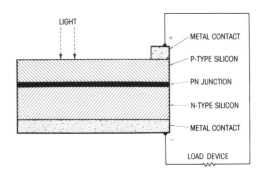

FIGURE 8–40
Silicon photovoltaic cell.

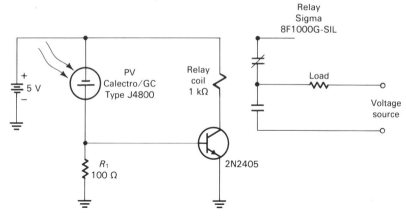

FIGURE 8–41
Photovoltaic cell relay control circuit.

Photoresistive Devices

Photoresistive devices are designed to change their electrical conductivity when variations of light energy occur. Such devices are also called *light-dependent resistors* (LDRs), since their resistance varies in inverse proportion to their conductivity. The cadmium sulfide (CaS) cell, shown in Figure 8–42, is a common type of photoconductive cell. When exposed to varying intensities of visible light, the cadmium sulfide cell changes resistance. An increase in light energy falling onto its surface increases the cell's conductivity. The cell is highly sensitive to variations of light intensity. These devices are typically used in alarm and relay control systems.

The operational principle of a photoconduc-

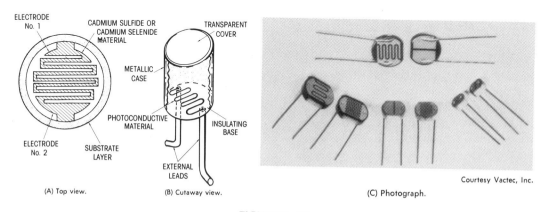

(A) Top view.

(B) Cutaway view.

(C) Photograph.

Courtesy Vactec, Inc.

FIGURE 8–42
Cadmium sulfide photoconductive cell.
(Courtesy of EG & G Vactec)

tive cell is that, when light strikes its surface, valence electrons of the semiconductor material are released from their atomic bonds. When electrons are released, the resistance of the material decreases. We may also say that the material becomes more conductive. If the light intensity is increased, more electrons are released and the material becomes more conductive. The resistance of photoconductive devices may range from several megohms in darkness to 50 to 100 Ω in fairly intense light. Note that the spectral response curve of a cadmium sulfide photoconductive cell very closely resembles the spectral response of the human eye.

An application of the photoconductive cell is shown in Figure 8–43. In this circuit, SCR$_1$ conducts when light is focused onto the photoconductive cell. When light strikes the photocell, its resistance decreases. The potential at point A becomes more positive and causes gate current (I_G) to flow. A sufficient amount of gate current triggers the SCR into conduction. When SCR$_1$ conducts, the load device is activated. The SCR then conducts until its anode circuit is opened. Variable resistor R_1 is used as a sensitivity adjustment to control the level of light required to cause the SCR to conduct.

Infrared Detectors

Another type of device that responds to radiant energy is referred to as an *infrared detector*. These devices respond to radiation in the infrared region of the electromagnetic spectrum (See Figure 8–2). Infrared detectors have been used for military applications for many years. These include guided missile systems, night detection scopes, haze detection, and infrared photography. Also, many industrial applications of infrared devices are now common. These include heat-sensitive control systems, optopyrometers, and infrared spectroscopy for gas analysis.

An important principle of infrared detection is that all objects emit infrared radiation. Infrared camera systems have been devised that can produce images in darkness by detecting infrared thermal radiation. Since the human body emits thermal infrared radiation, infrared detectors may be used to detect individuals in darkness with no light source used. This application is used in security applications.

Ultraviolet Detectors

Detectors have also been designed that respond to electromagnetic radiation in the ultraviolet range (see Figure 8–2). Many design problems have been encountered with ultraviolet detectors; therefore, they are not used as often as detectors for the visible light and infrared regions of the spectrum. Two types of optoelectronic devices that may be designed for use in the ultraviolet region are multiplier phototubes and cadmium selenide photoconductive cells.

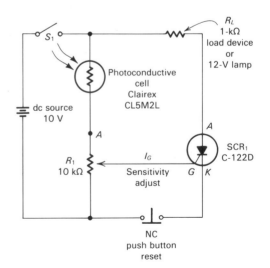

FIGURE 8–43
Photoconductive cell applications.

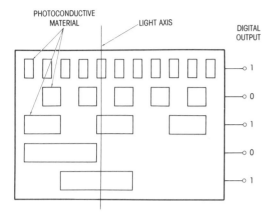

FIGURE 8–44
Digital readout position indicator.

Optoelectronic Position Detectors

Various types of optoelectronic devices have been designed to sense the position of a light beam. These devices ordinarily produce an electrical output based on the position of a light beam. These devices may be used with digital systems to produce electrical outputs as shown in Figure 8–44. The electrical signal output is based on the patterns of the photoconductive material onto which the light line is focused.

Photopotentiometric Devices

We previously discussed photoresistive devices. The photoresistive principle may be extended to design photopotentiometric devices. A photopotentiometer uses a light beam rather than a wiper contact such as a conventional potentiometer uses. Thus many of the problems associated with potentiometers may be avoided by using a photopotentiometer.

The operational theory of a photopotentiometer is shown in Figure 8–45. A precision wire-wound or composition resistive material is used to establish the potentiometer's maximum resistance between points A and C. Point B is the variable contact. A light beam is focused between the resistive material and a metal base. Between the metal base and the resistive material, a photoconductive material is used. The resistance of the photoconductive material varies according to the light exposed to its surface area. Conduction from either terminal A or terminal C to terminal B of the photopotentiometer depends on the position of the light beam. The light beam may be focused anywhere along the entire length of the resistive material. Thus a variable resistance between points A and B and C and B may be accomplished by adjusting the position of the light beam.

Optoelectronic Couplers

Optoelectronic couplers, which are sometimes referred to as *optoisolators,* provide a one-way transfer path for electrical signals. Optoelectronic couplers are commonly manufactured in dual in-line packages as shown in Figure 8–46(A). Note the equivalent circuit of the optoelectronic coupler [Figure 8–46(B)]. A light-

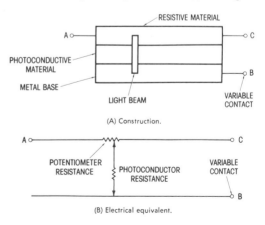

(A) Construction.

(B) Electrical equivalent.

FIGURE 8–45
Photopotentiometer.

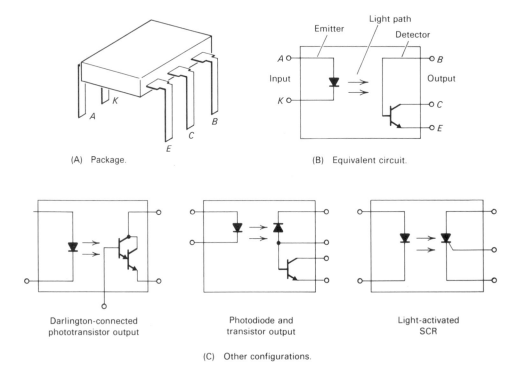

(A) Package.

(B) Equivalent circuit.

Darlington-connected
phototransistor output

Photodiode and
transistor output

Light-activated
SCR

(C) Other configurations.

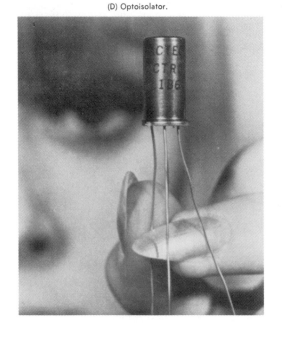

(D) Optoisolator.

FIGURE 8–46
Optoelectronic couplers: (A) package; (B) equivalent circuit; (C) other configurations; (D) optoisolator. (Courtesy of EG & G Vactec)

emitting diode (LED) or infrared emitting diode (IRED) is combined with a transistor amplifier in the same package. The input of this device is the LED; the output is the transistor circuit. The collector current of the transistor varies in direct proportion to the current through the LED. Therefore, when an input signal is applied to the LED, it emits light in proportion to the applied signal voltage. The light causes the transistor to conduct, thus increasing the collector current. This is achieved with no electrical connection between the devices that compose the coupler. Isolation of the two circuits is therefore achieved.

Optoelectronic couplers may be used advantageously for many coupling requirements.

They are not as bulky as transformers and they last for longer periods. Their input-output characteristics are relatively linear in terms of LED current versus transistor collector current. They may be used for rapid-response applications, as well as for isolation between a power source and the load and isolation of noise from electronic circuits. The amount of isolation between the two portions of the optoelectronic coupler is determined by the material in the light path and the distance between the LED and the transistor detector. As the distance between these portions increases, greater isolation is achieved. However, as the distance increases, the current transfer ratio between the two devices decreases, causing signal transfer to become poorer. Therefore, a compromise must be made between isolation and current transfer for optimum results. Other electronic couplers are available for voltage isolation requirements as high as 50,000 V.

Optoelectronic couplers may be manufactured in a variety of different ways. By adding additional electronic elements in combination with the detector, better sensitivity and response time can be achieved. The equivalent symbols for optoelectronic couplers using (1) a Darlington-connected phototransistor output detector, (2) a photodiode and transistor output detector, and (3) a light-activated silicon-controlled rectifier detector output are shown in Figure 8–46(C). Other configurations of emitters and detectors may be used for specialized coupling or isolation applications. Some typical applications of optoelectronic couplers are in telephone communications, relay control, dc power control, and high-voltage ac switching.

Optoelectronic couplers have numerous industrial applications. Figure 8–47(A) shows an optocoupler time-delay circuit. The time delay is brought about by the combination of R_1 and C_1. The LED is shunted by C_1, and therefore turn-on of the LED is delayed by the time constant of $R_1 C_1$. After the time interval required

to activate the LED, an output is produced at the collector of the transistor detector. In this circuit, the time-delay elements are isolated from the controlled circuit.

Figure 8–47(B) shows an optocoupler switch that uses an SCR detector. A trigger pulse applied to the LED causes the SCR to conduct. The conductive SCR then causes current to flow through an external load. Again, the detector is electrically isolated from the circuit that controls it.

Figure 8–47(C) illustrates a pair of LASCR optoelectronic couplers used as an ac relay. The optocouplers are connected in a back-to-back configuration so that a trigger pulse of

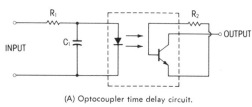

(A) Optocoupler time delay circuit.

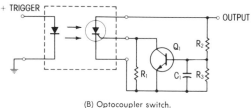

(B) Optocoupler switch.

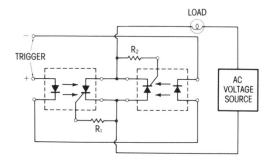

(C) Optocoupler ac relay.

FIGURE 8–47
Optoelectronic coupler applications.

proper polarity applied to either LED element causes the corresponding SCR detector to conduct. SCR conduction causes the load, which is connected to an ac source, to be activated.

Ruby Lasers

The development of the laser has had a significant impact on industrial systems and promises many more potential uses in the future. Lasers are presently used in welding and industrial measurement. The major advantage of lasers is that their radiation can travel long distances with relatively little divergence at one wavelength. This is in contrast to other light sources, which have poor directional and wideband wavelength characteristics.

The term *laser* means "light amplification by stimulated emission of radiation." This principle may be illustrated by referring to the simplified diagram of a ruby laser shown in Figure 8–48. When the xenon flash tube is activated, the chromium atoms contained in the ruby rod absorb photons of light owing to the xenon flash tube action. The chromium atoms then are caused to emit photons of energy. Many of these photons of light energy are reflected back and forth through the ruby rod by the mirrors on each end. The concentration of photon energy within the ruby causes *stimulated emission*. The chromium atoms emit photons of light energy owing to the initial action of the xenon flash tube. These atoms emit photons in the same direction and phase as the initiating photons from the xenon flash tube. The cumulative action that takes place causes a laser beam to be emitted through the partially reflecting mirror at one end of the ruby rod. The laser beam is very concentrated and penetrates the mirror due to stimulated emission or light amplification.

Gas Lasers

Another laser light source is the gas laser. A very popular type of gas laser is the helium–neon laser; however, many other types are now available that use basically the same operational principle. The helium–neon gas laser is shown in Figure 8–49. A high dc potential is applied to the plasma tube by means of a voltage multiplier circuit and a pulse transformer. The filament contained within the plasma tube is heated by a 6.3 V ac potential. This filament, when heated, is a source of electrons that are accelerated by the high dc potential.

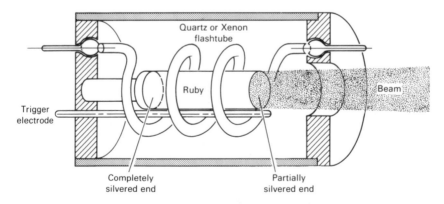

FIGURE 8–48
Ruby laser.

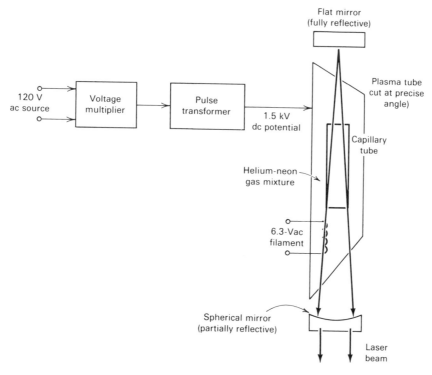

FIGURE 8–49
Helium–neon gas laser.

As the electrons from the filament are accelerated toward the high dc potential, they strike helium–neon gas atoms and cause them to ionize. The ionized gas causes the emission of light similar to the action of a fluorescent light. The light beams reflect from the flat, fully reflective mirror shown at the top of Figure 8–49. The plasma tube is cut at a precise angle to cause a controlled reflective angle through the capillary tube. The light is reflected back toward the partially reflective spherical mirror, where it is concentrated, owing to the action of this mirror, into a laser beam that is emitted through the mirror. A beam reflects back and forth between the mirrors several times before it is emitted. Again, the emitted light beam is produced by light amplification of stimulated emission. Other types of gas lasers are the argon laser, helium–cadmium laser, and CO_2 laser.

Semiconductor Lasers

It is possible today to generate laser beams by utilizing semiconductor principles. These lasers have a resonant cavity similar to other lasers except that they are formed on a chip of semiconductor material. A semiconductor injection laser is shown in Figure 8–50. This type of laser is very efficient and small in size compared to other types. Injection lasers are similar to light-emitting diodes in operational principle. The end faces of a gallium arsenide chip, shown in Figure 8–50(A), must be carefully fabricated so that they are parallel and

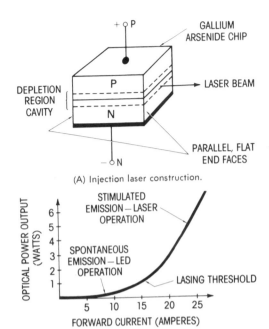

(A) Injection laser construction.

(B) Current versus optical power output.

FIGURE 8–50
Semiconductor lasers.

flat. Since gallium arsenide is a reflective material, no mirrors are needed to produce reflection. This is a distinct advantage of the semiconductor injection laser. In some injection lasers, a film of silver or gold is deposited over one end so that the other end will serve as the only emitter of light.

As mentioned previously, the semiconductor injection laser operates similarly to an LED. As current flows through the semiconductor chip, light is emitted from the material. Stimulated emission of light energy occurs when atoms collide near the *pn* junction of the material and cause the release of additional photons of energy. Due to the reflective properties of gallium arsenide, a wave of photons is developed between the flat, reflective surfaces of the material. The back and forth movement of this wave of photons creates the

resonant action required for the stimulated emission of radiation. Note in Figure 8–50(B) that the injection laser operates just as an LED until a value referred to as the *lasing threshold* is reached. Beyond the lasing threshold, stimulated emission results, as shown by the linear rise in power output with increases in forward current. Typical lasers of this type emit 0.5 to 50 W of energy at room temperature when operated in a pulsed condition (rather than continuously). The high current necessary to sustain emission would destroy the laser if it were applied continuously. For this reason, semiconductor injection lasers are often operated at cryogenic temperatures. Industrial applications of lasers are shown in Figure 8–51.

X-Ray Application

When we look at the electromagnetic spectrum of Figure 8–2 we find a band of frequencies, above the frequency of visible light, called x-rays. Certain industrial applications rely on x-rays. And we are all familiar with the applications of x-rays in medical technology. A rare metal called radium is known to emit three kinds of rays, called alpha, beta, and gamma rays. Some of these rays can pass through the human body and are frequently used in medical treatment and analysis.

It is possible to use a vacuum tube, such as illustrated in Figure 8–52, to produce rays similar to those emitted by radium. This x-ray tube has a cathode that is heated by the application of a filament voltage. The anode is constructed of very heavy metal and has a high positive potential applied. This high positive potential accelerates the electrons emitted from the cathode at a very rapid rate. The electrons strike the anode with such velocity that x-rays are generated and move away from the anode surface. If the dc anode–cathode potential is

(A) Laser interferometer system used for laser measurement applications.

(B) Laser system to align milling machine setup.

(C) Laser system used for measurement.

FIGURE 8–51
Industrial application of a laser. (Courtesy of Hewlett-Packard)

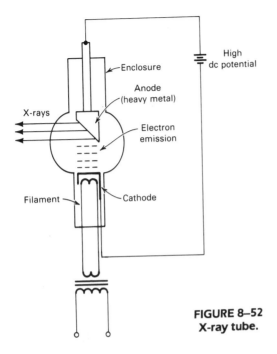

FIGURE 8–52
X-ray tube.

increased, the frequency of the generated x-rays also increases. An increase in frequency causes a corresponding decrease in wavelength.

X-ray tubes now operate with dc anode potentials in excess of 1 million volts. The x-rays produced by this high dc voltage are similar to the high-frequency gamma rays emitted by radium. X-rays in industry are used to analyze metals and to provide a means of controlling industrial processes that involve metals. The short wavelength of x-rays allows them to pass through metals and reveal the inner structural characteristics of various metal parts.

OPTOELECTRONIC SYSTEM APPLICATIONS

Several applications of optoelectronic systems in industry have been discussed in the previous sections. There are so many applications of op-

toelectronic systems today that it would be rather difficult to categorize all of them. An understanding of how these devices operate is basic to the design of circuits that incorporate them for a specific application. The previous sections have attempted to show some of the basic operational characteristics of typical optoelectronic devices.

Optoelectronic control systems in industry are becoming more prevalent each day. As new optoelectronic devices are developed, new ways of utilizing them will result. In the following sections, we will discuss some of the general types of controls that utilize optoelectronic devices and some circuits that may be used for optoelectronic control.

General Types of Industrial Optoelectronic Control

Many industrial manufacturing processes are now being controlled by optoelectronic systems. As a rule, it is rather difficult to categorize these processes into common groups. We will therefore attempt to discuss only those applications that are widely used. Some of the more popular applications are the following:

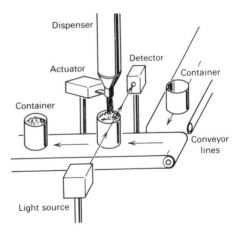

FIGURE 8–53
Level control.

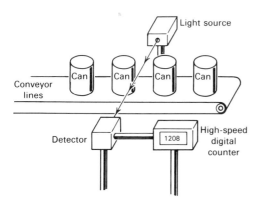

FIGURE 8–54
High-speed counting.

1. Level control
2. High-speed counting
3. Sorting and routing
4. Detecting position
5. Automatic inspection
6. Preventing conveyor jamming
7. Safety hazard detection
8. Automatic stacking
9. Measurement

Level Control

Level control is accomplished by placing the light source at the same height above the conveyor line as the desired level of fill of a container. In the illustration of Figure 8–53, containers on a conveyor line are positioned under a material dispenser. When the container is in position, the actuator causes the dispenser to allow material to pass into the container. When the material reaches the level of the light source, the light beam is interrupted. With no light striking its surface, the detector causes a relay to activate. The activated relay, in turn, causes the actuator on the dispenser to close. When another container is in position, the ac-

tuator opens once more. This control system ensures a uniform level of material in each container.

High-speed Counting

High-speed counting is also accomplished by the interruption of a light source. In this application, as shown in Figure 8–54, a precise beam of light is focused onto a detector. When the light beam is broken, the electronic counter is activated. High-speed counters may be used to count items at a rate of over 100 per second.

Sorting and Routing

Sorting and routing are conveyor processes that involve the sorting of unlike items and their routing to different locations. Items are typically sorted by size or by register marks. Figure 8–55 shows how cartons filled with different items may be sorted and routed by using register marks. A register mark is reflective and therefore causes a light-sensitive device to change condition when light focuses onto it. In the example shown, some cartons have one register mark and others have two marks. Cartons with one register mark activate the control, which pushes them onto conveyor line 1. Those cartons with two marks are pushed onto line 2. This system could be used for any number of conveyor lines.

Detecting Position

The detection of position is important for many industrial processes. Figure 8–56 shows one method of detecting position. In this case, the height of the items is detected. Items of each height are counted by separate optoelectronic counting circuits. The counting circuits are designed so that counter 1 counts the smaller items. Counter 2 counts only when both source

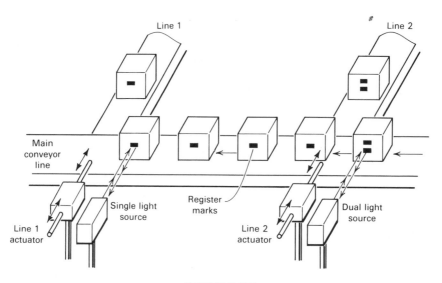

FIGURE 8–55
Sorting and routing.

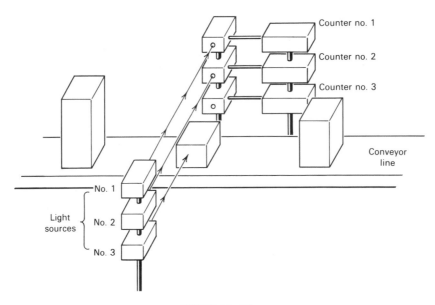

FIGURE 8–56
Detecting position.

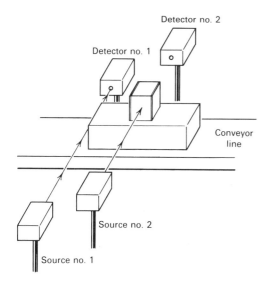

FIGURE 8–57
Automatic Inspection.

1 and source 3 are interrupted. Counter 3 counts when sources 1, 2, and 3 are interrupted. Therefore, the position, in this case height of the object, determines which counter is activated.

Automatic Inspection

Many industrial operations must be continuously or periodically inspected to ensure accuracy of construction or that no parts are defective or missing. Several types of inspection may be accomplished by optoelectronic systems. Figure 8–57 shows an example of how workpieces may be inspected for possible missing parts. As a workpiece passes down the conveyor line, source 1 is interrupted when the workpiece passes. Source 1 serves as a reference or locator. At the instant source 1 is interrupted, source 2 should also be interrupted. Source 2 is used to check the location of the portion of the workpiece located in the center.

If the center portion is missing, source 2 will not be interrupted. A control circuit is designed to cause an actuator to remove the workpiece from the conveyor line if the center portion of the workpiece is missing. This method could be used to make several inspections of more complicated workpieces.

Preventing Conveyor Jamming

Another common use of optoelectronic systems is to prevent conveyor jamming. Figure 8–58 shows an example of how this operation could be accomplished. Each part that passes through the light source interrupts the light beam and causes a timer to start. If the light beam remains interrupted by parts that are jammed together, the length of the timing period causes the conveyor motor to turn off or slow down so that jamming does not continue. Another timing period controls the amount of time that the conveyor motor remains off or slower in speed.

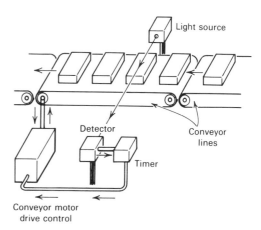

FIGURE 8–58
Preventing conveyor jamming.

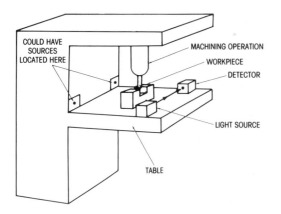

FIGURE 8–59
Safety hazard detection.

Safety Hazard Detection _____

Some machines used in industry are dangerous to use if not operated properly. Machine operators must be constantly alert to avoid accidents. It is possible to use optoelectronic sys-

tems to rapidly switch a machine off when the operator makes a mistake that might injure him or her in some way. An example of safety hazard detection is shown in Figure 8–59. When the machine operator places his or her hands on the table while the machine is running, a light beam is interrupted. Interruption of the light beam causes the machine to turn off. Thus, if the operator gets too near the machining operation, the machine automatically stops. This method could eliminate many industrial accidents.

Automatic Stacking _____

Figure 8–60 shows a conveyor line situation in which metal plates are being stacked onto a conveyor. It is possible to use optoelectronic systems to stack a desired amount of objects. In this case, a light source is interrupted as each metal plate passes through it from con-

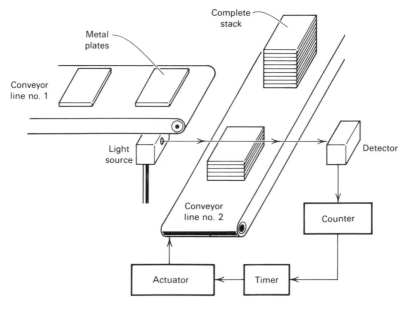

FIGURE 8–60
Automatic stacking.

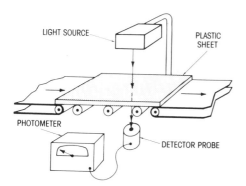

FIGURE 8–61
Optoelectronic measurement.

veyor line 1. When the light source is broken, the counter connected to it is activated. When the desired number of metal plates has been stacked, conveyor line 2 is moved so that another stack can be started. Automatic stacking could also be accomplished by positioning the light beam at the desired height of the stack. When the objects are stacked to this height, conveyor line 1 stops and conveyor line 2 moves so that another stack can be started.

Measurement _____

Optoelectronic systems are readily adaptable to several types of measurement. An instrument called a *photometer* is used to measure illumination. This meter may be used to measure the luminous intensity of light sources, to set light levels, and for other optical measurements. An example is shown in Figure 8–61 of an industrial measurement application using a photometer. The photometer uses an optoelectronic detector in its probe to serve as a transducer for the instrument. In the example shown, the density of sheet plastic is being checked by the deflection produced on the photometer. The probe detector is a photovoltaic cell that changes its electrical output with variations in

light. The density of the sheet plastic should be consistent and, therefore, cause uniform deflection on the photometer. If a sheet of plastic does not have uniform density, the meter will indicate this. Thus a photometer may be used to sense changes in density of a translucent material.

QUESTIONS

1. What is meant by the term *optoelectronic?*

2. What are some industrial applications of optoelectronic systems?

3. Discuss the electromagnetic spectrum.

4. Define the following terms:

   a. Micrometer

   b. Millimicrometer

   c. Angstrom

   d. Candela

   e. Nanometer

   f. Lumen

   g. Lux

5. What are three classifications of optoelectronic detector devices? Discuss each type.

6. Discuss the operational characteristics and list some applications for each of the following devices.

   a. Phototube

   b. Multiplier phototube

   c. Photodiode

   d. Phototransistor

   e. Darlington-connected phototransistor

   f. Avalanche photodiode

g. Photo-FET

h. LASCR

i. LED

j. Photovoltaic cell

k. Photoconductive cell

l. Infrared detector

m. Ultraviolet detector

n. Position detector

o. Photopotentiometer

p. Optical fiber

q. Optoelectronic coupler

r. Ruby laser

s. Gas laser

t. Semiconductor laser

u. X-rays

7. What are some industrial applications of optoelectronic systems for process control? Discuss each application.

8. What is meant by the terms *through beam*, *reflex*, and *proximity detection?* What is the purpose of each of them.

9. System design must take into account such things as component matching, transmission medium, and optical coupling considerations. Why are these considerations important?

PROBLEMS

1. In what portion of the electromagnetic spectrum would each of the following wavelengths be?

   a. 1 meter (m)

b. 10^{-8} m

c. 10^5 m

d. 10^{12} m

e. 500 nanometers (nm)

f. 6×10^3 nm

g. 200 nm

h. 4×10^4 nm

2. What colors of visible light are produced by the following wavelengths?
   a. 700 nm

   b. 400 nm

   c. 600 nm

   d. 550 nm

   e. 480 nm

   f. 590 nm

3. Convert each of the wavelengths of Problem 2 to micrometers, and then to angstroms.

4. Using the phototube characteristic curves of Figure 8–24, draw a load line at 150 V and 5 mA and determine the following:
   a. Load resistance $(R_L) = V_{AK}/I_P$

   b. I_P when the light intensity is 0.06 lumen

   c. I_P when the light intensity is 0.04 lumen

   d. V_{AK} at 0.04 lumen of light intensity

   e. V_{AK} at 0.02 lumen of light intensity

5. Using the photodiode characteristic curves of Figure 8–26, draw a load line at 40 V and 400 μA and determine the following:

   a. Load resistance (R_L)

   b. Current (μA) when the light source is 1500 lux

c. Current (μA) when the light source is 1000 lux

d. Diode voltage with a light source of 500 lux

e. Diode voltage with a light source of 1500 lux

6. Using the phototransistor characteristic curves of Figure 8–27, draw a load line at 50 V and 20 mA and determine the following:

a. Load resistance $R_L = V_{CC}/L_C$

b. I_C with a light intensity of 0.06 lumen

c. I_C with a light intensity of 0.04 lumen

d. V_{CE} at 0.04 lumen

e. V_{CE} at 0.08 lumen

ACTIVITIES

ACTIVITY 8–1: Photodiode Control Circuit

Objective: To construct a photodiode control circuit and become familiar with its operation and measure circuit operating conditions.

Procedure:

1. Construct the photodiode control circuit of Figure 8–29.

2. Apply operating power to the circuit.

3. Apply light from an incandescent lamp to the photodiode. If the circuit is functional, the relay will actuate and the load will turn on. Adjust the potentiometer (R_1) to the most sensitive position. This is the point where the circuit will be actuated with the least amount of light.

4. Measure the base–emitter voltage when the transistor is off and when it is conductive. Record these values.

5. Measure the voltage across the photodiode and R_1 with light applied and without light applied. Record the measurements and analyze your findings.

6. Explain how this circuit controls the actuation of the relay.

ACTIVITY 8–2: Phototransistor Control of an SCR

Objective: Construction of a phototransistor SCR control circuit to become familiar with the operating characteristics of a phototransistor and to evaluate the performance of the circuit.

Procedure

1. Construct the phototransistor SCR control circuit of Figure 8–31. The base of the phototransistor is connected. This permits the transistor to be more sensitive to changes in light. It is possible to connect this same transistor with the base floating or not connected. Operation is primarily the same.

2. Apply operating power to the circuit. If the circuit is functional, light applied to Q_1 will cause transistor Q_2 to be conductive. This in turn will cause the SCR to receive gate current and be triggered into conduction. Since the SCR is energized by dc, it will latch and hold the load in its conduction state. To reset the circuit, momentarily depress the reset button.

3. Test the operation of the circuit several times.

4. Measure and record the V_{CE} of Q_1 and Q_2 and the V_{AK} of the SCR when light is applied and without light applied to Q_1.

5. Describe the operation of this circuit using the measured voltage values.

ACTIVITY 8–3: Phototransistor Circuit Control

Objective: Construction of a phototransistor circuit to become familiar with transistor circuit applications and operating characteristics.

Procedure:

1. Construct the phototransistor control circuit of Figure 8–32.

2. Apply power to the circuit and test its operation. If the circuit is properly connected, light applied to Q_1 will increase the base current of Q_2 to cause it to conduct and actuate the relay.

3. Measure the voltage at the collector of Q_1, the base of Q_2, and the collector of Q_2 with respect to ground for applied light, ambient light, and darkness. Make a chart showing these values.

4. If time permits, measure and record the I_C of Q_1, I_B of Q_2, and I_C of Q_2 for different responses to light.

ACTIVITY 8–4: Reverse-connected LASCR Control

Objective: Construction of a reverse-connected LASCR circuit and evaluation of its operation.

Procedure:

1. Construct the reverse-connected LASCR control circuit of Figure 8–37

2. Apply power to the circuit and test its operation. If the circuit is functioning properly, no light applied to the LASCR will cause gate current to trigger SCR_1. With light applied to the LASCR, it becomes conductive and shunts I_G to ground. This turns off the SCR, which is energized by

ac. The load should be on without light and off with light applied to the LASCR.

3. Measure V_{AK} of the LASCR with and without light applied.

4. Measure and record I_G of the SCR with and without light.

5. With an oscilloscope, observe the wave forms across the LASCR, SCR, and R_L for applied light and no applied light. Make a sketch of the observed wave forms.

ACTIVITY 8–5: Forward-connected LASCR Control

Objective: Construction of a forward-connected LASCR control circuit and evaluation of its operation.

Procedure:

1. Construct the forward-connected LASCR control circuit of Figure 8–38.

2. Apply operating power to the circuit. If the circuit is properly connected, the load will be off. When light is applied to the LASCR, it will conduct and trigger the SCR into conduction. This, in turn, will actuate the load device. Without light applied, the load will be off.

3. With applied light to the LASCR, measure and record the voltage across R_1, V_{AK} of the SCR, and V_{RL}. These are dc voltage values. V_{R1} is dependent on conduction of the LASCR. Apply light to the LASCR and measure the same voltages again. Record your measured values.

4. With an oscilloscope, observe the wave forms across the LASCR, SCR, and R_L when light is applied and not applied to the LASCR. Make a sketch of the observed wave forms.

5. Explain how the circuit responds to changes in light applied to the LASCR.

ACTIVITY 8–6: Photovoltaic Cell Circuit Control

Objective: Contruction of a photovoltaic cell control circuit to evaluate its operation.

Procedure:

1. Construct the photovoltaic cell control circuit of Figure 8–41.

2. Apply operational power to the circuit. If the circuit is functioning, light applied to P_v will energize the relay and turn on the load device.

3. Measure and record V_{R1} and V_{CE} with and without light applied to P_v.

4. Measure and record the I_B and I_C of Q_1 with and without light applied to P_v.

5. Explain how a change in light intensity applied to P_v will cause Q_1 to be conductive or not conductive.

ACTIVITY 8–7: Photoconductive Cell Control of an SCR

Objective: Construction of a photoconductive cell control circuit and evaluation of its operation.

Procedure:

1. Construct the photoconductive cell control circuit of Figure 8–43.

2. Test the resistance of the cell with an ohmmeter when light is applied and without light applied. Record the change in resistance that occurs.

3. Apply operational power to the circuit. Apply light to P_c to trigger the SCR into conduction and actuation of the load. It may

be necessary to adjust the sensitivity control to a suitable level of light that will produce triggering. Note that the load will remain actuated once the SCR has been triggered. The reset button is used to turn off the load.

4. Measure the I_G and I_{AK} with light applied and without light applied to P_c.

5. Turn off the power source and connect an equivalent value of ac to the circuit. A 1N4001 diode should be placed in series with the gate. The cathode of the diode should be connected to the gate and the anode to the potentiometer.

6. Apply power to the circuit and test its operation. With light applied to P_c, the load will be triggered; without light, the load will turn off. How do you account for this difference in operation?

ACTIVITY 8–8: Optocoupler Time-delay Circuitry

Objective: Construction of an optocoupler time-delay circuit to evaluate its operation.

Procedure:

1. Construct the optocoupler time-delay circuit of Figure 8–47(A).

2. Apply power to the input. With a voltmeter, measure and record the voltage across C_1. If the input is functioning, this voltage should rise to approximately 6 V and then drop in value during one time constant of $R_1 \times C_1$.

3. Apply power to the output. If this part of the circuit is functioning properly, the LED should flash with each change in the input voltage.

4. Connect an oscilloscope across the input capacitor and make a sketch of the ob-

served wave form. Connect the oscilloscope across the output. Make a sketch of the observed output wave form.

5. Desribe how a signal is coupled or transferred between the input and output of this optocoupler.

ACTIVITY 8–9: Optocoupler SCR Switch

Objective: Construction of an optocoupler SCR switch to evalute its operational characteristics.

Procedure:

1. Construct the optocoupler SCR ac switch of Figure 8–47(B).

2. Apply power to the circuit and test its operation. Press the push button to energize the load. Since ac is applied to the SCR, the load will only receive half-wave output when it is energized. The load will respond to very rapid changes in the input.

3. If the circuit is responding to push-button changes, remove the dc source and replace it with a square-wave generator. Apply a suitable value of input voltage that will trigger the coupler. Vary the frequency of the input to determine the manner in which the coupler responds.

4. Connect an oscilloscope to the input of the coupler and observe the input signal. Change the oscilloscope to the output and monitor the wave form. If at all possible, monitor the two wave forms on a dual-trace oscilloscope to observe signal delay. Make a sketch of your findings.

5. Explain how the output of this circuit is half-wave when the source is ac.

ACTIVITY 8–10: Optocoupler AC Relay

Objective: Construct an ac optocoupler relay and examine its operating characteristics.

Procedure:

1. Construct the optocoupler ac relay circuit of Figure 8–47(C).

2. Apply power to the load first. Under normal circumstances, the load should not be energized. Apply power to the input. This should energize the load.

3. With an oscilloscope, observe the wave form across the load. Turn off the input while observing the load. Adjust the oscilloscope to produce approximately 10 complete wave forms on the screen.

4. Replace the dc input with a suitable square-wave generator. Adjust the frequency of the generator to produce 6 pulses per second. How does this alter the display of the output? Adjust the square-wave input to some other frequency and observe the response of the output.

5. Carefully disconnect one of the gate resistors from the coupler. What influence does this have on the output?

6. Explain why two optocouplers are needed to achieve ac switch operation.

Of all the manufacturing processes utilized by industry today, temperature measurement and manipulation are by far the most common. In fact, over 50% of all measured variables in related fields of industry tend to involve some form of temperature measurement or change. With improved technology, the trend will obviously be toward even better and more improved measurement and control techniques.

Systems that utilize thermal processing must produce or generate heat, provide a path for it to follow, initiate some type of control action, utilize energy to accomplish a specific work function, and ultimately record temperature variations through precise measurement techniques. These functions are a major concern of all industrial personnel involved in process control applications. A basic understanding of the thermal system, its applications, and measuring instrumentation is of paramount importance to someone pursuing this field as a career.

THERMAL PROCESS SYSTEMS

Manufacturing processes that respond in some way to temperature are commonly classified as *thermal systems*. In industrial applications, thermal systems are used to control a wide range of processes, from complex manufacturing operations to single-function systems that control only one process. Our primary concern here is directed toward thermal system basics that can be applied to any application regardless of its size or complexity.

A thermal system must have a primary energy source, transmission path, control, a load, and possibly one or more indicators in order to function properly. These parts, you may recall, are the basic elements of all functioning systems. To distinguish this type of system from others, further classification is required. In

9

Thermal Systems

general, a thermal process system is defined as any system that responds in some way to changes in temperature. These systems may generate heat to produce molding or forming operations or respond to temperature changes that are used to control another process.

The energy source of a thermal system also requires some additional classification in order to distinguish it from other systems. Energy, for example, is present in three basic forms: heat, light, and mechanical motion. It is also available in the form of electricity, chemical action, and nuclear energy. These six forms of energy are all related to some extent. This relationship is based on the fact that energy of one form can be readily changed or transferred into one of the other existing forms. The energy source of a thermal system usually operates by changing energy from one form into something of a different type. In this regard, electricity and chemical action generally serve as the primary energy source of most industrial thermal systems. In addition, the sun can also be used as a primary source of thermal energy. A great deal of research is presently being done to make better use of the sun as a primary source of energy. Thermal energy may also be obtained by friction, compression, and mechanical action. Energy in any of these forms is generally rather difficult to harness as a primary source for an operating system.

The transmission path of a thermal system is unique when compared with other systems. The material of the path may be anything that is either solid, liquid, or gas. If one end of a solid metal bar is placed in an open-flame heat source, the other end of the bar will soon become hot. The process by which heat is transferred from the heated end of the bar to the cold end is called *conduction*. According to the kinetic theory of energy, conduction is the transfer of heat through the collision of molecules. Essentially, heat from the source causes molecules at one end of the bar to move more rapidly. Increased molecule velocity ultimately

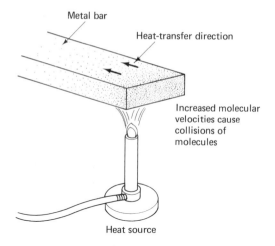

FIGURE 9–1
Heat-conduction principle.

causes collisions with neighboring molecules, which in turn cause them to move faster. The process continues until molecular motion has increased throughout the bar. In solid materials the metals are the best thermal conductors, whereas nonmetals in general serve as insulators, or nonconductors, of heat. Figure 9–1 shows an example of the conduction principle of heat transmission.

Liquids and gases are primarily heated by the convection process. When a container of liquid is placed on a heat source, at first only the liquid at the bottom of the container receives heat. In this case heat is transferred by conduction. Since most liquids are rather poor conductors of heat, very little heat is transferred to other parts of the liquid. As the bottom layer of the liquid begins to expand, it becomes less dense than the cooler water above it. The warmer liquid therefore moves to the top of the container and the colder liquid circulates to the bottom. In this manner, different layers of liquid begin to move, thus causing circulation currents. *Convection,* therefore, is the transfer of heat through circulating currents that occur when liquids or gases are heated.

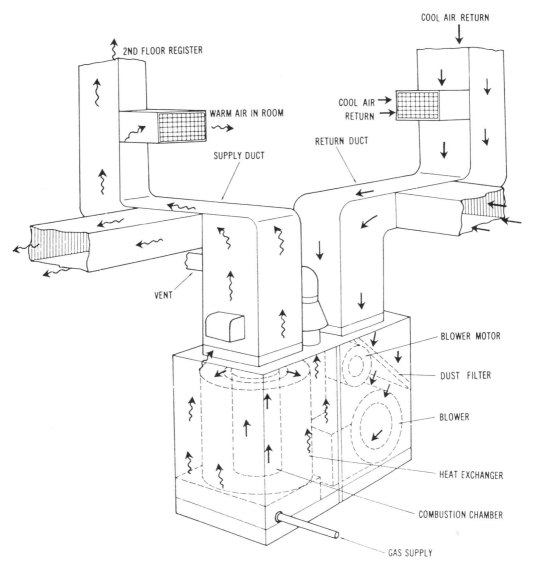

FIGURE 9–2
Forced-air gas furnace employing the
convection principle. (Courtesy of American
Gas Assoc., Inc.)

Figure 9–2 shows an example of the convection principle in a forced-air heating system.

Heat may also be transmitted from a source through the *radiation* of waves where matter does not exist. A prime example of this is the heat that reaches the earth from the sun. In ef-

fect, thermal energy is given off or radiated away from a heat source through infrared rays. Any object possessing heat gives off these rays or waves. In theory, discrete bundles or quanta of energy move away from the thermal source in wavelike patterns at the speed of light. En-

ergy released from atoms having the greatest mass has the shortest wavelength and the highest frequency. Heat produced by radiation has rather limited application in industrial thermal systems. Figure 9–3 shows an example of heat transfer by the radiation principle.

The control function of a thermal system alters the flow path of heat between the primary energy source and the load device. Specific devices called *controllers* are usually responsible for this operation. These devices attempt to maintain system temperature at a desired level. Two-position control, which causes on and off conditions, and proportioning control, which causes less pronounced variations in temperature, are the most common methods of control. System controllers respond by sensing level changes between temperature output and set-point values. The control function of a thermal system is somewhat limited because of the basic nature of the energy being manipulated.

The load part of a thermal system represents the work function or material that is to be maintained at a specified temperature. Since heat flows away from a body of higher temperature and toward a substance of lower temperature, the load must be directly dependent on the source. The thermal demand of the load may be of a steady nature for a prolonged period, variable, or cyclic. The application of the system usually determines the characteristic nature of the load.

Thermal indicators of instrumentation represent the part of the system that is primarily responsible for measurement. This operation may be performed at a number of different locations, depending on the demands of the system. Typically, temperature indicators are attached to the output or system load, the controller, or the source. Periodic monitoring of the indicator generally ensures operating efficiency within the designed limits of the system.

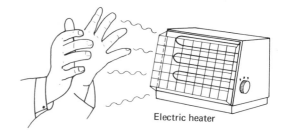

Electric heater

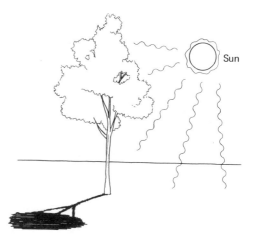

Sun

FIGURE 9–3
Radiation principle.

Temperature measurements are made in a number of ways. Nonelectrical indicators, such as thermometers, are designed to respond to temperature variations caused by changes in liquid volume and gas or vapor pressure and to the dimensional changes of solid materials. Electronic indicators respond by measuring the temperature of solids, liquids, or gases by direct contact through thermoelectric transducers or indirectly through infrared radiation detection. The range and span of the temperature being measured, accuracy, and speed of response are the primary factors to consider when selecting an indicator for a specific application.

INDUSTRIAL THERMAL SOURCES

The heat of an industrial thermal system is primarily produced by a change in the state of matter. Heat produced as the result of a fire is a prime example. Burning changes the state of coal, wood, or whatever fuel is being used. In theory, the fuel is united with oxygen, and both fuel and oxygen are changed to another material. Carbon of the burning fuel also unites with oxygen in the air and produces a different type of matter called carbon dioxide. The union produced when carbon and oxygen are combined is also responsible for liberating heat.

There are many examples of heat being produced by uniting certain substances with air. In the human body, oxygen in the air we breathe combines with our food to produce body heat. Iron exposed to the oxygen of outside air produces rust and a measurable amount of heat. The amount of heat produced in this case is not very significant because the combining process is very slow.

Heat is also produced when a liquid or gas changes form. The transition of water to ice is a prime example of this principle. In a similar manner, heat is given off when steam or gas is condensed into water. Steam heating systems operate on this principle.

INDUSTRIAL FOSSIL-FUEL HEAT SOURCES

The most common industrial fossil-fuel heat source is the furnace. This type of device is built of metal, brick, or a combination of these fireproof materials. After the structure has been built, fuel is burned in the center or fire chamber to produce heat. Furnaces are used to develop heat for comfort, for heat treating, or to melt materials for different manufacturing purposes. This source is primarily designed to provide the greatest amount of heat from the fuel being used and to concentrate it where it does the most effective work.

Warm-air furnaces are designed to heat air and distribute it through ducts to different rooms or parts of a building to provide a comfortable temperature there. Forced warm-air furnaces employ a blower or electric fan to move greater volumes of air through the system. This type of system permits the furnace to be located a greater distance away from the area being heated by the system. The fuel for these furnaces may be wood, coal, coke, fuel oil, or natural gas. Three representative comfort heating furnaces (coal or coke, gas, and oil) are shown in Figure 9–4.

Fossil fuel is also used as a source of energy for large industrial furnaces used in heat-treating operations and in the production of iron, steel, bricks, cement, glass, and many other materials. These furnaces differ from the warm-air type of unit by producing extremely high temperatures. Again, coal, coke, fuel oil, and natural gas are typical fossil fuels used as the primary source of heat energy. Metal-refining furnaces usually force large quantities or blasts of air into the fire chamber to increase the heat produced. This type of heat source is commonly called a blast furnace. Figure 9–5 shows a representative iron-ore blast furnace.

Small gas-fired heat-treating furnaces of the batch type are commonly found in many industrial applications. These units are used in applications that require precise control of temperature, time, and atmosphere. Figure 9–6 shows a partial cutaway view of a carbonizing heat-treating furnace. The operating range of this unit is 1450° to 1750°F (787° to 954°C).

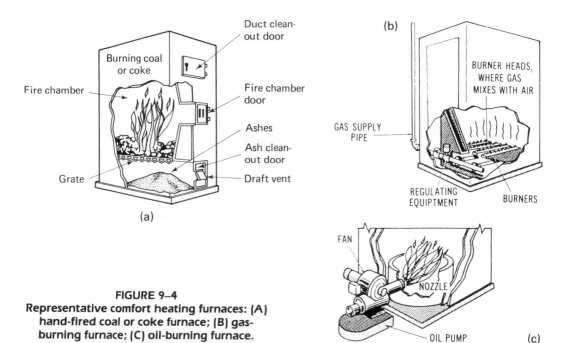

FIGURE 9-4
Representative comfort heating furnaces: (A)
hand-fired coal or coke furnace; (B) gas-
burning furnace; (C) oil-burning furnace.

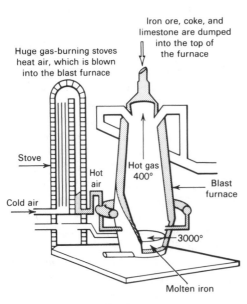

FIGURE 9-5
Iron blast furnace.

Steam and hot-water heating systems represent an additional type of heating system that finds widespread use in industry. Systems of this type may be used for facility heating purposes, for manufacturing process applications, or in power generation. This type of system is generally considered to be very dependable and provides a uniform distribution of heat throughout the system.

The essential parts of a steam or hot-water system are the boiler, distribution pipes, and unit heaters or radiators. The boiler is where fuel is burned to produce heat and ultimately changed into steam or hot water. In steam systems, steam is circulated at a temperature of 170° to 200°F. In a steam pumping system, the distribution lines are kept free from air, which keeps the system at somewhat less than normal barometric pressure. As a result of this condition, steam is produced at a lower temperature. Temperatures in the range of 170°F can be

used effectively to produce steam in this type of system.

The radiators or load of a steam or hot-water system give off heat by conduction, convection, and radiation. Conduction is quite small, with convection and radiation being the most significant methods of heat transfer. The radiator is located where heat is to be supplied to the system. The temperature of the area where the radiator is located determines the load placed on the radiator. Steam or hot-water systems usually have many radiators located throughout the system. The load is a composite of all the radiators connected to the system.

Steam-heated industrial heat-treating furnaces of the batch type are frequently found in many industrial applications. These units may contain their own boiler unit or may be attached to a central distribution system. Units of this type combine the benefits of a protective steam atmosphere, forced circulation heating, and accurate temperature control in a single unit. Figure 9–7 shows a partial cutaway view of the interior of an industrial steam-energized heat-treating furnace. Units of this type operate at temperatures of 0° to 1500°F (17° to 815°C). A thermocouple is generally used as a sensor for the control element. Proportioning control is widely used. This type of control

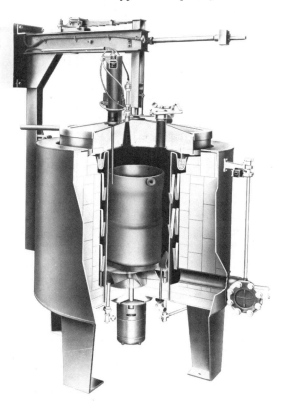

FIGURE 9–6
View of a gas-fired furnace. (Courtesy of Lindberg, A Unit of General Signal)

FIGURE 9–7
Industrial-type steam-energized heat-treating furnace. (Courtesy of Lindberg, A Unit of General Signal)

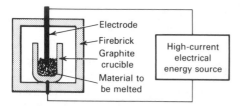

(A) Simplified diagram.

FIGURE 9–8
Electric-arc furnace. (Courtesy of Whiting
Corp.)

(B) Overview.

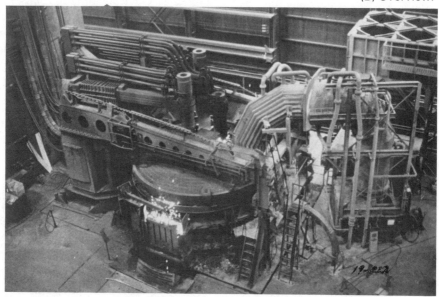

permits the unit to come up to temperature quickly and smoothly without overshoot, while holding for the duration of the cycle.

ELECTRICAL HEAT SOURCES

Electrically energized heat sources have a number of advantages over nearly all other industrial heating methods. In furnaces, electricity can be used to produce temperatures in the range from 3500° to 5000°F (1926° to 2760°C). In addition, electric heat does not produce gases that may have a harmful effect in metal processing. Temperature is more ac-

curately controlled and the entire process is more efficient and cleaner to operate.

Three common types of electric heating sources used in industrial applications today are the arc, resistance, and induction furnaces. Each general type uses electricity as the primary energy source and produces heat as the end result or output of the load device.

A simplified diagram of an electric arc furnace is shown in Figure 9–8(A). With high-current electricity applied across the carbon electrode and the graphite crucible, an electric arc is produced when the electrode touches metal. After an arc has been started, the electrode is withdrawn slightly. Temperatures of 3500°F are typical of electric furnaces. Figure

9–8(B) shows a large electric arc furnace used in the smelting of steel.

An electric resistance furnace is very similar in operation to the oven of a home-type electric range or bread toaster. When current is forced to pass through a conductor, heat is produced as a result of conductor resistance. These special-resistance heating elements are placed around an insulated chamber where small batches of materials are placed for heat treating. Figure 9–9 shows the heating element of an electric heat treating oven. This type of oven has forced convection so that all surfaces of the workpiece are exposed to heat. It provides rapid heating and uniform distribution of heat and atmosphere inside the chamber. The controller of this unit responds to a thermocouple located inside the chamber. A duration-adjusting type of control proportions heat input to meet the demands of the load. Control of this is smooth without overshoot and holds the temperature at precise levels.

Electrical conduction furnaces send high-frequency alternating current through a wire coil wound around an insulated container that holds a material that is to be heated. If the material placed in the container is iron, a magnetic field is developed in the iron as a result of the applied ac. With high-frequency ac applied, the magnetic field of the iron is in a state of constant change. As a result of this action, molecules of the metal continually shift position. This, in turn, produces intense levels of heat due to internal molecular friction. Induction furnaces develop intense levels of heat in very short periods of operating time.

If nonmagnetic materials are placed in the container of an induction furnace, they will become hot due to the resistance of the material. For nonmetallic materials, heating is achieved by changing the insulated container at the center of the coil to a carbon crucible. The furnace then generates heat by induction into the container. Then, by conduction, heat is transferred to the nonmetallic material within the container. Induction heating can be achieved very quickly with rather significant levels of accuracy.

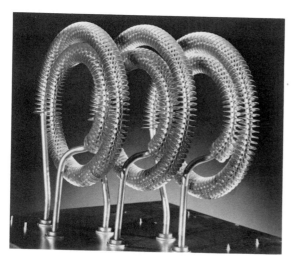

FIGURE 9–9
Heating element of an electric unit heater.
(Courtesy of Modine Manufacturing Co.)

TEMPERATURE SYSTEM CONTROLLERS

The controller function of a thermal system is primarily achieved by a combination of components placed in a unit known as a controller. The function of this unit is to sense the temperature of the system and to determine the amount of heat flow needed to meet the demands of the operating set point of the system. In achieving this function, several factors affect the accuracy of the controller. These include temperature gradients, thermal lag, component location, and controller operation-mode selection. Mean temperature consistency and system bandwidth are primarily affected by these factors.

Thermal Gradients

Measurement of different temperature values, starting at the heat source and moving toward the load, indicates that a decided drop in temperature occurs near the load end of the system. This variation in temperature is commonly called the *thermal gradient* of the system.

Thermal gradients in general occur in all temperature systems, and it is quite important to recognize where they exist. Since heat is effectively transferred from the source to the load in only one direction, thermal gradients are inevitable and necessary. System control can be effective only when thermal gradients are taken into account. It therefore becomes imperative that all measurement affecting the control function be made as near as possible to the area being influenced by the controller. If these measurements are taken near the source end of the system, the readings are somewhat higher than those that actually appear at the load. Ideally, the controller sensing element should be attached to the load or placed in the actual work area of the system. The set point of the controller must take into account the thermal gradient and be adjusted or compensated for relative to its location in the system.

A number of things can be done to minimize the gradients that occur in a thermal system. These include balancing heater capacity against heat demand, proper sensing element location, sensing element control range, and general system insulation against heat loss. In practice, it is desirable to minimize the thermal gradients in order to improve the accuracy of the controller.

Thermal Lag

Thermal lag is another inevitable condition that is present to some extent in all temperature systems. *Thermal lag* is primarily a delay in heat distribution that occurs between that leaving the source and ultimately arriving at the load. The distance between the source and load and the resistance to heat flow are the primary factors that influence this kind of delay.

Accurate system control is largely dependent on thermal lag. When the delay factor is low, controller action closely follows system set-point adjustments. Long delay periods, by comparison, tend to cause temperature overshoot. This represents more heat to the load than what the system actually needs to recover from the temperature drop. In addition, the sensing element may not be able to respond quickly enough to deliver the necessary heat needed by the load. The term undershoot usually describes this condition. Both overshoot and undershoot cause the width of the control range to be expanded quite significantly during normal operation.

In practice, thermal lag cannot be entirely eliminated. With proper system design, however, a large amount of delay can be minimized and some degree of compensation can be made for the remainder of those lags that still exist. Proper selection of the transmission path material between the source and the load is a prime factor in system design. Typically, solids, liquids, or gases are all used in the transmission path. As a general rule, however, material selection is primarily dictated by the application of the system. When close control is desired, several transmission path factors must be considered. These are described in the following statements:

1. When liquids, air, or gas are used in the transmission path, they should be in a continuous state of agitation.

2. All metals used in the transmission path should have a high level of thermal conductivity.

3. Thermal path insulating materials should possess a low conductivity.

4. Avoid conditions in the transmission path that cause air or liquids to become stagnant.

Thermal lag, in general, can produce some misleading information about the performance of a rapidly changing temperature system. In some systems the effects of excessive lag can be so great that the sensing element at the load may be calling for more heat when the system is just beginning to respond to heat from a previous change. Systems with fast-response controllers and slower-responding indicators, such as mercury thermometers, usually have inherent delay problems of this type.

System Component Placement

In an operating thermal system, component placement has a great deal to do with the effectiveness of the control function. If the heat source, the sensing element, and the load could be grouped together in a compact central area, there would be very little problem with control. A short heat path from the source to the load would enable the sensing element to respond very quickly to any and all system changes. This would minimize overshoot, undershoot, thermal lag, and thermal gradients.

In most industrial thermal system applications, it is rather difficult to achieve intimate component grouping arrangements. The size of the system and the remote location of the source and load pose typical problems. In practice, there is no single answer to system component placement. Designers generally try to arrive at a compromise that will permit the best level of control for a particular system.

A general rule to consider when selecting the location of thermal system components is based on the nature of the control characteristic. For systems where the desired heat demand is steady, the sensing element should be positioned closer to the source. Where system demand is of a variable nature, the sensing element should be oriented closer to the load area.

In liquid and gas systems where the demand for heat is of a rather steady nature, the sensing element should always be placed above the heat source. This is done to minimize the bandwidth of the control range. The transfer of heat in this type of system is primarily achieved by the convection process. Figure 9–10 shows a realistic way to place the sensing element in this type of system. The agitator of this system is used to distribute convection currents and to minimize thermal gradients and thermal lag.

Thermal System Controller Selection

Selection of an appropriate controller for a specific thermal system involves a number of important considerations. Essentially, controller performance should first match the application of the system in order to ensure that it achieves the desired level of control. In addition, the selection process should also take into account temperature operating range, response time, resolution sensitivity, mode of control, and sensor type. When these factors are satisfied,

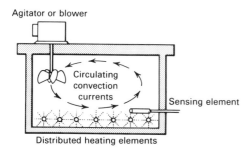

FIGURE 9–10
Sensing element placement in steady-heat systems.

the controller should ultimately be compatible with the system and its application.

The temperature operating range of a controller refers specifically to the upper and lower temperature extremes over which a controller will respond. This range of operation is primarily determined by the type of sensing element employed and the mechanical or electrical operation of the controller. The sensing element is basically responsible for detecting a change in temperature. Typical electrical sensors respond to temperature by generating a voltage, changing resistance, comparing colors, or responding to radiation. Liquid-filled sensors, by comparison, respond to temperature variations by producing changes in liquid volume, changes in gas or vapor pressure, or dimensional changes of solid materials.

In practice, the temperature range of a controller varies a great deal among different manufacturers. Some representative ranges are $-100°$ to $600°F$, $200°$ to $1500°F$, and $-20°$ to $275°F$ ($-73°$ to $315°C$, $93°$ to $815°C$, and $-28°$ to $135°C$) for thermostat and thermoswitch sensing elements. In liquid-filled systems, representative ranges may be $350°$ to $650°F$ ($176°$ to $343°C$) wide or somewhere within a $-450°$ to $1400°F$ ($-267°$ to $760°C$) limit. Thermocouple systems generally respond to the widest range of temperature, with extremes ranging from $-400°$ to $3200°F$ ($-240°$ to $1760°C$). Thermoresistive systems cover a range of $-430°$ to $1800°F$ ($-256°$ to $982°C$). Because of nonlinearity problems over a wide range, thermistor systems have a narrower temperature operating range. This range can be extended, however, by using alternate sensing elements in a system.

The response time of a controller is a measure of the time that it takes the sensing element to generate a signal that will ultimately initiate a system state change. To a large extent this factor is also determined by the type of sensing element employed by the system.

Response time is normally based on the time that it takes the sensor to initiate a 63.2% change in value over its calibrated output. Typical electrical sensors are of the bimetal-strip switch or thermostat type, or are thermocouples, thermoresistor detectors, and thermistors. Nonelectrical sensors are of the gas- or fluid-filled type. The response time of the sensing element is a major factor in the selection of a controller. When high-speed response is needed, thermistor and thermoresistor detector elements are applicable. Response times ranging from 0.035 to 5 seconds (s) are typical. The response time of a thermocouple is next, with a range of 0.04 to 7.5 s. Thermostats and thermoswitches are somewhat slower, with response time starting at 1 s. Filled sensing elements overlap some of the electrical sensors, with a response time of 0.5 to 10 s or more.

To demonstrate the response time of a sensor, we will describe how a thermistor responds electrically. A thermistor changes its resistance value according to the temperature of the environment where it is placed. Response time is generally expressed in time constants. The time constant of a thermistor is the time required, in seconds, for it to change 63% of its resistance value when subjected to a new or different environment. In this regard, a thermistor taken from an environment of 72°F and placed in an environment of 172°F will change to a temperature of 135°F in one time constant. This is based on the fact that 172°F minus 72°F produces a span of 100°F, and 63% of 100° is 63°. Then 72 + 63 = 135°F. Essentially, this means that a thermistor goes through a 63% change in temperature and resistance in one time constant. In practice, five time constants are required for a thermistor to completely reflect a new environmental temperature change.

In general, response time is not very significant in systems where the temperature remains fairly constant for long periods. In systems where the temperature changes occur fre-

quently and rapidly, however, the response time becomes a very important consideration of the system.

Resolution sensitivity of a controller normally refers to the specific amount of temperature change needed by a particular controller to initiate a state change. Typical expressions of sensitivity are given in a specified number of degrees or as some percentage of the controller's total operating range or scale. In practice, sensitivity is a good measure of the controller's temperature bandwidth. The process of changing good controller sensitivity into correspondingly accurate control generally calls for a number of rather careful design procedures. As a rule this means that good sensitivity is somewhat more costly to achieve. For most applications, controller sensitivities of 2° to 5°F (1.1° to 2.7°C) are more than adequate when the system is properly installed. Some representative sensitivities for thermostats and thermoswitches are 0° to 1°F, 1° to 5°F, 5° to 10°F, and 2° to 8°F (0° to 0.5°C, 0.5° to 2.7°C, 2.7° to 5.5°C, 1.1° to 4.4°C). In liquid-filled controllers, a representative sensitivity is 2° to 8°F (1.1° to 4.4°C). Thermistor and thermocouple elements are by far the most sensitive of all detectors, with values of 1°F or 0.2% of the temperature span being typical values.

Mode of control essentially describes the method by which a controller adjusts system temperature in order to restore it to a desired level. In practice, thermal systems either employ the two-position mode (on–off) or proportioning control. In the *two-position mode* of operation, the source is simply turned off when the load temperature has exceeded the set-point value. Then when the temperature of the load drops below the set-point value, the source is turned on again to return it to the desired level. Figure 9–11 shows a typical temperature response of a two-position controller. As noted, there is a great deal of overshoot–undershoot oscillation in this mode of control.

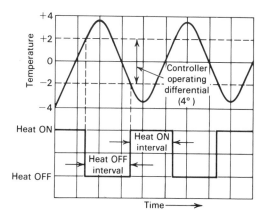

FIGURE 9–11
Response of a two-position controller.

The *proportioning mode* of control provides a means of variable temperature adjustments which reduces the overshoot–undershoot problems of the two-position mode of operation. In electrical thermal systems, proportioning control is achieved simply by altering the amount of power applied to the heating element source. One type of proportioning control is called *time rate control*. This process is accomplished by regulating the number of cycles of electrical power supplied to the source in a given period (see Figure 9–12). Systems that employ this type of control produce a very low level of electrical interference because the power is turned on and off at the zero point. Some controller manufacturers refer to this type of control as *zero-voltage switching*.

An alternate method of achieving electrical proportioning control employs the *phase angle firing principle*. In this method a triac or dual SCRs are used to turn on the electrical power to the system heating element for only a portion of the cycle (see Figure 9–13). Phase angle firing as a rule generates some rather pronounced transient spikes in the ac power line. A system employing this type of control must have some form of transient spike suppression.

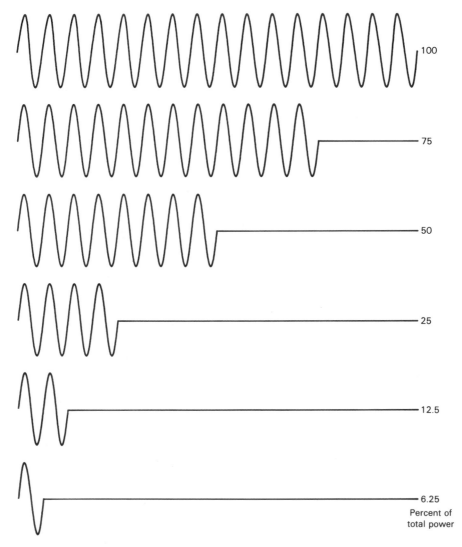

FIGURE 9–12
Time-rate temperature control.

In addition to the electrical control process, proportioning control can also be employed by filled systems. Changes in sensor output can be used to change the wiper arm of a potentiometer. Through this action, a motorized valve can be adjusted to different temperature levels. Through this control process, valve positions can be altered to any position from closed to 100% open, depending on the deviation of the set point. Figure 9–14 shows a proportioning potentiometer and Figure 9–15 shows an electrical controller circuit that can be used for either two-position or proportioning control.

Sensor element operation is an extremely important consideration when selecting a thermal system controller for a specific applica-

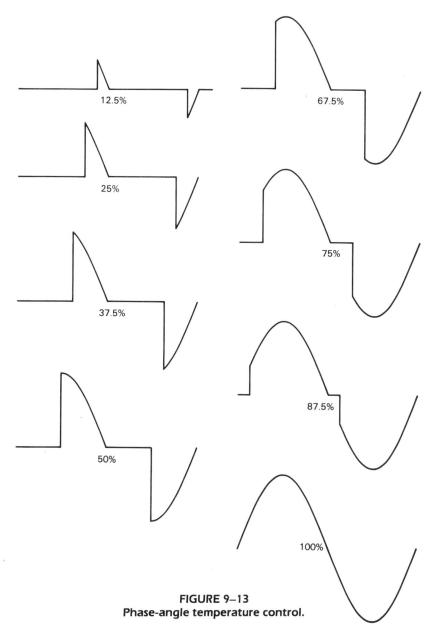

FIGURE 9–13
Phase-angle temperature control.

tion. Such things as response time, temperature operating range, resolution sensitivity, and repeatability are very dependent on the sensor element. In addition, the physical size of the sensor has a great deal to do with component location and installation design procedures.

Filled sensing elements are primarily designed to respond to changes in temperature by producing a physical change in a pressure- or volume-sensitive component. Controllers of this type employ a sensing element or bulb, a capillary tube, and a pressure- or volume-sen-

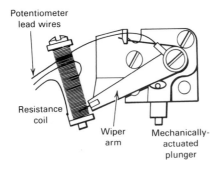

FIGURE 9–14
Proportioning potentiometer.

sitive component such as a Bourdon tube, bellows, or diaphragm. Figure 9–16 shows an internal view of a filled system instrument with a capillary tube and bulb sensing element.

The sensing element or bulb of a filled system contains a fluid or gas that changes its volume or pressure with temperature. The pressure- or volume-sensitive part of the system responds to these changes by delivering a motion or physical change that is applied to the control element. Comparisons of the set-point value and sensor output are then made to determine the action of the controller.

Class I filled systems employ liquids other than mercury. An inert hydrocarbon, such as xylene, is very common. Sensors of this type have an expansion rate that is six times greater than that of mercury. A characteristic of this sensor is its small size.

Class II pressure elements have the filled medium in both liquid and gaseous form. The combination of the two interface in the sensing bulb to produce a vapor. There are four different combinations of liquid–gas elements, which are labeled IIA, B, C, or D.

Class III refers to gas-filled systems. Nitro-

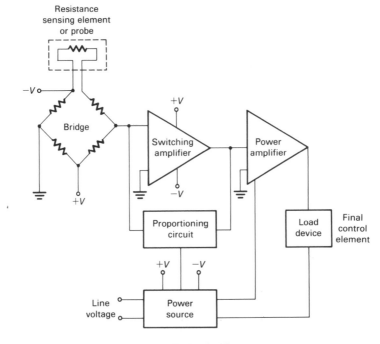

FIGURE 9–15
Electrical temperature controller.

gen is used up to 800°F and helium is used for extremely low temperatures. In practice, this type of sensor is made rather large and somewhat longer than others to reduce temperature interference along the capillary.

Class V filled systems employ mercury as the medium. Mercury has rapid response, is very accurate, and provides a great deal of physical power to actuate the pressure-sensing element. At high temperatures, pressures may reach 1200 psi (8.274 MPa), while dropping to values of 400 psi (2.758 MPa) at the low-temperature end of the range. Mercury-filled systems are commonly used in industrial applications.

Thermostats and thermoswitch sensors in general are somewhat slower in response time compared with other sensing elements. For example, they must produce switching action by physically distorting a bimetal strip with the application of heat. As a rule, some degree of response time is needed to cause the bimetal material element to react. Standard response times range from 1 to 10 s or more. Figure 9–17 shows the internal structure of a rapid-re-

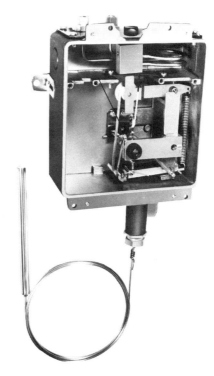

FIGURE 9–16
Internal view of a filled temperature controller. (Courtesy of Fenwal, Inc.)

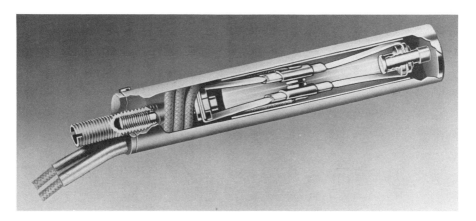

FIGURE 9–17
Internal structure of a thermoswitch.
(Courtesy of Fenwal, Inc.)

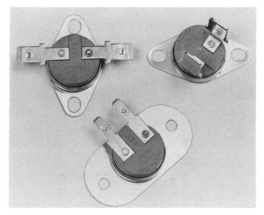

(A) Three views.

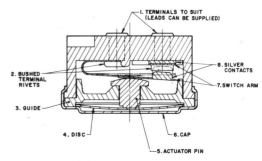

(B) Cutaway drawing.

FIGURE 9–18
Bimetal disc thermostats. (Courtesy of Airpax
Corporation, Frederick Division)

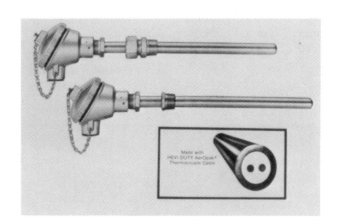

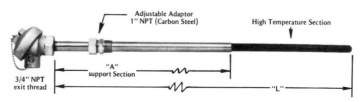

FIGURE 9–19
Thermocouples. (Courtesy of ARI Industries,
Inc.)

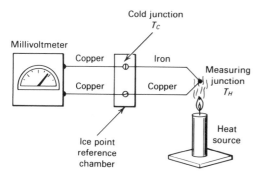

FIGURE 9–20
Thermocouple circuit.

Thermostats of this type are calibrated at the factory and housed in a tamperproof enclosure.

A thermocouple sensing element is composed of two dissimilar metal wires connected in isothermal contact. Figure 9–19 shows a partial cutaway view of a thermocouple in a thermowell assembly and an external view of several different thermocouples. The isothermal connection may be achieved by welding, fusing, or twisting the two wires together.

When a thermocouple is connected into a circuit as in Figure 9–20, it serves as the heat-sensing junction (T_H). If one junction is maintained at a reference temperature (T_C), the magnitude of the resulting current will be directly proportional to the temperature at the measured junction (T_H).

In practice, the output of a thermocouple sensor is measured in millivolts. In some applications the millivolt output of a thermocouple is transposed into temperature for indication on a calibrated scale. In controller operation, thermocouple output voltage is

sponding thermoswitch. This element has a high-expansion outside shell and a low-expansion internal strut assembly. The temperature at which the contacts make and break can be adjusted by the temperature-adjusting screw.

A thermostat with a bimetal disc assembly is shown in Figure 9–18. This sensing element has positive reinforced snap action, which is known for its repeatability and reliability.

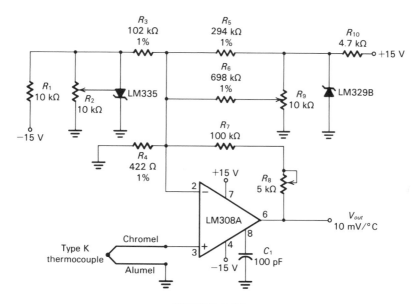

FIGURE 9–21
Thermocouple amplifier.

compared with the set-point adjustment voltage to ultimately determine the action of the controller. As a rule, some type of amplification is usually required to make this comparison. Op-amps are used exclusively to achieve this level of amplification today.

Figure 9–21 shows a thermocouple input amplifier with cold-junction compensation. This circuit has a 10-mV/°C output. Gain is achieved by adjustment of the feedback network composed of resistors R_7 and R_8. The LM335 is a special precision-calibrated temperature sensor IC. It responds as a two-terminal zener diode whose breakdown voltage is directly proportional to absolute temperature at $+10$ mV/K. This device permits cold-junction temperature compensation of the thermocouple. The LM329B is a precision temperature-compensated 6.9-V zener reference diode. The LM308A is an op-amp that responds well to low input currents and has an extremely low offset voltage. In a controller, the output of this circuit is connected to one input of a voltage comparator. The alternate input comes from the set-point circuit. The values of these two voltages are compared and determine the output of the circuit. A variety of modifications can be made to permit this circuit to be used in a controller.

Thermoresistive sensing element operation is based on the resistance property of certain metals to change with temperature. These changes in resistance can then be used to alter the current in an electric circuit or to develop changing voltage that can be amplified to a level that will permit control. Of all the materials currently being used in thermoresistive elements, platinum tends to have the most desirable characteristics. As shown in Figure 9–22, the resistance of platinum is very linear from 0° to 800°C. In addition, the melting point of platinum is high and does not change physically for temperatures below 1200°C. The tensile strength of platinum is 18,000 psi

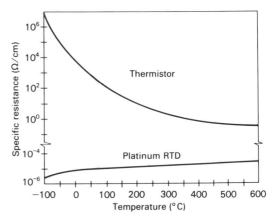

FIGURE 9–22
Resistance–temperature graph of thermistors and platinum RTDs.

(124.1 MPa), and its resistance is 60.0 Ω/circular mil at 0°C or 9.83 $\mu\Omega$/cm. Industrial thermoresistive elements are usually called resistance temperature detectors or RTDs. These elements have a response time of 0.035 to 5 s for temperatures of $-100°$ to $+1000°$F ($-73°$ to 537°C), with a 0.1% tolerance and a $+0.01\%$ repeatability.

The resistance change of an RTD is generally quite small under normal operating conditions. As a rule, it can be used directly to sense temperature changes as a variation in voltage across a current-driven resistor or by output resistance changes in a bridge circuit. Normally, the developed voltage is then amplified before it can be used to effectively control a load device. Op-amps are used exclusively today in controllers that respond to RTD sensors.

Figure 9–23 shows the circuitry of an adjustable reference op-amp temperature-sensing circuit. The RTD of this circuit is connected in the feedback path of the op-amp. The resistance of the RTF varies from 100 to 200 Ω over the temperature range. The gain of the

op-amp is altered by these changes. The AD584 is an adjustable multireference IC that is set for 6.2-V output at the emitter of the 2N2219 transistor. Potentiometer R_2 is used to alter this reference voltage. Potentiometers R_4 and R_6 adjust the span and offset of the op-amp. The span adjustment is made first by altering R_6 to produce a 1.8-V output when 266°C is applied. The offset adjustment is made by altering the value of R_4 so that the output is 0 V at 0°C. The scale of the circuit is somewhat arbitrary. In general, the output voltage range is primarily based on the device being fed by the circuit. This circuit permits temperatures of 0° to 266°C to be measured as voltages of 0 to 1.8 V.

Thermistors are an additional type of thermoresistive sensing element of the semiconductor or solid-state type. As the name implies, a thermistor is a temperature-sensitive resistor. The differences of the thermistor compared to a platinum thermoresistive element are shown in Figure 9–22. The resistance of the thermistor, as noted, drops in value as temperature increases. This characteristic is known

as a *negative temperature coefficient*. Platinum, by comparision, increases in resistance with an increase in temperature, which indicates a *positive temperature coefficient*. The response time of a thermistor compares rather favorably with that of a thermoresistive element. Device resistance of a thermistor can be selected from a number of values that range from several megohms at −100°C to values less than 1 Ω at 400°C.

The use of a thermistor as a control element to drive a load device generally necessitates some degree of amplification. As a rule, the amount of amplification needed to achieve control is based on the load device being driven by the controller. Op-amps are used rather commonly in industrial controllers today. The controller can be used to achieve on–off, proportional, or proportional with integral and derivative control. The thermistor senses a change in temperature by altering its resistance. This is translated into a change in voltage and amplified. The voltage is then used to alter the load device according to the type of controller mode desired.

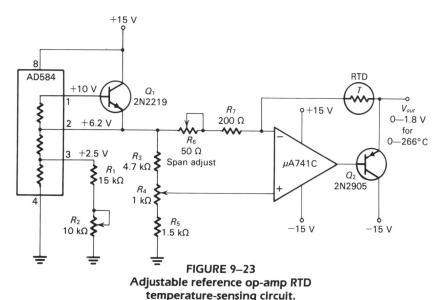

FIGURE 9–23
Adjustable reference op-amp RTD
temperature-sensing circuit.

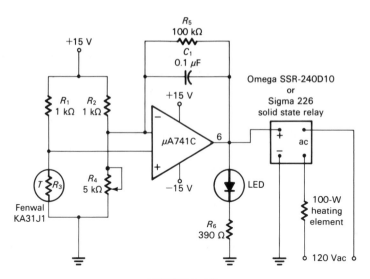

FIGURE 9–24
On–off temperature controller.

Figure 9–24 shows the circuitry of a rather simplified on–off temperature controller. The thermistor is used in a bridge circuit. Balancing the bridge is the equivalent of adjusting the set point of the circuit to some desired temperature. A change in thermistor temperature causes the bridge to go out of balance and produce a corresponding change in voltage at the input of the op-amp. This voltage is then amplified and applied to the load device. If a load, such as a heating element, is controlled by a relay or SCR, on–off control can be achieved. When a power transistor or IC is used to alter conduction of the load, some degree of variability is achieved. This permits proportional or PID control.

TEMPERATURE INSTRUMENTATION

Instrumentation is a common term for describing devices or procedures used in the measurement and evaluation of industrial process applications. Temperature instrumentation is somewhat more specialized because it applies to those things that are primarily used to test and evaluate the temperature of a system. Precise measurement of temperature is a key factor in nearly all manufacturing operations regardless of the product involved. In thermal systems, instrumentation may be applied to any discrete part of the system. It is therefore essential that a person working with this type of system, or with a process control application that responds in some way to temperature, have an understanding of the basic principles of instrumentation.

A rather general way of classifying all temperature-measuring instruments is made by comparing the temperature operating range of each device. Figure 9–25 shows an instrument operating range comparison chart. Note that several instruments may be capable of measuring temperatures over the same given range. However, not all instruments are equally suited for a given temperature measurement. Selection of a specific instrument, therefore, must take into account something other than the

temperature range. This includes such things as response time, accuracy, life expectancy, and the basic method of operation. In general, the measuring instrument should be compatible with the capabilities of the controller, process, and system.

NONELECTRICAL INSTRUMENTATION

Temperature measurement is commonly divided into two general classifications: those that are electrical or electronic and those that are not. Nonelectrical instrumentation was developed first and probably has more applications today than the electrical or electronic

classification. Nonelectrical instrumentation essentially exemplifies the expansion principle. Changes in temperature cause dimensional changes in solid materials or cause gas, vapor pressure, or liquids to expand. As a result of this action, temperature can be transformed into a physical or mechanical change that can be read on a calibrated scale.

Filled-system Indicators

The principle of volumetric liquid expansion with increasing temperature is probably one of the oldest methods employed for the determination of temperature. The glass stem thermometer, which utilizes this principle, was developed by G. D. Fahrenheit in the eighteenth century. In the general range of −500° to

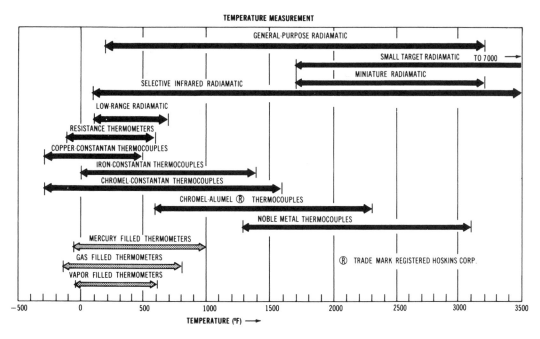

FIGURE 9–25
Temperature instrument measuring range.
(Courtesy of Honeywell, Inc.)

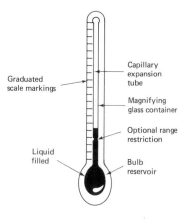

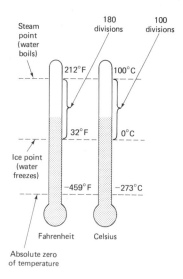

FIGURE 9–26
Filled thermometer.

of the tube is sealed, we have a closed thermal expansion system.

Liquid in a sealed container that has a fixed but larger volume area will expand according to ambient temperature. The expansion of pure mercury is 0.01% per degree Fahrenheit and is very linear from its approximate freezing point of −38°F (−38.8°C) to its boiling point of 1000°F (537.7°C).

Industrial applications of the thermometer are still rather common. Some thermometers are permanently attached to a system, while others are portable. In both cases the thermometer is limited to only direct reading applications that are not adaptable to recording or automatic control situations. With some degree of modification, it is possible to adapt the thermometer principle to perform these operations. Filled temperature-measuring instruments are the results of this modification.

A filled temperature-measuring instrument is very similar for all practical purposes to the sensing element, capillary tube, and pressure–volume element of a filled-system controller. In a temperature-measuring instrument, the end result of its operation is a usable reading on a calibrated scale. The term *temperature recorder* is often used to describe this type of device in industry.

Typical industrial filled-system thermometers usually employ a circular chart as a calibrated scale with a recording pen attached to the pressure element. Figure 9–27 shows recording and indicating temperature instruments of the filled type. The center unit is a disassembly of the indicating instrument. Note that the sensor and capillary tube are exterior components. The pressure-sensing element is a spiral Bourdon tube. Figure 9–28 shows an enlargement of the spiral Bourdon element of a recording instrument. Instruments of this type are available for class I, II, or III operation, with ranges from −450° to 1450°F (−267.7° to 787.7°C).

1000°F (−295° to 537.7°C), this type of indicator is about as important as any other method of measurement today.

A filled thermometer is essentially a glass tube that has a small hole bored lengthwise, with a bulb reservoir at one end (see Figure 9–26). When the reservoir is filled with liquid, the remaining tube air is removed, and the top

FIGURE 9–27
Recording and indicating temperature
instruments. (Courtesy of AMETEK)

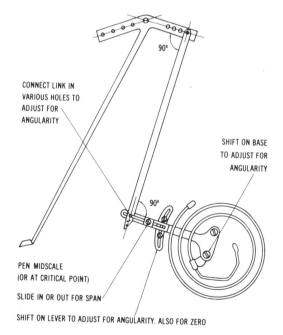

CONNECT LINK IN
VARIOUS HOLES TO
ADJUST FOR
ANGULARITY

90°

SHIFT ON BASE
TO ADJUST FOR
ANGULARITY

90°

PEN MIDSCALE
(OR AT CRITICAL POINT)

SLIDE IN OR OUT FOR SPAN

SHIFT ON LEVER TO ADJUST FOR ANGULARITY, ALSO FOR ZERO

FIGURE 9–28
Bourdon pressure-sensing element.

Bimetallic Thermometers

Bimetallic thermometers are nonelectrical temperature-measuring instruments that find about the same amount of acceptance in industry as the glass bulb thermometer. Bimetallic thermometers essentially make use of the coefficient of linear expansion principle, which states that a solid material will change dimensionally when its temperature is changed. If two different kinds of metal strips are bonded together and heated, the resulting strip will bend in the direction of the metal with the lower expansion rate. The amount of resulting deflection that occurs is proportional to the square of the length and the total change in temperature, and is inversely related to material thickness.

To take full advantage of the expansion principle, the element of a bimetal thermometer should be rather long. In practice, the element is formed into a flat spiral or a single helix. The outside end of the element is then mounted to a structure and an indicating hand

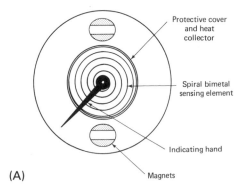

(A)

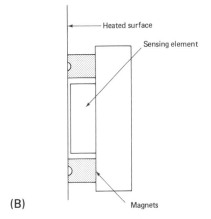

(B)

(C)

FIGURE 9–29
Bimetal thermometer. (Courtesy of Whal Instruments, Inc.)

is attached to the inside of the loose end. An increase in temperature causes the element to wind up, which produces a clockwise deflection. Movement of the indicating hand registers a change in temperature on a calibrated scale.

Figure 9–29 shows an example of a spiral-element bimetal thermometer. The sensing element in this case is exposed for quick and accurate response to surface temperature. Where applications demand better protection, the element may be covered with a protective cover.

ELECTRICAL AND ELECTRONIC INSTRUMENTATION

Electrical instrumentation is somewhat different from nonelectrical measuring techniques. First, electricity must be supplied by an auxiliary source to make the system function. Second, a transducer is employed to change temperature variations into electrical signals. This type of instrumentation also has the advantage of small-mass sensing elements that can be located an effective distance from the measuring area. In addition, electronic instrumentation lends itself well to portable applications that increase the versatility of the measuring equipment.

Electrical and electronic instrumentation is primarily classified according to the fundamental operation principle of the sensing element. In practice, this includes resistance changes, voltage generation, radiation, and optical comparisons. The sensing element or transducer of these instruments must have the ability to distinguish between temperature changes and judge the amount of heat in an object.

Temperature-measuring transducers are very similar to those used in the sensor element of a controller. In fact, sensor elements are often

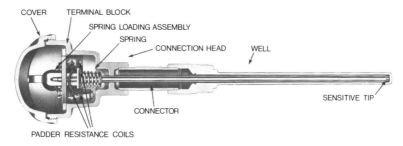

COVER   TERMINAL BLOCK

SPRING LOADING ASSEMBLY

SPRING

CONNECTION HEAD   WELL

SENSITIVE TIP

CONNECTOR

PADDER RESISTANCE COILS

FIGURE 9–30
Cross-sectional view of an RTD. (Courtesy of
Foxboro Co.)

used interchangeably in controllers and temperature recorders. These functions are frequently combined to achieve both control and temperature indications in a recording type of controller. We will now direct our attention to the operation of some of the important commercially available instruments used by industry.

Thermoresistant Instrumentation

Thermoresistant instrumentation is based on the property of certain metals to change resistance when subjected to heat. In general, all metals possess this characteristic to some extent. The most significant of these considerations is the purity of the metal and its ability to be formed into fine wire. In addition, the metal should respond to rapid changes in temperature, have a repeatable temperature coefficient, respond over a linear resistance range, and possess a high resistance–temperature change ratio.

The sensor of a thermoresistant instrument is simply a long piece of wire formed into the shape of a coil wound around a ceramic core. The entire assembly is then enclosed in a protective sheath. Connection to the wire coil is made by passing leads through the ceramic core, forming a stress relief junction. Figure

9–30 shows an internal view of a typical resistance thermal detector or RTD element. Note that the active length of the sensor is quite small compared with the rest of the assembly. Thermoresistive sensing elements are constructed from a number of common metals and alloys. Among these, platinum, nickel, tungsten, and copper are frequently used, while vanadium, rhodium, silver, iron, and tantalum are used occasionally. Of these metals, platinum is the best suited for industrial applications. It is readily available in nearly a pure state and can be easily formed into wire. In addition, it has linear resistance over a very useful range. The accuracy of platinum is so good that it serves as the international standard for measuring temperatures between $-297.35°$ and $1102.9°F$ ($-182.9°$ to $594.9°C$).

The display or readout of a thermoresistive instrument is ordinarily obtained by connecting the sensing-element output to a bridge circuit. Two-, three-, and four-wire bridge circuit configurations are in use today. A simple two-wire bridge circuit is shown in Figure 9–31. Note that the RTD element is connected to the bridge as R_x.

The resistance relationship of a bridge circuit (Figure 9–31) when it is balanced is expressed by the formula

$$\frac{R_2}{R_1} = \frac{R_3}{R_x}$$

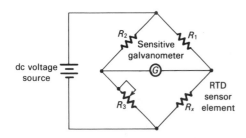

FIGURE 9–31
Two-wire bridge temperature-measuring circuit.

When balance occurs, the current through R_2 and R_3 equals that through R_1 and R_x or the RTD element. A zero deflection of the meter shows this condition.

To determine temperature, the resistance of the RTD sensor must first be determined. In practice, R_3 is adjusted to produce a balance indication on the galvonometer after the RTD has changed value. Resistance of the RTD is then determined by the formula

$$\text{RTD} = \frac{R_1}{R_2} \times R_3 \quad \text{when balanced}$$

When the value of the RTD element is determined, temperature can be determined by this value on a resistance–temperature graph.

Typical temperature bridge circuits often have R_3 calibrated in temperature values instead of resistance. As a result, when the circuit is balanced, the temperature is read directly from a calibrated dial or on a scale. Figure 9–32 shows a representative resistance thermometer bridge of this type.

An automatic self-balancing Wheatstone bridge resistance thermometer circuit is shown in Figure 9–33. With this type of circuit, any condition of imbalance caused by heat applied to the resistance element is recognized and corrected by the slide-wire resistor balancing motor. An indication of this change is then recorded on a suitable scale or chart.

The operation of a self-balanced bridge

thermometer is based on the dc voltage developed across the bridge circuit as a result of the resistance element. Any dc voltage appearing at points A–A is changed into an alternating current by action of the op-amp chopper circuit. By input transformer action, this ac is stepped up and applied to a voltage amplifier at points B–B. The output of the voltage amplifier at points C–C is then used to drive the power amplifier. Power amplifier output at points D–D then controls the rotation and direction of the balancing motor. Mechanical connection of the motor and slide-wire potentiometer is made through points E–E. As a result of this action, an increase or decrease in element resistance is automatically transposed into a physical change in slide-wire resistance, which nulls the bridge. This action can also be used to drive a recording stylus or deflect a meter, thus indicating the temperature of the resistance element. Temperature recorders of this type are commonly used to monitor continuous temperature values in process control applications.

An addition to the thermoresistant measuring device family is the portable digital readout type of instrument. Figure 9–34 shows an in-

FIGURE 9–32
Resistance thermometer bridge. (Courtesy of Leeds and Northrup Instruments, A Unit of General Signal)

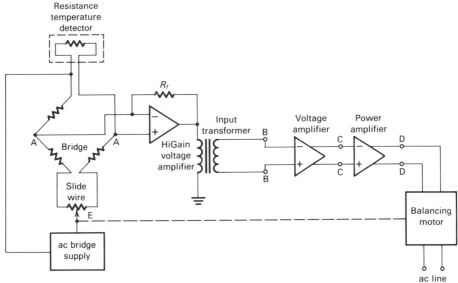

FIGURE 9–33
Automatic self-balancing thermometer.

strument of this type that will measure temperatures over a range of −50° to 900°F (−45.5° to 482.2°C). The resolution of this instrument with a platinum RTD probe is 0.1°F (0.05°C). Similar models have ranges for −50° to 500°C, 0° to 2000°F, and 0° to 1370°C. By placing the sensor probe on a surface, in liquids, powders, air, or gases can cause an instant digital reading to be obtained.

A simplified block diagram of a representative digital thermometer is shown in Figure 9–35. The operation of this circuit centers around an analog-to-digital converter. This part of the circuit is designed to change temperature or analog information into a digital signal. A variety of different conversion methods can be used today. Typically, the A/D converter is a voltage-to-frequency conversion process. In this regard, a change in temperature causes a change in voltage. The voltage change is then translated into a frequency. The frequency appears as a series of pulses that are representative of binary information. These data are then

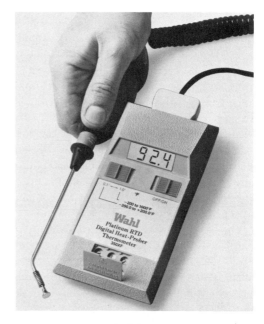

FIGURE 9–34
Portable digital thermometer with RTD probe. (Courtesy of Wahl Instruments, Inc.)

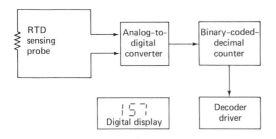

FIGURE 9–35
Block diagram of a digital thermometer.

counted, decoded, and applied to the readout as a display of temperature. The display response time is very rapid. Some models of the thermometer will trigger and hold momentarily at the maximum sensing temperature. The versatility of this device and its operational simplicity and accuracy make it a very popular industrial temperature-measuring instrument.

Thermocouple Indicators

Thermocouple temperature indicators respond to the electrical property that when two dissimilar metals are heated at a common connection point, a dc voltage is generated. The resulting voltage measured across the free ends of the thermocouple wires can be used to indicate the temperature applied to the measuring junction. Figure 9–36 shows a simplified circuit diagram of a thermocouple temperature indicator. In industrial applications, this type of instrument is commonly called a *millivolt pyrometer* or simply a pyrometer.

The basic components of a millivolt pyrometer include a d'Arsonval type of galvanometer, a thermocouple sensing element, and a compensating resistor. When heat is applied to the thermocouple measuring junction, a resulting voltage appears at the free ends or reference junction. This voltage causes a corresponding current in a series circuit formed by the meter coil, compensating resistor, and ther-

mocouple. The resulting current through the meter coil produces an electromagnetic field. This electromagnetic field is in opposition to the permanent magnetic field of the horseshoe-shaped magnet surrounding the coil. An interaction between the electromagnetic field and the permanent magnetic field causes the meter coil to move or deflect. An indicating pointer attached to the coil displays the amount of deflection in degrees of temperature or millivolts.

Several different types of thermocouples are available today for industrial applications. The combination of metals must possess a reasonably linear temperature–millivolt relationship to be of value in this type of measurement. Figure 9–37 shows the temperature–millivolt characteristic of several common types of thermocouples.

An indicating recorder circuit diagram for a continuous balance thermocouple temperature-measuring system is shown in Figure 9–38. Note that this circuit is very similar to the self-balancing Wheatstone bridge resistance thermometer of Figure 9–33. The primary differ-

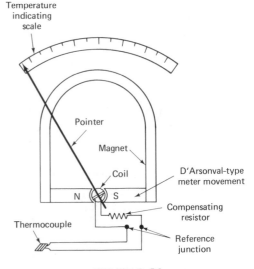

FIGURE 9–36
Temperature pyrometer.

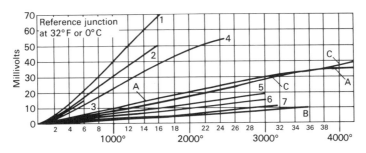

Legend:
1   Type E chromel-constantan
2   Type J iron-constantan
3   Type T copper-constantan
4   Type K chromel-alumel
5   Type R (platinum 13% rhodium-platinum)
6   Type S (platinum 10% rhodium-platinum)
7   Type B
    platinum 30% rhodium-platinum 6% rhodium

Tentative curves:
A   Tungsten 5% rhenium-tungsten 26% rhenium
B   40% iridium 60% rhodium-iridium
C   Tungsten-tungsten 26% rhenium

FIGURE 9–37
Temperature–millivolt characteristic of typical thermocouples.

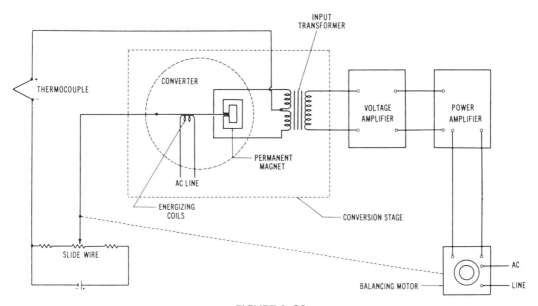

FIGURE 9–38
Thermocouple indicating temperature recorder for continuous balance. (Courtesy of Honeywell, Inc.)

TABLE 9–1
Thermistor Resistance–temperature Conversion Table.

RESISTANCE-TEMPERATURE CONVERSION TABLE

R-T CURVE NO.	1	2	3	4	5	6	7
MATERIAL	TYPE T	TYPE P	TYPE H	TYPE H	TYPE H	TYPE H	TYPE H
TYPE UNITS	DISCS	DISCS	STD. LG. BEADS MINI-PROBES STD. PROBES	STD. LG. BEADS MINI-PROBES STD. PROBES	STD. LG. BEADS MINI-PROBES STD. PROBES	STD. LG. BEADS MINI PROBES STD. PROBES	STD. LG. BEADS MINI PROBES STD. PROBES
**Ro RANGES (OHMS) NOTE—FOR DISCS: Size DIA. (IN.) F .050 J .1 K .2 C .3 L .4 D .5 M .6 N .77 Z 1.0 *P .070 NOTE—FOR RODS: Size DIA. (IN.) Q .053 R .110 T .173	DISCS Size Ro F 45K-180K J 22K-100K K 5.5K-50K C 3.5K-24K L 2K-14K D 1300-9K M 1100-6K N 725-3700 Z 550-2200	DISCS Size Ro F 50K-200K J 25K-110K K 6K-55K C 4K-27K L 2.2K-15K D 1400-10K M 1200-7K N 800-4K Z 600-2400 P 200K-1 MEG.	Ro NOM. 300K RANGE 100K-500K BEADS .043 DIA. MINI .060 DIA. STD. .100 DIA.	Ro NOM. 500K RANGE 300K-1 MEG. BEADS .043 DIA. MINI .060 DIA. STD. .100 DIA.	Ro NOM. 1 MEG. RANGE 600K-3 MEG. BEADS .043 DIA. MINI .060 DIA. STD. .100 DIA.	Ro NOM. 5 MEG. RANGE 2 MEG.-10 MEG. BEADS .043 DIA. MINI .060 DIA. STD. .100 DIA.	Ro NOM. 50 MEG. RANGE 20 MEG.-80 MEG. BEADS .043 DIA. MINI .060 DIA. STD. .100 DIA.
PART NUMBERS PREFIXED BY:	FT, JT, KT, CT, LT, DT, MT, NT, UT, ZT	FP, JP, KP, CP, LP, DP, MP, NP, PP, ZP	GH	GH	GH	GH	GH
BETA IN °K	4138 ± 86	4290 ± 100	4227 ± 86	4349 ± 87	4540 ± 86	4850 ± 86	5584 ± 86
RATIO Ro @ 0/50°C	10.45 ± 5%	11.60 ± 4.5%	10.99 ± 5%	11.78 ± 5%	13.12 ± 5%	15.65 ± 5%	23.71 ± 5%
RATIO TEST LIMITS 0/50°C	9.93-10.97	11.08-12.12	10.44-11.54	11.19-12.37	12.46-13.78	14.87-16.43	22.52-24.90
RATIO Ro @ 25/125°C	38.07	48.08	42.20	46.57	56.60	75.50	147.5
TEMPERATURE CO-EFFICIENT (α_T) @ 25°C	−4.7% / °C	−4.9% / °C	−4.8% / °C	−4.9% / °C	−5.1% / °C	−5.5% / °C	−6.3% / °C

°F	°C	1	2	3	4	5	6	7
−76	−60	—	—	183.3	201.4	223.9	349.6	455.5
−58	−50	—	92.08	86.03	94.18	107.4	151.1	205.5
−40	−40	40.155	45.50	42.24	45.95	52.87	68.47	94.97
−22	−30	20.640	23.31	21.61	23.31	26.69	32.41	44.89
−4	−20	11.034	12.08	11.47	12.22	13.80	15.97	21.68
14	−10	6.119	6.70	6.314	6.642	7.247	8.169	10.69
32	0	3.510	3.71	3.591	3.733	3.942	4.323	5.376
50	10	2.078	2.20	2.107	2.157	2.227	2.354	2.710
68	20	1.2674	1.30	1.272	1.284	1.297	1.322	1.405
77	25	1.0000	1.00	1.000	1.000	1.000	1.000	1.000
86	30	.79422	.796	.7895	.7860	.7764	.7644	.7469
104	40	.51048	.505	.5021	.4934	.4772	.4538	.4068
122	50	.33591	.320	.3267	.3170	.3004	.2762	.2267
140	60	.22590	.212	.2173	.2092	.1936	.1725	.1315
158	70	.15502	.140	.1475	.1409	.1275	.1106	.07831
176	80	.10837	.0957	.1020	.09663	.08562	.07191	.04780
194	90	.077077	.0671	.07178	.06744	.05858	.04786	.02985
212	100	.055693	.0470	.05132	.04784	.04077	.03244	.01904
230	110	.040829	.0337	.03725	.03432	.02882	.02238	.01240
248	120	.030333	.0242	.02743	.02499	.02070	.01569	.008239
257	125	.026266	.0208	.02366	.02144	.01764	.01322	.006764
266	130	.022810	.0178	.02047	.01845	.01508	.01118	.005578
284	140	.017343	.0134	.01546	.01379	.01140	.008077	.003842
302	150	.013319	.0101	.01182	.01044	.008335	.005916	.002690
320	160		*.00768	.009136	.008003	.006325	.004390	.001916
356	180		*.00464	.005629	.004860	.003761	.002506	.001014
392	200		*.00292	.003600	.003071	.002366	.001494	.0005658
428	220		*.00191	.002377	.002012	.001484	.0009256	.0003291
464	240		*.00129	.001619	.001359	.0009767	.0005942	.0002050
500	260		*.000893	.001134	.0009417	.0006622	.0003942	.0001276
536	280		*.000637	.0008156	.0006677	.0004615	.0002694	.0000846
572	300		*.000461	.0006000	.0004836	.0003294	.0001890	.0000581

* 160°C THOUGH 300°C USED FOR PART NUMBERS PREFIXED BY PP, PB & PA ONLY. **Ro = RESISTANCE @ 25°C, Zero Power Applied
P DIA. REFERS TO GLASS ENVELOPE DIA.

TABLE 9–1 (Continued)

Table shows curves of thermistors made of different types of materials. To determine resistance of thermistor at specified temperature, first determine RT curve number, material, type unit, and then select appropriate vertical column. Multiply resistance of thermistor at 25°C by appropriate horizontal value in line with the specified temperature to obtain resistance.

8	9	10	11	12	13	14	15	16
TYPE D	TYPE C	TYPE B	TYPE B	TYPE B	TYPE A	TYPE A	TYPE A	TYPE A
GLASS COATED BEADS & PROBES DISCS	GLASS COATED BEADS & PROBES	DISCS WASHERS RODS	GLASS COATED BEADS & PROBES	GLASS COATED BEADS & PROBES	GLASS COATED BEADS & PROBES	GLASS COATED BEADS & PROBES	GLASS COATED BEADS & PROBES	DISCS WASHERS RODS
STD. SMALL BEADS (.014 DIA.) 250 — 1K STD. LG. BEADS & PROBES (.043 DIA.) 50-250 DISCS Size Ro F 30-50 J 15-75 K 4-35 C 2.5-18 L 1.5-10 D .9-6.5 M .7-4.5 PROBES MICRO-MINI (.020 DIA.) 250 — 1K SUB-MINI (.030 DIA.) 150-650 MINI (.060 DIA) 50-250 GD BEADS & PROBES — DISCS — FD, JD, KD, CD, LD, DD, MD, UD	STD. SMALL BEADS (.014 DIA.) 1K-5K STD. LG. BEADS & PROBES (.043 DIA.) 250-2K PROBES MICRO-MINI (.020 DIA.) 1K-5K SUB-MINI (.030 DIA.) 600-2K GC	DISCS Size Ro F 600-2800 J 300-1400 K 75-700 C 50-350 L 30-180 D 20-125 M 15-85 N 10-50 Z 7.5-30 P 2.5K-15K WASHERS 10-60 RODS Size Ro Q 4K-20K R 1K-15K T 350-7.5K DISCS FB, JB, KB, CB, LB, DB, MB, NB, PB, UB, ZB WASHERS WB RODS GB, RB, TB	STD. SMALL BEADS (.014 DIA.) 7K-30K STD. LG. BEADS (.043 DIA.) 1K-5K PROBES MICRO-MINI (.020 DIA.) 7K-30K SUB-MINI (.030 DIA.) 4K-18K MINI (.060 DIA.) 1K-5K STD. PROBES (.100 DIA.) 1K - 5K GB	STD. SMALL BEADS (.014 DIA.) 40K-50K STD. LG. BEADS (.043 DIA.) 5K-10K PROBES MICRO-MINI (.020 DIA.) 40K-50K SUB-MINI (.030 DIA.) 23K-30K MINI (.060 DIA.) 5K-10K STD. PROBES (.100 DIA.) 5K - 10K GB	STD. SMALL BEADS (.014 DIA.) 50K-200K STD. LG. BEADS (.043 DIA.) 10K-30K PROBES MICRO-MINI (.020 DIA.) 50K-200K SUB-MINI (.030 DIA.) 30K-120K MINI (.060 DIA.) 10K-30K STD. PROBES (.100 DIA.) 10K - 30K GA	STD. SMALL BEADS (.014 DIA.) 200K-400K STD. LG. BEADS (.043 DIA.) 30K-60K PROBES MICRO-MINI (.020 DIA.) 200K-400K SUB-MINI (.030 DIA.) 110K-230K MINI (.060 DIA.) 30K-60K STD. PROBES (.100 DIA.) 30K - 60K GA	STD. SMALL BEADS (.014 DIA.) 500K-1 MEG. STD. LG. BEADS (.043 DIA.) 75K-200K PROBES MICRO-MINI (.020 DIA.) 500K-1 MEG. SUB-MINI (.030 DIA.) 280K-600K MINI (.060 DIA.) 75K-200K STD. PROBES (.100 DIA.) 75K - 200K GA	DISCS Size Ro F 4400-20K J 2200-10K K 550-5K C 375-2500 L 200-1400 D 130-900 M 110-600 N 72-375 Z 55-220 P 20K-100K WASHERS 70-425 RODS Size Ro Q 25K-125K R 6K-120K T 2.5K-42.5K DISCS FA, JA, KA, CA, LA, DA, MA, NA, PA, UA, ZA WASHERS WA RODS QA, RA, TA
2758±175	3000±175	3400±80	3442±90	3574±93	3894±90	3976±93	4118±95	3887±51
4.80±10%	5.50±10%	6.95±4.5%	7.04±5%	7.59±5%	9.1±5%	9.53±5%	10.33±5%	9.1±3%
4.32-5.28	4.95-6.05	6.63-7.26	6.69-7.39	7.21-7.97	8.65-9.56	9.05-10.01	9.81-10.85	8.83-9.37
10.30	13.51	19.05	19.85	22.73	29.42	31.72	38.05	29.27
−3.1%/°C	−3.4%/°C	−3.9%/°C	−3.9%/°C	−4.0%/°C	−4.4%/°C	−4.5%/°C	−4.7%/°C	−4.4%/°C
38.2	45.3	73.04	76.08	89.45	145.2	152.5	174.0	140.49
21.7	25.8	38.95	40.10	46.03	68.88	72.00	81.6	67.01
12.90	15.1	21.51	22.07	24.75	34.28	37.268	40.2	33.65
8.03	9.24	12.33	12.60	13.83	17.92	18.40	20.6	17.70
5.16	5.81	7.307	7.430	8.009	9.792	10.20	11.0	9.707
3.42	3.76	4.476	4.530	4.796	5.560	5.767	6.12	5.533
2.34	2.50	2.825	2.850	2.961	3.274	3.363	3.51	3.265
1.64	1.70	1.830	1.839	1.882	1.992	2.022	2.08	1.990
1.17	1.19	1.216	1.219	1.227	1.250	1.256	1.27	1.249
1.00	1.00	1.000	1.000	1.000	1.000	1.000	1.00	1.000
.857	.846	.8267	.8265	.8197	.8053	.8030	.794	.8057
.640	.615	.5742	.5730	.5598	.5316	.5264	.510	.5327
.486	.454	.4067	.4048	.3903	.3595	.3528	.336	.3603
.376	.341	.2937	.2915	.2773	.2482	.2417	.226	.2488
.295	.261	.2160	.2138	.2006	.1747	.1690	.155	.1752
.234	.202	.1615	.1594	.1475	.1252	.1203	.108	.1255
.189	.158	.1229	.1205	.1101	.09126	.08698	.0771	.09153
.154	.125	.0946	.09235	.08335	.06754	.06395	.0557	.06783
.127	.101	.0740	.07185	.06396	.05076	.04769	.0408	.05103
.106	.0817	.0585	.05655	.04969	.03867	.03608	.0303	.03893
.0971	.0740	.0525	.05038	.04399	.03399	.03154	.0262	.03417
.0889	.0670	.0471	.04500	.03906	.02988	.02765	.0228	.030093
.0755	.0554	.0382	.03620	.03104	.02327	.02144	.0173	.023527
.0647	.0462	.0314	.02940	.02491	.01843	.01682	.0133	.018597
		*.0259	.02408	.02019	.01470	.01332	.0105	*.0147
		*.0180	.01727	.01362	.009700	.008615	.00656	*.0097
		*.0130	.01248	.009491	.006600	.005769	.00427	*.0066
		*.0098	.00940	.006805	.004700	.003981	.00286	*.0047
		*.0076	.007294	.005004	.003500	.002831	.00197	*.0035
		*.0060	.005758	.003763	.002600	.002065	.00140	*.0026
		*.0048	.004607	.002888	.002100	.001541	.00101	*.0021
		*.0040	.003839	.002256	.001700	.001173	.000745	*.0017

(Courtesy of Fenwal)

ence in the two circuits is in the thermocouple connection to the bridge. The final operation of this circuit is essentially the same as the previous circuit. The conversion stage of this circuit uses an electromagnetic unit instead of the op-amp. This type of conversion has been available for a number of years. It is very reliable and is widely used in temperature recorders.

When more accurate thermocouple measurements are desired, it is rather common practice to use cold-junction compensation. In this situation a reference junction is placed between the thermocouple and the meter or readout device. The reference junction is then maintained at a constant temperature of 0°C or 32°F. With this addition to the circuit, the only variables that remain are the cold-junction temperature and the resistance of the reference-junction readout lead wires. Special cold-junction compensators and ice-point cells simplify this measuring technique.

Thermistor Instrumentation _____

Thermistors are one of the simplest and most versatile temperature-measuring components available. This component, being a solid-state device, differs from its RTD counterpart by having a negative temperature coefficient of resistance. As a result, increases in temperature cause a corresponding decrease in resistance. This effect is the reverse of that in a metal that has a positive temperature coefficient.

The resistance of a thermistor is primarily controlled by the temperature of its environment. When using a specific thermistor, it is possible to predict how it will respond to a change in temperature. In this regard, if its reference temperature resistance is known and the temperature of the environment in which it is placed is known, its new resistance can be determined. In the same manner, if the reference

temperature resistance and its environment resistance are known, its temperature can be determined. Predictions of this type can be achieved by using the manufacturer's resistance–temperature tables.

The resistance–temperature tables shown in Table 9–1 are used to determine the resistance of a thermistor when its temperature ranges from −60° to 300°C. This particular table has 16 different columns of temperature coefficients. Each column represents a distinct type of thermistor or different material used in its construction. Note the material designation in the second horizontal row. The construction type is indicated in the third row as type units. Ranges and prefixes are shown in the next two rows. The coefficient values are indicated by the last eight rows. Notice that these are indicated for both degrees Celsius and Fahrenheit.

To use the table, first find the temperature of the environment in which the thermistor is placed. This is indicated in the left-hand column. Moving from this temperature horizontally and to the right to a particular column will identify a specific coefficient value. The coefficient is then used to determine the temperature of the thermistor. This is achieved by multiplying the thermistor's reference value by the coefficient. Reference values are generally rated at 25°C or 77°F. This is often called ambient or room temperature referencing.

Assume that we are using a KB31J1 Fenwal thermistor to evaluate the temperature of a specific environment. The specific size of the thermistor is indicated by the letter K. The B designation of this number denotes the type. This is found in column 10 of the table. Specifically, this thermistor has a resistance of 1 kΩ at a reference temperature of 25°C. Let us now see how the thermistor responds when it is placed in an environment of 100°C. To determine the resistance, we find the coefficient of the thermistor to be 0.0946 in column 10 for 100°C. This shows that the resistance of the

thermistor will be 94.6 Ω when it is placed in an environment of 100°C. This is determined by multiplying 1000 × 0.0946 = 94.6 ohms.

Using the reverse procedure, it is possible to determine temperature by finding a coefficient that reflects the value change in resistance. In this regard, asume that the same KB31J1 thermistor is placed in an environment with an unknown temperature. Its resistance changes to a value of 216 Ω. To determine the unknown temperature, divide the measured resistance (216 Ω) by the reference resistance (1000 Ω) to find a coefficient value of 0.216. This value is then found in column 10 and projected to the left for the temperature value. A coefficient of 0.216 indicates a temperature of 70°C or 158°F. The temperature–resistance table is a very valuable tool in predicting temperature and resistance values of a thermistor.

The process of measuring temperature with a thermistor simply involves a process of monitoring corresponding circuit changes in current or voltage. The circuit of Figure 9–39 shows a dc energy source, a variable resistor, a thermistor, and a microammeter. Any temperature change that takes place around the thermistor will produce a change in circuit. With the meter calibrated in temperature values, direct readings can be obtained from the meter. In this type of circuit the thermistor may be located a long distance from other circuit components without adversely affecting accuracy. Additional copper wire, for example, only adds a negligible amount of circuit resistance to a normally high resistance circuit.

The variable resistor (R_1) provides calibration for the thermistor circuit of Figure 9–39. The range of the microammeter has a great deal to do with the setting of R_1. It is generally advisable to make a multipoint calibration for a circuit of this type. A typical thermistor does not ordinarily have a wide range of linearity. It is also important to have the voltage source stabilized when the circuit is used for long pe-

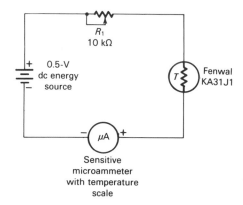

FIGURE 9–39
Thermistor temperature-measuring circuit.

riods of time to assure proper calibration. The source voltage should be kept at a minimum value in order to reduce the self-heating effect of the thermistor.

Thermistors are generally used in a bridge type of circuit configuration. A bridge usually has improved sensitivity over the series type of circuit. Bridges can be energized by either an ac or dc power source; they have a voltmeter or ammeter indicator and four resistance arms. The sensitivity of the indicator determines the temperature-range capabilities of the circuit. In some cases a full-scale deflecton of the meter may correspond to a reading of only 1°C.

Figure 9–40 shows a simple four-arm bridge in which the thermistor forms one of the arms. A microammeter or millivoltmeter is used as an indicator. The variable resistor is used for balancing the bridge. The bridge may be balanced to null at any temperature within the operating range of the thermistor. When the bridge is nulled, $R_1/R_3 = R_2/R_4$. The value of R_2 could then be determined by transposing the formula so that

$$R_2 = R_1 \times \frac{R_4}{R_3}$$

Thus, if R_3 and R_4 are of an equal value, the

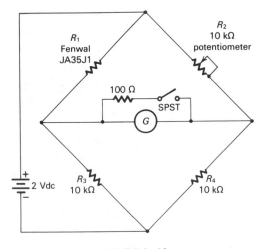

FIGURE 9–40
Thermistor bridge.

term R_4/R_3 becomes a 1. This means that the setting of R_2 therefore indicates directly the resistance of the thermistor. Thermistor resistance for any temperature can therefore be known very accurately if a precision adjustable resistor is used for R_2. A decade resistance box or calibrated slide-wire resistor is generally used to achieve this value. The null resistance

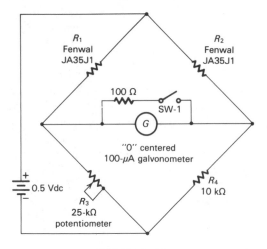

FIGURE 9–41
Differential thermistor bridge.

can then be converted to temperature units in degrees Celsius or Fahrenheit according to the value of the thermistor used. In a commercially prepared thermistor bridge, the resistance setting of R_2 may be graduated directly in degrees. Temperature values are taken directly from the setting of the resistor.

When two thermistors are used in a bridge, differential comparisons can be made. If the two thermistors are placed in different arms of the bridge, a greater circuit imbalance will occur with a change in temperature. If matched thermistors are used, it will be possible to detect temperature changes as low as 0.0005°C. Figure 9–41 shows a two-thermistor bridge circuit.

When a thermistor is used to drive a device to achieve some form of measurement, it generally necessitates amplification. In this regard, the thermistor is used to acquire data such as a change in temperature to achieve control of a circuit or load device. A rather simplified thermistor control circuit is shown in Figure 9–42. When the circuit is energized by the switch, resistor R_1 must be adjusted to produce a null identification on the milliammeter. This calibrates the circuit to ambient temperature. Grasping the thermistor with your fingers

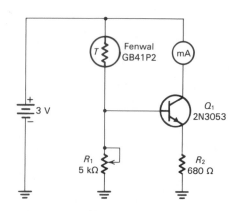

FIGURE 9–42
Thermistor control circuit.

should cause an imbalance and produce a current reading on the milliammeter. Removing your fingers from the thermistor should cause the circuit to return to the null state. As a rule, any change in thermistor resistance will cause a response in the output of this circuit. Resistor R_2 could be exchanged for the dc input of a solid-state relay and provide control of a rather substantial load. The power-handling capabilities of a thermistor are generally quite small. It cannot very effectively control a load device without some type of amplification.

Thermistor temperature-measuring circuits are inherently sensitive, stable, and fast responding and require rather simple circuitry. Lead length is not a significant problem and device polarity does not effectively alter circuit operation. In addition, the thermistor does not require reference temperatures or cold-junction compensation and it is rather inexpensive. Its disadvantages are nonlinearity over wide spans and instability for temperatures in excess of 200°C. The ability of a thermistor to produce changes in resistance that are almost entirely a function of temperature makes it a vital industrial measuring device.

RADIATION PYROMETERS

Radiation pyrometry refers to a method of measuring the temperature of an object by the amount of thermal energy radiated from its surface. Through this method of measurement, temperatures can be determined without direct contact with the object. A special type of optical system is employed that collects visible and infrared energy and focuses it on a detector element. The detector then changes this concentrated energy into an electrical signal. The signal is then amplified and applied to a readout or display element. Temperature is ultimately indicated by meter deflection, chart recording, or a display of digital numbers. See the diagram of a radiation pyrometer system in Figure 9–43.

The energy detector of a radiation pyrometer frequently employs a device known as a thermopile. Technically, a *thermopile* is described as a number of discrete thermocouples connected together in series. The composite output of this device is a dc voltage that is directly proportional to the amount of thermal energy falling on its surface. See the enlarged view of a thermopile in Figure 9–44(A) and the phantom view of the radiation head of a radiation pyrometer in Figure 9–44(B)

Figure 9–45 shows a portable version of a radiation pyrometer with a digital readout. This device uses a special vacuum-deposited ultrastable sensor of the CMOS integrated-circuit family. This instrument is primarily designed to measure general-purpose heated areas with a range of 0° to 600°F or 0° to 500°C. An alternate unit measures temperatures from 200° to 1000°F or 100° to 1000°C. The target size at 0 to 1 m is 50 mm in diam-

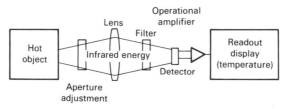

FIGURE 9–43
Simplified radiation pyrometer temperature-measuring system.

(A) Enlarged view of thermopile.

(B) Phantom view of radiation head.

FIGURE 9–44
Parts of a radiation pyrometer. (Courtesy of
Honeywell, Inc.)

FIGURE 9–45
Digital infrared thermometer. (Courtesy of
Whal Instruments, Inc.)

(A)

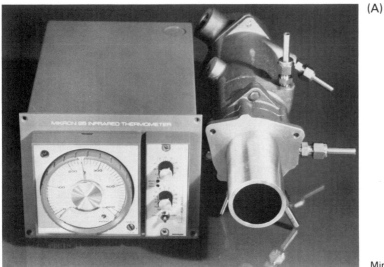

FIGURE 9–46
(A) Infrared prometer (Courtesy of Mikron Inc.); (B) diagram of an infrared pyrometer.

(B)

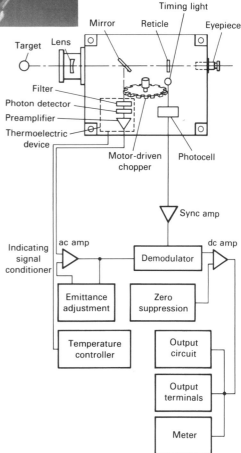

eter with a working distance of 20 ft or 6 m.

A radiation pyrometer system that measures temperatures between 70° and 3500°F or 21° to 1926°C with a target as small as 6 mm is shown in Figure 9–46(A). The diagram of this unit is shown in Figure 9–46(B). A special photon detector element is used in this unit to change infrared energy into dc electrical energy. The signal is then interrupted 1380 times per second by a motor-driven chopper, which changes the dc into an ac signal. This signal is then amplified and applied to a demodulator. Another chopper signal with pulses in synchronism with the original signal is applied to the demodulator input. The demodulator output is a dc signal that is applied to a meter or indicating unit. Instruments of this type are ideally suited to measure temperature in furnace atmospheres and of moving objects in

rolling mills, or for temperatures beyond the range of thermocouples.

QUESTIONS

1. Describe the basic parts of a thermal system.

2. What is the primary function or role played by each part of a thermal system?

3. What are some of the sources of heat used in industrial thermal systems?

4. What are some common factors that affect the accuracy of a thermal controller?

5. What considerations are taken into account when selecting a controller for a thermal system?

6. What is meant by the term *industrial filled-system thermometer?*

7. How does a filled system respond to changes in temperature?

8. How is the coefficient of linear expansion principle used in bimetal thermometers?

9. What is meant by the term *thermoresistant instrumentation?*

10. Explain how a change in temperature applied to an RTD element causes a bridge circuit to respond.

11. How does the thermocouple differ from other temperature-sensing elements?

12. How does a thermistor differ from an RTD or thermocouple?

13. Why are cold-junction references used in some temperature-measuring applications?

14. How does the radiation pyrometer develop an indication for changes in temperature?

PROBLEMS

1. In the bridge circuit of Figure 9–40, adjusting R_2 to 7kΩ causes the circuit to be balanced. What is the resistance of the thermistor?

2. Assume that the bridge of Figure 9–40 has the value of R_3 at 5kΩ and R_4 at 10kΩ. Balancing occurs when R_2 is adjusted to 5kΩ. What is the resistance of the thermistor?

3. In Figure 9–40, assume that adjusting R_2 to 5kΩ causes the circuit to be balanced. Prove that a millivolt meter or microampere meter placed across the output will in fact equal zero.

4. In Figure 9–39, when the potentiometer is adjusted to 1kΩ, the meter indicates 250 μA. What is the resistance of the thermistor?

5. Using the resistance–temperature table of Table 9–1, determine the resistance of a KA31J1 thermistor (1kΩ, type A) when it is placed in an environment of 50°C.

6. A KA31J1 thermistor changes value to 125.5 Ω when placed in an unknown environment. What temperature does this indicate?

7. A 5-kΩ thermistor is taken from an environment of 0°C and placed in an environment of 100°C. After one time constant, what is the resistance of the thermistor and what is its temperature?

8. How many time constants are required for a thermistor to complete a change in temperature–resistance?

9. The time constant of a thermistor is 0.5 s and its resistance is 5 kΩ. If it is taken

from an environment of 0°C and placed in an environment of 100°C, what is its temperature and resistance after 1.5 s?

ACTIVITIES

ACTIVITY 9–1: Thermocouple Sensor

Objective: Construction of a thermocouple sensor circuit, calibration of it, and evaluation of its operation.

Procedure:

1. Construct the thermocouple circuit of Figure 9–21. The thermocouple should be connected in close proximity to the LM335.

2. Momentarily disconnect the thermocouple from the noninverting input. Apply a 1- or 2-mV dc input signal to the noninverting input. Adjust resistor R_8 so that the op-amp has a gain of 245.7. Disconnect the calibration voltage from the noninverting input.

3. Connect a ground lead to the noninverting input of the LM308A and to the cathode of LM329B. Adjust R_2 so that the output voltage of the LM308A is 2.982 V at 25°C.

4. Remove the ground from the LM329B and adjust R_9 so that the voltage output is 246 mV at 25°C.

5. Remove the ground from the noninverting input and connect the thermocouple.

6. Test several temperature samples to evaluate the accuracy of the circuit. The output voltage of the amplifier should be 10 mV/°C.

7. Why does the output of a thermocouple usually necessitate some degree of amplification to effectively achieve control?

ACTIVITY 9–2: RTD Temperature Sensing

Objective: To construct an RTD amplified temperature-sensing circuit, calibrate the circuit, and evaluate its operation.

Procedure:

1. Construct the adjustable reference op-amp temperature-sensing circuit of Figure 9–23.

2. Apply power to the circuit and adjust resistor R_2 to produce 6.2 V at the emitter of the 2N2219 transistor.

3. Potentiometers R_4 and R_6 adjust the span and offset of the op-amp. The span adjustment is made first. When 266°C is applied to the RTD, it should produce an output voltage of 1.8 V. This heat may be derived from a heat gun, heating cone, or propane torch. A digital thermometer should be used to determine the tempearture as a reference. Practice some with the heat source so that it can be accurately predicted when 266° is reached. Apply heat to the RTD and quickly adjust the span control to produce an output of 1.8 V.

4. Apply 0°C to the RTD and adjust R_4 to produce 0-V output. Freeze mist, a container of crushed ice, or an icepoint reference chamber can be used as a source of 0°C.

5. After the calibration process, test several temperature samples to see how the circuit responds. Compare the accuracy with that of a digital voltmeter.

6. What is the voltage–degree Celsius relationship of this circuit?

ACTIVITY 9–3: On–Off Thermistor Temperature Controller

Objective: Construction of an on–off thermistor temperature controller and evaluation of circuit operation.

Procedure:

1. Construct the temperature control circuit of Figure 9–24. The heating element should be placed in a metal box or container of some type. The thermistor must be attached to the metal box or placed inside the box to sense the inside temperature. Avoid having the remainder of the circuit close to the metal container so that it will not be overheated by the source.

2. Apply power to the circuit and the heater. Monitor the inside temperature of the container with a thermometer. Adjust the setpoint control to a value 10° to 20°C above room temperature. After a short period of time, the circuit should settle down and remain fairly constant.

3. The LED connected to the output of the op-amp shows when the load is actuated. Alter the temperature of the container by opening a door or forcing cool air across its surface. Monitor the duty cycle of the heating element with the LED indicator. The duty cycle is determined by time on/time off + time on. The times can be monitored with a watch.

4. There should be a noticeable oscillation of the temperature above and below the setpoint value. Note how these oscillations are affected by the duty cycle.

ACTIVITY 9–4: Thermistor Bridge Circuit

Objective: Construction of a thermistor bridge circuit that will sense a change in temperature.

Procedure:

1. Construct the thermistor bridge of Figure 9–41.

2. Before applying power to the circuit, close the resistor meter shunt switch. This reduces the sensitivity of the circuit and protects the meter from large imbalance currents.

3. Apply power to the bridge and adjust R_2 to produce the best balance indication on the meter. Open the shunt switch and carefully rebalance the bridge again.

4. The bridge is now balanced for normal room temperature.

5. Grasp the thermistor between your thumb and finger and hold it for a few seconds. This should cause the bridge to become imbalanced. Note the time needed to cause the bridge to change from its balanced to an unbalanced condition.

6. Try a different source of heat and see how the circuit responds. Note the polarity of the meter when the bridge becomes unbalanced.

7. Place a piece of ice or spray the thermistor with freeze mist. Does a decrease in temperature cause the bridge to become imbalanced? Is there any difference in the indication of imbalance shown by the meter?

ACTIVITY 9–5: Differential Thermistor Bridge

Objective: Construction of a differential thermistor bridge circuit and evaluation of its operation as a temperature-measuring device.

Procedure:

1. Construct the thermistor bridge circuit of Figure 9–41. By having two thermistors in the bridge, the response will be twice as great as it would be with just one thermistor.

2. Close the meter shunt switch before applying power to the circuit.

3. Turn on the power and adjust the potentiometer to balance the bridge. Turn off the meter shunt switch and rebalance the bridge.

4. Shield R_1 while blowing on R_2. Describe how the meter responds.

5. Shield R_2 while blowing on R_1. Describe how this alters the bridge.

6. Position R_1 and R_2 so that they are in close proximity to one another. Blow on the two thermistors at the same time. What kind of response does the meter have to this action?

7. Try grasping one thermistor and blowing over the second thermistor. Then reverse the procedure on the two thermistors. How does this action alter the condition of the bridge?

ACTIVITY 9–6: Transistor Thermistor Control Circuit

Objective: Construction of a thermistor temperature control circuit that actuates a transistor and an analysis of circuit operation.

Procedure:

1. Construct the thermistor circuit of Figure 9–42.

2. Energize the circuit and adjust R_1 to produce a zero reading or null indication on the meter. This calibrates the circuit for ambient temperature.

3. Grasp the thermistor between your thumb and forefinger for about 3 min and record the current indicated by the milliammeter. Note the response time of the circuit. Remove your fingers from the thermistor and note how long it takes the circuit to return to its balanced state.

4. Measure and record V_B, V_E, and V_C of the transistor in its balanced state.

5. Place the thermistor in a cup of warm water. Measure and record the V_B, V_E, and V_C of the circuit when it is out of balance.

6. How could this circuit be calibrated for another temperature?

A very large portion of all industrial manufacturing is achieved today through some type of automatic processing equipment. Information or data that are used by this type of equipment are often described as *control signals* or *commands*. For these signals to be made usable, they must be manipulated in a variety of ways. This includes storing in memory, transmission, reading, counting, encoding, and decoding. As an end result, the system may perform a precision machining operation or alter some delicate control process.

10

Digital Electronic Systems

INTRODUCTION

As a general rule, most industrial equipment is controlled by signals that contain some type of numerical information. Specific number elements, which are typically described as digits, therefore become important. A decimal system, for example, has 10 elements or digits that are used repeatedly in the counting process. Any device that employs a numerical signal in its operation is therefore classified as a digital system. Computers, pocket calculators, digital display instruments, numerical control or NC equipment, and timing devices are common industrial applications included in this classification.

Industrial applications of a digital system may be operated electronically, hydraulically, or pneumatically. The manipulation of digital information is primarily the same for all three system types. Digital systems of the fluidic type are primarily limited to rather low speed operations that process only small quantities of data. Practically unlimited quantities of digital information can be processed in nanoseconds (10^{-9} second) of time electronically. With operational speed being of prime importance in industry today, digital electronic applications tend to be used more frequently than any of the

other systems. We will therefore direct the attention of this chapter to digital electronic system applications that are used in industry.

THE DIGITAL SYSTEM

Digital systems, as a rule, are quite different from other electrical or electronic systems. An electrical energy source is first needed to energize the entire system. DC electricity is commonly used to achieve this function. The dc energy is manipulated by various electronic devices in such a way that it ultimately appears as a number of electrical pulses that occur within a given time. Electronic clock circuits or generators are employed to produce the pulses. The resulting output is called a *digital signal*. This signal is then processed through the system to develop the unique counting capability of the digital system. In a strict sense, this system has a primary energy source and a digital pulse signal source.

The transmission path, control, load, and indicator parts of a digital system are also different. They are energized by the primary source, but must process pulses that represent digital signal information. In the remainder of this chapter, we will discuss the digital signal processing that is used to achieve industrial control functions.

Digital System Numbers

The most common number system in operation today is the decimal system. Ten digits are used in this numbering system to achieve counting: 0, 1, 2, 3, 4, 5, 6, 7, 8, and 9. The number of discrete digits of the system is commonly called its *base* or *radix*. The decimal system, therefore, has a radix or base of 10.

Nearly all modern numbering systems are

described as having *place value*. This term refers to the placement of a particular digit with respect to others in the counting process. The largest digit that can be used in a specific place or location is determined by the base of the system. In the decimal system, the first position to the left of the decimal point is called the *unit's place*. Any digit from 0 to 9 can be used in this place. When number values greater than 9 are to be used, they must be expressed in two or more places. The next position to the left of the unit's place is the 10's place in a decimal system. The number 99 is the largest digital value that can be expressed by two places in the decimal system. Each place added to the left extends the capability of this system by a power of 10.

A specific number value of any base can be expressed by addition of weighted place values. The decimal number 1346, for example, would be expressed as $(1000 \times 1) + (3 \times 100) + (4 \times 10) + (6 \times 1)$. Note that these values increase progressively for each place

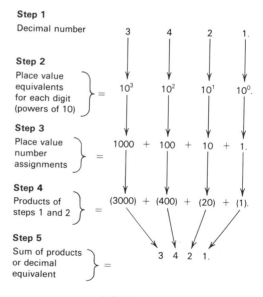

Step 1
Decimal number

Step 2
Place value equivalents for each digit (powers of 10)

Step 3
Place value number assignments

Step 4
Products of steps 1 and 2

Step 5
Sum of products or decimal equivalent

FIGURE 10–1
Components of decimal number 3421.

extending to the left of the starting position or decimal point. These place or position factors can also be expressed as powers of the base number. In the decimal system this would be 10^3, 10^2, 10^1, and 10^0, with each succeeding place being expressed as the next power of base 10. Mathematically, each place value is expressed as the digit number times a power of the radix of the numbering system base. The decimal number 3421 is expressed this way in Figure 10–1.

The decimal numbering system is commonly used today and is very convenient in our daily lives. Electronically, however, it is rather difficult to employ. Each digit of a base 10 system, for example, would require a specific value associated with it. Electronically, a system using this numbering method would require a special detection process to distinguish between different number values. The problems associated with defining and maintaining these ten levels are very difficult to solve.

Binary Numbering System

Practically all electronic digital systems in operation today are of the binary type. This type of system has 2 as its base or radix. The largest digital value that can be expressed in a specific place by this system is the number 1. Essentially, this means that only the numbers 0 or 1 are used in the binary system. Electronically, the value of zero can be expressed as a very low voltage value or no voltage. The number 1 can then be indicated by some voltage-value assignment larger than or more significant than zero. Binary systems that use this voltage-value assignment are described as having *positive logic*. Negative logic by comparison has voltage assigned to the zero and no voltage assigned to the number 1. In the discussion that follows, only positive logic will be used.

The two operational states of a binary system, one and zero, can be considered as natural circuit conditions. When a circuit is turned off or has no voltage applied, it is considered to be in the off or 0 state. An electrical circuit that has voltage applied or is operational, is therefore considered to be on or in the 1 state. A binary digit can therefore be either a 1 or a 0. The term *bit* is commonly used to describe this condition. A bit is a shortened version of the words *bi*nary digi*t*.

The basic principles of numbering that are used by the decimal or base 10 numbers apply in general to binary numbers. The radix of the binary system, for example, is 2. This means that only the digits 0 and 1 can be used to express a specific place value. The first place to the left of the starting point, or, in this case, the binary point, represents the unit's or 1's location. Places that follow to the left of the binary point refer to the powers of 2. Some of the digital values of numbers to the left of the binary point are $2^0 = 1$, $2^1 = 2$, $2^2 = 4$, $2^3 = 8$, $2^4 = 16$, $2^5 = 32$, $2^6 = 64$, $2^7 = 128$, and so on.

As a general rule, when different numbering systems are used in a discussion, they must incorporate a subscript number to identify the base of the numbering system being used. The number $110._2$ is a typical expression of this type. This would be described as one–one–zero instead of the decimal equivalent of one hundred and ten.

The number $110._2$ is equivalent to six to the base ten, or 6_{10}. Starting at the first digit to the left of the binary point, this number would have place value of $0 \cdot 2^0 + 1 \cdot 2^1 + 1 \cdot 2^2$ or $0 + 2._{10} + 4._{10} = 6._{10}$. The conversion of a binary number to an equivalent decimal number is shown by steps in Figure 10–2.

A simplified version of the binary-to-decimal conversion process is shown in Figure 10–3. In this method of conversion, write down the binary number first. Starting at the binary

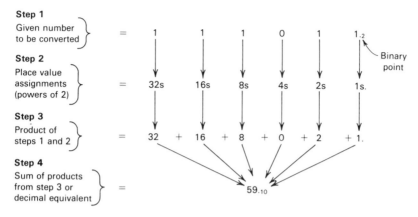

FIGURE 10–2
Conversion of a binary number to a decimal number.

point, indicate the decimal equivalent powers-of-2 numbers for each binary place location where a 1 is indicated. For each zero in the binary number, leave a blank space or indicate a zero. Add the place value assignments and record the decimal equivalent. Practice this method on several binary numbers until you are proficient in this conversion process.

The conversion of a decimal number to a binary equivalent is achieved by repetitive steps of division by the number 2. When the quotient is even with no remainder, a 0 is recorded. When the quotient has a remainder, a 1 is recorded. The steps needed to convert a

decimal number to binary number are shown in Figure 10–4.

The conversion process, in this case, is achieved by writing down the decimal number $(35._{10})$. Divide this number by the base of the system, or 2. Record the quotient and remainder as indicated. Move the quotient of step 1 to step 2 and repeat the process. The division process continues until the quotient becomes zero. The binary equivalent is simply the remainder values in their last-to-first placement order. You may want to practice this process on several numbers to gain some degree of proficiency.

Binary Coded Decimal Numbers

When large numbers are to be indicated by binary numbers, they become somewhat awkward and difficult to use. For this reason, the binary coded decimal method of counting was devised. In this type of system, four binary digits are used to represent each decimal digit. To illustrate this procedure, we have selected the number $329._{10}$ to be converted to a binary

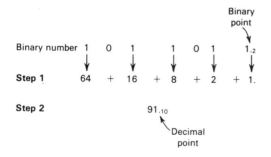

FIGURE 10–3
Simplified binary conversion process.

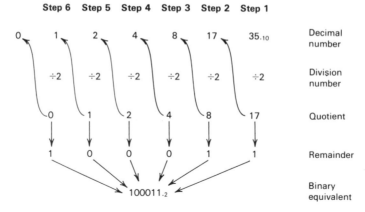

Step 6 Step 5 Step 4 Step 3 Step 2 Step 1

0	1	2	4	8	17	35.$_{10}$	Decimal number
÷2	÷2	÷2	÷2	÷2	÷2		Division number
0	1	2	4	8	17		Quotient
1	0	0	0	1	1		Remainder

100011.$_2$ Binary equivalent

FIGURE 10–4
Conversion of a decimal number to a binary
number.

coded decimal or BCD number. In straight binary numbers, $329._{10} = 101,001,001._2$.

To apply the BCD conversion process, the base 10 number is first divided into discrete digits according to place values (see Figure 10–5). The number $329._{10}$ therefore equals the digits 3–2–9. Converting each digit to binary would permit us to display this number as 0011–0010–$1001._{BCD}$. Decimal numbers up to $999._{10}$ could be displayed and quickly interpreted by this process with only 12 binary numbers. The dash line between each group of digits is extremely important when displaying BCD numbers.

Given decimal number		329.$_{10}$	
Step 1 Grouping of digits	(3)	(2)	(9)
Step 2 Conversion of each digit to binary group	(0011)	(0010)	(1001)
Step 3 Combine group values	0011 / 0010 / 1001.$_{BCD}$		

FIGURE 10–5
Converting a decimal number to a BCD
number.

The largest digit to be displayed by any group of BCD numbers is 9. This means that six digits of a number coding group are not being used at all in this system. Because of this the octal, or base 8, and the hexadecimal, or base 16, systems were devised. Digital systems still process numbers in binary form but usually display them in BCD, octal, or hexadecimal values.

Octal Numbering Systems

Octal or base 8 numbering systems are commonly used to process large numbers through digital systems. The octal system of numbers uses the same basic principles outlined with the decimal and binary counting methods.

The octal numbering system has a radix or base of 8. The largest number displayed by the system before it changes the place value is seven. The digits 0, 1, 2, 3, 4, 5, 6, and 7 are used in the place positions. The place values of digits starting at the left of the octal point are the powers of 8: 8^0 = units or 1's, 8^1 = 8's, 8^2 = 64's, 8^3 = 512's, and 8^4 = 4096's, and so on.

The process of converting an octal number

Step 1
Octal number   =   2 6 5.$_8$

Step 2
Place value equivalents (powers of 8)

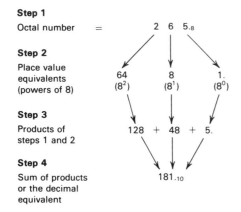

64   8   1.
(8^2)   (8^1)   (8^0)

Step 3
Products of steps 1 and 2

128 + 48 + 5.

Step 4
Sum of products or the decimal equivalent

181.$_{10}$

FIGURE 10–6
Conversion of an octal number to a decimal number.

Given octal number   127.$_8$

Step 1
Grouping of digits   (1) (2) (7).

Step 2
Conversion of digits to binary group

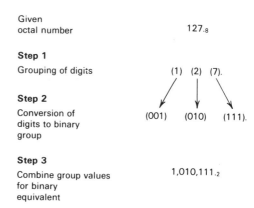

(001)   (010)   (111).

Step 3
Combine group values for binary equivalent   1,010,111.$_2$

FIGURE 10–7
Conversion of an octal number to a binary number.

to a decimal number is the same as that used in the binary-to-decimal conversion process. In this method, however, the powers of 8 are employed instead of the powers of 2. Suppose now that the number 265.$_8$ is to be changed to an equivalent decimal number. See the procedure outlined in Figure 10–6.

Converting an octal number to an equivalent binary number is very similar to the BCD conversion process discussed previously. The octal number is first divided into discrete digits according to place value. Each octal digit is then converted into an equivalent binary number using only three digits. The steps of this procedure are shown in Figure 10–7. You may want to practice this conversion process to gain proficiency in its use.

Converting a decimal number to an octal number is a process of repetitive division by the number 8. After the quotient has been determined, the remainder is brought down as the place value. When the quotient is even with no remainder, a zero is transferred to the place position. Assume now that the number 4098.$_{10}$ is to be converted to an octal equivalent. The procedure for making this conversion is outlined in Figure 10–8.

Converting a binary number to an octal number is a very important conversion process found in digital systems. Binary numbers are first processed through the equipment at a very high speed. An output circuit then accepts this signal and may convert it to an octal signal that can be displayed on a readout device.

Assume now that the number 10,110,101.$_2$ is to be changed into an equivalent octal number. The digits must first be divided into

Step 5   Step 4   Step 3   Step 2   Step 1

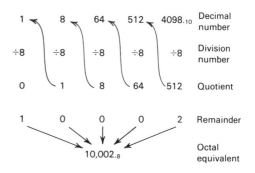

1	8	64	512	4098.$_{10}$	Decimal number
÷8	÷8	÷8	÷8	÷8	Division number
0	1	8	64	512	Quotient
1	0	0	0	2	Remainder

10,002.$_8$ Octal equivalent

FIGURE 10–8
Conversion of a decimal number to an octal number.

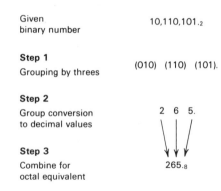

Given binary number	$10,110,101._2$
Step 1 Grouping by threes	(010) (110) (101).
Step 2 Group conversion to decimal values	2 6 5.
Step 3 Combine for octal equivalent	$265._8$

FIGURE 10–9
Conversion of a binary number to an octal number.

groups of three, starting at the octal point. Each binary group is then converted into an equivalent octal number. These numbers are then combined, while remaining in their same respective places, to represent the equivalent octal number. Refer to the conversion steps outlined in Figure 10–9.

Hexadecimal Numbering System

The hexadecimal numbering system is used in digital systems to process large number values. The radix or base of this system is 16, which means that the largest number used in a place is 15. Digits used to display this system are the numbers 0 through 9 and the letters, A, B, C, D, E, and F. The letters A through F are used to denote the digits 10 through 15, respectively. The place value of digits to the left of the hexadecimal point are the powers of 16: $16^0 = 1$'s, $16^1 = 16$'s, $16^2 = 256$'s, $16^3 = 4096$, $16^4 = 65,536$, $16^5 = 1,048,576$, and so on.

The process of changing a hexadecimal number to a decimal number is achieved by the same procedure outlined for other conversions. Initially, a hexadecimal number is recorded in proper digital order as outlined in Figure 10–10. The place values or powers of the base are then positioned under each respective digit in step 2. The values of steps 1 and 2 can then be multiplied to indicate discrete place-value assignments. In a hexadecimal conversion, step 3 is usually added to simplify letter digit assignments. Steps 2 and 3 are then multiplied together. Step 4 represents the addition of these product values. Adding these values together in step 5 represents the decimal equivalent of a hexadecimal number.

The process of changing a hexadecimal number to a binary equivalent is a simple grouping operation. Figure 10–11 shows the operational steps for making this conversion. Initially, the hexadecimal number is separated

Step 1:	Hexadecimal number	=	1		2		A	$F._{16}$
Step 2:	Place value equivalents (powers of 16)	=	4096s		256s		16s	1s.
Step 3:	Place value digits	=	1		2		10	15.
Step 4:	Product of steps 2 and 3	=	4096	+	512	+	160 +	15.
Step 5:	Sum of products or decimal equivalent	=	$4783._{10}$					

FIGURE 10–10
Conversion of a hexadecimal number to a decimal number.

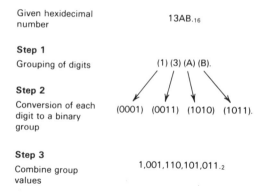

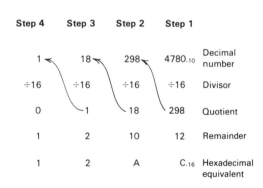

FIGURE 10–11
Converting a hexadecimal number to a
binary number.

FIGURE 10–12
Conversion of a decimal number to a
hexadecimal number.

into discrete digits in step 1. Each digit is then converted to an equivalent binary number using only four digits per group. Step 3 shows the binary groups combined to form the equivalent binary number.

The conversion of a decimal number to a hexadecimal number is achieved by the repetitive division process used with other number systems. In this procedure, however, the division factor is 16 and remainders can be as large as 15. Figure 10–12 shows the necessary procedural steps for achieving this conversion.

Converting a binary number to a hexadeci-

mal equivalent is a reverse of the hexadecimal to binary process. Figure 10–13 shows the fundamental steps of this procedure. Initially, the binary number is divided into groups of four digits, starting at the hexadecimal point. Each grouped number is then converted to a hexadecimal value and combined to form the hexadecimal equivalent.

DIGITAL SYSTEM OPERATIONAL STATES

Digital systems require a precise definition of operational states or conditions in order to be useful. In actual circuit design applications, binary signals are considered to be far superior to those of the octal, decimal, or hexadecimal systems just discussed. In practice, binary signals can be processed very easily through electronic circuitry because they can be represented by two stable states of operation. These states can be easily defined as on or off, 1 or 0, up or down, voltage or no voltage, right or left, or any other two-condition designations. There must be no in-between step or condition.

Given
binary number $1,001,001,111,101._2$

Step 1
Grouping by fours $(0001)(0010)(0111)(1101).$

Step 2
Group conversion   1   2   7   13
to hexadecimal   ↓   ↓   ↓   ↓
values   1   2   7   D

Step 3
Combine for
hexadecimal $127D._{16}$
equivalent

FIGURE 10–13
Binary number conversion to a hexadecimal
equivalent.

These states must be decidedly different and easily distinguished.

The symbols used to define the operational state of a binary system are very important. In positive binary logic, such things as voltage, on, true, or a letter designation such as A are used to denote the 1 operational state. No voltage, off, false, or the letter $\overline{A}$ are commonly used to denote the alternate or 0 condition. An operating system can be set to either state, where it will remain until something causes it to change conditions.

Any device that can be set in one of two operational states or conditions by an outside signal is said to be *bistable*. Switches, relays, transistors, diodes, and ICs are commonly used today to achieve this operation. In a strict sense, a bistable device has the capability of storing one binary digit or bit of information. By employing a number of these devices, it is possible to build an electronic circuit that will make decisions based on the applied input signals. The output of this circuit is therefore a decision based on the operational conditions of the input. Since this application of a bistable device makes logical decisions, it is commonly called a *binary logic circuit* or simply a logic circuit.

Binary Logic Functions

Any bistable circuit that is used to make a series of decisions based on two-state input conditions is called a *binary logic circuit*. Three basic circuits of this type have been developed to make simple logic decisions: the AND circuit, the OR circuit, and the NOT circuit. The logic decision made by each circuit is unique and very important in digital system operations.

Electronic circuits designed to perform specific logic functions are commonly called *gates*. This term refers to the capability of a circuit to pass or block specific digital signals. A simple if–then type of sentence is often used to describe the basic operation of a logic gate. For example, if the inputs applied to an AND gate are all 1, then the output will be 1. If a 1 is applied to any input of an OR gate, then the output will be 1. If any input is applied to a NOT gate, then the output will be reversed.

The fundamental operation of a digital system is based directly on gate applications. Technicians working with digital systems must therefore be very familiar with each basic gate function. The input–output characteristics and operation of basic logic gates will serve as the basis of our next discussion.

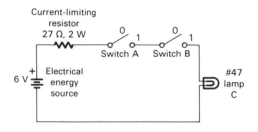

(A) Simple AND gate circuit.

(B) AND gate symbols.

ANS symbol   NEMA symbol

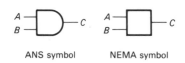

Switch A	Switch B	Lamp C
0	0	0
0	1	0
1	0	0
1	1	1

(C) AND gate truth table.

**FIGURE 10–14
AND gate information.**

AND Gates

An AND gate is designed to have two or more inputs and one output. Essentially, if all inputs are in the 1 state simultaneously, then a 1 will appear in the output. Figure 10–14 shows a simple switch-lamp analogy of the AND gate, its symbol, and an operational table. In Figure 10–14(A), when a switch is turned on it represents a 1 condition, while off represents a 0. The lamp also displays this same condition by being a 1 when it is on and 0 when turned off. Note that the switches are labeled A and B while the output lamp is C.

The operational characteristics of a gate are usually simplified by describing the input–output relationship in a table. The table in Figure 10–14(C) shows the 1 or 0 alternatives at the input and the corresponding output that will occur as a result of this input. As a rule, such a description of a gate is called a *truth table*. Essentially, it shows the predictable operating conditions of a logic circuit.

Each input to an AND gate has two operational states of 1 and 0. A two-input AND gate would therefore have 2^2, or 4, possible combinations that would influence the output. A three-input gate would have 2^3, or 8, combinations, while a four input would have 2^4, or 16, combinations. These combinations are normally placed in the truth table in binary progression order. For a two-input gate, this would be 00, 01, 10, and 11, which shows the binary count of 0, 1, 2, and 3 in order.

Functionally, the AND gate of Figure 10–14(A) will only produce a 1 output when switches *A* and *B* are both 1. Mathematically, this action is described as $A \cdot B = C$. This expression shows the multiplication operation. In a punch-press operation, this type of gate will not actuate the drive motor until the operator presses the L push button with the left hand and the R button with the right hand at the same time.

The symbol representations of an AND gate shown in Figure 10–14(B) are very common. The square symbol is a typical National Electrical Manufacturer's Association (NEMA) representation; the round diagram is the American National Standard (ANS) symbol.

OR Gates

An OR gate is designed to have two or more inputs and a single output. Like the AND gate, each input to the OR gate has two possible states: 1 or 0. The output of this gate will produce a 1 when either or both inputs are 1. Figure 10–15 shows a simple lamp-switch anal-

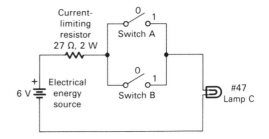

(A) Simple OR gate circuit.

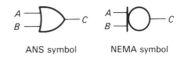

ANS symbol   NEMA symbol

(B) OR gate symbols.

Switch A	Switch B	Lamp C
0	0	0
0	1	1
1	0	1
1	1	1

(C) OR gate truth table.

FIGURE 10–15
OR gate information.

ogy of the OR gate, its symbol, and a truth table.

Functionally, an OR gate will produce a 1 output when both switches are 1 or when either switch A or B is a 1. Mathematically, this action is described as $A + B = C$. This expression shows OR addition. Applications of this gate are used to make logic decisions as to whether or not a 1 appears at either input. The over-head or dome-lamp system of an automobile is controlled by an OR type of circuit. Individual door switches and the dash panel switch all control the lamp from a different location.

NOT Gates

A NOT gate has a single input and a single output, which makes it unique compared with the AND and OR gates. The output of a NOT gate is designed so that it will be opposite to that of the input state. Figure 10–16 shows a simple switch-controlled NOT gate, its symbol, and truth table. Note that when the SPST switch is on or in the 1 state it shorts out the lamp. Likewise, placing the switch in the off condition causes the lamp to be on or in the 1 state. NOT gates are also called *inverters*. The significance of a NOT gate should be rather apparent after the following discussion of gates.

Combination Logic Gates

When a NOT gate is combined with an AND gate or an OR gate, it is called a combination logic function. A NOT–AND gate is normally called a NAND gate. This gate is an inverted AND gate, or simply NOT an AND gate. Figure 10–17 shows a simple switch-lamp circuit analogy of this gate, along with its symbol and truth table.

The NAND gate is an inversion of the AND gate. When switches A and B are both on or in

the 1 state, the lamp C is off. When either or both switches are off, the lamp C is in the on or 1 state. Mathematically, the operation of a NAND gate is expressed as $A \cdot B = \overline{C}$. The bar over C denotes the inversion or negative function of the gate.

A combination NOT–OR or NOR gate produces a negation of the OR function. Figure 10–18 shows a simple switch-lamp circuit analogy of this gate, along with its symbol and truth table. Mathematically, the operation of a NOR gate is expressed as $A + B = \overline{C}$. A 1 will only appear in its output when A is O and B is O.

Logic Gate Circuits

The switch-lamp analogy of different gate circuits was primarily used to show basic logic operating characteristics in simplified form. In actual circuit applications, logic gates show very little resemblance at all to this type of circuit construction. Transistors, diodes, and numerous other components are commonly connected together to achieve gate functions. The switching action of a gate can then be achieved very quickly by applying either forward or reverse biasing to solid-state components.

At one time, logic circuits of the discrete component type were very popular. Developments in integrated-circuit technology have now brought about a tremendous reduction in applications of discrete-component logic circuits. Multiple gate structures are now being built inexpensively on single IC chips. Through these devices it is possible to construct complex logic circuits by simply interconnecting different logic gates. An understanding of basic logic functions is therefore much more important today than it has ever been in the past. The truth table of a specific gate and its logic symbol terminal connections seem to be the two most important items

(B) NOT gate symbols.

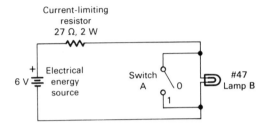

(A) Simple NOT gate circuit.

Switch A	Lamp B
0	1
1	0

(C) NOT gate truth table.

**FIGURE 10–16
NOT gate information.**

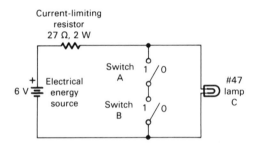

(A) NAND gate circuit.

(B) NAND gate symbols.

Switch A	Switch B	Lamp C
0	0	1
0	1	1
1	0	1
1	1	0

(C) NAND gate truth table.

**FIGURE 10–17
NAND gate information.**

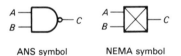

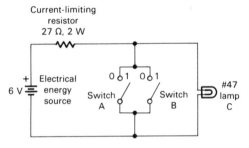

(A) NOR gate circuit.

(B) NOR gate symbols.

Switch A	Switch B	Lamp C
0	0	1
0	1	0
1	0	0
1	1	0

(C) NOR gate truth table.

**FIGURE 10–18
NOR gate information.**

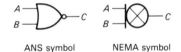

375

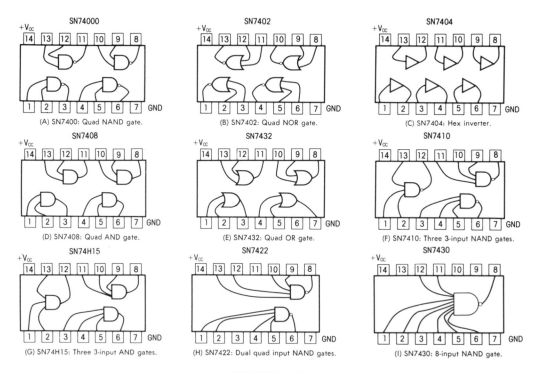

FIGURE 10–19
Typical IC pin configuration diagrams.

needed in selecting an IC to perform a particular function. Figure 10–19 shows some typical pin connection diagrams of transistor–transistor logic or TTL ICs.

BOOLEAN ALGEBRA

Boolean algebra is a special form of algebra that was designed to show the relationships of two-state variable logic operations. This form of algebra is ideally suited for the analysis and design of binary logic systems. Through the use of Boolean algebra, it is possible to write mathematical expressions that describe specific logic functions. Boolean expressions seem to

be much more meaningful than complex word statements or elaborate truth tables. The laws that apply to Boolean algebra may also be used to simplify complex expressions. Through this type of operation, it may be possible to reduce the number of logic gates needed to achieve a specific function before it is built.

In Boolean algebra the variables of an equation are commonly assigned letters of the alphabet. Each variable then exists in states of 1 or 0 according to its condition. The 1 or true state is normally represented by a single letter such as A, B, or C. The opposite state or condition is then described as 0 or false and is represented as $\overline{A}$ or A'. This is described as NOT A or A negated or complemented.

Boolean algebra is somewhat different from

conventional algebra with respect to mathematical operations. The Boolean operations and two other conventions are expressed as follows:

Multiplication: A AND B, AB, $A \cdot B$

OR addition: A OR B, $A + B$

Negation or complementing: NOT A, $\overline{A}$, A'

Equivalency: A equals B, $A = B$

Using Boolean Algebra

Assume now that a logic circuit is used to control the operation of an ac servomotor that actuates a rotary table. In this case the table will rotate according to information sent to it from three input variables, A, B, and C. The motor should operate when only C is on by itself or when A, B, and C are on at the same time.

Expressing this statement in a Boolean expression would describe the desired output. Eight different combinations of A, B, and C exist in this expression because there are three inputs. Only two of those combinations must generate an output signal that will actuate the motor. When a variable is not on, or 0, it is expressed as a negated letter. The original statement would therefore be expressed: With A, B, and C on, or with A off, B off, and C on, motor operation (X) will occur.

$$ABC + \overline{A}\overline{B}C = X$$

Developing a truth table for this equation would show if it achieves the given expression. Table 10–1 shows how this truth table is developed in operational steps. In step 1, ABC is achieved by multiplying the three inputs together. A 1 only appears when the A, B, and C inputs are all 1. Steps 2 and 3 are achieved by negating inputs A and B, respectively. Step 3 shows the product of inputs C, $\overline{A}$, and $\overline{B}$. Step 5 shows the addition of ABC (step 1) and $\overline{A}\overline{B}C$ (step 4). The output of this equation shows that a 1 is generated only when $\overline{A}\overline{B}C$ is 1 or when ABC is 1.

The process of constructing a logic circuit from a Boolean expression is shown in Figure 10–20. Initially the equation must be analyzed for its primary operational function. Step 1 shows the original equation. The primary function in this case is addition. This function influences all parts of the equation in some way. Step 2 shows the primary function changed to a logic gate diagram with branch parts of the equation applied to it. Step 3 shows the branch parts of the equation expressed by logic diagrams. In this case, AND gates are used to combine terms. Step 4 completes the process by connecting all inputs together. The circles at inputs $\overline{A}\overline{B}$ of the lower AND gate are used to achieve the negation function of these branch parts.

The general rules for changing a Boolean equation into a logic circuit diagram are very similar to those outlined. Initially, the original equation must be analyzed for its primary mathematical function. This is then changed into a gate diagram that is fed by second-level or branch parts of the equation. Each branch operation is then analyzed and expressed in gate form. The process continues until all branches are completely expressed in diagram

TABLE 10–1
Truth Table of Boolean Expression
$ABC + \overline{A}\overline{B}C = X$

Inputs			Step 1	Step 2	Step 3	Step 4	Step 5 ABC + $\overline{A}\overline{B}C$
A	B	C	ABC	$\overline{A}$	$\overline{B}$	$\overline{A}\overline{B}C$	Output
0	0	0	0	1	1	0	0
0	0	1	0	1	1	1	1
0	1	0	0	1	0	0	0
0	1	1	0	1	0	0	0
1	0	0	0	0	1	0	0
1	0	1	0	0	1	0	0
1	1	0	0	0	0	0	0
1	1	1	1	0	0	0	1

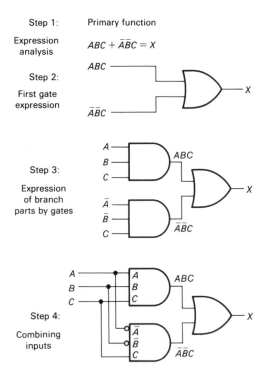

Step 1:

Expression analysis

Primary function

$ABC + \bar{A}\bar{B}C = X$

Step 2:

First gate expression

Step 3:

Expression of branch parts by gates

Step 4:

Combining inputs

FIGURE 10–20
Steps in logic circuit construction from Boolean equation.

form. Common inputs are then connected together if they are present.

DIGITAL LOGIC DEVICES

Digital systems employ a number of devices that are not classified specifically as logic gates. These devices usually play some special role in the operation of a digital system. Such things as flip-flops, counters, decoders, and memory devices are included in this classification. A presentation of the truth tables, logic symbols, and the operational characteristics of these devices will be made so that they may be used more effectively when the need arises. As a general rule, most of these devices are constructed entirely on IC chips. Operation is based to a large extent on the internal circuit construction of the IC. Very little can be done to alter the operation of these devices other than to modify the input or use its output to influence the operation of a secondary device.

Flip-flops

Flip-flops are commonly used to generate signals, shape waves, and achieve division. In addition to these operations, a flip-flop may also be used as a memory device. In this capacity, it can be made to hold an output state even when the input is completely removed. It can also be made to change its output when an appropriate input signal occurs.

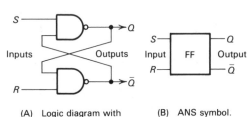

(A) Logic diagram with NAND gates.

(B) ANS symbol.

Unpredictable

Applied inputs		Previous outputs		Resulting outputs	
S	R	Q	$\bar{Q}$	Q	$\bar{Q}$
0	0	1	0	1/0	0/1
0	1	1	0	1	0
1	0	1	0	0	1
1	1	1	0	1	0
0	0	0	1	0/1	1/0
0	1	0	1	1	0
1	0	0	1	0	1
1	1	0	1	0	1

Unpredictable

(C) R-S flip-flop truth table.

FIGURE 10–21
RS flip-flop information.

The reset–set or RS flip-flop of Figure 10–21 is a typical digital system control device. The logic diagrams, ANS symbol, and truth table of the flip-flop are shown in the figure. Note that the truth table for this device is somewhat more complicated than that of a simple logic gate. For example, it must show the different states of the device before an input pulse occurs and then show how it changes after the input has arrived. Note that two of the operating conditions produce an unpredictable output. In this state of operation, the first arriving pulse will produce an output only by coincidence.

In many digital system applications, flip-flops must be set and cleared at specific times with respect to other operating circuits. This type of operation can be achieved by manipulating flip-flops in step with a clock pulse. In this case, the appropriate RS inputs and clock pulse must all be present in order to cause a state change. A device of this type is called an RS triggered flip-flop or simply an RST flip-flop.

The truth table of an RST flip-flop is basically the same as that of the RS flip-flop of Figure 10–21. It will only initiate a state change when the clock pulse arrives at the T input. A two-input AND gate is simply added to the set and reset inputs to accomplish this operation. Figure 10–22 shows this modification, the corresponding ANS logic symbol, and the truth table for the RST flip-flop.

Another important flip-flop device that is commonly used in digital systems is the JK flip-flop. This device is somewhat unusual because it has no unpredictable output states. It can be set by applying a 1 to the J input and can be cleared by feeding a 1 to the K input. A 1 signal applied to both J and K inputs simultaneously causes the output to change states or toggle. A 0 applied to both inputs at the same time does not initiate a state change. The inputs of a JK flip-flop are controlled directly by clock pulse application.

Figure 10–23 shows a logic diagram, ANS symbol, and truth table for the JK flip-flop. Notice that there are no unpredictable output states for this device. Several versions or modifications of the basic JK flip-flop are available today. These include devices with preset and preclear inputs that can be used to establish sequential operations at a precise moment. Flip-flops are commonly used as the basic logic ele-

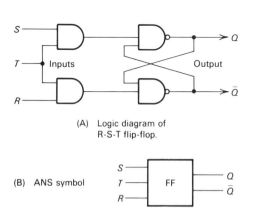

(A) Logic diagram of R-S-T flip-flop.

(B) ANS symbol

Applied inputs			Previous outputs		Resulting outputs		
S	R	T	Q	$\bar{Q}$	Q	$\bar{Q}$	
0	0	0	1	0	1/0	0/1	←
0	1	1	1	0	1	0	
1	0	0	1	0	0	1	Unpredictable
1	1	1	1	0	1	0	
0	0	0	0	1	0/1	1/0	←
0	1	1	0	1	1	0	
1	0	0	0	1	0	1	
1	1	1	0	1	0	1	

(C) R-S-T flip-flop truth table.

FIGURE 10–22
RST flip-flop.

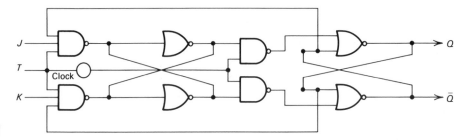

(A) Logic diagram of JK flip-flop.

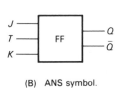

(B) ANS symbol.

Applied inputs			Previous outputs		Resulting output	
J	K	T	Q	Q̄	Q	Q̄
0	0	0	0	1	0	1
0	1	1	0	1	0	1
1	0	0	0	1	1	0
1	1	1	0	1	1	0
0	0	0	1	0	1	0
0	1	1	1	0	0	1
1	0	0	1	0	1	0
1	1	1	1	0	0	1

←Toggle state

FIGURE 10–23
JK flip-flop information.

(C) JK flip-flop truth table.

ment for counting operations, temporary memory, and sequential switching operatons.

Digital Counters

One of the most versatile and important logic devices of a digital system is the counter. This device, as a general rule, can be employed to count a wide variety of objects in a number of different digital system applications. While this device may be called upon to count an endless number of objects, it essentially counts only one thing, electronic pulses. These pulses may be produced electronically by a clock mechanism, electromechanically, photoelectrically, acoustically, or by a number of other processes. The basic operation of the counter, however, is completely independent of the pulse generator.

Binary Counters

A common application of the digital counter is used to count numerical information in binary form. This type of device simply employs a number of flip-flops connected so that the Q output of the first device drives the trigger or clock input of the next device. Each flip-flop therefore has a divide-by-2 function.

Figure 10–24 shows JK flip-flops connected to achieve binary counting. The counter in Figure 10–24(A) is commonly called a binary ripple counter. Each flip-flop in this circuit has the J and K inputs held at a logic 1 level. Each clock pulse applied to the input of FF_1 will then cause a change in state. The flip-flops only trigger on the negative-going part of the clock pulse. The output of FF_1 will therefore alternate between 1 and 0 with each pulse. A

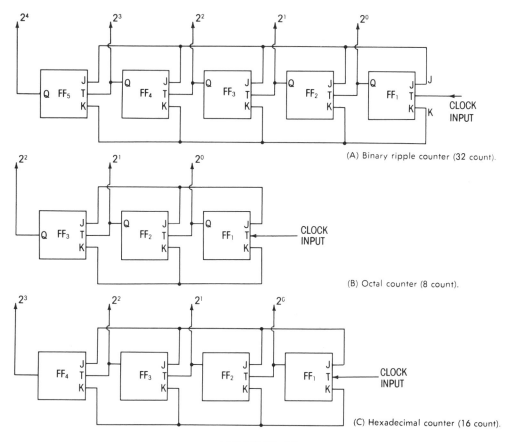

FIGURE 10–24
Digital counters achieved with JK flip-flops.

1 output will appear at Q of FF_1 for every two input pulses. This means that each flip-flop has a divide-by-2 function. Five flip-flops connected in this manner will produce a 2^5, or 32, count. The largest count in this case is $11111._2$; that is, $31._{10}$ occurs when each Q output is 1. The next applied pulse clears the counters so that 0 appears at all the Q outputs.

By grouping three flip-flops together [Figure 10–24(B)], it is possible to develop the units part of a binary coded octal or BCO counter. Therefore, $111._2$ would be used to represent the seven count or seven units of an octal counter. Two groups of three flip-flops connected in this manner would produce a maximum count of $111–111._2$, which represents $77._8$ or $63._{10}$.

By placing four flip-flops together in a group [Figure 10–24(C)], it is possible to develop the units part of a binary coded hexadecimal or BCH counter. Thus $1111._2$ would be used to represent $F._{16}$ or $15._{10}$. Two groups of four flip-flops could be used to produce a maximum count of $1111–1111._2$, which would

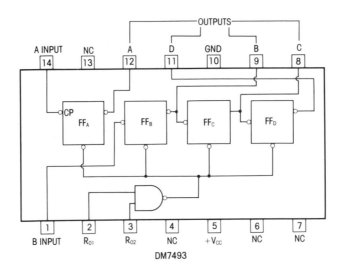

FIGURE 10–25
Four-bit binary counter IC.

represent $FF._{16}$ or $255._{10}$. Each succeeding group of four flip-flops would be used to raise the counting possibility to the next 16.

Binary counters that contain four interconnected flip-flops are commonly built on one IC chip. Figure 10–25 shows the logic connections of a 4-bit binary counter. When used as a 4-bit counter, the FF_A will now produce a maximum count of $1111._2$ or $15._{10}$. By disconnecting FF_A from FF_B, and applying the clock to FF_B input, we have a 3-bit or BCO counter. The outputs of flip-flops FF_A through FF_D are labeled A, B, C, and D, respectively.

Decade Counters

Since most of the mathematics that we use today is based on the decimal or base 10 system, it is important to be able to count by this method. Digital systems are, however, designed to process information in binary form because of the ease with which a two-state signal can be manipulated. The output of a binary

counter must therefore be changed into a decimal form before it can be used by an individual not familiar with binary numbers. The first step in this process is to change binary signals into a binary coded decimal or BCD form.

Consider now the 4-bit binary counter of Figure 10–26(A). In this counter, 16 natural counts are achieved by the four flip-flops. To convert this counter into a decade counter, we must simply cause it to skip some of its natural counts. Notice the 16 natural counts listed below the binary counter, reading right to left.

A method of converting a binary counter into a decade counter is shown in Figure 10–26(B). In this method the first seven counts occur naturally, as shown. Through these steps FF_D stays at 0. The $\overline{Q}$ output of FF_D therefore remains at 1 during these counts. This is applied to the J input of FF_B, which permits it to trigger with each clock pulse.

At the seventh count, 1's appearing at the Q outputs of FF_B and FF_C are applied to the AND gate. This action produces a logic 1 and applies it to the J input of FF_D. Arrival of the

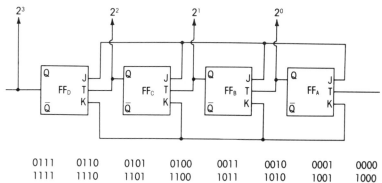

(A) Four-bit binary counter.

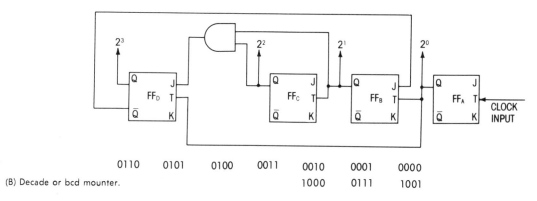

(B) Decade or bcd mounter.

FIGURE 10–26
Binary counter to decade or BCD counter
conversion.

next clock pulse triggers FF_A, FF_B, and FF_C into the off state and turns on FF_D. This represents the eight count.

When FF_D is in the on state, Q is 1 and $\overline{Q}$ is 0. This causes a 0 to be fed to the J input of FF_B, which now prevents it from triggering until cleared. Arrival of the next clock pulse causes FF_A to be set to a 1. This registers a $1001._2$, which is the ninth count. Arrival of the next count clears FF_A and FF_D instantly. Since FF_B and FF_C were previously cleared by the seventh count, all 0's appear at the outputs. The counter has therefore cycled through the

ninth count and returned to zero ready for the next input pulse. BCD counting of this type can be achieved in a number of ways. This method is quite common in IC devices today.

Figure 10–27 shows an IC BCD counter. The operation of this IC is essentially the same as the one just described. When this IC is used as a BCD counter, the output of FF_A must be connected to the BD input. Omitting this connection and applying the clock pulses to the BD input produces a five count. With this option the counter is somewhat more versatile. The two NAND gates of this IC are used to set

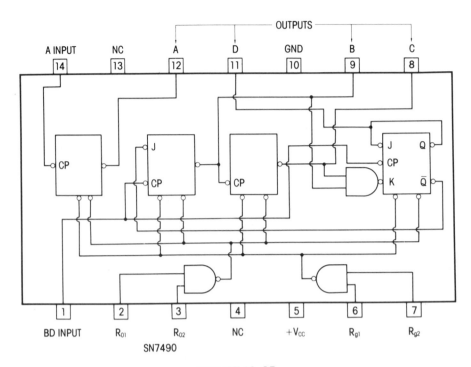

FIGURE 10–27
BCD decade counter IC.

or reset the four flip-flops from an outside source. This counter triggers only on the negative-going part of the clock pulse.

DIGITAL SYSTEM DISPLAYS

As a general rule, the average person called on to read the output of a digital system will not be familiar with the BCD method of displaying numbers. Digital systems must therefore change this information into a suitable method of display in order to be practical. Alphanumeric displays are commonly used today to achieve this operation. These devices can be used to display both number and letter information. In this case we are only concerned with the display of numerical information.

Three common methods of displaying nu-

merical information are available today. This includes the discrete number method, bar matrix displays, and the dot matrix. Each method represents a unique device designed to change electrical energy into light energy. The basic characteristics of the device dictate such things as operating voltage, current, illumination level, and quality of the display character.

The three basic methods of digital display are shown in Figure 10–28. Each display produces a particular type of character that is easily recognized. The electronic processes involved in producing a particular display include the ionization of a gas and powering incandescent elements, light-emitting diodes, and liquid-crystal display elements. Each method of display has a number of features and characteristics that must be taken into consideration when selecting a device for a specific application.

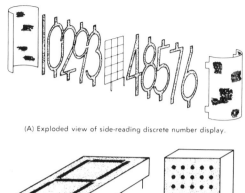

(A) Exploded view of side-reading discrete number display.

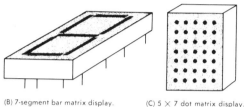

(B) 7-segment bar matrix display.

(C) 5 × 7 dot matrix display.

FIGURE 10–28
Digital display methods.

Gaseous Display Devices

The gaseous display tube has been used for a number of years as a digital readout device. The construction of this device includes a common anode and multiple cathodes shaped as discrete numbers or segmented bars. The numbers, or bar segments, remain somewhat transparent until energized electrically. With voltage of a specific value applied between the anode and a selected cathode, a characteristic orange glow appears around the appropriate cathode. This glow is a result of neon gas ionization within the display enclosure.

Figure 10–29 shows two types of gaseous display devices and their corresponding electrical circuits. In the discrete number display [Figure 10–29(A)], each switch completes an electrical circuit between the anode and a selected cathode. A dc source voltage of 170 V or more is needed to ionize the neon gas in this device to make it operate. The switching action that controls operation is normally achieved by a decoder IC. This device simply completes a return path to ground when the

appropriate number is needed in a display.

The operation of a seven-segment gaseous display device [Figure 10–29(C)] is very similar to that of the discrete number unit just discussed. The method of display, however, is somewhat different. It is achieved by energizing a combination of two or more discrete segments. The number 8, for example, is displayed when all segments are energized. The number 0 is displayed when all segments are energized except the center. The segmented bars of this display are labeled a, b, c, d, e, f, and g, respectively, and positioned to form a box 8 number. Displays of this type are manufactured with one or more discrete numbers formed into a single unit. The segment connection pins for this type of display extend from the back side of the display area.

Incandescent Display

Seven-segment incandescent display devices are used in some industrial digital systems today. These display units contain seven discrete resistive elements suspended between supporting posts. One side of each element is connected to a common tie point. Illumination occurs when current flows through a specific element and the common point. Usually, 5 V of ac or dc electricity is needed to produce a desired degree of illumination. Display devices of this type are commonly called Numitrons. RCA is the principal manufacturer of this device today.

Figure 10–30 shows a picture of a DR2000 Numitron and its electrical circuit. Note that this display produces a block type of seven-segment number similar to that of the gaseous display device. The chief advantage of the Numitron is its variable intensity characteristic. The filament segments of this device are, however, somewhat fragile when they are energized.

When a discrete segment of a Numitron is electrically energized, heat occurs. If enough

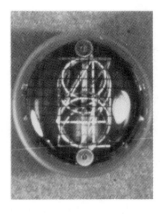

(A) Discrete number display.

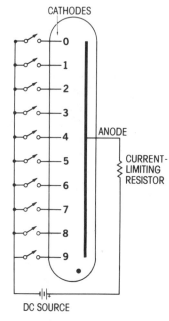

(B) Construction of (A).

(C) 7-segment display.

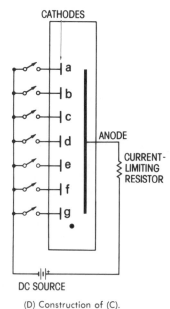

(D) Construction of (C).

FIGURE 10–29
Gaseous display devices.

heat is developed, the filament wire changes to a dull orange appearance and produces light energy. The degree of illumination produced is quite evident when compared with an unenergized element. As a result, this noticeable change is used to indicate segment illumination.

The discrete filament segments of a Numitron are commonly connected to form a single tie point. This essentially means that each filament presents a parallel path for the current from the source. As a result of this construction, filament current increases a set amount when each segment is energized. The number

(A) Photograph.

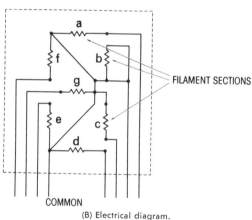

FILAMENT SECTIONS

COMMON

(B) Electrical diagram.

FIGURE 10–30
Numitron display device.

8 therefore demands the largest amount of current from the source when it is displayed.

The circuitry of a Numitron is somewhat simplified when compared with other seven-segment display devices. For example, it does not necessitate a current-limiting resistor. This resistance is built in or self-contained in each

filament element. The common tie point is typically connected to the positive side of the source, and each segment is energized by connecting its other side to ground.

Light-emitting Diode Displays

Light-emitting diodes are commonly used in seven-segment and 5 × 7 dot matrix displays. The LEDs of these devices produce visible light when forward biased and no light when reverse biased. As a result of this two-state condition, discrete segments or dots can be illuminated when diodes are energized. Typically, the positive side of the energy source is applied to the anodes of each diode through a current-limiting resistor. The cathode of a respective diode is then grounded by switching action. When the circuit is complete, the diode is energized, thus producing light.

Seven-segment LED display devices often contain four or more discrete diodes connected in parallel to form a segment. This type of construction usually necessitates only one current-limiting resistor for each segment. The amount of voltage needed to produce illumination is typically 3.5 to 5 V dc.

Figure 10–31 shows the circuitry of seven-segment and 5 × 7 dot matrix LED display devices. The LEDs in both circuits are similar in all respects. The switching method needed to energize specific diodes is somewhat special. In the seven-segment device [Figure 10–31(B)], each segment is controlled by a single switch. The dot matrix circuit [Figure 10–31(D)], by comparison, is controlled by two or more switches. A discrete diode can be energized by two switches such as row 4, column 5. A complete vertical row would require one column switch and all seven row switches. A complete horizontal row would be energized by one row switch and all five column

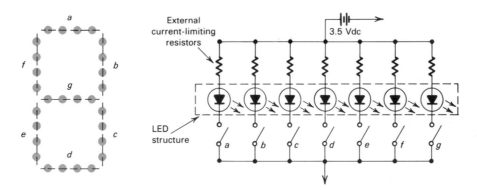

(A) 7-segment LED display
with 4 diodes per segment.

(B) Diagram showing connections of segments.

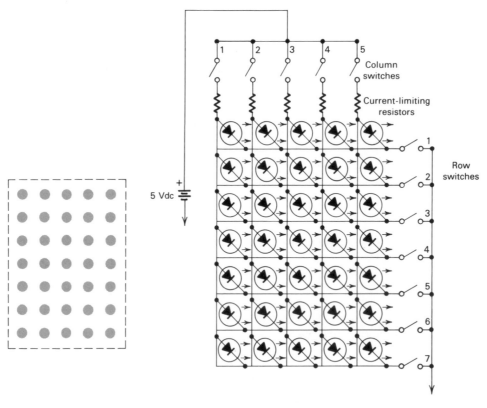

(C) 5 × 7 LED dot matrix display.

(D) 5 × 7 LED dot matrix diagram.

FIGURE 10–31
LED display devices.

switches. As a general rule, dot matrix display devices are used to produce letter displays more so than numbers. LED display devices are used more frequently in industrial applications today than all other devices combined.

Liquid-crystal Displays

Liquid-crystal display units represent a fourth major classification of display devices. This method of display is achieved by applying electrical energy in the form of voltage to discrete bars of phosphorized silicon. When voltage is applied, the crystal material changes from a transparent state to an opaque condition that reflects ambient light. In a strict sense, this action takes place when the phosphors are

bombarded by electrons from the energy source.

Liquid-crystal digital display devices are typically of the seven-segment type. The circuit construction is very similar to that of the seven-segment LED display of Figure 10–31. Each segmented bar responds as an LED when energized. As a general rule, liquid-crystal displays are commonly used in wristwatches, pocket calculators, and portable digital devices. Very small amounts of electrical energy are needed to produce a significant readout display.

Liquid-crystal displays are primarily designed to reflect normal room light when they are energized. This type of display therefore develops significantly less light intensity when compared with other displays. Liquid-crystal

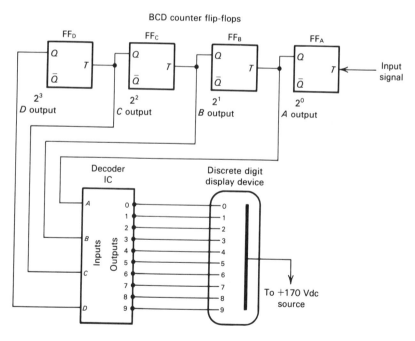

FIGURE 10–32
Discrete number display decoder–counter unit.

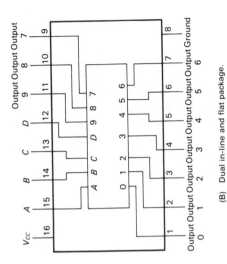

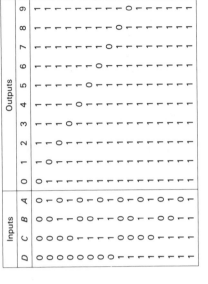

(B) Dual in-line and flat package.

(C) Truth table.

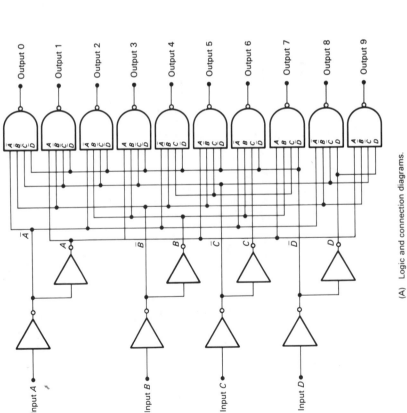

(A) Logic and connection diagrams.

FIGURE 10–33
BCD to decimal decoder IC. (Courtesy of National Semiconductor Corp.)

units are rarely ever used in industrial applications today because of this deficiency.

DIGITAL SYSTEM DECODING

Before a display device can be effectively used to develop a digital number, it must receive an appropriate actuating signal from the counter. The counter output signal in this case normally contains information in binary form. This information must therefore be decoded in such a way that it will energize a display when a specific number occurs. Decoding of this type is achieved by a number of four-input gates connected to the A, B, C, and D outputs of a BCD counter. When an appropriate combination of binary number signals appears at the input of the decoder, the output will energize a display device by grounding a specific number or bar segment. In a strict sense, the manual switches of the previous display devices can be replaced by an automatically controlled decoder.

Two distinct types of decoders are available today to drive display devices used in digital systems. The discrete number type of display requires a decoder that has 10 distinct output signals in order to be energized properly (Figure 10–32). Only one output must be energized at a time. The seven-segment type of display device is energized by two or more signals at a time. When the number 8 is displayed, all segments must be energized at one time. This necessitates an entirely different type of decoder circuit. The basic method of driving specific gates, however, is very similar for both types of decoders.

BCD-to-Decimal Decoders

The logic diagram of a BCD-to-decimal decoder is shown in Figure 10–33. This entire circuit is conveniently built on a single IC chip and produced in either a dual in-line or flat-package housing. In this IC, the A, B, C, and D inputs are either inverted once or twice before being applied to their respective NAND gates. When an appropriate input number combination is applied, it causes the corresponding NAND gate to be actuated. A zero or ground output then appears at its output. This, in turn, energizes the appropriate cathode of the display by forming a complete electrical circuit. When something other than the appropriate number combination is applied to each NAND gate, a 1 output is generated. This type of output will not produce a ground, which causes the respective cathode to see only an open circuit.

Assume now that a BCD counter produces a binary signal of $0101._2$ and applies it to the input of the decoder. From the truth table of Figure 10–33(C), this signal represents the decimal number 5. The decoder input sees A as 1, B as 0, C as 1, and D as 0. Directing the 1 inputs of A and C into two inverters causes A and C to remain at the 1 input level when applied to NAND gate 5. Inputs B and D to the NAND gate, by comparison, are directed through only one inverter or NOT gate. As a result, they are inverted and appear as $\overline{B}$ and $\overline{D}$ at the input of NAND gate 5. Since $\overline{B}$ and $\overline{D}$ were originally 0, $\overline{B}$ and $\overline{D}$ will now both appear as 1's at the NAND gate input. Four 1 inputs applied to this gate therefore generate a 0 or ground at the output. This completes the cathode path of the display device, thus energizing the number 5. A similar action would be achieved by each of the decoder outputs. Through this action, the decoder generates a single output for each number combination applied to its input.

BCD to Seven-segment Decoders

The logic block of a BCD to seven-segment decoder is shown in Figure 10–34. The entire circuit of this block is built on a single IC chip

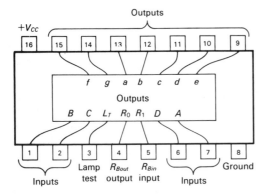

(A) IC connection diagram.

BCD inputs				7-segment outputs						
A	B	D	D	a	b	c	d	e	f	g
0	0	0	0	0	0	0	0	0	0	1
0	0	0	1	1	0	0	1	1	1	1
0	0	1	0	0	0	1	0	0	1	0
0	0	1	1	0	0	0	0	1	1	0
0	1	0	0	1	0	0	1	1	0	0
0	1	0	1	0	1	0	0	1	0	0
0	1	1	0	0	1	0	0	0	0	0
0	1	1	1	0	0	0	1	1	1	1
1	0	0	0	0	0	0	0	0	0	0
1	0	0	1	0	0	0	0	1	0	0

"0" output = grounded element
"1" output = open circuit

(C) Truth table.

(B) Numbers and corresponding segments.

FIGURE 10–34
BCD to seven-segment decoding.

and is manufactured in either a dual in-line or flat-package housing. Inputs A, B, C, and D are applied to either one or two inverters as in the decimal decoder. The decoding process is very similar in nearly all respects to that of the decimal decoder. The very nature of a seven-segment decoder, however, necessitates two or more outputs generated at the same time according to the number being displayed. In this decoder, each NAND gate output will produce a 0 or ground when it receives four 1 inputs.

The different decoding combinations needed to display the decimal numbers 0 to 9, respectively, are shown in the truth table of Figure 10–34(C). The A, B, C, and D inputs and respective a, b, c, d, e, f, and g outputs reflect the possible combinations needed to produce a specific number output. Seven-segment LED, Numitron, and liquid-crystal display devices can be energized by this type of decoder. Decoders with a seven-segment display are more commonly used in industrial applications than the discrete digit type of display unit.

DIGITAL SYSTEM INPUT

Industrial applications of a numerical system must employ some type of input device that changes real-world data into digital signals that can be processed electronically. Most real-world data that are of concern to a numerical system are either of a continuous changing value type or of the on–off variety. Physical quantities such as pressure, temperature, liquid level, and fluid flow tend to change value rather gradually on a continuous basis. Changes of this type can produce a large number of discrete values before ever reaching a final state. Quantity changes of this type are usually described as *analog* values.

Input data that switch very abruptly from one state to another without any in-between value changes are described as *digital* quantities. A number of objects passing through a production line counter produces a signal of this type. Any two-state condition of operation is classified as a digital quantity. Holes or no holes in a strip of paper tape or card can be used to produce digital input signals for some systems. As a rule, digital input signals are the easiest to achieve when compared with analog inputs.

The input of an industrial digital system has a large number of possibilities depending on its application. Paper tape, punched cards, magnetic tape, photoelectric control, and electromagnetic-controlled devices are typical digital inputs. Time, voltage, current, pressure, distance, speed, resistance, temperature, and light levels are some of the more common analog input possibilities. Special analog-to-digital or A/D converters are employed to make this transition possible.

The primary responsibility of the digital system input is to get numerical data into the system so that they can be processed. This part of the system is often called the real world-to-machine interface unit. It must be capable of sensing or detecting information very accurately at high speeds. Input sensitivity and accuracy of the developed data are of primary concern in digital systems today.

DIGITAL COUNTING SYSTEMS

A very simple application of the digital system in industry today is a counter. This type of device is often used to count the number of items passing a given point on a production line. Each passing item simply triggers the input device in such a way that the display device advances one count. A two-state input device such as a photoelectric detector cell or some mechanical actuating element is commonly used to trigger this type of system.

Figure 10–35 shows the primary parts of a production line counter. In this application, an object passing along the conveyor belt interrupts the light beam from the source momentarily. This action triggers the light detector, which in turn causes a state change to occur. A binary signal is generated each time the light beam is broken. Applying this signal to a BCD counter causes it to advance one count. The output of the counter is then fed into a BCD decoder, which is used to drive the digital display device. This type of system is quite simple, very accurate, and relatively inexpensive to maintain. Nearly all digital systems operate on this basic principle.

The input sensing section of a digital counter primarily represents the major difference in basic system design. Photoelectric devices, electromagnetic pickups, mechanical actuators, motor drive units, capacitance, and electrical changes are commonly used to develop input signals. The accuracy of a digital system cannot be any greater than the accuracy of the input information applied to it. Typical

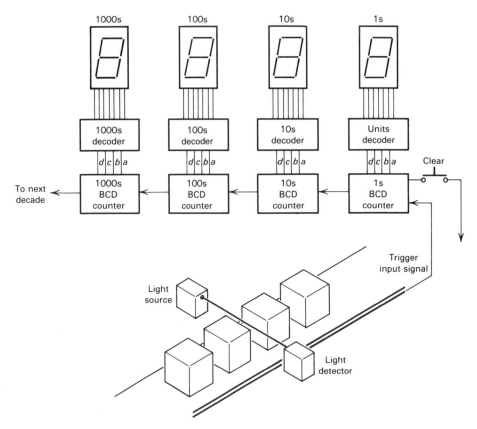

FIGURE 10–35
Production line counter.

accuracies for this type of system are limited to plus or minus one count of the number being displayed. Input device inaccuracies can add to the error factor quite significantly.

DIGITAL INSTRUMENTS

Practically any value that needs to be measured in industry today can be achieved by a digital type of instrument. The quantity being measured is primarily limited to the capabilities of the input device. Fluid flow rates, pressure, electrical quantities, temperature, time, speed, distance, light level, radiation, and sound level are typical digital instrument applications.

With such a wide range of digital instrument applications today, one would immediately think that these devices must be extremely complex. To the contrary, however, all instruments contain a number of common elements. The digital display unit, for example, is basic to practically all instruments. In addition, the counter is nearly always of the BCD type. Its output is generally used to drive a decoder of either the seven-segment or discrete number type of display. This basic unit

is designed to achieve the counting function of a digital instrument.

The input part of a digital instrument is undoubtedly the most unusual section of the entire system. Special devices such as analog-to-digital or A/D converters are commonly used to achieve this operation. These devices are designed to change analog information such as pressure, temperature, vibration, sound, or light into equivalent digital signals. When these signals enter the system, their output must be capable of driving the counting unit. Figure 10–36 is a diagram of a digital instrument showing the relationship of these parts.

Digital Voltmeters

One of the most widely used digital instruments in operation today is the digital voltmeter or DVM. This instrument is designed to change variable voltage values into signals that can be displayed in digital form. The measurement of such things as resistance, current, temperature, and pressure can then be achieved by simply changing these quantities into different voltage values. The operating principle of a DVM is basic to all digital instruments.

The input of a DVM represents the most unusual part of the entire instrument. This particular part is primarily responsible for converting an unknown voltage into a usable digital signal. It must do this accurately, be capable of rejecting extraneous electrical noise to some extent, and be reasonably stable over a suitable operating range. Three rather common conversion techniques are used today to achieve this function. These are voltage-controlled oscillators, ramp function instruments, and the dual-slope method of conversion. The input part of a DVM is actually an analog-to-digital converter.

Voltage-controlled Oscillator Techniques

When the frequency of an oscillator changes with voltage, it is commonly called a voltage-controlled oscillator or VCO. The output frequency of this oscillator can then be counted during a fixed interval of time and displayed as a digital output.

Figure 10–37 shows a block diagram of a digital voltmeter with a VCO. The frequency

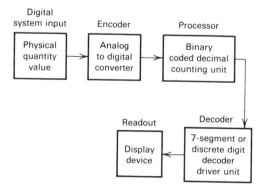

FIGURE 10–36
Block diagram of a digital instrument.

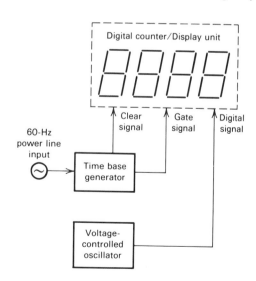

FIGURE 10–37
Block diagram of a VCO digital voltmeter.

of the VCO is commonly scaled so that it has a certain output for each volt of input. One volt should appear as a count of 1000 on the display. For a DVM with a power-line time-base generator, the VCO would need a frequency range of 0 to 60 kHz/V sensitivity.

The time-base generator of a VCO digital voltmeter may come from the ac power line or a separate crystal-controlled oscillator. Power-line frequency, time-base units are very common and rather easy to achieve. The accuracy of the 60-Hz line frequency is quite adequate for most industrial applications of the DVM. The accuracy of this section could be improved by employing a crystal-controlled oscillator. Typically, a 100-kHz frequency is generated and scaled down to base values of 10, 100, 1000, and 10,000, according to system needs. A time-base generator is primarily responsible for turning on or gating the output of the VCO for a specific frequency count.

The basic operation of a digital voltmeter with a VCO is really quite simple. Assume that an unknown voltage of 1 V is applied to the input of the VCO. An instrument with a 60 kHz/V sensitivity would immediately advance in frequency to 60 kHz. The power-line time-base generator would then turn on the output of the VCO for 1/60 s. And one-sixtieth of 60,000 Hz would therefore produce a count of 1000. A decimal point control circuit would show this value as 1.000 or 1 V. After a short delay, the counter would clear and reset to zero, where it starts the next count. The signal processing section of this instrument simply counts the VCO output, decodes it, and ultimately drives the display device.

Ramp-type DVM Input

The ramp type of DVM is a rather special circuit that employs a gate, ramp generator, and comparator attached to its input. The output of

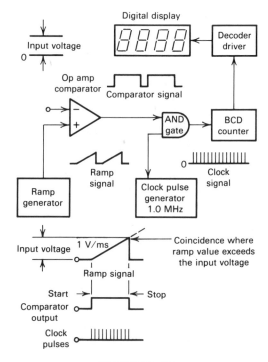

FIGURE 10–38
Block diagram of a ramp-type DVM.

this unit drives the same counter, decoder, and display devices found in other DVMs. Basically, this input technique compares an applied voltage to that developed by the linear ramp generator. When the ramp voltage is less than the input, the comparator produces an output signal. This signal, along with that of a clock pulse generator, is then applied to the input of the AND gate. These two inputs produce an output of clock pulses that is counted and ultimately displayed.

When the ramp generator voltage of this DVM rises in value and exceeds the input voltage, it causes the comparator to change polarity. This in turn causes a 0 to appear at the input of the AND gate. As a result, the clock pulse signal stops and the readout holds its display. The duration of the count is therefore ac-

curately controlled by the linear rise time of the ramp generator. Figure 10–38 shows a block diagram of a ramp type of DVM with a representative voltage-to-time comparison.

The ramp voltage of a DVM is commonly designed to rise at a rate of 1 V/ms. This, in a sense, means that the input voltage can be exceeded within a prescribed amount of time. As a result, this action causes a change in comparator polarity, which generates a 0 output. This closes the AND gate. The clock pulses immediately stop passing into the counter. The

number of counts in the display is then proportional to the value of the input voltage.

Assume now that 2 V is to be measured by the DVM. With this voltage applied, the 1.0-V/ms rise time of the ramp generator would also be started immediately. The output of the op-amp comparator produces a 1 and applies this to the AND gate. Also, 1's from the clock pulse generator applied to the AND gate cause it to produce an output. After 2 ms, the ramp voltage exceeds the value of the input voltage. When this occurs, the op-amp comparator changes to the 0 state and turns off the AND gate. The pulse repetition rate of the clock is accurately at 1,000,000 Hz during this period of operation. As a result, 2 ms or 0.002 of 1,000,000 is 2000. A decimal point control circuit would cause this number to appear as 2.000 on the display, which indicates a measured value of 2 V.

DVM's of the ramp type are subject to many things that produce inaccurate measurements. The nonlinearity of the ramp, instability of the clock generator, and noise rejection are some of the more critical problems. The accuracy of this type of DVM is somewhat limited because of these problems. As a general rule, a DVM of this type is still better than the typical 3% accuracy of a portable analog-type instrument.

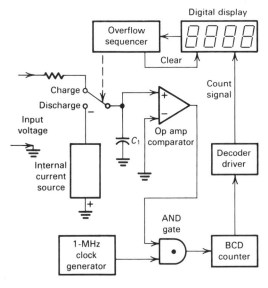

(A)   Dvm circuit.

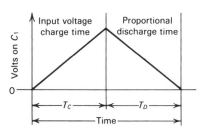

(B)   Capacitor charge and discharge.

FIGURE 10–39
Dual-slope DVM.

Dual-slope DVM Input

The dual-slope input of Figure 10–39 has improved accuracy and is somewhat more sophisticated than the ramp or VCO types of DVM circuits. This type of DVM is designed to measure a true average of the input over a given period. Nonlinear effects are canceled and the entire input is rather immune to noise.

The operation of a dual slope DVM occurs in two steps as shown in Figure 10–39(A). The first step occurs when an unknown voltage is

applied to the DVM input through the switch. This action causes C_1 to charge to a ramp type of slope that is proportional to applied input, as shown in Figure 10–39(B). During this time, a positive voltage applied to the + or noninverting input of the comparator causes a positive or 1 to be applied to the AND gate. Positive clock pulses applied to this gate at the same time cause the clock signal to be transferred to a BCD counter. This count is then applied to the display device.

The second operational step of the DVM occurs when the display produces an overflow signal. This takes place on the next count after 9999 appears. The overflow detector turns on, clears the display, and switches S_1 to the discharge position. At this time, C_1 begins to discharge into the internal current source. The positive input of the comparator continues to apply a 1 to the AND gate. As a result, a new count is now applied to the display unit. This count continues until C_1 reaches zero charge or returns to its original value. This in turn causes the comparator to produce a 0 and apply it to the AND gate. As a result, the AND gate changes to a zero state and the clock signal will not pass. The number indicated on the display now shows capacitor discharge voltage in digital form. After a short time delay, the sequencer will clear the display and return S_1 to the charge position to repeat the operational cycle. The sequencer is typically a 555 IC timer used as an astable multivibrator to clear the display at prescribed intervals.

discussed. A number of refinements such as temperature compensation circuitry, multiplexed displays with increased digits, and memory functions are some of the possible alterations found in these instruments. Regardless of the degree of sophistication involved, the instrument must basically employ an encoder, digital signal processor, decoder, and a display or actuating device.

Figure 10–40 shows a typical digital multimeter or DMM. To measure current, this instrument is designed to determine the voltage drop across a resistance and display this as current in amperes, milliamperes, or microamperes. For linear measurement of resistance, an internal constant-current source is supplied. Resistance is then determined by measuring the voltage developed across an unknown resistive value. AC or dc voltages are easily measured by adding an op-amp connected as a full-wave rectifier. Automatic polarity display is very common with this type of instrument.

Many specialized measurements can be achieved by monitoring specific voltage changes. Pressure, for example, can be measured with a transducer that produces a voltage output. Temperature, moisture, liquid levels, pH or acid content, light, sound levels, and radiation are only a few of the quantities measured by digital instruments in operation today. Improved accuracy, display reading ease, and reduced loading effects are some of the obvious reasons why this type of instrument will find more applications in the future.

OTHER DIGITAL INSTRUMENTS

Practically all the digital instruments used in industry today respond to voltage, frequency, or a time period. These instruments are primarily a variation of the circuits we have just

NUMERICAL CONTROLS SYSTEMS

Another very important digital system application found in industry today is called numerical control or NC. In this application, a series of numerical-coded instructions are used to con-

FIGURE 10–40
Digital multimeter. (Courtesy of Sencore)

trol the operation of a machine automatically. Duplicate parts may be produced by this process, or specific assembly operations may be performed automatically. Manufacturing consistency is a major advantage of machinery controlled by this process.

The term *numerical control* actually refers to two distinct functions that are interrelated. The term *numerical* refers specifically to the instructional information applied to the machine. This generally represents digital information punched into a paper tape or card that is read by the input part of the system. Two-state conditions such as holes or no holes in a

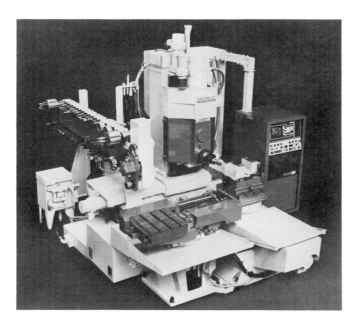

FIGURE 10–41
Typical NC machine. (Courtesy of Cincinnati Milacron)

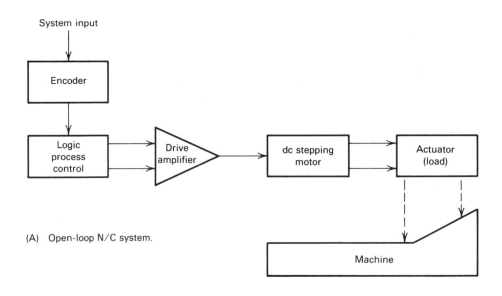

(A) Open-loop N/C system.

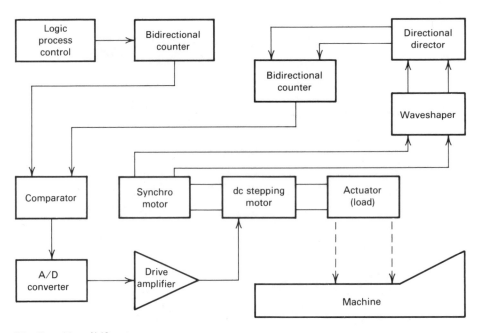

(B) Closed-loop N/C system.

**FIGURE 10–42
NC system diagrams.**

paper tape are used to instruct the machine. The digital console is primarily responsible for this operation.

The *control* function of an NC system refers to the physical changes that take place by the machine after it has been commanded to do something. Timing, sequencing, positioning, guiding, directing, altering speed, and clamping are typical machine control operations. Electromechanical, hydraulic, and pneumatic operations are used to achieve this function independently or through a combination of all three operations working together.

Figure 10–41 shows a typical NC milling machine unit. The operator's control console is located on the right side of the machine. This unit employs a paper-tape drive unit and the digital logic components needed to control different machine operations. Electrical disconnect switches, control transformers, spindle speed power control, and auxiliary operating functions are controlled by the console of this system.

Physical changes that take place in the operation of an NC machine are achieved electrically, hydraulically, or by pneumatic actuators. DC stepping motors and ac servomotors are commonly used to drive the different axes of the work table electrically. Table position can then be monitored by synchromotors to relay accurate position information back to the control console for precise reference correction. Vertical position of the work table, tool selectors, coolant circulation, spindle feed, and turret rotation are typical hydraulic and pneumatic control operations. Control of this type may be energized electrically or mechanically and actuated hydraulically or pneumatically.

The operation of an NC machine can be simplified somewhat by placing it in the framework of a basic system structure. Figure 10–42 shows two distinct types of NC machine control systems. The open-loop system [Figure 10–42(A)] in its simplest form only necessi-tates a logic processor and amplifier to drive stepping motors to achieve specific control operations. The theory behind the operation of this system is that the stepping motor is usually reliable enough to act on a command without fail. Systems of this type are less expensive and generally easier to maintain and operate than closed-loop systems. The key to this type of system is a reliable stepping motor. A number of basic milling machines and machine lathes are controlled by this type of system.

Traditionally, NC machines have nearly all been of the closed-loop type [Figure 10–42(B)]. Commands applied to the input are processed and applied to the actuators. Feedback signals developed by the actuator are then returned to the processor for comparison. Input and feedback signals are then compared, and a correction signal is used to modify the control process should the need arise. Systems of this type are quite sophisticated when compared with the open-loop type of system. The intended work function of the system is primarily used to decide the need for open- or closed-loop control.

NC INPUT

For an NC machine to operate, it must receive digital information from its input. Coded digital instructions are usually prepared in advance and can be placed on perforated paper tape, punched cards, or magnetic tape. Today, perforated paper tape has been established as a standard input medium for NC systems. Instructions placed on this tape are punched in eight horizontal channels that run the length of the tape. Holes punched in different channel locations are done in accordance with an established code. Figure 10–43 shows representative codes of the EIA 244A and ASCII. The EIA code was developed by the Electronics In-

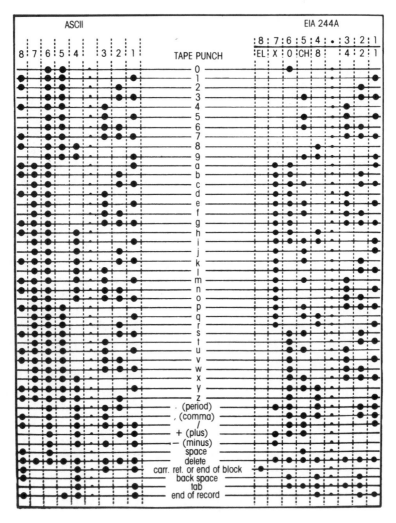

FIGURE 10–43
EIA 244A and ASCII paper tape codes.

dustry Association. ASCII refers to a code developed by the American Standards Institute for Information Interchange.

The EIA code is commonly described as an *odd-parity* code. This refers to the fact that each character punched into the tape produces an odd number of holes. The small sprocket drive hole between channels 3 and 4 does not

enter into this count. The EIA 244A code was the original code established by EIA. Today this code is being replaced by the new RS 358. As a general rule, most NC inputs accept both EIA codes without any modification.

The ASCII of Figure 10–43 is considered an *even-parity* code. Each character punched into the tape produces an even number of

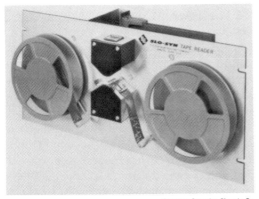

Courtesy Superior Electric Co.

(A) Tape reader.

FIGURE 10–44
NC tape reader equipment. (Courtesy of
Ingenorsfirma Terco AB-Sweden, Superior
Electric Co.)

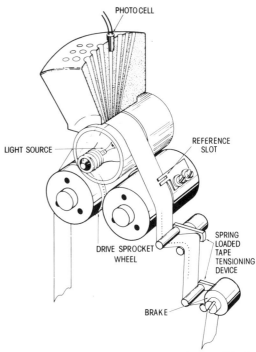

Courtesy Ingenörsfirma Terco AB-Sweden

(B) Photocell pickup and drive unit.

holes. Because of the differences in odd- and even-parity codes, EIA and ASCII codes are not used interchangeably in NC inputs.

Tape perforation is primarily prepared by a special electric typewriter. This typewriter is very similar to a standard electric typewriter. In addition to the standard carriage and keyboard controls, this typewriter is equipped with a tape perforator and tape reader. A specific NC is typed on paper and punched on tape at the same time. The tape reader function permits a prepared tape to be read and reproduced by the typewriter as a printout that is easily read. The perforated tape prepared by this typewriter is ready for the tape reader of the NC input.

Tape Readers

The primary input of an NC machine is a tape-reading device. This device is needed to interpret the information prepared in the program of instructions and direct it to the process control unit. Essentially, a tape reader gathers digital information from the holes punched in the paper tape. In a strict sense, a tape reader detects two-state or binary coded information and changes it into a digital signal.

Figure 10–44(A) shows a typical NC paper tape reader. Holes punched in the tape pass light from the source to a specific photocell above each channel. When light reaches a specific cell, it generates an output signal. Readers of this type are well suited for high-speed operation and show very little part wear for long hours of operation.

Figure 10–44(B) shows an enlargement of a photoelectric cell pickup and sprocket drive assembly unit. From 100 to 600 transverse rows of coded information can be read by this device in 1 s. Photoelectric tape readers of this type are used more frequently today in NC ma-

chines than any of the other pickup methods. Reliability seems to be the most prevalent reason for such widespread acceptance of this type of tape reader.

NC Machine Control Unit

The machine control unit or MCU of an NC system is the primary link between the programmed information placed on tape and actual machine operations. This part of the system acts on the digital input signal from the tape reader and converts it into actual machine motions through actuators.

One thing that makes the MCU of an NC machine somewhat difficult to discuss in general terms is the large number of different system options available today. Each option obviously changes the operation and circuitry of a system a great deal. One manufacturer lists several distinct types of control units for NC applications. A rather simple unit is designed for two-axis, point-to-point positioning and straight-line machine operations. This is a rather compact unit with logic circuits, control panel, silicon motor drive transistors, and a self-contained power supply. Control can be achieved by tape drive or by manual overriding switches. Systems of this type are typically of the open-loop type.

Another MCU by the same manufacturer has two-, three-, or four-axis control of the contouring type. Cutting, welding, and milling operations can be applied to contouring surfaces automatically by this unit. It can be operated by a paper tape or by its own built-in typewriter keyboard, or it can be interfaced with a computer. This unit is a closed-loop system that samples the position of each axis and corrects itself according to a tolerance level controlled by the program. As a general rule, the MCU of an NC machine is primarily designed around the specific needs of the machine and its intended applications.

NC Load Actuators

The end result or work function of an NC machine is commonly applied to the system load through an actuator. Rotary actuators such as dc stepping motors or ac servomotors are commonly used to achieve this operation.

The rotary motion of a dc stepping motor is commonly changed into linear motion by driving a lead screw. When the motor moves one step, it may cause the screw to turn 1/200 of a revolution. Two-hundred continuous steps can be used to rotate the lead screw one complete revolution. Typical NC stepping motor accuracy is $\pm 0.09°$ of the desired shaft position. This level of accuracy is usually not cumulative, which makes it quite accurate for low-tolerance machining operations.

Figure 10–45 shows a typical NC machine positioning table. The horizontal or x axis of this table is controlled by a servomotor attached to the left end of the table. Actuation of this motor causes accurate rotation of a lead screw. Each revolution of the motor causes the lead screw to advance 0.100 in. or 1 mm, according to the design of the unit. Dials attached to the lead screw are commonly divided into 100 equally spaced slots out into its periphery. Rotation of the lead screw produces coded information that is relayed back to the control console as an indication of position.

Front-to-back or y axis movement of the positioning table is also controlled by a servomotor. This motor is attached to the front part of the table. A lead screw driven by this motor produces control that is very similar to that of the x-axis actuator.

Machine spindle feeds are often controlled automatically by hydraulic or pneumatic actuators. This type of load control may drive the spindle fast initially and at a slower rate when it nears the work and during its operation. Special tool-holder turrets are often attached to an NC machine to permit multiple tool machining capabilities. Specific load actuators must be

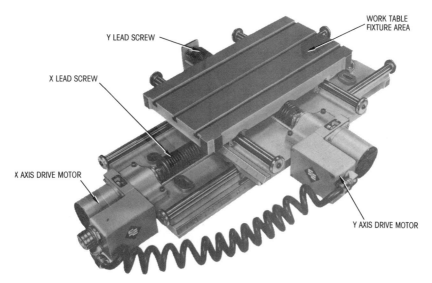

FIGURE 10–45
NC milling machine positioning table.
(Courtesy of Superior Electric Co.)

designed to be compatible with the machine and the MCU.

Future of NC

The future of NC is almost unlimited for industrial manufacturing process control equipment. Traditionally, NC applications have been limited to basic machine tool operations. With the development of microcomputers that are attached directly to the machine, NC manufacturing processes will obviously see a tremendous change in the future. For example, computer-aided design has been used for some time now to help in product design problems. Computer-aided manufacturing or CAM systems are now being used in process equipment. This type of automation will obviously have an impact on NC in the future. The entire field of digital electronics will also have a tremendous impact on all industrial applications.

QUESTIONS

1. What are the basic parts of a digital system?

2. What is meant by the term *base* or *radix* and how does it apply to numbering systems?

3. Why is the two-state operating condition of an electronic device important in digital systems?

4. Why are BCD counters in common use in digital instruments?

5. Compare the input–output characteristics of two-input AND, OR, NAND, and NOR gates.

6. How are flip-flops used to achieve binary counting?

7. What are the 10 distinct 1/0 condition states of a BCD counter?

8. What is the basic difference between a counter and a DVM?

9. Why are such things as temperature, pressure, light, and sound more difficult to measure with digital devices than a simple counting operation?

10. Briefly explain one method of DVM analog-to-digital conversion.

11. What are some of the major differences between seven-segment and discrete digit decoding?

12. What is the primary difference between open- and closed-loop NC control?

13. What are the basic parts of an NC system?

14. In general terms, what would be the difference between a digital instrument and an NC machine?

15. How is linear movement achieved in an NC machine?

PROBLEMS

1. How can the operation of the following gates be expressed mathematically?

   a. AND

   b. OR

   c. NOT

   d. NAND

   e. NOR

2. Convert the following numbers to base 10:

   a. $11011._2$

   b. $110001._2$

   c. $11000011._2$

   d. $23._8$

   e. $131._8$

   f. $11A._{16}$

   g. $149D._{16}$

3. Convert the following numbers to base 2:

   a. $37._{10}$

   b. $61._{10}$

   c. $123._{10}$

   d. $127._8$

   e. $105._8$

   f. $14A._{16}$

   g. $23D._{16}$

4. Develop a truth table and logic diagram for the expression $ABC + B = X$.

5. What are the general rules for changing a Boolean expression into a logic diagram?

6. Develop a truth table and logic diagram for the expression $\overline{A}B + \overline{B}A = X$.

7. Express the following numbers in BCD form:

   a. $137._{10}$

   b. $486._{10}$

   c. $195._{10}$

ACTIVITIES

ACTIVITY 10–1: Logic Gate Analysis

Objective: Construction of discrete component logic gates using switches and lamps to become familiar with the basic functions of a logic circuit.

Procedure:

1. Construct the AND gate of Figure 10–14.

2. Using the four different switch combinations, verify the truth-table accuracy of this gate.

3. Construct the OR gate of Figure 10–15 and verify the truth-table accuracy.

4. Construct the NOT gate of Figure 10–16 and verify the accuracy of the truth table.

5. Construct the NAND gate of Figure 10–17 and verify the accuracy of the truth table.

6. Construct the NOR gate of Figure 10–18 and verify the accuracy of the truth table.

ACTIVITY 10–2: IC Logic Gate Analysis

Objective: To construct basic logic gates using TTL ICs and to become familiar with IC circuit construction techniques.

Procedure:

1. The following IC construction procedures must be followed in order to complete the circuits of this activity:

   a. Each IC must be energized by a dc source. In this case, 5 V will be used.

   b. The chip selected for this activity generally has more than one gate in its construction. Select any one of the gates for this activity.

   c. A SPDT toggle switch is used as the control input for each gate. The switch should be connected so that the input will either be $+5$ V or ground (O V), depending on the position of the switch.

   d. An LED connected in series with a current-limiting resistor of 390 Ω should be attached to the output of each switch. When the switch is in the 5-V or 1 position, the LED should be illuminated. It should be off when the switch is in the O-V or 0 position.

   e. The output of a switch should be connected to the input of the gate.

   f. The output of a gate should be connected to an LED in series with a 390 Ω resistor. When the output is on or in the 1 state, the LED should be illuminated, and off when it is low or in the 0 state.

2. Construct an AND gate using an SN7408 IC. Using input switches with LEDs and an output LED indicator, develop a truth table showing the function of one specific gate of the IC. If time permits, test one other gate of the IC.

3. Using the same procedure, evaluate the operation of an SN7432 IC.

4. Construct a test circuit to evaluate the gates of an SN7410.

5. Construct a test circuit to evaluate the gates of an SN7400.

6. Construct a test circuit to evaluate the gates of an SN7402.

ACTIVITY 10–3: Binary Counters

Objective: Construction of a binary counter that is controlled by manual switching in order to evaluate the operation of a counter.

Procedure:

1. Construct the binary counter of Figure 10–46. The SN7413 is a Schmitt trigger and the SN7493 is a counter. Arrange the output LEDs so that A is in the 1's position, B is in the 2's position, C is in the 4's position, and D is in the 8's position.

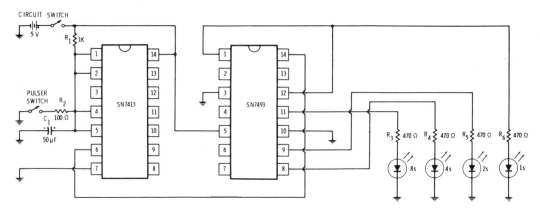

FIGURE 10–46
Binary counter.

2. Apply power to the circuit. First test the operation of the Schmitt trigger. Connect a voltmeter to the output (pin 6). Each time the pulser switch is altered, there should be a change in the output level. When this level change is applied to the counter, it causes a change in the output.

3. Test the counter by pulsing a signal into the counter.

4. If the counter is functioning properly, clear the output so that all LEDs are off.

5. Apply one pulse to the input circuit and note the output response.

6. Develop a truth table of the output showing how it responds to progressive counts from 0 to 16.

7. What is in the physical construction of a counter that will permit it to achieve binary counting?

ACTIVITY 10–4: Binary Coded Decimal Counters

Objective: Construction of a BCD counter

to evaluate its operation and to become more familiar with IC circuit construction.

Procedure:

1. Construct the BCD counter of Figure 10–47.

2. Apply power to the circuit and test the operation of the Schmitt trigger. If it is working properly, a voltage level change should occur at the output (pin 6) for each change in the pulser switch.

3. Pulse through several counts while observing the output indicators.

4. If the output of the counter is working properly, cycle it until a 0000 appears in the output.

5. Assume that the first count is zero or 0000. Pulse a count into the input and see the response of the output.

6. Make a truth table showing the output for each step of one complete operational cycle.

7. How does the output of this counter differ

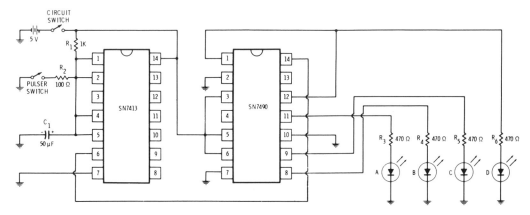

FIGURE 10–47
BCD counter.

from that of the binary counter of Activity 10–3?

ACTIVITY 10–5: Seven-segment LED Displays

Objective: To test a seven-segment LED display to determine the segment assignments and current needed to produce operation.

Procedure:

1. Connect the LED seven-segment display of Figure 10–48.

2. Apply power and turn on the circuit switch.

3. Alternately connect each of the 390-Ω resistors to the ground or common of the power source. Label the specific pin number that causes illumination of each segment of the display.

4. Measure and record the current needed to illuminate each segment.

5. Connect the resistor combinations needed to produce the number 8. Measure and record the combined current needed to produce this number.

6. Connect the combination of resistors needed to produce the numbers 0 through 9.

7. Why must an independent resistor be used for each segment of the display?

ACTIVITY 10–6: A 5 × 7 LED Dot Matrix Display Analysis

Objective: Construction of a 5 × 7 LED dot matrix display and analysis of its operating procedure.

Procedure:

1. Construct the 5 × 7 dot matrix display circuit of Figure 10–31. The current-limiting resistors of this display should be 390 Ω. The pin out of this device is not shown with the diagram. Use the manufacturer's data sheet for the device used in this activity. A 2517 or 2518 are common dot matrix displays.

2. Apply power to the circuit. To test the operation of the circuit, a combination of row switches and column switches must be actuated.

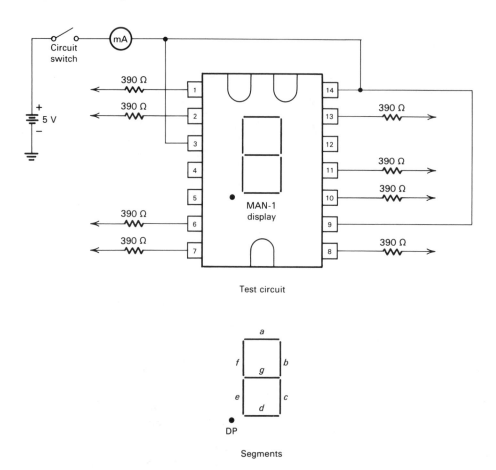

FIGURE 10–48
LED seven-segment display test circuit.

3. With all switches in the off position initially, turn on column 1 and row 1. This should energize LED 1 in the upper left corner. Try several different combinations and predict the LED that will be energized.

4. Determine the switch configuration needed to produce the letter C. Test the combination to see if it will in fact produce a letter C.

5. Determine the switch combinations needed to produce several other letters. Try out the combination to see if it produces the appropriate letter on the display.

6. Measure and record the current that flows when one LED is actuated. How much current is needed to produce a specific letter such as C?

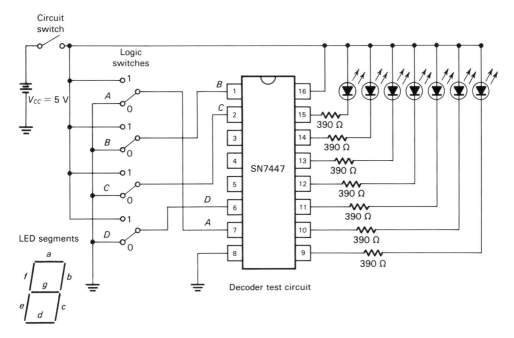

FIGURE 10–49
Seven-segment decoder test circuit.

ACTIVITY 10–7: BCD Decoding and Seven-segment Driving

Objective: Construction of a BCD to seven-segment decoder test circuit for evaluation of a decoder driver.

Procedure:

1. Construct the BCD to seven-segment decoder test circuit of Figure 10–49.

2. Arrange each lettered LED in its specific seven-segment location as indicated.

3. Turn on the power source and circuit switch. All switches should be in the 1 position initially. Momentarily connect pin 3 to ground. This is the lamp test function of the decoder. If the circuit is correctly wired, all seven LEDs will be illuminated. Test your circuit and modify it if necessary to make it function properly. Disconnect pin 3 from ground and proceed.

4. When a particular input switch (A–B–C–D) is connected to ground, it represents a low or 0 state. When a switch is in the 1 position, it has voltage applied to the input. Starting with 1–1–1–1, evaluate the resulting output of the display. Record what switch combination is needed to produce the display of numbers 0 through 9.

ACTIVITY 10–8: BCD Counters

Objective: Construction of a BCD counter that will decode and drive a seven-segment LED display.

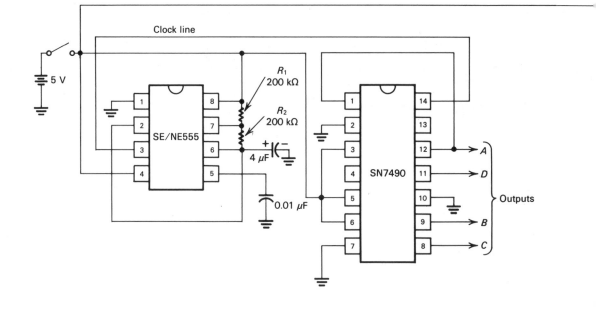

FIGURE 10–50
Counter system.

Procedure:

1. The counter of this activity should be assembled in three steps. Refer to the circuit
   of Figure 10–50. Construct the decoder
   driver and seven-segment display first. Energize the circuit and test the display by
   momentarily connecting pin 3 of the
   SN7447 to ground. If the circuit is properly
   wired, all segments and the decimal point
   will be illuminated. If this occurs, proceed.
   If it does not, correct the problem by re-
   checking the wiring and devices.

2. Turn off the power source and connect the
   BCD counter to the decoder. Apply power
   to the combined circuit. Momentarily connect pin 14 of the SN7490 to ground and

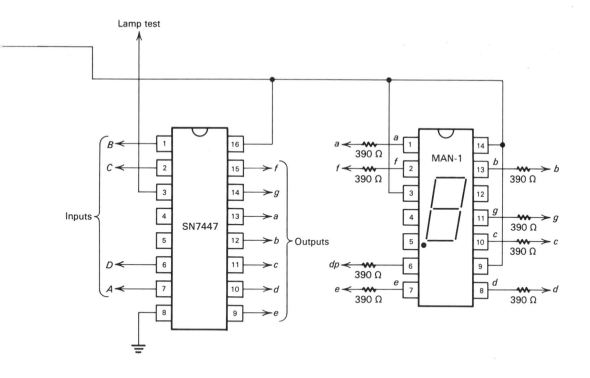

FIGURE 10–50 (Continued)

then to +5 V. Each state change of this type should cause the display to produce a number output. If it does, the circuit is correct, so proceed to the next step. If it does not respond, recheck the wiring of the SN7490 or the device.

3. Turn off the power source and connect the clock circuit.

4. Apply power to the entire circuit. If every-

thing is functioning properly, the counter should change states with each clock pulse. If it does not do this, check the wiring of the clock pulse generator.

5. A square-wave output should appear at pin 3 of the clock. Connect an oscilloscope to the output of the clock and make a sketch of the observed wave form.

6. Explain the function of each section of the BCD counter.

11

Microprocessor Systems

Computer technology has brought a significant number of changes to the field of industrial electronics. Centralized or mainframe computers have been used for a number of years to perform a wide range of control operations in automatic process applications. Elaborate calculations can be performed quickly, data can be stored and retrieved at a moment's notice, and deductions can be made from data that will influence the operation of a system. All this has caused industry to become more dependent on the computer and has placed a higher premium on computer operational time.

Large mainframe computers had their beginning in 1946 with development of the ENIAC. This unit was a large-scale calculating machine that used vacuum tubes. The cost of the unit was rather prohibitive and operational time was very expensive. The ENIAC was primarily used to solve only very important problems.

A few years after the ENIAC was developed, mainframe computers were built with discrete solid-state devices. This was the beginning of the computers as we know them today. Mainframe computers employed millions of discrete components that were hard-wired into complex circuits. As a rule, these computers were extremely bulky and rather expensive to operate and maintain. They were not very widely used at this time because of the cost and operational complexity. Miniaturized construction techniques and advances in solid-state logic circuitry then caused a significant change in computer design.

Around 1963, minicomputers appeared on the scene to provide computer technology for industrial applications not requiring the capacity of the large mainframe computer. These units were significantly less costly, were ruggedly constructed, and were much smaller than the mainframe units. Instant success demonstrated the usefulness of this unit with a wide range of applications. Cathode-ray tube dis-

plays were included with the computer to present an immediate display of information for the operator. Information could be placed into the unit through a typewriter keyboard, magnetic disks, or analog transducers.

Microcomputers were introduced by a number of manufacturers in the early 1970s. These computers were primarily an extension of the technology employed by the minicomputer. Large-scale integration or LSI technology was used to place thousands of discrete solid-state components on a single integrated-circuit chip. Microcomputers are composed of three main parts like those of the mainframe and minicomputers: the central processing unit, memory, and input/output circuits. The network of processing circuitry is commonly called the central processing unit or CPU. The input is responsible for accepting signals from external devices such as switches, transducers, and sensors. Analog signals are converted into digital voltages that actuate the central processing unit. The CPU performs logical and computational operations on these signals as directed by the control program held in memory. CPU output signals are commands sent to the output circuits. The output is reasonable for converting logic-level signals to actuating power for load device control.

Modern microcomputers are often called microsystems or microprocessors. These systems frequently have the CPU, input/output, and memory all built on a single IC chip. The entire unit is extremely small and can be easily housed in an instrument or the machine being controlled. This permits machinery to be controlled by its own computer. Microsystems are often considered to be dedicated computers. This means that they are designed to control a specific machine or instrument. The capacity of the system can generally be expanded according to the control capabilities desired. Microprocessor technology has virtually revolutionized industrial system operation by providing inexpensive computers that can be attached directly to a machine.

COMPUTER BASICS

The term *computer* is a rather broad general term that can be used to cover a number of functions. It primarily refers to a device that will perform automatic computations when provided with the appropriate information. Computers range from pocket calculators to complex centralized mainframes that may be used to serve an entire industry. Electrical energy is needed to energize the unit and operation is performed through electronic components. Information processed by the computer comes in two states.

Digital computers use numbers represented by the presence or absence of voltage at a particular level. A voltage level or pulse usually is taken to represent a 1 state, whereas no voltage indicates the 0 state. A voltage value or single pulse is described as a *bit* of information, from the words "*bi*nary" and "digi*t*." A binary number has two states or conditions of operation and belongs to the base 2 counting system. A group of pulses or voltage-level changes produces a word. A byte consists of 8 bits.

A computer system, regardless of its complexity, has a number of fundamental parts that are the basis of its operation. These parts may be arranged in a variety of different ways and still achieve the same primary function. The internal organization and design of each block differ considerably between manufacturers. Figure 11–1 shows a block diagram of a digital computer.

A digital computer is essentially an electronic unit that consists of input and output devices, arithmetic/logic and control circuitry, and some form of memory. Before the com-

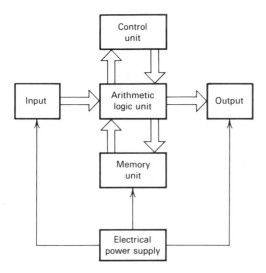

FIGURE 11–1
Block diagram of a digital computer.

puter can be placed into operation, a special set of instructions called a *program* must be supplied. These instructions must be written in a *language* that the computer understands. This information is then supplied to the input as a digital signal.

Input data supplied to the computer are first translated into some type of number code or machine language before operation progresses. The arithmetic/logic control unit then manipulates the input data according to its programmed instructions. After all the manpulative operations are complete, the coding process is reversed. In this case, machine language is translated back into a real-world language. This information is then used to actuate the output device.

The memory section of a computer primarily serves as a place to store the operating instructions that direct the CPU control function. Coded pieces of data in the form of 1's and 0's are written into memory through directions provided by a program. The CPU then reads these instructions from memory in a logical sequence and uses them to initiate processing op-

erations. When the program structure is logical, processing proceeds in an intelligible manner with useful results.

All computers in operation today employ one or more output ports that permit the CPU to communicate with the outside world. Video terminal displays for operator monitoring, hard-copy on-line printers, magnetic tape or disk storage, and direct load device actuation are some representative output devices. Operational speed is generally an important characteristic of the output device.

The functional parts of a computer are basically the same for mainframe computers, minicomputers, and microcomputers. The differences between these units are in the physical makeup of the individual block function. Mainframe computers usually employ components and logic functions that are mounted on printed-circuit boards or cards. This type of unit is also characterized by an enormous memory capacity, high-speed operation, and simplified program routines. Typically, 32 or more bits of information are used to make programming words.

Minicomputer systems are made from logic function chips of the LSI type that are also arranged on printed-circuit boards. This type of unit generally has reduced memory capacity, requires a longer cycle time, and is less costly. Microcomputers, by comparison, were primarily designed for applications not requiring the capacity of a mainframe computer. Program word size is normally 8 to 16 bits. The differences in computer classifications today are not very well defined. In general, only the price, capacity, and packaging differences distinguish one computer from another.

Microcomputer systems are tiny units built around single-chip IC technology. The microprocessor of this system can be a single-chip IC package that performs the arithmetic/logic and control function. These units are inexpensive off-the-shelf items that can be used to

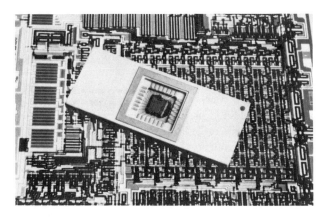

FIGURE 11-2
Microcomputer IC. (Courtesy of Analog Devices)

achieve an enormous number of industrial control applications. They are somewhat more difficult to program than larger computers because of the reduced word size (4 to 16 bits), and they usually have reduced memory capacity. In practice, microcomputer systems are generally used to serve a specific need, solve a specific type of problem, or handle one application.

MICROCOMPUTER SYSTEMS

Microcomputer systems are one of the most significant developments to take place in the industrial electronics field in the last decade. The potential capabilities of the microcomputer system have not been fully realized at this time. Benefits such as faster development times, smaller equipment size, increased reliability, easy serviceability, and lower product cost are only a few of the major considerations to keep in mind. A microcomputer built on a single IC chip is shown in Figure 11-2.

A microcomputer, as a general rule, is quite complex when viewed in its entirety. For example, it has a microprocessor, memory, an interface adapter, and several distribution paths called *buses*. To simplify this system, it is better to first look at a stripped-down version of its physical makeup (see Figure 11-3).

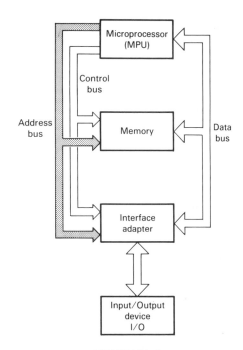

FIGURE 11-3
Microprocessor system.

The simplified version of our microcomputer is very similar to the basic computer diagram of Figure 11–1. The microprocessor, in this case, has replaced the arithmetic/logic unit and control unit. Data or information handled by this system are primarily of two types: instructions and data. In a simple addition problem, such as $7 + 3 = 10$ the numbers 7, 3, and 10 are data, and the plus sign is an instruction. The data are distributed by the data bus to all parts of the system. Instructions are distributed by the control bus in the same manner but through a separate path. The address bus of the unit forms an alternate distribution path for the distribution of address data. It is normally used to place information into memory at an appropriate address. By an appropriate command from the microprocessor, data may be removed from memory and distributed to the output.

Our investigation of microcomputers will now be directed to some of the functions and parts of the system. Numbering, for example, deals with the data and information signals utilized by the system. This area of investigation deals with the numbers that are actually manipulated by the computer. Octal and hexadecimal numbers are primarily used in microprocessor systems. These numbering systems were discussed in Chapter 10. Second, the hardware of a microprocessor will be discussed. This section is concerned with the physical makeup of the microprocessor. Memory is the third major area of concern. Read/write memory and read-only memory will be discussed in this section. The fourth area will be directed toward input/output techniques. This deals with placing information into the computer from an outside source and converting its output into a usable signal. The fifth and last major area deals with microcomputer software. Program development, execution, and MPU languages are presented in this section. Through this approach you should begin to have some understanding

of the microcomputer and see how it can be practically implemented to perform a number of useful control functions.

MICROPROCESSOR UNIT

A microprocessor or MPU is the arithmetic/logic unit and control section of a computer scaled down so that it fits on a single IC chip. Typical chip sizes measure approximately ½ cm^2 and contain thousands of transistors, resistors, and diodes. Over 20 U.S. companies are now manufacturing these chips in more than 30 different designs with prices ranging from a few dollars to over one hundred dollars. Industrial applications of this device are increasing at a remarkable rate.

A microprocessor is essentially a digital device that is designed to receive data in the form of 1's and 0's. It may then store these data for future processing, perform arithmetic and logic operations in accordance with previously stored instructions, and deliver the results to an output device. In a sense, a microprocessor is a computer on a chip.

A block diagram of a typical microprocessor shows that it contains a number of basic components connected in a rather unusual manner (see Figure 11–4). Included in its construction are the arithmetic/logic unit, an accumulator, a data register, address registers, program counter, instruction decoder, and sequence controller.

Arithmetic/Logic Unit

All microprocessors contain an arithmetic/logic unit, which is usually designated ALU. The ALU is a calculator chip that performs mathematical and logical operations on the data words supplied to it. It is made to work auto-

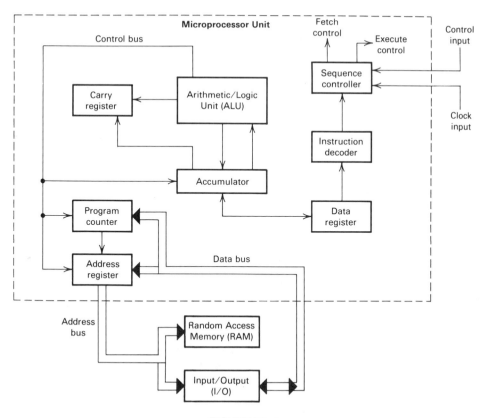

FIGURE 11–4
Microprocessor block diagram.

matically by control signals developed in the instruction decoder.

The ALU simply combines the contents of its two inputs, which are called the data register and the accumulator. As a general rule, addition, subtraction, and logic comparisons are the primary operations performed by the ALU. The specific operation to be performed is determined by a control signal supplied by the instruction decoder.

The data supplied to the inputs of an ALU are normally in the form of 8-bit binary numbers. Upon being received at the input, these data are combined by the ALU in accordance with the logic of binary arithmetic. Since a mathematical operation is ultimately performed on the two data inputs, the latter are often called *operands*.

To demonstrate the operation of the ALU, assume now that two binary numbers are to be added. In this case, let us consider the addition of the number 6_{10} and 8_{10}. Initially, the binary number 00000110_2 is placed in the accumulator. The second operand, 00001000_2, representing the number 8_{10}, is then placed into the data register. When a proper control line to the ALU is activated, binary addition is performed, producing an output of 00001110_2, or

14_{10}, which is the sum of the two operands. This value is then stored in the accumulator, where it replaces the operand that appeared there originally. The ALU only responds to binary numbers.

Accumulators

The accumulators of a microprocessor are temporary registers that are designed to store operands that are to be processed by the ALU. Before the ALU can perform, it must first receive data from an accumulator. After the data register input and accumulator input are combined, the logical answer or output of the ALU appears in the accumulator. This particular function is essentially the same for all microprocessors.

In microprocessor operation, a typical instruction would be to "load the accumulator." This instruction enables the contents of a particular memory location to be placed into the accumulator. A similar instruction might be "store accumulator." In this operation the instruction causes the contents of the accumulator to be placed in a selected memory location. Essentially, the accumulator serves in one capacity as an input source for the ALU and then as a destination area for its output.

Data Registers

The data register of a microprocessor serves as a temporary storage location for information applied to the data bus. Typically, this register will accommodate an 8-bit data word. An example of a function of this register is operand storage for the ALU input. In addition, it may be called on to hold an instruction while the instruction is being decoded or it may temporarily hold data prior to the data being placed in memory.

Address Registers

Address registers are used in microprocessors to temporarily store the address of a memory location that is to be accessed for data. In some units this register may be programmable. This means that it permits instructions to alter its contents. The program can also be used to build an address in the register prior to executing a memory reference instruction.

Program Counter

The program counter of a microprocessor is a memory device that holds the address of the next instruction to be executed in a program. As a general rule, this unit simply counts the instructions of a program in sequential order. In practice, when the MPU has fetched instructions addressed by the program counter, the count advances to the next location. At any given point during the sequence, the counter indicates the location in memory from which the next information will be derived.

The numbering sequence of the program counter may be modified so that the next count may not follow a numerical order. Through this procedure, the counter may be programmed to jump from one point to another in a routine. This permits the MPU to have branching capabilities should the need arise.

Instruction Decoders

Each specific operation that the MPU can perform is identified by an exclusive binary number known as an *instruction code*. Eight-bit words are commonly used for this code. Exactly 2^8 or 256_{10} separate or alternative operations can be represented by this code. After a typical instruction code is pulled from memory and placed in the data register, it must be de-

coded. The instruction decoder simply examines the coded word and selectively decides which operation is to be performed by the ALU. The output of the decoder is first applied to the sequence controller.

Sequence Controller

The sequence controller performs a number of very vital functions in the operation of a microprocessor. Using clock inputs, this circuitry maintains the proper sequence of events required to perform a processing task. After instructions are received and decoded, the sequence controller issues a control sign that initiates the proper processing action. In most units the controller has the capability of responding to external control signals.

Buses

The registers and components of most microprocessors are connected by a bus-organized type of network. The term *bus,* in this case, is defined as a group of conductor paths that are used to connect data words to various registers. A simplification of registers connected by a common bus line is shown in Figure 11–5.

The utility of bus-connected components is the ease with which a data word can be transferred or loaded into registers. In operation, each register has inputs labeled clock, enable, load, and clear. When the load and enable input lines are low or at 0, each register is isolated from the common bus line.

To transfer a word from one register to another, it is necessary to make the appropriate inputs high or at the 1 state. For instance, to transfer the data of register A to register D, place enable A (EA) and load D (LD) inputs both in the 1 state. This will cause the data of register A to appear on the common bus line.

When a clock pulse arrives at the common inputs, the transfer process is completed.

The word length of a bus is based on the number of conductor paths that it employs. Buses for 4, 8, and 16 bits are commonly used in microprocessors. New MPUs tend to use an 8-bit data bus and a 16-bit address bus.

Microprocessor Architecture

The physical layout or architecture of a microprocessor is generally much more complex than the stripped down version of the one pre-

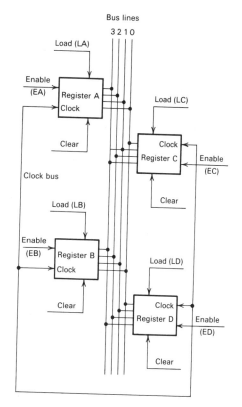

FIGURE 11–5
Registers connected to a common bus line.

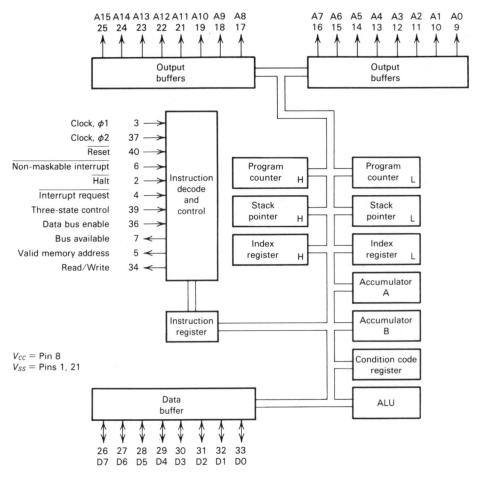

FIGURE 11–6
Block diagram of the MC6800 microprocessor.

sented earlier. In practice, it is not really necessary to know what goes on inside a microprocessor other than to have some idea of its primary functions. As a rule, the operation is so complex that if we attempt to analyze a specific unit it is easy to get bogged down in details. An expanded block diagram of a representative microprocessor is shown in Figure 11–6 to compare its architecture with the simplified unit presented previously.

The MC6800 is the nucleus of Motorola's microcomputer family. It is housed in the 40-pin dual-in-line package shown in Figure 11–7. Two accumulators, an index register, a program counter register, a stack pointer register, and a condition code register are included in its physical makeup. Only two of these registers differ from those of our simplified model. Let us look briefly at these differences, starting with the accumulator.

MOTOROLA
Semiconductors
BOX 20912 • PHOENIX, ARIZONA 85036

MICROPROCESSING UNIT (MPU)

The MC6800 is a monolithic 8-bit microprocessor forming the central control function for Motorola's M6800 family. Compatible with TTL, the MC6800, as with all M6800 system parts, requires only one +5.0-volt power supply, and no external TTL devices for bus interface.

The MC6800 is capable of addressing 65K bytes of memory with its 16-bit address lines. The 8-bit data bus is bidirectional as well as 3-state, making direct memory addressing and multiprocessing applications realizable.

- Eight-Bit Parallel Processing
- Bi-Directional Data Bus
- Sixteen-Bit Address Bus — 65K Bytes of Addressing
- 72 Instructions — Variable Length
- Seven Addressing Modes — Direct, Relative, Immediate, Indexed, Extended, Implied and Accumulator
- Variable Length Stack
- Vectored Restart
- Maskable Interrupt Vector
- Separate Non-Maskable Interrupt — Internal Registers Saved In Stack
- Six Internal Registers — Two Accumulators, Index Register, Program Counter, Stack Pointer and Condition Code Register
- Direct Memory Addressing (DMA) and Multiple Processor Capability
- Clock Rates as High as 1 MHz
- Simple Bus Interface Without TTL
- Halt and Single Instruction Execution Capability

PIN ASSIGNMENT

L SUFFIX
CERAMIC PACKAGE
CASE 715

NOT SHOWN: P SUFFIX
PLASTIC PACKAGE
CASE 711

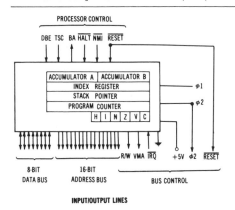

INPUT/OUTPUT LINES

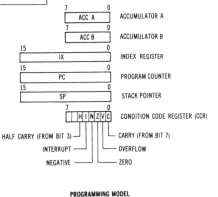

PROGRAMMING MODEL

FIGURE 11–7
Partial MC6800 data sheet. (Courtesy of
Motorola Semiconductor Products, Inc.)

Accumulators

The MC6800 MPU has two accumulators, instead of one, which are labeled AA and AB. Each accumulator is 8 bits wide, which is indicated by the numbers 0 to 7 in the programming model of Figure 11–7. These numbers are used to show the programming capacity of the chip. Each accumulator is designed to hold operands or data from the ALU.

Program instructions for each accumulator include a mnemonic of its name and the operation to be performed. The loading of accumulator A is LDAA, and LDAB is the mnemonic for loading accumulator B. Storing data in accumulator A is STAA, with STAB achieving the same operation for accumulator B. With two accumulators in the MPU, arithmetic and logic operations can be performed on two different numbers at the same time without shifting to memory.

Index Register

The index register of the MC6800 has a 16-bit or 2-byte capacity that is used to store memory addresses. This register has the capability of being loaded from two adjacent memory bytes, which allows its contents to be stored in two adjacent memory locations. Through this feature, data can be moved in 2-byte groups. The contents value increases by 1 when given the increment index register instruction or INX. A DEX instruction applied to the unit causes it to decrease by 1. This latter instruction is called *decrementing* the index register.

Program Counter

The program counter or PC of the MC6800 is a 16-bit register that holds the address of the next byte to be fetched from memory. It can accommodate 2^{16} or $65,536_{10}$ different mem-

ory addresses. Two 8-bit bytes are used for obtaining a specific address location.

Stack Pointer

The stack pointer or SP of the MC6800 is a special 16-bit or 2-byte register that uses a section of memory that has a last-in, first-out capability. With this capability, the status of the MPU registers may be stored when branch or interrupt subroutines are being performed.

An address in the SP is the starting point of sequential memory locations in memory where the status of MPU registers is stored. After the register status has been placed into the stack pointer, it is decremented. When the SP is accessed, the status of the last byte placed on the stack serves as the first byte to be restored.

Condition Code Register

The condition code register or CCR of the MC6800 is a special 8-bit register that is actuated by the execution of an instruction. The outputs of this register are indicated by the instruction, 11 HINZVC. The carry in or borrow condition is indicated by the letter C in the zero bit position. When C = 1, it indicates a carry for addition or a borrow for subtraction. The C = 0 condition indicates the reset state when no borrow or carry occurs.

A 1 appearing at the V output location is used to indicate the results of an overflow condition when the two's complement arithmetic operation has been performed. When V = 0, the overflow condition does not occur.

The Z or zero output location of the register indicates when the output of an arithmetic operation is zero. A Z = 0 indicates a resulting zero, and a Z = 1 state indicates a notzero condition.

The N or negative bit of the condition code register indicates the status of bit 7 after an

arithmetic operation. When bit 7 is 1, N = 1. This is used to denote a negative value for a two's complement operation. When N = 0, the seventh bit of the operation is zero, which indicates a positive status.

When the I bit of the condition code output is equal to 1, the MPU cannot respond to an interrupt request from an outside source. An I = 0 state permits interrupts to occur.

The H bit of the CCR output is used to indicate a half-carry during adding, adding with carry, or adding accumulator operations. When H = 1 during an execution of instructions, it indicates there is a resulting carry from bit 3 to 4. An H = 0 state indicates no resulting carry from the bit 3 position.

Bit positions 6 and 7 of the CC register output are not specific indicators in normal operation. They remain at the 1 state during regular operation.

MEMORY

Microcomputer applications range from a number of single-chip microprocessor units to some rather complex networks that employ several auxiliary chips interconnected in a massive system. As a general rule, the primary difference in this broad range of applications is in the memory capabilities of the system. Single-chip microprocessors are obviously quite limited in the amounts of memory that they can possess owing to the large number of essential logic functions needed to make the unit operational. Additional memory, in general, can be achieved much more economically through the use of auxiliary chips. The potential capabilities of a microcomputer system are primarily limited by the range of memory that it employs.

Memory, in general terms, refers to the capability of a device to store logical data in such a way that a single bit or a group of bits can be easily accessed or retrieved. In practice, memory can be achieved in a variety of different ways. Microcomputer systems are usually concerned with read/write memory and read-only memory. These two classifications of memory are accomplished by employing numerous semiconductor circuit duplications on a single IC chip.

Read/Write Memory

Read/write semiconductor memories are the most widely used form of electronic memory found in microcomputer systems today. Read/write chips of the large-scale integration (LSI) type have been capable of storing 16,384 or 16K bits of data in an area of less than $\frac{1}{2}$cm^2. New technologies have caused the 64K memory now to be common, with 256K and 512K units coming into use. The structure of the chip includes a number of discrete circuits, each having the ability to store binary data in an organized rectangular configuration. Access to each memory location is provided by coded information from the microprocessor address bus. The read/write function indicates that data can be placed into memory or retrieved at the same rate.

A simplification of the memory process is represented by the 8 × 8 state memory unit of Figure 11–8. As noted here, memory ICs are usually organized in a rectangular pattern of rows and columns. This particular diagram employs eight rows that can store 8-bit words or 64 single bits of memory. To select a particular memory address, a 3-bit binary number is used to designate a specific row location and three additional bits are used to indicate the column location. In this example, the row address is 3_{10}, or 011_2, and the column address is 5_{10}, or 101_2. The selected memory cell address is at location 30.

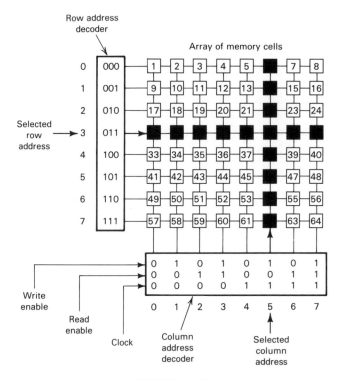

FIGURE 11–8
Simplification of the memory location
process.

Many read/write memory chips employ a single MOS transistor for each memory location (see Figure 11–9). Binary information is stored in the transistor as a charge on a small capacitor. No charge across the transistor gate–channel electrodes indicates a 0 state, and a charge appearing across the two electrodes represents a 1. When a row select line is activated, it energizes the gate of each transistor in the entire row. When a column line is selected, it energizes the source–drain electrodes of each transistor in the column. Simultaneous activation of a row and column energizes a specific transistor memory cell.

A charge placed on the discrete MOS transistor of a memory cell must be restored periodically in order to overcome leakage. Charge regeneration is generally achieved by a special

transistor thresholding amplifier. In practice, charge regeneration occurs every few milliseconds on a continuous basis.

Eight-bit word storage is achieved in our memory unit by energizing one row and all eight columns simultaneously. The row and column decoders perform this operation. Some of the read/write memory units available today have capacities of 8×8, 32×8, 128×8, 1024×8, and 4096×8.

To write a word into memory, a specific address is first selected according to the data supplied by the address bus. See the block diagram of the read/write memory unit of Figure 11–10. The address decoder, in this case, selects the appriopriate row and column select lines. A high or 1 write enable signal applied to the control unit causes the data bus signal to

be transferred to the selected memory address. These data then charge the appropriate memory cells according to the coded 1 or 0 values. Removing the write enable signal causes the data charge accumulations to remain at each cell location. The output is disconnected from the data bus after the write operation has been completed.

To read the charge accumulation appearing at each memory cell, the read enable control line must be energized. Selecting a specific memory location causes charge data to appear at the data bus as memory output signals. Charge restoration from the thresholding amplifier continuously maintains the same charge at each cell. This means that reading from memory does not destroy the charge data at each cell. All this takes place as long as the memory unit is energized electrically. A loss of electrical power or turning the unit off destroys the data placed at each memory location. Essentially, solid-state read/write memory is classified as volatile because of this.

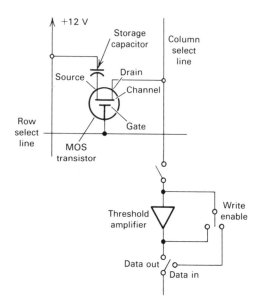

FIGURE 11–9
MOS transistor memory cell.

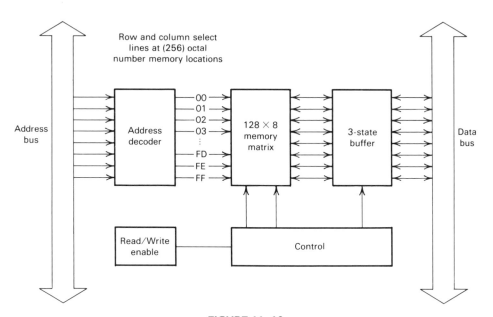

FIGURE 11–10
Read/write memory block diagram

Read-only Memory

Most microcomputer systems necessitate memories that contain permanently stored or rarely altered data. A prime example of this would be math tables and permanent program data. Storage of this type is provided by read-only memory (ROM). Information is often placed in this type of memory unit when the chip is manufactured. ROM data are nonvolatile, which means that they are not lost when the power source is removed or turned off.

Read-only memory is achieved in a variety of ways. One process employs fusible links built into each memory cell. A data pattern can then be placed into memory by "blowing out" the unwanted fusible links. This action may be used to open interconnecting conductors, place a diode between two connections, or place a small capacitor between two electrodes. Obviously, a fusible link cannot be reformed after it has once been destroyed. The fusible-link principle is used only once to program a read-only memory chip.

Programmable read-only memory or PROM can be optically erased by exposure to an ultraviolet light source. After UV light exposure, each cell of the entire unit goes to a zero state. Writing data into the chip again initiates the new program.

Figure 11–11 shows a cross-sectional view of an ultraviolet erasable ROM. The floating gate of the MOS transistor in this case is not electrically connected to anything. Data to be stored in the cell are written into the transistor by applying 25 V between the gate and drain electrodes while the source and substrate are at ground potential. This action causes a static field to appear between the gate and source, which in turn causes electron movement with considerable velocity. Electrons that move through the thin silicon dioxide insulator become trapped on the floating gate. The charged gate–drain therefore serves as a small capaci-

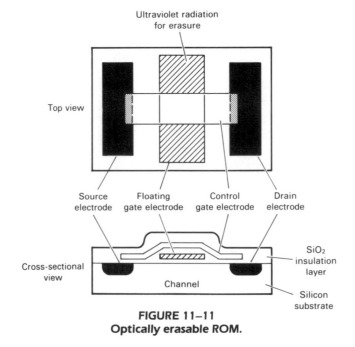

FIGURE 11–11
Optically erasable ROM.

tor. A charged condition represents a 1 state in memory and an uncharged condition indicates a 0 state. The charged cell condition produced by each transistor is nonvolatile.

Erasing the charged data of each MOS cell is achieved by exposing the chip to ultraviolet light. This action temporarily makes the silicon dioxide insulation layer somewhat more conductive. As a result, excessive leakage causes the floating gate charge to dissipate. In practice, each cell of the chip is discharged by the exposure process at the same time. Memory can be restored by writing data back into each transistor cell. PROMs of this type can be altered while in the circuit board if the need arises.

An alternative to the optically erasable read-only memory is the electrically alterable read-only memory (EAROM). This type of chip permits erasures of individual cells or word locations instead of the entire chip. Cell structure is very similar to the optically erasable ROM. The floating-gate structure of each cell is, however, altered by having a discrete interface insulation strip between it and the drain. Selective charge and discharge of each cell can be achieved by signals applied to the gate connection. The potential usefulness of the EAROM is quite large today. It has not yet, however, found its way into many applications because of cost, access time, and long-term retention problems.

MICROCOMPUTER FUNCTIONS

Certain functions are basic to almost all microcomputer systems. Included in these operations are timing, fetch and execution, read memory, write memory, input/out transfer, and interrupts. An understanding of these basic functions is important when examining the operation of a specific microcomputer.

Timing

The operational activities of a microcomputer system are achieved by a sequence of cycling instructions. The MPU, for example, fetches an instruction, executes the required operations, fetches the next instruction, executes it, and continues to operate in a cycling pattern. This means that all actions occur at or during a precisely defined time interval. An orderly sequence of operations like this necessitates some type of a precision clock mechanism. In practice, a free-running electronic oscillator or clock is primarily responsible for this function. In some systems the clock may be built into the MPU; in others it is provided by an independent unit that feeds the system through a separate clock control bus. The entire sequence of operations is controlled by the timing signal.

Sequential operations such as fetch and execute are normally achieved within a period called the MPU cycle. The fetch portion of this cycle always consists of the same series of instructions. It therefore takes the same amount of time for each instruction. The execute phase of an operation, by comparison, may consist of many events and sequences, depending on the specific instruction being performed. This portion of the cycle will therefore vary a great deal with the particular instruction being performed.

The total interval that it takes a timing pulse to pass through a complete cycle from beginning to end is called a *period*. In practice, one or more clock periods may be needed to complete an operational instruction such as fetch. The execute operation, as a rule, may require an even larger number of timing periods to cycle through its sequence. Essentially, this

means that the machine cycle of a system may be quite variable, whereas the period of a timing pulse is very consistent.

Fetch and Execute Operations

After programmed information has been placed into the memory of a microcomputer, its action is directed by a series of fetch and execute operations. This sequence of operations is repeated over and over again until the entire program has cycled to its conclusion. This program essentially tells the MPU specifically what operations it must perform.

The entire operation begins when the start function is initiated. This signal actuates the control section of the MPU, which in turn automatically starts the machine cycle. The first instruction that the MPU receives is to fetch the next instruction from memory. In a normal sequence of events, the MPU issues a read operational code instruction and the contents of the program counter are sent to the program memory. It, in turn, responds by returning the next instruction word. The first word of this instruction is then placed into the instruction register. If more than one word is included in the instruction, a longer cycling time is needed to complete the instruction. After the complete instruction word is in the MPU, the program counter is incremented by one count. The instruction is then decoded. This action prepares the unit for the next fetch instruction.

The execution phase of operation is primarily based on which instruction is to be performed by the MPU. This instruction may call for such things as read memory, write in memory, read the input signal, transfer to output, or any one of several MPU operations such as add registers, subtract, or register-to-register transfer. The magnitude or time of this operation is dependent on programmed information that is placed in memory.

The popular 8080 microprocessor, made by Intel Corporation, takes a number of the clock periods to perform its operations. This particular chip can be operated at a clock rate of 2 MHz. A single cycle of the clock has a period 1/2,000,000 or 0.0000005 s. Periods this small are best expressed in microseconds (0.5 μs) or nanoseconds (500 ns). The fastest instruction change that can be achieved by this chip requires four clock periods or 4×500 ns = 2 μs. Its slowest instruction requires 18 periods or 18×500 ns = 9 μs. The operational time of an MPU is a good measure of its effectiveness and how powerful it is as a functional device.

Read Memory Operation

The read memory operation is an instruction that calls for data to be read from a specific memory location and applied to the MPU. To initiate this operation, the MPU issues a read operation code and sends it to the proper memory address. In return, the read/write memory unit sends the data stored at the selected address into the data bus. This 8-bit number is ultimately fed to the MPU, where it is placed in the accumulator after an appropriate timing pulse has been initiated.

Figure 11–12 shows a simplification of the read memory operation in a series of sequential steps. In step 1 the address bus supplies an 8-bit memory select address to the decoder. These data come from the programmed instructions and are initiated by the MPU. Step 2 is performed by the address decoder, which generates the appropriate row and column select lines that actuate the memory location. These address input lines allow any one of the 1024 locations to be addressed. When several memory chips are used, a specific chip is selected first, and then the desired address is selected. This operation involves two steps called chip selection and address selection.

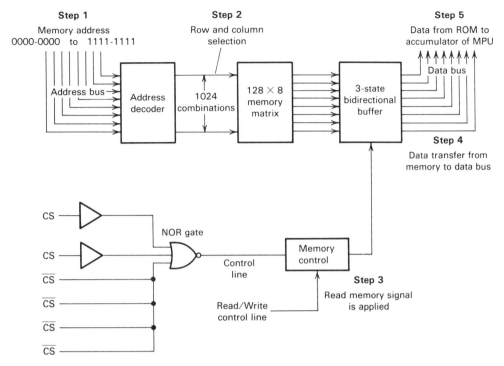

FIGURE 11–12
Operational sequence steps for read memory.

Step 3 is a control function. When the read memory signal is applied to the read/write control line, the data transfer direction of the three-state buffer is decided. The reading operation directs data from memory to the data bus line.

Step 4 deals with the chip select control signal. An appropriate 6-bit binary code energizes the NOR gate control line. This action causes the three-state buffer to change from a high-impedance condition to low impedance. As a result of this action, data are transferred from memory into the data bus. Step 5 shows data being ultimately transferred to the accumulator of the MPU, which completes the read memory operation.

Write Memory Operation

The write memory operation is an instruction that calls for data to be placed into or stored at a specific memory location. This function is initiated when the MPU issues a write operation code and sends it to a selected read/write memory unit. Data from the data bus are then placed into the selected memory location for storage. In practice, 8-bit numbers are usually stored as words in the memory unit.

Figure 11–13 shows a simplified block diagram of the write memory operation in a series of sequential steps. In step 1 the MPU places an 8-bit address location into the address bus. In step 2 these data are applied to the address

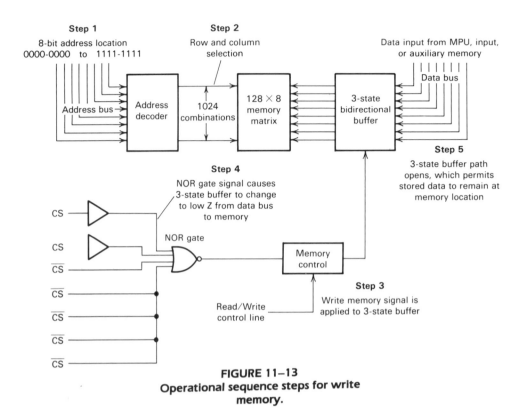

FIGURE 11–13
Operational sequence steps for write memory.

decoder, where they generate the desired row and column select lines that actuate the memory location. Any one of 1024 locations can be selected in this particular example. If more than one memory chip is used, the operation is preceded by a chip select signal applied to the CS inputs. The complete operation thus involves two steps: chip selection and address selection within the chip.

Step 3 is a control operation that prepares the chip to receive data. When the write-in memory signal is applied to the read/write control line, the data transfer direction of the three-state buffer is decided. The writing operation directs data from the data bus into the buffer. Notice the direction of the data flow arrows. The data, in this case, may come from the MPU, from an alternate memory source, or through the system input.

Step 4 deals with the chip select control signal. A 6-bit binary code energizes the NOR gate control line. This action causes the three-state buffer to change so that it is low impedance from the data bus to the memory matrix. Data are then transferred into the matrix where they actuate specific memory cells according to a prescribed level. Step 5 opens the path through the three-state buffer, which in turn prevents any further change in the stored data at this location.

Input/Output Transfer Operations

In a microcomputer system, input/output (I/O) transfer operations are very similar to the read/write operation just discussed. The major dif-

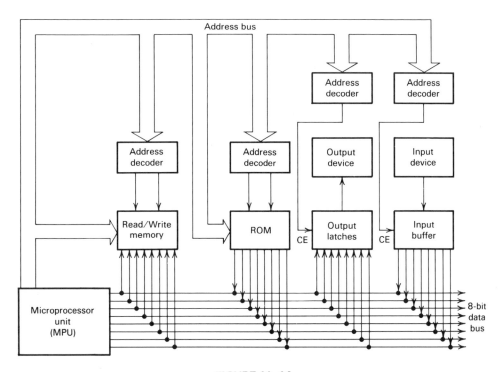

FIGURE 11–14
Simplification of MPU address bus and data
bus connections.

ference, for all practical purposes, is the opcode data number that is used to call up the operation. When the MPU issues an input/output opcode, it actuates the appropriate I/O port, which in turn either receives data from the input or sends it to the output device according to the coded instruction.

A simplification of a microcomputer system with a read/write memory, read-only memory, output, and input connected to a common address bus and data bus is shown in Figure 11–14. In this type of system, all data are acted on by the MPU. As noted by the data bus arrows, data move in either direction to the read/write memory and flow only from the ROM or input into the data bus. The output only flows from the data bus to the output device.

In a bus-controlled system, data from a spe-cific source must be transferred independently of the others. This is accomplished by assigning each destination or potential data source a different address. The chip enable pin of each data source is selected by an activating code that energizes the desired data source.

The address assigned to each data source is primarily dependent on the capacity of the memory being employed. If a 512_{10}-byte read/write memory is used, it might possibly be assigned memory locations from 0000 to $01FF_{16}$. A 1024_{10}-byte ROM if used is usually assigned locations near the upper extreme of the data bus capacity. In this case, locations might be $FC00_{16}$ to $FFFF_{16}$. When any of these memory address locations appears on the address bus, its data can be transferred to the data bus when the appropriate chip enable code is applied.

The latch circuit of the output and buffer of the input are also assigned specific address locations. When these address locations are selected, the data are transferred to the output or brought into the data bus via the input device. This action occurs only when a chip enable control signal is received by the appropriate component.

The output of each data source must not interfere with or upset the data appearing at the other source when they are placed on the data bus. To prevent cross-interference, each data source is commonly fed through a three-state logic device. When a specific data source is disabled, it automatically assumes a high-impedance state with the data bus. When enabled, it immediately changes to a low-impedance state that provides connection to the data bus. Through this kind of circuitry, only one data source appears on the data bus at a particular time.

Interrupt Operations

Interrupt operations are often used to improve the efficiency of a microcomputer system. Interrupt signals are generated by peripheral equipment such as keyboards, displays, printers, or process control devices. These signals are generated by peripheral equipment and applied to the MPU so as to inform it that a particular peripheral device needs some type of attention.

Consider now a microcomputer system that is designed to process a large volume of data, some of which is to be output to a line printer. The MPU, in this case, can output data at a very high rate compared to the time needed to actuate a character representing a specific data byte. Essentially, this means that the MPU would have to remain idle while waiting for the printer to complete its task.

If an interrupt capability is employed by the MPU of a microcomputer system, it can output a data byte and then return to processing while the printer completes its operation. When the printer is ready for the next data byte, it simply requests an interrupt. Upon acknowledging the interrupt, the MPU suspends program execution and automatically branches to a subroutine that will output the next data byte to the printer. The MPU operation is not restricted by slow-speed peripheral equipment.

In practice, the interrupt operation is achieved by using registers within the MPU in conjunction with instructions stored in memory. Upon receipt of an interrupt request, it is necessary to freeze the contents of the MPU internal registers. This is usually achieved by storing them in the memory locations of the stack pointer register. This register has last-in, first-out memory capabilities. When the program is resumed again, data at the interrupted point can be lifted from the stack pointer, which calls for execution to be restored.

Interrupt operations are only needed in systems where the MPU has a task to perform that can be undertaken while a particular peripheral device is progressing through its sequence. In industrial process control applications where a limited amount of data are being moved, the interrupt operation is generally avoided.

PROGRAMMING

The term *program* generally refers to a series of acceptable instructions developed for a computer that permit it to perform a prescribed operation or function. In microcomputer systems, some programs are hard-wired, some are in read-only memories called firmware, and others are described as software. A dedicated system that is designed to achieve a specific function is generally hardware programmed, which means that it cannot be adapted for other tasks

FIGURE 11–15
Software package for measurement tasks.
(Courtesy of Analog Devices)

without a physical circuit change. Firmware systems have programmed material placed on ROM chips. Program changes for this type of system can be achieved by changing the ROMs. A software type of program has the greatest level of flexibility. This type of program is created on paper and transferred to the system by a keyboard, magnetic disk, or magnetic tape. Instructions are stored at read/write memory locations and performed by calling for these instructions from memory.

Most microcomputer systems used in industrial process applications are replacements for hard-wired logic systems. The design of the system and its purpose usually dictate the type of programming method employed. Combined firmware and software programmed systems with a keyboard are very common today (see Figure 11–15).

Instructions

The instructions for a microprocessor system normally appear as a set of characters or symbols that are used to define a specific operation. These symbols, which may appear alone or together with other characters, are similar to those that appear on an ordinary typewriter. Included are decimal digits 0 through 9, letters A through Z, and in some cases punctuation marks and specialized keyboard characters. The presentation of symbolized instructions may appear as binary numbers, hexadecimal numbers, or as mnemonic codes.

Microprocessors may employ any one of several different codes in a program according to its design. As a general rule, each type of MPU has a unique *instructional set* or repertoire of instructions that it is designed to understand and obey. These instructions primarily appear as binary data symbols and words. *Machine instructions* of this type are normally held in a read-only memory unit that is address selected and connected to the MPU through the common data bus. Instructional sets of this type are an example of firmware because they are fixed at a specific memory location and cannot be changed by program material.

Microprocessor instructions usually consist of one, two, or three bytes of data. This type of data must follow the instruction commands in successive memory locations. These instructions are usually called *addressing modes*. There are several distinct types of addressing modes in a typical microcomputer system.

Inherent-mode addressing. One-byte instructions are often described as inherent-mode instructions. These instructions are primarily designed to manipulate data to the accumulator registers of the ALU. As a rule, no address code is needed for this type of instruction because it is an implied machine instruction. The instruction CLA, for example, is a one-byte opcode that clears the contents of accumulator A. No specific definition of data is needed, nor is an address needed for further data manipulation. This instruction simply clears the accumulator register of its data.

Inherent-mode instructions differ a great deal between manufacturers. Some representa-

TABLE 11-1
Opcode Instructions

Mnemonic	Opcode	MEANING
ABA	1B	Add the contents of accumulators A and B. The result is stored in accumulator A. The contents of B are not altered.
CLA	4F	Clear accumulator A to all zeros.
CLB	5F	Clear accumulator B.
CBA	11	Compare accumulators: Subtract the contents of ACCB from ACCA. The ALU is involved but the contents of the accumulators are not altered. The comparison is reflected in the condition register.
COMA	43	Find the ones complement of the data in accumulator A, and replace its contents with its ones complement. (The ones complement is simple inversion of all bits.)
COMB	53	Replace the contents of ACCB with its ones complement.
DAA	19	Adjust the two hexadecimal digits in accumulator A to valid BCD digits. Set the carry bit in the condition register when appropriate. The correction is accomplished by adding 06, 60, or 66 to the contents of ACCA.
DECA	4A	Decrement accumulator A. Subtract 1 from the contents of accumulator A. Store result in ACCA.
DECB	5A	Decrement accumulator B. Store result in accumulator B.
LSRA	44	Logic shift right, accumulator A or B.
LSRB	54	$0 \rightarrow \boxed{b_7\ b_6\ b_5\ b_4\ b_3\ b_2\ b_1\ b_0} \rightarrow \boxed{C}$
SBA	10	Subtract the contents of accumulator B from the contents of accumulator A. Store results in accumulator A.
TAB	16	Transfer the contents of ACCA to accumulator B. The contents of register A are unchanged.
TBA	17	Transfer the contents of ACCB to accumulator A. The contents of ACCA are unchanged.
NEGA	40	Replace the contents of ACCA with its twos complement. This operation generates a negative number.
NEGB	50	Replace the contents of ACCB with its twos complement. This operation generates a negative number.
INCA	4C	Increment accumulator A. Add 1 to the contents of ACCA and store in ACCA.
INCB	5C	Increment accumulator B. Store results in AACB.
ROLA	49	Rotate left, accumulator A or B.
ROLB	59	$\boxed{C} \leftarrow \boxed{b_7\ b_6\ b_5\ b_4\ b_3\ b_2\ b_1\ b_0}$ Carry/borrow in condition register.
RORA	46	Rotate right, accumulator A or B.
RORB	56	$\boxed{C} \rightarrow \boxed{b_7\ b_6\ b_5\ b_4\ b_3\ b_2\ b_1\ b_0}$
ASLA	48	Shift left, accumulator A or B (arithmetic).
ASLB	58	$\boxed{C} \leftarrow \boxed{b_7\ b_6\ b_5\ b_4\ b_3\ b_2\ b_1\ b_0} \leftarrow 0$ In condition code register — Always enters zeros
ASRA	47	Shift right, accumulator A or B (arithmetic).
ASRB	57	$\boxed{b_7\ b_6\ b_5\ b_4\ b_3\ b_2\ b_1\ b_0} \rightarrow \boxed{C}$ Retains sign bit

(Courtesy of Motorola Semiconductor Products, Inc.)

tive opcode instructions are shown in Table 11-1. Note particularly that the meaning of the instruction, its code in hexadecimal form, and a mnemonic are given for each instruction. In practice, each microcomputer system has a number of inherent instructions of the one-byte type that contain only an opcode.

Immediate addressing. Immediate addressing is accomplished by a two-byte instruction that contains an opcode and an operand. In this addressing mode, the opcode appears in the first 8-bit byte followed by an 8-bit operand. A common practice is to place intermediate addressing instructions in the first 256 memory

locations. Through this procedure, these instructions can be retrieved very quickly and this is the fastest mode of operation.

An example of an intermediate address instruction would be to "load accumulator A with the number 53_{16}." This instruction would appear as

Memory Location	Hexadecimal	Binary	Function
0010	86	1000–0110	LDA (opcode)
0011	53	0101–0011	(Data)

The number 86_{16} of this instruction is an indication of the hexadecimal opcode LDA A located at memory address 0010. The number 53_{16} are the data to be manipulated. It appears at the next consecutive memory location. Ultimately, this means that the number 53_{16} or $0110–0011_2$ has been loaded into accumulator A.

Relative addressing. Relative addressing instructions are primarily designed to transfer program control to a location other than the next consecutive memory address. In this type of addressing, two 8-bit bytes are used for the instruction. Transfer operations of this type are often limited to a specific number of memory locations in front or in back of their present locations. An example of this would be 127 forward and 128 reverse locations.

The two-byte instruction contains an opcode in the first byte and an 8-bit memory location in the second byte. The second byte points to the location of the next instruction that is to be executed. This type of instruction is primarily designed to achieve branching operations.

Indexed addressing. Indexed addressing is achieved by a two-byte instruction and is very similar to the relative addressing mode of instruction. In this type of addressing, the second byte of the instruction is added to the contents of the index register to form a new or *effective address*. This address is obtained during program execution rather than being held at a predetermined location as with the other addressing modes. The newly created effective address is also held in a temporary memory address register so that it will not be altered or destroyed during the processing operation.

Direct addressing. Direct addressing is generally the most common of all modes of instruction. In this type of instruction, the address is located in the next byte of memory following the opcode. This permits the first 256 bytes of memory, from 0000 to $00FF_{16}$, to be addressed.

An example of direct addressing would be

Memory Location	Contents	Function
0010	96_{16}	LDAA (opcode)
0011	62_{16}	Location of Data

The number 96_{16} is used as the opcode command for direct addressing of accumulator A. The mnemonic LDAA describes this operation. The number 62_{16} is an indication of the address where data are to be fetched from memory. Whatever data appear at this location are then transferred through the data bus to accumulator A. In direct addressing, the second byte of the instruction is considered to be the absolute memory address.

Extended addressing. Extended addressing, as its name implies, is a method of increasing the capability of direct addressing so that it can accumulate more data. This mode of address-

ACCUMULATOR AND MEMORY INSTRUCTIONS

		IMMED			DIRECT			INDEX			EXTND			IMPLIED			BOOLEAN/ARITHMETIC OPERATION (All register labels refer to contents)	COND. CODE REG.					
OPERATIONS	MNEMONIC	OP	~	#	OP	~	#	OP	~	#	OP	~	#	OP	~	#		5 H	4 I	3 N	2 Z	1 V	0 C
Add	ADDA	8B	2	2	9B	3	2	AB	5	2	BB	4	3				A + M → A	↕	•	↕	↕	↕	↕
	ADDB	CB	2	2	DB	3	2	EB	5	2	FB	4	3				B + M → B	↕	•	↕	↕	↕	↕
Add Acmltrs	ABA													1B	2	1	A + B → A	↕	•	↕	↕	↕	↕
Add with Carry	ADCA	89	2	2	99	3	2	A9	5	2	B9	4	3				A + M + C → A	↕	•	↕	↕	↕	↕
	ADCB	C9	2	2	D9	3	2	E9	5	2	F9	4	3				B + M + C → B	↕	•	↕	↕	↕	↕
And	ANDA	84	2	2	94	3	2	A4	5	2	B4	4	3				A · M → A	•	•	↕	↕	R	•
	ANDB	C4	2	2	D4	3	2	E4	5	2	F4	4	3				B · M → B	•	•	↕	↕	R	•
Bit Test	BITA	85	2	2	95	3	2	A5	5	2	B5	4	3				A · M	•	•	↕	↕	R	•
	BITB	C5	2	2	D5	3	2	E5	5	2	F5	4	3				B · M	•	•	↕	↕	R	•
Clear	CLR							6F	7	2	7F	6	3				00 → M	•	•	R	S	R	R
	CLRA													4F	2	1	00 → A	•	•	R	S	R	R
	CLRB													5F	2	1	00 → B	•	•	R	S	R	R
Compare	CMPA	81	2	2	91	3	2	A1	5	2	B1	4	3				A − M	•	•	↕	↕	↕	↕
	CMPB	C1	2	2	D1	3	2	E1	5	2	F1	4	3				B − M	•	•	↕	↕	↕	↕
Compare Acmltrs	CBA													11	2	1	A − B	•	•	↕	↕	↕	↕
Complement, 1's	COM							63	7	2	73	6	3				M̄ → M	•	•	↕	↕	R	S
	COMA													43	2	1	Ā → A	•	•	↕	↕	R	S
	COMB													53	2	1	B̄ → B	•	•	↕	↕	R	S
Complement, 2's	NEG							60	7	2	70	6	3				00 − M → M	•	•	↕	↕	①	②
(Negate)	NEGA													40	2	1	00 − A → A	•	•	↕	↕	①	②
	NEGB													50	2	1	00 − B → B	•	•	↕	↕	①	②
Decimal Adjust, A	DAA													19	2	1	Converts Binary Add of BCD Characters into BCD Format	•	•	↕	↕	↕	③
Decrement	DEC							6A	7	2	7A	6	3				M − 1 → M	•	•	↕	↕	④	•
	DECA													4A	2	1	A − 1 → A	•	•	↕	↕	④	•
	DECB													5A	2	1	B − 1 → B	•	•	↕	↕	④	•
Exclusive OR	EORA	88	2	2	98	3	2	A8	5	2	B8	4	3				A ⊕ M → A	•	•	↕	↕	R	•
	EORB	C8	2	2	D8	3	2	E8	5	2	F8	4	3				B ⊕ M → B	•	•	↕	↕	R	•
Increment	INC							6C	7	2	7C	6	3				M + 1 → M	•	•	↕	↕	⑤	•
	INCA													4C	2	1	A + 1 → A	•	•	↕	↕	⑤	•
	INCB													5C	2	1	B + 1 → B	•	•	↕	↕	⑤	•
Load Acmltr	LDAA	86	2	2	96	3	2	A6	5	2	B6	4	3				M → A	•	•	↕	↕	R	•
	LDAB	C6	2	2	D6	3	2	E6	5	2	F6	4	3				M → B	•	•	↕	↕	R	•
Or, Inclusive	ORAA	8A	2	2	9A	3	2	AA	5	2	BA	4	3				A + M → A	•	•	↕	↕	R	•
	ORAB	CA	2	2	DA	3	2	EA	5	2	FA	4	3				B + M → B	•	•	↕	↕	R	•
Push Data	PSHA													36	4	1	A → Msp, SP − 1 → SP	•	•	•	•	•	•
	PSHB													37	4	1	B → Msp, SP − 1 → SP	•	•	•	•	•	•
Pull Data	PULA													32	4	1	SP + 1 → SP, Msp → A	•	•	•	•	•	•
	PULB													33	4	1	SP + 1 → SP, Msp → B	•	•	•	•	•	•

Operations	Mnemonic	IMMED OP ~ =	DIRECT OP ~ =	INDEX OP ~ =	EXTND OP ~ =	IMPLIED OP ~ =	Boolean/Arithmetic Operation	H	I	N	Z	V	C
Rotate Left	ROL			69 7 2	79 6 3		M	●	●	↕	↕	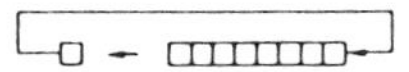 ⑥	↕
	ROLA					49 2 1	A	●	●	↕	↕	⑥	↕
	ROLB					59 2 1	B	●	●	↕	↕	⑥	↕
Rotate Right	ROR			66 7 2	76 6 3		M	●	●	↕	↕	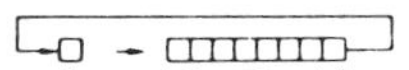 ⑥	↕
	RORA					46 2 1	A	●	●	↕	↕	⑥	↕
	RORB					56 2 1	B	●	●	↕	↕	⑥	↕
Shift Left, Arithmetic	ASL			68 7 2	78 6 3		M	●	●	↕	↕	 ⑥	↕
	ASLA					48 2 1	A	●	●	↕	↕	⑥	↕
	ASLB					58 2 1	B	●	●	↕	↕	⑥	↕
Shift Right, Arithmetic	ASR			67 7 2	77 6 3		M	●	●	↕	↕	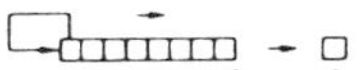 ⑥	↕
	ASRA					47 2 1	A	●	●	↕	↕	⑥	↕
	ASRB					57 2 1	B	●	●	↕	↕	⑥	↕
Shift Right, Logic	LSR			64 7 2	74 6 3		M	●	●	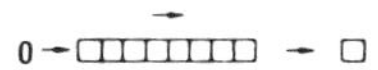 R	↕	⑥	↕
	LSRA					44 2 1	A	●	●	R	↕	⑥	↕
	LSRB					54 2 1	B	●	●	R	↕	⑥	↕
Store Acmltr	STAA		97 4 2	A7 6 2	B7 5 3		A → M	●	●	↕	↕	R	●
	STAB		D7 4 2	E7 6 2	F7 5 3		B → M	●	●	↕	↕	R	●
Subtract	SUBA	80 2 2	90 3 2	A0 5 2	B0 4 3		A − M → A	●	●	↕	↕	↕	↕
	SUBB	C0 2 2	D0 3 2	E0 5 2	F0 4 3		B − M → B	●	●	↕	↕	↕	↕
Subtract Acmltrs	SBA					10 2 1	A − B → A	●	●	↕	↕	↕	↕
Subtr with Carry	SBCA	82 2 2	92 3 2	A2 5 2	B2 4 3		A − M − C → A	●	●	↕	↕	↕	↕
	SBCB	C2 2 2	D2 3 2	E2 5 2	F2 4 3		B − M − C → B	●	●	↕	↕	↕	↕
Transfer Acmltrs	TAB					16 2 1	A → B	●	●	↕	↕	R	●
	TBA					17 2 1	B → A	●	●	↕	↕	R	●
Test, Zero or Minus	TST			6D 7 2	7D 6 3		M − 00	●	●	↕	↕	R	R
	TSTA					4D 2 1	A − 00	●	●	↕	↕	R	R
	TSTB					5D 2 1	B − 00	●	●	↕	↕	R	R

LEGEND

OP   Operation Code (Hexadecimal)
~   Number of MPU Cycles.
=   Number of Program Bytes.
+   Arithmetic Plus.
−   Arithmetic Minus.
·   Boolean AND.
MSP Contents of memory location pointed to be Stack Pointer.

+   Boolean Inclusive OR.
⊙   Boolean Exclusive OR.
M̄   Complement of M.
→   Transfer Into.
0   Bit Zero.
00   Byte Zero.

Note   Accumulator addressing mode instructions are included in the column for IMPLIED addressing

CONDITION CODE SYMBOLS

H   Half carry from bit 3.
I   Interrupt mask
N   Negative (sign bit)
Z   Zero (byte)
V   Overflow, 2's complement
C   Carry from bit 7
R   Reset Always
S   Set Always
↕   Test and set if true, cleared otherwise
●   Not Affected

FIGURE 11–16
MC6800 instruction set. (Courtesy of Motorola Semiconductor Products, Inc.)

439

ing is used for memory locations above $00FF_{16}$ and requires three bytes of data for the instruction. The first byte is a standard 8-bit opcode. The second byte is an address location for the most significant or highest order of the data in 8 bits. This is followed by the third byte, which holds the address of the least significant or lowest 8 bits of the data number being processed.

A representative extended memory instruction would appear as

Memory Location	Contents	Function
0010	$B6_{16}$	LDA A (opcode)
0011	40_{16}	Address of highest 8 bits of data
0100	53_{16}	Address of lowest 8 bits of data

The number $B6_{16}$ of this instruction indicates the opcode command for extended loading of accumulator A. The mnemonic LDA A describes the operation. The number 40_{16} is an indication of the address of the most significant 8 bits of data. The second half of the number, or least significant 8 bits of data, is stored at location 53_{16}. After the instruction has been executed, the combined data at the designated locations are transferred to the data bus, where they are ultimately loaded into accumulator A.

A Programming Example

To demonstrate the potential capabilities of a microcomputer system, we will discuss its ability to solve a straight-line computation problem. In this problem the system will be used to simply add two numbers and then indicate the resulting sum. This type of problem is obviously quite simple and could be easily solved without the help of a microcomputer system. It is used in this situation to demonstrate a principle of operation and to show a plan of procedure.

In practice, a microcomputer system could not solve even the simplest type of problem without the help of a well-defined program that works out everything right down to the smallest detail. After the program has been developed, the system simply follows this procedure to accomplish the task. Programming is an essential part of nearly all computer system applications.

Before a program can be effectively prepared for a microcomputer system, the programmer must be fully aware of the specific instructions that can be performed by the system. In general, each microcomputer system has a unique list of instructions that are used to control its operation. The instruction set of a microcomputer is the basis of all program construction. Figure 11–16 shows an instruction set for the Motorola MC6800 microprocessor system.

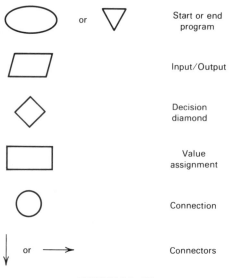

FIGURE 11–17
Flow-chart symbols.

Assume now that the programmer is familiar with the instruction set of the system being used to solve our straight-line computation problem. The next step in this procedure is to decide what specific instructions are needed to solve the problem. A limited number of operations to perform can generally be developed without the aid of a diagrammed plan of procedure. Complex problems, by comparison, usually require a specific plan in order to reduce confusion or to avoid the loss of an important operational step. Flow charts are commonly used to aid the programmer in this type of planning. Figure 11–17 shows some of the flow-chart symbols that are commonly used in program planning.

The first step in preparing a program to solve our problem is to make a flow chart that shows the general plan of procedure to be followed. In this case we will set up the program to accomplish the following:

Find: the number N (a decimal value)

Use equation: $x + y = N$

Let: $x = 0A$ (operand)

$y = 07$ (operand)

Figure 11–18 shows a simple flow-chart plan of procedure to be followed by our program to solve the problem. The first step, numbered 0, is a simple statement of the problem. Steps 1 and 2 are then used as the operands of the problem and indicate the values of x and y. After these values have been obtained, each is placed into a specific accumulator. Step 3 is then responsible for the addition operation. Since this system deals with binary numbers, conversion to decimal values is also necessary. Step 4 is a converson operation that changes binary numbers to BCD values. This value can then be used to energize an output so that it would produce a decimal readout. The fifth and final step of the program is an implied halt opcode that stops the program.

A programming sheet for our problem example is shown in Table 11–2. Notice that this sheet indicates the step number, a representative memory address in hexadecimal values, instruction bytes in hexadecimal values, opcode mnemonics, binary equivalents, addressing mode, and a description of each function. The memory address locations employed in the program begin with 66_{16}. In practice, it is a common procedure to reserve the first 100 memory locations, or 00 to 63_{16}, for branch instructions. We have arbitrarily selected location 66_{16} or 102_{10} in order to avoid those addresses being reserved for branching operations.

The program example used here is only one of literally thousands of programs that can be employed by a microcomputer to perform use-

Steps

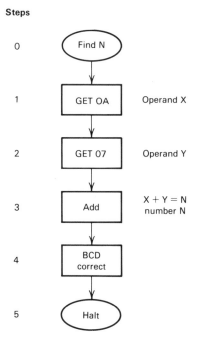

FIGURE 11–18
Flow-chart plan of a problem.

TABLE 11–2
Programming Sheet

	Title: X + Y = N Date: _____
	Purpose: Find N Time: _____
Steps	Memory Address (Hexadecimal)	Instruction Byte 1	Byte 2	Byte 3	Opcode	Addressing Mode	Operand (Binary)	Description	
1	66	86	–	–	LDA A	Immediate		Load accumulator A	
	67	–	0A	–			0000 1010	Use data 0A₁₆	
2	68	C6	–	–	LDA B	Immediate		Load accumulator B	
	69	–	08	–			0000 1000	Use data 08₁₆	
3	6A	1B	–	–	ABA	Inherent		Add the contents of accumulators A and B	
4	6B	19	–	–	DAA	Inherent		Correct for bcd output	
5	6C	3E	–	–	HLT	Inherent		Stop all operations	

ful industrial operations. We have in this case tried to show only one simple problem that could be achieved by a microcomputer. The potential capabilities of this type of system are virtually unlimited. The type of microprocessor employed by a system and its unique instructional set are the primary factors that govern its operation in program planning.

QUESTIONS

1. Compare the functional differences between a central computer, a minicomputer, and a microcomputer system.

2. Explain what is meant by the terms *bit, byte, word*, and a *two-state number*.

3. What is the basic organizational pattern of a computer system?

4. What is meant by the terms *radix, place value, octal, binary, hexadecimal*, and *BCD?*

5. What does the ALU of a microprocessor do?

6. What is an accumulator and what function does it perform?

7. Describe the purpose of a data register.

8. What is the architecture of a microprocessor such as the MC6800?

9. Compare the basic differences between read/write and ROM chips.

10. Explain how data can be written into memory.

11. Explain how data can be read from a read/write memory.

12. What role does the address decoder play in a read/write memory unit?

13. Why is a read/write memory unit considered to be volatile?

14. How are data originally placed in a ROM?

15. How are data optically erased from a ROM?

16. What is an EAROM?

17. Why is timing an essential microcomputer function?

18. Explain the fetch and execute operations of a microcomputer.

19. What are the sequential steps of a read memory operation?

20. Explain how the write memory operation is achieved by sequential steps.

21. How are data transferred in a microcomputer system between I/O ports?

22. What is the purpose of the interrupt operation of the microcomputer system?

23. What is an instructional set for a microcomputer?

24. Explain the differences between:

    a. Inherent-mode instruction

    b. Immediate addressing

    c. Relative addressing

    d. Indexed addressing.

    e. Direct addressing

25. Plan a program that will add four numbers together.

12

Programmable
Controllers

For a number of years industrial control has been achieved by electromechanical devices such as relays, solenoid valves, motors, linear actuators, and timers. These devices were used to control large production machines where only switching operations were necessary. Most controllers were of the two-state type and were called on to simply turn the load device on or off. In addition, some basic logic functions could also be achieved. Production line sequencing operations were achieved by motor-driven drum controllers with timers. As a rule, nearly all electromagnetic controllers were hard-wired into the system and responded as permanent fixtures. Modification of the system was rather difficult to accomplish and somewhat expensive. In industries where production changes were frequent, this type of control was rather costly. It was, however, the best way and in many cases the only way that control could be effectively achieved with any degree of success.

In the late 1960s, solid-state devices and digital electronics began to appear in controllers. These innovations were primarily aimed at replacing the older electromechanical control devices. The transition to solid-state electronics has, however, been much more significant than expected. Solid-state electronic devices, digital logic ICs, and microprocessors have led to the development of programmable controllers (PCs). These devices have capabilities that far exceed the older relay controllers. Programmable controllers are extremely flexible, have reduced downtime when making changeovers, occupy very little space, and have improved operational efficiency.

Early PCs, like their electromagnetic relay counterparts, could only perform a limited number of logic functions. AND and OR functions were the extent to which logic could be performed. Today, PCs can perform a variety of computer calculations. In fact, the ability to do simple arithmetic calculations is the pri-

mary thing that distinguishes a PC from the electromagnetic controller. A PC can therefore be used to respond to numerical data such as size, weight, temperature, or pressure. For example, it can accept a temperature signal, multiply it by a constant, and print out the results in degrees Fahrenheit. The resulting control action can be retained in memory, recorded, displayed on a cathode-ray tube, or used to energize an alarm. PCs can also be equipped to solve problems involving mathematical functions such as sine, cosine, tangent, xy, square root, and logarithms. These calculations are important in energy management, process control, process modeling, real-time error correction, and production line control. PCs are extremely versatile and can be easily modified to meet the demands of a complex control situation.

In a programmable controller, instructions can be entered or changed without learning complex languages and routines. The operator only needs to have a good understanding of relay-type logic and its design. Relay symbols appear on a display when a key is depressed or the symbols may be inscribed on the buttons of a keyboard. System functions can be altered by simply depressing a few keys to change the logic sequence. In many cases, an entire system modification can be achieved without altering anything other than the keys of the controller unit. Once the system has been modified to meet a specific need, the program can be retained in memory and used when desired.

PROGRAMMABLE CONTROLLER SYSTEMS

The concept of a programmable controller is not particularly new in the systems approach that we have used in this text. The controller, for example, is primarily responsible for alter-

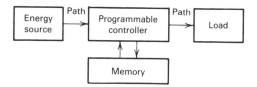

FIGURE 12–1
Programmable controller system.

ing a system so that it conforms with some desired operating function. A block diagram of a simplified programmable control system is shown in Figure 12–1. Note that the control function of the system is achieved entirely by the programmable controller. Programmable controllers, in general, are more complex than indicated by a single block. A programmable controller, for example, has several particular parts. Functionally, these are described as the input/output or I/O structure, the processor, the memory unit, the display unit, and the programmer. Figure 12–2 shows an expansion of the control block of a programmable controller to include these parts.

The block diagram of a programmable controller is very similar to that of a small computer. In fact, most programmable controllers are classified as dedicated computers. This type of unit is usually designed to perform a number of specific control functions in the operation of a machine or industrial process. The degree of sophistication or "power" of a pro-

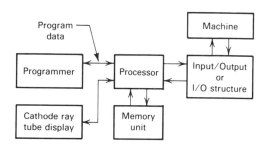

FIGURE 12–2
Programmable controller parts.

grammable controller is dependent on its application. Many PCs may respond as a computer terminal and interface with a mainframe computer. Other units may be completely independent and respond only to those things that are needed to control a specific machine operation. Figure 12–3 shows a representative programmable controller of the plug-in module type. Expansion of the unit is achieved by simply adding modules to the system.

Programmable Controller Components

A programmable controller is basically a software-based equivalent of the older electromagnetic relay control panel. Essentially, the PC is a flexible system that can be easily modified and still be used as a general-purpose control device. Most PCs can be programmed to con-

trol a variety of machine functions at one time. When a production change is necessitated, the program can be altered by a keyboard to make the system conform with the needed changes. The new control procedure may be entirely different from the original operating order. Figure 12–4 shows a rack-mounted programmable controller. This unit employs modular construction that permits it to be expanded to fit a variety of applications. The upper rack of this system houses the power supply. This particular unit has a standard power supply and a backup assembly in case of power failure. This assures continuous power to the system in the event the main power supply fails. The center rack of the assembly houses the central processing unit (CPU). It also has slot locations for interface modules and specific expansion of the CPU. The lower rack houses the I/O modules and has slot locations for additional expansion.

FIGURE 12–3
Programmable controller hardware.
(Courtesy of Industrial Solid State Controls, Inc.)

FIGURE 12–4
Rack-mounted programmable controller.
(Courtesy of Eagle Signal Co.)

The central processing unit or CPU is the nerve center of a programmable controller system. The unit shown in Figure 12–4 uses an INTEL 8080A microprocessor as its basic logic element. The 8080 microprocessor is an 8-bit IC. It has 16 address outputs accommodating a 64K address bus. The 8-bit data bus is bidirectional. This unit requires two clock signals and three separate power sources of −5, +5, and +12 V. Two or more machine cycles are needed for each instruction. Each machine cycle requires three or more clock periods to function. The CPU is housed in an independent module and located in the center rack of the assembly.

The arithmetic processing unit (APU) of the programmable controller unit of Figure 12–4 is housed in the center rack of the assembly. Number manipulation is accomplished by the APU. Basic arithmetic, logarithmic, and trigonometric functions are computed for both fixed and floating-point numbers. The APU generally delays CPU operations during the initializing sequence. After this, the APU functions on an independent basis. Note the location of this module in the center of the rack assembly. It is an independent module that provides for expansion of the PC assembly.

The center rack of the programmable controller of Figure 12–4 also houses the memory modules. In this particular PC, there is a choice of two basic expandable memory options. An ultraviolet erasable programmable read-only memory (UV-PROM) and a semiconductor random-access memory (RAM) are available in modules. Both types of memory can be intermixed in the rack assembly. Each memory word is 8 bits long and has 16K capacity per module. Memory can be expanded to 48K words with additional modules.

The data entry/display and push-button modules of the programmable controller of Figure 12–4 are also housed in the center rack of the assembly. Figure 12–5 shows a close-up

view of these modules. The push-button module permits front panel control of variable data through a keyboard assembly. These data are then displayed on a four and a half-digit readout with a decimal point and a plus/minus indicator, as well as an eight-symbol annunciator panel that indicates the units being monitored. The push-button module also has four independent control buttons. These buttons may be assigned or identified with a variable function such as timer control, parts count, or temperature. Peripheral interface modules may also be included with the push-button assembly. A broad selection of interface possibilities can be achieved. Sixteen different interfaces are available that will permit the PC to accommodate printers, teletype, color or monochrome CRT terminals, cassette tape loading, telephone (modem) input, diskette drive, and multicomputer interconnections. As a rule, each interface possibility is achieved by an independent module.

FIGURE 12–5
Data entry–display module of a programmable controller. (Courtesy of Eagle Signal Co.)

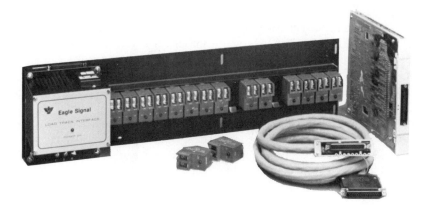

(A) Single track programmable
controller unit.

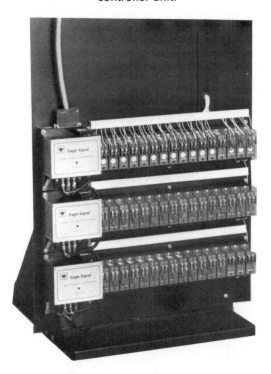

(B) Multiple track programmable
controller unit.

FIGURE 12–6
**Track-mounting programmable controller
units. (Courtesy of Eagle Signal Co.)**

Further expansion of the PC of Figure 12–4 can be achieved by using an alternate track-mounted assembly. Figure 12–6 shows two versions of the track assembly. Sixteen individual optically isolated I/O modules can be connected to one track. If additional expansion is needed, other track units can be ganged together on a common frame. The three-track assembly shows this alternative. Expansion through the use of track units permits this system to accommodate up to 2048 input/output units. Each track necessitates a drive module interface. This module is located on the left side of the track assembly.

The input/output (I/O) of the PC of Figure 12–4 is generally achieved by plug-in modules. These modules are housed on the lower rack of the assembly. An output module may be a solid-state relay, electromechanical relay, timer, or power transistor. This type of construction eliminates the hard-wired circuit problem and reduces interfacing between the system and the load. The output module essentially makes a direct connection between the PC and the load device. Input modules, by comparison, are designed to interface signals with the PC. These modules appear the same as an output module in the assembly. The circuitry of an input module is, however, design-

FIGURE 12–7
Portable industrial CRT terminal. (Courtesy of
Industrial Solid State Controls, Inc.)

ed to accommodate such things as an RTD, thermocouples, light sensors, and practically any type of analog input signal.

Communication with a programmable controller may be achieved with an external CRT terminal. This type of unit may be housed in a ruggedized case, which can be easily moved to the work site where a controller is located. This type of unit must be designed for operation in harsh industrial environments. It is suited for locations where electromagnetic noise, high temperature, humidity, and mechanical shock are prevalent. Figure 12–7 shows a portable industrial CRT terminal. When the environment is not too harsh, a standard CRT terminal may be used to program the PC. Figure 12–8 shows two conventional CRT terminals. The terminal on the right has built-in dual cassette drives. The terminal on the left has a larger CRT and a double-density, dual

FIGURE 12–8
CRT terminals. (Courtesy of Eagle Signal Co.)

diskette drive subsystem. Both types of terminals can be effectively used to program information into the PC. CRT terminals connect directly to the PC and provide a method of programming information into the processor.

Mini-Programmable Controller Systems

Recent improvements in large-scale integration IC manufacturing and power transistor manufacturing technology are responsible for the development of mini-PCs. These systems can be used economically to control simple machine operations and numerous manufacturing processes. A number of companies are now producing mini-PCs. Figure 12–9 shows a representative mini-PC.

Mini-PCs are classified as systems that can economically replace as few as four relays in a control application. They are capable of providing timer and counter functions, as well as relay logic, and are small enough to fit into a standard 19-in. rack assembly. Most systems of this type have less than 32 I/O ports or modules. Some units can be expanded to drive up to 400 I/O devices. Typically, the I/O of this type of system responds to digital signals. Some units have the capability of responding to analog information. This makes it possible for the system to respond to temperature, pressure, flow, level, light, weight, and practically any analog process control application.

Mini-PCs, in general, can achieve the same control functions as the larger programmable controller only on a smaller basis. Mini-PCs are usually smaller, less expensive, simpler to use, and rather efficient devices compared with mainframe programmable controllers. Mini-units are just now beginning to make their way into the PC field. In the future, these systems will obviously play a greater role in the control of industrial electronic systems.

PROGRAMMING THE PC

Instructions for the operation of a programmable controller are given to the PC through push buttons, a keyboard programmer, magnetic

FIGURE 12–9
**Mini-programmable controller. (Courtesy of
Eagle Signal Co.)**

disks, or cassette tape. Each PC has a special set of instructions and procedures to make it functional. How the PC performs is based on the design of its programming procedure. In general, PCs can be programmed by relay ladder diagrams, logic diagrams, and Boolean equations. These procedures can be expressed as language words or as symbolic expressions on a CRT display. One manufacturer describes these methods of programming as *assembly language* and *relay language*. Assembly language is generally used by the microprocessor of the system. Relay language is a symbolic logic system that employs the relay ladder diagram as a method of programming. This method of programming relies heavily on relay symbols instead of words and letter designations.

Assembly Language

Assembly language is a basic instructional set that is based on the microprocessor used in the construction of the PC. For the Intel 8080 microprocessor, the assembly language program is a combination of mnemonics and labels that the programmer uses to solve a control problem. If the system is programmed directly with binary numbers, the programmer will probably use a lookup table to write the program in assembly language. It is usually easier to keep track of loops and variables in an assembly language. It is also easier for someone else to look at the program when they are trying to see how it works. Ultimately, the programmer must type the coded information into the computer in binary form. This generally means that an assembly language program needs to be translated into binary data before it can be entered. This can be done by laboriously writing down each mnemonic and label line by line and then entering the translation into memory. A convenient alternative to this procedure is to

have a program that takes lines of assembly language as its input and does the translation for the programmer automatically. A program called *assembler* functionally does this operation. It actually puts together the operational codes and addresses that take the place of mnemonics and labels. When the procedure is complete, the assembler has a duplicate of the assembly language in the machine language of the microprocessor. These data can then be entered by the programmer manually, but they are generally applied directly to the input since it is in memory when the translation is completed.

For the Intel 8080 microprocessor, assembly language incorporates bit and byte I/O modes and provides the user with a number of special functions for system control. It has 244 instructions with one to three bytes of code per instruction (one byte of operand and zero to two bytes of data). Executions of the code range from 2 to 9 μs, with 4 μs being a typical execution time. Some sample instructions are as follows:

> LAL   Load the accumulator with the content of the L register.
>
> AD   Add 1 to the contents of the accumulator and store the result in the accumulator.
>
> LLE   Load the L register with the contents of the E register.

Assembly language is generally considered to be a low-level language. It is very efficient with respect to the amount of memory needed and execution time required. It is also somewhat difficult to use and debug unless the programmer is very adept at programming or works with the language on a frequent basis. As a rule, the other languages used by a PC are variations or developments of the assembly language.

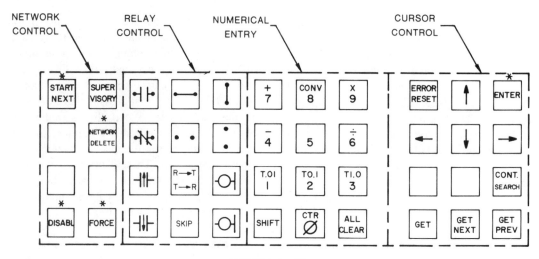

FIGURE 12–10
Layout of a relay logic PC keyboard.
(Courtesy of Gould/Modicon Division)

Relay Language or Logic _____

The processor of a programmable controller dictates the language and programming procedure to be followed by the system. Essentially, it is capable of doing arithmetic and logic functions. It can also store and handle data and continuously monitor the status of its input and output signals. The resulting output being controlled is based on the response of the signal information being handled by the system. The processor is generally programmed by a keyboard panel, program panel, or CRT terminal. Figure 12–10 shows the layout of a relay logic PC keyboard. Note that it has network control, relay control, and a numerical entry section.

In a relay language system, the basic element of programming is the relay contact. This contact may be normally open (NO) or normally closed (NC). Figure 12–11 shows the symbolic expression of these contacts. Note that the normally open contacts are on the left and the normally closed contacts are on the right. The line on the right side of the two

lower contacts is for connection to branch circuits. This is generally an optional circuit possibility. Below each contact is a four-digit reference number. This number is used to identify specific contacts being used in the system. The contact is then connected in either series or parallel to form a horizontal rung of the relay ladder diagram.

Figure 12–12 shows the programming format of a relay ladder used by one PC manufac-

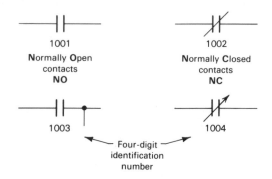

FIGURE 12–11
Programming format of relay contacts.

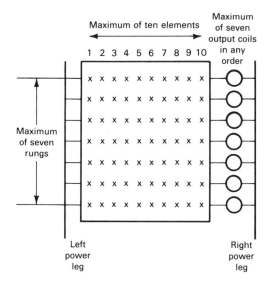

Maximum of ten elements

Maximum of seven output coils in any order

1 2 3 4 5 6 7 8 9 10

Maximum of seven rungs

Left power leg

Right power leg

FIGURE 12–12
Relay ladder programming format.

turer. This specific format allows for up to 10 elements in each horizontal rung and up to 7 rungs per network. In the makeup of the network, power flow is only from left to right. The operating sequence occurs vertically from top to bottom. It can be recycled from the bottom back to the top in loop operations.

Once a relay program has been entered into the PC, it may be monitored on the CRT and modified by a keystroke. Monitoring the operation of a program is achieved by illuminating the current path by making it brighter than the remainder of the circuit components. Modification of the diagram can be achieved by simply placing the cursor of the CRT on the device to be altered and making the change with a keystroke. Cursor control is achieved by manipulation of the four arrow keys on the right of the keyboard. Contact status can be changed or bypassed and different outputs can be turned on or off by this procedure. Each input or output has a four-digit number that can be altered

by the numerical data entry part of the keyboard.

All the control components of a PC are identified by a numbering system. As a rule, each manufacturer has a unique set of component numbers for its system. One manufacturer has a four-digit numbering system for referencing components. The numbers are divided into discrete component references and register references. A discrete component is used to achieve on and off control operations. Limit switches, push buttons, relay contacts, motor starters, relay coils, solenoid valves, and solid-state devices are examples of discrete component references. Registers are used to store some form of numerical data or information. Timing counts, number counts, and arithmetic data may be stored in register devices. All component references and register references are identified by a numbering system. Each manufacturer has a particular way of identifying system components.

Each I/O module of a programmable controller has a distinct reference number or address to identify its location in the system. Figure 12–13 defines the exact reference of each I/O module installed in a specific channel. The second channel would have its address locations increased by a factor of 128. The same holds true for channels 3 and 4. Notice that the outputs are identified by a number beginning with a zero. Inputs are identified by a number beginning with a one. The identity of each specific I/O device is extremely important in the programming procedure. These numbers cannot be altered or used more than once to achieve control of a specific I/O.

Assume now that a relay diagram has been placed into the PC by selection of the proper number data entries and symbol selections. The PC must examine this network and solve the interconnected logic elements in their numerical sequence. In doing this, network 1 must be solved first, then network 2, 3, and 4

I/O REFERENCE CONFIGURATION

Module Number (Top to Bottom)	Circuit Number	CHANNEL ONE HOUSING NUMBER							
		ONE		TWO		THREE		FOUR	
		Output	Input	Output	Input	Output	Input	Output	Input
1	1	0001	1001	0033	1033	0065	1065	0097	1097
	2	0002	1002	0034	1034	0066	1066	0098	1098
	3	0003	1003	0035	1035	0067	1067	0099	1099
	4	0004	1004	0036	1036	0068	1068	0100	1100
2	1	0005	1005	0037	1037	0069	1069	0101	1101
	2	0006	1006	0038	1038	0070	1070	0102	1102
	3	0007	1007	0039	1039	0071	1071	0103	1103
	4	0008	1008	0040	1040	0072	1072	0104	1104
3	1	0009	1009	0041	1041	0073	1073	0105	1105
	2	0010	1010	0042	1042	0074	1074	0106	1106
	3	0011	1011	0043	1043	0075	1075	0107	1107
	4	0012	1012	0044	1044	0076	1076	0108	1108
4	1	0013	1013	0045	1045	0077	1077	0109	1109
	2	0014	1014	0046	1046	0078	1078	0110	1110
	3	0015	1015	0047	1047	0079	1079	0111	1111
	4	0016	1016	0048	1048	0080	1080	0112	1112
5	1	0017	1017	0049	1049	0081	1081	0113	1113
	2	0018	1018	0050	1050	0082	1082	0114	1114
	3	0019	1019	0051	1051	0083	1083	0115	1115
	4	0020	1020	0052	1052	0084	1084	0116	1116
6	1	0021	1021	0053	1053	0085	1085	0117	1117
	2	0022	1022	0054	1054	0086	1086	0118	1118
	3	0023	1023	0055	1055	0087	1087	0119	1119
	4	0024	1024	0056	1056	0088	1088	0120	1120
7	1	0025	1025	0057	1057	0089	1089	0121	1121
	2	0026	1026	0058	1058	0090	1090	0122	1122
	3	0027	1027	0059	1059	0091	1091	0123	1123
	4	0028	1028	0060	1060	0092	1092	0124	1124
8	1	0029	1029	0061	1061	0093	1093	0125	1125
	2	0030	1030	0062	1062	0094	1094	0126	1126
	3	0031	1031	0063	1063	0095	1095	0127	1127
	4	0032	1032	0064	1064	0096	1096	0128	1128

FIGURE 12–13
Input/output reference assignments of a PC.
(Courtesy of Gould/Modicon Division)

until the sequence is solved. The solving of each network is achieved by a scanning process. Essentially, scanning is achieved by a series of pulses that occur at a high rate. Each pulse must pass through the network following the proper sequence. Scanning occurs in the system the instant power is applied to the processor and continues as long as it remains energized. This permits each network to be solved from the left rail to the right rail and from the top to the bottom.

In most PCs, scanning occurs at a very rapid rate. In general, it occurs so rapidly that it appears to solve the logic steps instantly. The result of this action is that each network is immediately avialable to all subsequent net-

works regardless of whether there is a change in its status or a change in numerical value. This assures that each network is solved in the correct order of its numerical step number and not by the numerical value assigned to a specific coil or contact.

Programming Basics

Programmable controllers are provided with the capability to program or simulate the function of relays, timers, and counters. Programming is achieved on a format of up to 10 elements in each horizontal row or rung of a relay diagram, and up to 7 of these rungs connected to form a network. A network can be as simple as a single rung or a combination of several rungs as long as there is some interconnection between the elements of each rung. The left rail of the ladder can be the common connecting element. Each network can have up to seven coils connected in any order to the right rail of the ladder. These coils can be assigned any valid number for identification. The coil number can only be used once in the operational sequence. The quantity of discrete de-

vices and registers available for use depends on the power or capacity of the system.

When programming a relay ladder diagram into a PC, the discrete devices and registers are placed in the component format of Figure 12–12. Each component in this case is assigned a four-digit identification number. The specific reference number depends on the memory size of the system. In a low-capacity system, number assignments could be 0001 to 0064 for output coils and 0258 to 0320 for internal coils. A system with a larger capacity might use number assignments of 0001 to 0256 for output coils and 0258 to 0512 for internal coils. Any coil output or internal coil can only be used once in the system. References to contacts controlled by a specific coil can be used as many times as needed to complete the control operation. Output coils that are not used to drive a specific load can be used internally in the programming procedure.

When programming the response of a particular input module, it may be identified as a relay contact. In this regard, the symbol may be a normally closed (NC) contact or a normally open (NO) contact. The coil or actuating member of the contact takes on the same numbering assignment. The coil, however, is identified as a circle on the diagram and the contacts are identified by the standard contact symbol. Figure 12–14 shows some examples of the symbol identification procedure. The number designation is used to identify specific devices and contacts. The contacts can be programmed to achieve either the NO or NC condition according to their intended functions.

Any external input that is considered to be normally closed, such as a safety switch, overload switch, or stop push button, must be treated differently. An external NC push button, for example, would not be entered on the CRT as closed contacts. It would produce the opposite effect internally from that of a NO contact. Inverting the external contact func-

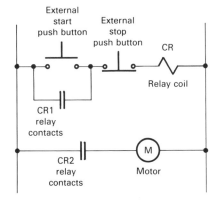

FIGURE 12–14
Relay ladder diagram symbols.

tion, as well as its signal, constitutes a double-inversion operation. It is for this reason that all normally closed external contacts or switches are programmed as normally open on the CRT.

Assume now that the simple start–stop motor controller of Figure 12–14 is to be connected by a programmable controller. The start and stop buttons are located externally. Pushing the start button energizes the relay coil. This action latches the relay coil by closing contacts CR1 across the start button. Contacts CR2 close at the same time, completing the energy path to the motor, thus causing it to run. The motor continues to run as long as energy is supplied from the source. Pushing the stop button turns off the motor and removes the latch from the start button.

A programmable controller equivalent of the motor starter of Figure 12–14 is shown in Figure 12–15. The number assignments refer to the specific components of the PC. Input devices are numbered 1001 and 1002. This includes the input module and its resulting switching operation. The output device is numbered 0049. The start and stop buttons are externally connected and do not have a module

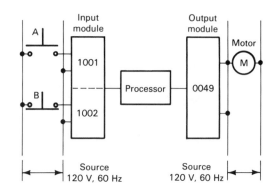

FIGURE 12–16
Actual PC circuit of a motor controller.

number assignment. Operation of the PC equivalent circuit will achieve the same control procedure as the original relay ladder diagram.

The actual PC circuit for a motor start–stop control operation is shown in Figure 12–16. This diagram shows how the I/O modules are interfaced with the microprocessor. Note that the input modules and output modules are treated as independent parts of the system that are controlled by the microprocessor. This circuit would be displayed on the CRT and could be modified with a few simple keystrokes. The PC equivalent is somewhat more complex than its ladder diagram equivalent. It is, however, more versatile and can be modified very quickly by a program change. Programming is simply a process of entering the appropriate component number assignment and then designating the function to be achieved by each component. The procedure can then be placed in memory and retained for future use or used immediately according to the needs of the system.

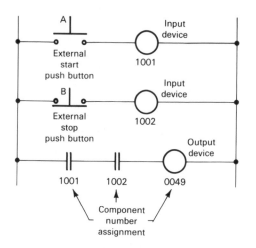

FIGURE 12–15
PC equivalent of a motor starter circuit.

Timing Function

Timing is frequently used as a control function in the operation of a programmable controller. A PC can be easily modified and programmed

to achieve the timing function. The timer is a register device that can be placed anywhere in a network where sufficient space exists. More than one timer can be placed in the network if the need arises. Timers are represented as a block in a ladder diagram and have a rectangular shape when they are displayed on a CRT. Two elements are included in the makeup of the timer. One element is used to store the preset time, and the second element is used to keep track of the elapsed time. Together these two functions can be used to achieve the timing function.

Figure 12–17 shows a representation of the timer format. Note that there are two entry points to the timer on the left. The upper point determines when the unit accumulates time and the lower point determines when the unit resets to zero. Essentially, the timer is enabled when the lower input receives power and resets when no power is available. The upper input, or set element, is responsible for a preset value that limits the maximum time capability of the unit. This preset value is determined by a three-digit setting of 0001 to 0999. This can be used to represent time as 999 in seconds, 99.9 in

tenths of a second, or as 9.99 in hundredths of a second. The time function can never exceed its preset value. The lower input or reset element refers to a storage location within the makeup of the controller where actual time can be stored. In the center of the timer block is a number designation preceded by the letter T. This denotes the time rate by which the timer has been programmed to respond. The designation $T1.0 =$ seconds, $T0.1 =$ tenths of seconds, and $T.01 =$ hundredths of a second. The lower number designation of the timer denotes the storage register reference number. One manufacturer has this number preceded by a 4 and followed by three digits. The final three digits continue consecutively to the maximum number of the memory size that can be used.

The right side of the timer block of Figure 12–17 indicates where the logical output is available. These two outputs provide power to coils, shunts, contacts, or solid-state devices that appear on the right of the timer. The upper output has power only when the timer is at its preset value. This output is de-energized or stops providing power when the reset is not receiving power. When the output is energized, the timer stops and there is no further accumulation of time beyond the preset value. The lower or NOT output is an inversion or negation of the upper output terminal. The NOT output stops providing power only when the timer is at its preset value.

A timer is enabled when the lower input or reset lead receives power. This action causes an accumulation of time whenever the control input receives power. The control signal can be turned *on, off,* or *on* as many times as necessary, and the unit will determine how long the signal was on up to the preset value. Each time the control lead is re-energized, time begins to accumulate from the previous value held in storage, regardless of how long the signal was in the off state. Thus the timer has a

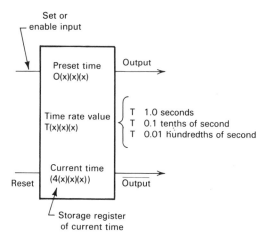

FIGURE 12–17
Timer format of a PC.

cumulative function. It can be reset by the lower-left input and is completely retentive in the event of a power failure. Whenever the reset signal is removed, the timer returns to zero and holds this state until the reset is re-energized.

Figure 12–18 shows one of the possible timing combinations that can be achieved with a programmable controller. The contact numbers, time rate, storage reference number, and output coil designations are only used by one manufacturer. The preset time in this case is 10 s, as indicated by the number 0010 in the timer block. Output coil 0025 will be energized and coil 0026 will be de-energized if NO contacts 1001 have been closed for a total of 10 s provided that contacts 1002 remain closed. The elapsed time of operation is stored in register 4003. This represents the delay-on function for output 0025.

Sequencing Operations

Sequencing is a control operation that a programmable controller is frequently called on to perform. A sequencer responds the same as a stepping relay that actuates a load device in each of its stepping positions. This application is widely used in automatic assembly operations and in production line control applica-

tions. Each PC manufacturer has a unique way of identifying the operation, its location in memory, the actuating procedure, and the numbering of its components. In general terms, a sequencer is represented as a block in ladder diagrams and as a rectangle when displayed on a CRT.

Figure 12–19 shows a rather common way of representing sequencer operation in its programming format. The block in this case achieves the sequencing operation. The number of steps being controlled is indicated by the top four-digit number. In this sequencer, the number 0006 indicates six steps. In general, sequencers can achieve up to 0032 steps. This number can be altered by simply programming the desired number of steps into the sequencer by data-entry keystrokes.

The sequencer is essentially a counting register. Its counting information is stored in a specific register. The sequencing register of Figure 12–19 is identified by a four-digit number. In this case, the number is 4053. The least significant digit is used to identify a specific sequencing register series. Control of a se-

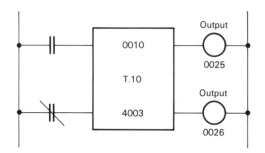

FIGURE 12–18
Timing circuit.

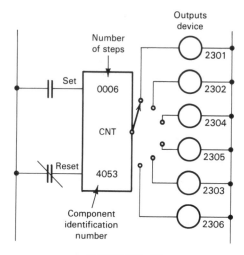

FIGURE 12–19
Sequencing circuit.

quencer is similar to that of other registers. It has two inputs that are identified as set and reset. Each time the set input is energized, the value of the register is incremented by a count of 1. This is the equivalent of moving a stepper relay one step or position. When three steps are achieved, it actuates the third output device. In this case, a four-digit numbering system is used to identify the output device. Output device 2503 would be actuated by the third input step. Notice that the output of the sequencing register is attached to six independent output devices.

When the reset input of a sequencer is energized, the stepping count goes to zero and the sequence returns to its starting position. This is not dependent on the location of its present count or step position. The sequencer will not energize any of the outputs during the transition period.

Each sequencer responds in a completely independent manner since it is controlled by separate register values. Sequencer references can be used as often as necessary in a PC circuit and may appear anywhere that a relay contact may be appropriate. By using calculated logic, it is possible to get the sequencer to skip steps, advance forward, or move backward according to some prescribed procedure. Intermediate references are not energized during this unusual procedure. Sequencers are updated as soon as a change is made in the content of a sequence register. One independent network can be used to drive a sequencer and a second network can be used to update the most recent value changes. Sequencers in general cannot be used on transitional contacts in PC control applications.

Arithmetic Functions

In addition to the normal relay functions, a programmable controller is capable of several data-manipulation functions. These functions

are capable of achieving some arithmetic operations. An arithmetic operation has three elements, usually registers, placed vertically one above the other in a block or rectangular-shaped box. The top and middle elements can be either a fixed or three-digit variable value not exceeding a maximum of 0999. The bottom element is a holding register. The registers are all assigned reference numbers for identification. A particular number assignment would vary between different manufacturers. In this explanation the numbers used have been developed by the manufacturer of one PC system. They would be different when applied to a system made by a different manufacturer. We are only using the number assignments here to serve as general identification of the particular registers being discussed.

Figure 12–20 shows the programming format of an arithmetic element. The upper element represents data or the numerical content of a register. This normally has a register identification number where its content is stored. The enable input on the left side of the block is used to achieve control of the function. The middle element is usually the same as the upper element. It represents data entry or the contents of data stored in a register. It is usu-

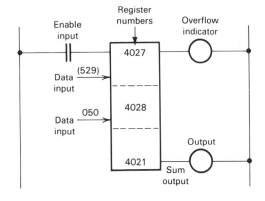

FIGURE 12–20
Arithmetic format.

ally identified by a different numbering sequence to distinguish it from the upper register. The lower element is a holding register that derives its data from the upper two registers. These data can be the sum, difference, product, or quotient of the data in the upper two registers. The arithmetic function of the unit determines the data value that appears in the lower register. Each arithmetic unit has up to three output possibilities depending on the function of the unit. These appear on the right side of the block. The outputs are updated after each scan of the enable input. Organization of the data and how it is manipulated is a programmable function that can be altered by a keystroke operation of the programming unit.

Addition

The addition function is achieved by adding the contents of the upper register to the contents of the middle register and placing the sum in the holding register. The upper and middle registers can be fixed or variable values from 000 to 999. In the addition function, gen-

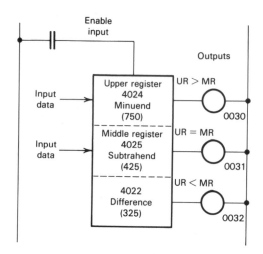

FIGURE 12–21
Subtraction format.

erally only one output is developed. This is used to represent the content of the holding register. In most units, the result of the addition function cannot be greater than the three-digit number 999. Values greater than this will only indicate the three least significant digits. In some cases, an overflow indication will appear when the sum is greater than 999. The overflow may be stored in a separate register, with the three least significant digits stored in another register.

Figure 12–20 shows an example of the addition function and some representative identification numbers used in a programmable controller. The four-digit numbers are register identification numbers. The numbers in brackets are the data values to be added and the sum of the two values. In this case, the sum is less than 999, so the overflow indicator is not actuated. The addition function, in this example, is updated each time that the system is scanned when the enable input is in its active or on state. The addition function of a programmable controller is generally limited to rather small number values. This is purposely done so that the function can be achieved with a small number of electronic components.

Subtraction

The subtraction function of a programmable controller is achieved by the same type of circuitry as that of the addition function. The difference between the two functions is the data value placed in the holding register. In the adder, the sum of the top and middle register is placed in the holding register. In a subtractor, the difference between the upper and middle register is placed in the holding register. In addition, a subtractor generally has three output conditions. The upper output passes power to the load when the upper register is greater than the middle register. The middle output passes

power to the load when the upper and middle registers are equal. The lower output is actuated when the upper register is less than the middle register. The three outputs can be selected or used according to the demands of the control function being utilized.

Figure 12–21 shows an example of the subtraction function and some of the component numbers that can be identified with the programming procedure. When the enable input is energized, it causes data stored in the respective registers to be applied to the subtractor unit. Notice that each register is identified by a four-digit number. The bracketed numbers represent data that appear at each register. Respective outputs are represented by four-digit numbers of the 0030 series. With the indicated data applied, output coil 0030 would be energized because the upper register is greater than the middle register. The data value placed in the holding register is the actual difference between the upper and middle registers. The subtraction function occurs and is updated each time that the enable input is scanned. This takes place very rapidly, and the entire process appears to be functioning on a continuous basis. The largest data number that can appear at any of the three registers is 999.

Multiplication

The multiplication function of a programmable controller is very similar to that of the other arithmetic functions. Three registers are involved in the function. This function has data applied to the upper and middle registers. The product of the two register values appears in the holding register. As a rule, the holding register is divided into two sections that accommodate the numbers 999 and 999. The three least significant digits are considered to be low-order values. The three most significant digits are considered to be high-order values.

The combined high- and low-order values permit a six-digit value to be produced as the product of the two registers. The product is an actual data value that is placed in a combination holding register. A multiplier generally has only one output. This indicates when the multiplication process is being performed by the assembly.

Figure 12–22 shows the multiplication programming format of a programmable controller. Four-digit numbers are used to identify the specific registers involved in this function. The enable input is actuated by contacts 1018. Each time that the enable input is energized, it causes the multiplication function to be performed and updated with each scanning cycle. In general, this function appears to take place instantly and occurs on a continuous basis. The bracketed numbers are representative of the data applied to each register. Note that the upper register is 250 and the middle register is 125. The product is 031 250 and divided between two registers. The multiplication output can be used if the system requirements demand some indication that the function is being per-

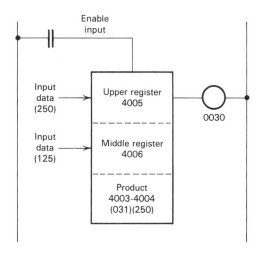

FIGURE 12–22
Multiplier format.

formed. The product of the two values appears as an actual data value.

Division

The division function of a programmable controller is similar to that of the multiplication function. The holding register indicates the quotient of the two numbers appearing in the upper and middle registers. The data value of the upper register is the dividend and the middle register is the divisor. The dividend is divided by the divisor and the quotient appears in the holding register. The dividend generally takes two consecutive registers to accommodate its value. Data values of up to 999,999 can be used as the dividend. The divisor and quotient utilize a single register with a maximum value of 999. A divider generally has three outputs. These indicate when the division operation is successful, if the quotient is greater the 999, and a divide by zero indication.

The programming format of a divider is shown in Figure 12–23. The four-digit num-

bers are used to identify the register. Registers 4005 and 4006 form the upper register or dividend. Register 4008 serves as the divisor and 4030 is the quotient. The bracketed numbers are representative of the data being manipulated by the divider. In this case, 002 750/50 = 55. The dividend is held in two consecutive registers. Output 0030 would be energized by this operation, indicating that the division function has been successfully performed. The quotient appears in register 4030 as an actual data value. The entire operation can be performed only when the enable input is energized. When enabled, the operaton is performed on a continuous basis and appears to take place instantly. Only a limited value of division can be achieved by a programmable controller.

Move Function

The transfer of data between different registers in a programmable controller is described as the move function. Essentially, data in an input or holding register can be transferred or moved to another holding register within the controller through this function. The data are not altered during the transferring operation. Moving takes place very quickly because it is initiated by the scanning signal.

Two types of moving are achieved by a programmable controller: register to table and table to register. The format of the move function is primarily the same for both operations. A table is a group of consecutive registers all holding data. Moving the data of a table is achieved by a pointer register. The pointer identifies each register of the table and causes its data to be transferred during the scanning operation. The table data are not altered during the transfer operation. The data at the new location are destroyed and replaced with new data from the table.

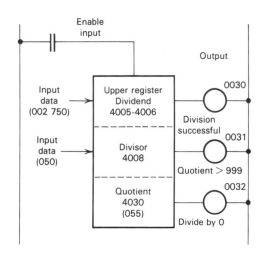

FIGURE 12–23
Divider format.

Figure 12–24 shows symbolic representations of the move function. When a scan pulse arrives at the set input, it enables the function. The contents of the register at location 4003 are transferred to the output. The lower register, identified as 4004, is used as the pointer. Its content determines the transfer location of the data moved from register 4003. Through this procedure, the content of a register can be transferred to a table or the content of a table can be transferred to a register. The letter designation R-T denotes register to table, and T-R refers to the table-to-register moving function.

Conversion

The conversion function of a programmable controller is used to change BCD data into binary form. This permits a variety of different devices to be connected to discrete input/output modules. Each input module, having four circuits, is capable of interfacing one BCD digit. Up to three consecutive modules are combined to provide coverage of numbers from 000 to 999 for a single register. Each data value will be converted and applied to or from the I/O module during a scanning cycle.

Figure 12–25 shows the general format of a converter. Assume in this application that the output of the digital meter is in BCD form. The BCD value of 357 is shown being applied to the input register. Each of the three BCD values is represented by a combination of four output lines. These lines are connected to an input module that has four lines for each input digit. The input module is divided into three sections according to digital values. When an enable signal is applied to the set input, it

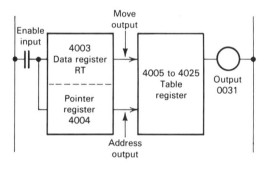

(A)   Register to table moving.

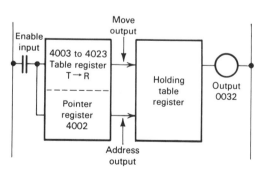

(B)   Table to register moving.

FIGURE 12–24
Data-moving function.

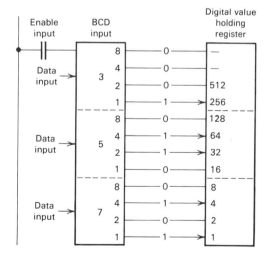

FIGURE 12–25
BCD-to-digital converter format.

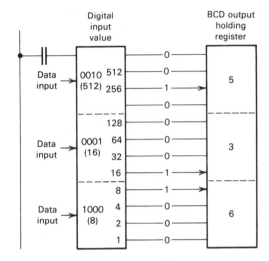

FIGURE 12–26
Digital-to-BCD converter format.

causes the BCD value of the input register to be applied to the digital ranked values of the corresponding input holding register. The binary equivalent is 0001–0110–0101. This digital value is then placed in the holding register for storage.

Conversion is also used to change digital data into BCD data to actuate an output device such as a meter or LED display. The conversion process is the reverse of the input conversion function of Figure 12–25. Figure 12–26 shows the format of an output converter. In this situation, the input is a digital signal that is divided into three sections of four lines each that represent the digital value of 0010–0001–1000. This input signal generally comes from a holding register. When an enable input signal is applied, it causes the digital signal to be transferred to three consecutive connected holding registers. The resulting output is the BCD equivalent or 536, which is the original digital input value. Conversion of this type is used to interface the PC with an instrument that has a digital display or response.

QUESTIONS

1. What are the fundamental parts of a programmable controller?

2. Explain the function of each fundamental part of a programmable controller?

3. What is meant by the expression, "a PC is a software-based control unit"?

4. What is a mini-PC and how does it differ from a full-scale PC?

5. What is the meaning of the expression *assembly language?*

6. How does the relay language of a PC differ from other general programming languages?

7. What are some of the programming basics that must be taken into account when using relay language to program a PC?

8. How is the timing function of a programmable controller achieved?

9. What is sequencing, and how is it achieved in a programmable controller?

10. Arithmetic functions achieved by a PC have a number of common features. What are they?

11. How is adding achieved in a programmable controller?

12. How is the subtracting function achieved in a PC?

13. What things distinguish multiplication from other arithmetic functions in a programmable controller?

14. How is division achieved in a programmable controller?

15. What is the purpose of the move function of a PC?

16. How is the conversion function of a PC achieved and what is the difference between input and output conversion?

PROBLEMS

1. Assume that a programmable controller is used to control the operation of an ac motor. A start push button, stop push button, and overload protection device are used in the control procedure. The start push button is latched by relay contacts when it is actuated. Draw a relay ladder diagram that would exemplify the operation of this type of circuit.

2. A sequencing operation is needed for an automatic assembly procedure. The sequence has six devices that will be placed into operation in order from 1 to 6. The sequence is then repeated in the same order. Explain how this can be achieved by the sequencer of a PC. Draw a ladder diagram that will achieve this operation.

3. A time-delay operation is needed for the control of an industrial process. This function involves a set of contacts to energize the timer, which has its output connected to a device that will be actuated 10 s after the contactor has been actuated. Draw a ladder diagram that will achieve this function. Explain how the circuit configuration responds.

4. An industrial control application calls for the addition of two number values of 202 and 18. The process is controlled by one enable input switch. The sum of the function appears in the output of the adder. Draw a ladder diagram that would achieve this function. Explain the operation of the circuit as if it were used in a programmable controller.

5. An industrial control application calls for the subtraction of two data values of 325 and 120. The subtractor is controlled by a single enable contact. When data enter the subtractor, its output should indicate when the value being subtracted (subtrahend) is greater than the number from which it is being subtracted (minuend). The output should also indicate when the two values are equal and when the minuend is greater than the subtrahend. Each of these three indicators should be connected to an independent output. Draw a ladder diagram that shows the format needed to achieve this function.

ACTIVITIES

The activities described in the following material require an operational programmable controller in order to be performed. A variety of PCs are commercially available through different manufacturing concerns. The specific PC being used will obviously have unique hardware and software operational procedures. It is recommended that the manufacturer's training manuals and programming material be reviewed before using the unit to achieve these functions. The activities presented here are in general terms and can be adapted to conform to any available PCs. The output of the PC can be connected to lamps, motors, solenoid valves, and a variety of devices to simulate the function of a system load.

ACTIVITY 12–1: PC Programming Panel Familiarization

Objective: To become familiar with the front or programming panel of a programming controller.

Procedure:

1. Attach the programming panel to the PC and connect a variety of load devices to several selected outputs.

2. Energize the system.

3. There should be features described as network control, relay control, and numerical entry on the panel. If a CRT or liquid-crystal display is included with the unit, the program panel will have some type of cursor control section.

4. Describe the layout of the control panel of your PC.

ACTIVITY 12–2: Identification of PC Components

Objective: To familiarize the user with the location of specific PC components and their identification procedure.

Procedure:

1. This activity is primarily directed toward physical component location in a functioning programmable controller.

2. With the aid of the manufacturer's operational manual, locate the position of the following hardware components:

   a. Controller or microprocessor unit

   b. Input devices and the number included in the system

   c. Output devices and the number included in the system

   d. Input/output registers and the type available in the unit

   e. Peripheral equipment included with the unit

   f. Memory unit and its capacity

3. With the aid of the manufacturer's opera-

tional manual, explain the component addressing procedure. Generally, a number or letter sequence is assigned to each series of components. Outline the address assignments of the PC being used.

ACTIVITY 12–3: Programming Procedure

Objective: To investigate the general programming procedure of a PC.

Procedure:

1. It is assumed that the PC is properly connected to an energy source and the components are attached to the appropriate distribution rails. A variety of electrical devices should be connected to the system to simulate the response of the loads.

2. The operating procedure of each PC will obviously vary a great deal between different systems. Review the manufacturer's programming manual and briefly summarize the procedure for starting a relay network. A network is the equivalent of a rung in the ladder diagram. This should include such things as the starting procedure, display response, address assignments, and entering data into the network.

3. Develop a programming procedure that will implement a simple relay network that has one contact, one output coil, and a two-state condition of operation.

ACTIVITY 12–4: Relay Network Programming

Objective: To program a relay network for the operation of a programmable controller.

Procedure:

1. Using the appropriate programming procedure outlined for your system, develop a control circuit for the motor controller of Figure 12–14.

2. If the system being used has a display, make a sketch of the diagram shown on the display.

3. Test the operation of the ladder diagram to see if it achieves the desired level of control.

ACTIVITY 12–5: Component Programming

Objective: To program a variety of register devices into a PC system and test the operation of the system.

Procedure:

1. Using the programming procedure for your system, develop diagrams that will permit the inclusion of the following items into a functional system: (a) timer, (b) sequencer, (c) adder, (d) subtractor, (e) multiplier, (f) divider, and (g) converter.

2. Each item should be programmed into a network independently. It should have an enable contact and a method of applying data to the register and be used to actuate an output device that will drive a simulated load.

3. Make a sketch of each diagram employed and explain the general procedures for adding data to the register part of the diagram.

4. Explain how each device responds in the system when it is achieving control.

13

Industrial Robotic Systems

A recent significant development in industry is the use of automated manufacturing equipment and industrial robots. Industrial robots are a specialized type of automated manufacturing equipment. A new technology has evolved from innovations in automated manufacturing. It is called *industrial robotics*.

DEVELOPMENT OF INDUSTRIAL ROBOTIC SYSTEMS

Robots have been used as imaginary characters in movies and television for many years. When the word "robot" is mentioned, most people visualize something similar to those shown in Figure 13–1. The purpose of an industrial robot is to accomplish some type of work. In many instances, robots can be used in industry to perform work that is boring, unpleasant, or hazardous for human beings to perform. Industrial robots are defined as programmable, multifunction manipulators designed to move materials, parts, tools, or special devices through programmed motions for the performance of a variety of tasks. A robot is a machine that can be programmed and reprogrammed to do several tasks. Because of its programmable capability, a robot can function in many different types of jobs.

Some people feel that robots are the answer to some of society's problems. Although this is not true, robots can be used to boost industrial productivity. Robots are not necessarily faster than humans, but they can work at a steady pace. Thus they outperform many workers, especially those doing repetitive jobs.

Industrial robots were first developed in the late 1950s and early 1960s. Their applications have become widespread in the 1980s. There are now many manufacturers of industrial robots in the United States and worldwide. Sev-

(A)

(B)

FIGURE 13–1
Robots.

eral types of industrial robots are shown in Figure 13–2. There are many different sizes and configurations of robots.

PARTS OF A ROBOTIC SYSTEM

A robotic system consists of three major components: (1) the mechanical unit, known as the *manipulator*, (2) the brain, known as the *controller*, and (3) the *power supply*. Figure 13–3 shows these components and their relationship to one another. The manipulator is a mechanical unit that does the work. The manipulator's main responsibility is to perform the manipulative function of positioning the robot's hand. The robot's hand is referred to as the *end effector*. To provide the manipulator with a certain amount of dexterity, several mechanical

linkages and joints are employed. Movement of the various joints and linkages of the manipulator is accomplished by *actuators*. The actuator is a motor or transducer that converts electrical, hydraulic, or pneumatic energy to produce motion of the robot. Actuators can be mounted directly at each joint or they can drive the robot indirectly through the use of gears, cables, chains, or lead screws. Other components used with the manipulator vary according to the type of power supply employed and the level of sophistication. If the robot is a *closed-loop system,* internal sensors may be used to communicate to the controller. Feedback sensors such as encoders or resolvers may be used in communicating the various segments or joint location positions.

Some robots employ more than one type of sensor. This is especially true if we are interested in controlling velocity as well as positioning. The less sophisticated robot, the *open-*

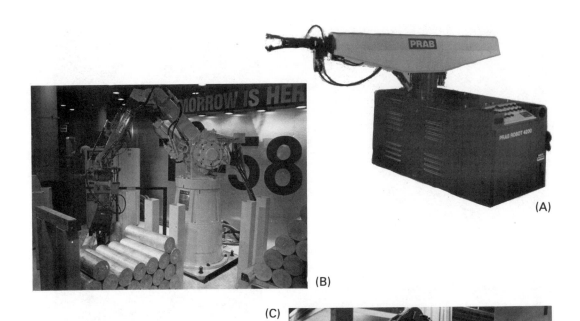

(A)

(B)

(C)

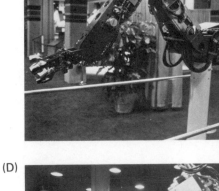

(D)

(E)

FIGURE 13–2
Types of industrial robots.

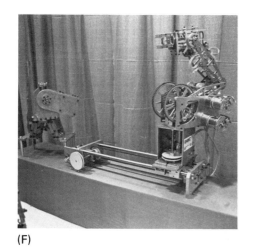

(F)

(I)

(G)

(J)

(H)

FIGURE 13–2 (Continued)

loop system, may use a simple limit switch. The switch may be activated by the robot arm, indicating that the robot's arm has reached its destination. In addition to sensors, various control valves are employed on the manipulator. Hydraulic and pneumatic units use control valves to regulate and control the flow of air or oil to the various actuators. The manipulator of an industrial robot not only includes the various segments and joints but also the actuators, sensors, switches and control valves.

A key factor leading to the increased use of industrial robots has been the improvements made in the robot controller. With new developments in integrated circuit technology, the controller is more powerful and considerably

(A) Manipulators.

(B) Controllers.

FIGURE 13–3
Components of a robotic system.

cheaper today. Programmable controllers, microprocessors, and minicomputers are now available on many robots at a reasonable cost. The controllers on an industrial robot vary in complexity and capability. For the more sophisticated or *intelligent robot,* a microprocessor or minicomputer is used. The minicomputer has greater memory power for storing positions and sequence data. This increased storage capacity provides a smoother movement of the manipulator. The controller functions as memory by storing the necessary positioning and sequence data. The controller also controls the movement of the manipulator by initiating and terminating various moves. The controller also communicates with the peripheral equipment, such as by turning on adjacent equipment or performing a waiting function until adjacent equipment cycles. In the more sophisticated arrangement where external sensors are used, the controller can be programmed to recognize certain conditions and make the necessary adjustments.

The power supply provides the energy to drive the actuator. The three basic power supplies are *electric, hydraulic,* and *pneumatic.* The selection of the type of power supply is generally determined by the application. If the application is a lightweight pick-and-place operation that requires speed and accuracy, a pneumatic source may be preferred. If the application is in an explosive area, a pneumatic or hydraulic source should be used. For operations that require the handling of heavy objects, the hydraulic unit is recommended. Hydraulic units are considered faster than electrical units. The hydraulic unit can achieve good accuracy and repeatability when used with accurate feedback sensors. The use of electrical power supplies is increasing, especially since greater emphasis is being placed on automated assembly. The electrical unit is

(C) Power supply.

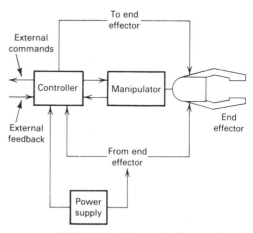

(D) Relationships of robot components.

FIGURE 13–3 (Continued)

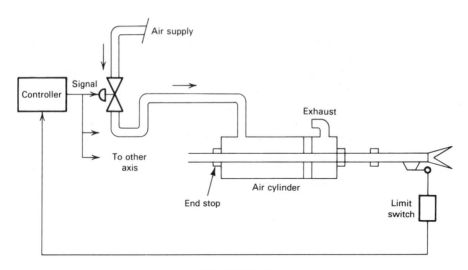

FIGURE 13–4
Non-servo robotic system.

not as strong or fast as the hydraulic unit but it requires less floor space. Another advantage is the electrical unit makes less noise than the hydraulic units.

CLASSIFICATION OF ROBOTIC SYSTEMS

In the United States, robots are often classed into two major categories: (1) *nonservo* and (2) *servo*. Sometimes three major categories are used. The nonservo robot is considered a *non-intelligent robot,* while servo robots are classified as either *intelligent* or *highly intelligent* robots. The nonservo robot is an *open-loop system*. The input signal to the system is not dependent on the output of the system. Nonservo robots are the simplest form of robot. They are often referred to as limited-sequence robots, pick-and-place, fixed stops, or bang-bang robots. A nonservo robot system is shown in Figure 13–4. The diagram is used to represent a four-axis pneumatic robot. At the

beginning of the cycle, the controller begins to move the robot through its various steps of sequence. At the first step, the controller sends a signal to the control valve of the manipulator. As the control valve opens, air is allowed to pass to the actuator or cylinder, causing the rod of the cylinder to move. As long as the valve remains open, this segment of the manipulator continues to move until it is restrained by the end stops on the rod of the cylinder. After the rod of the cylinder reaches its length of travel, a limit switch is activated. This tells the controller to close the control valve. The controller then sends a signal to the control valve to close it. The controller then moves to the next step in the program and initiates the necessary signals. The process is repeated until all the steps in the program have been completed.

The servo robot is a more sophisticated *closed-loop* system. The signal from the controller is dependent on the output of the system. A servomechanism is a control system used to detect and correct errors.

Figure 13–5 is used to explain the operating

principle of the servo robot. The diagram is a simplified version of a six-axis robot with a hydraulic power supply. When the start of the cycle is initiated, the controller addresses the first desired location and interprets the actual locations of the various axes. The desired location signal generated by the controller is compared with the feedback signals from the resolver. The difference in the signals, known as the *error signal,* is amplified and applied to the servo valve. The valve opens proportionally to the level of the command signal generated by the amplifier. The open valve admits fluid to the actuator on the manipulator. The actuator then moves the manipulator. New signals are generated as the manipulator moves. When the error signal reaches *zero,* the servo control valve closes, shutting off the flow of fluid. The manipulator comes to rest at the desired position. The controller then addresses the next point in memory. The process is repeated until all steps of the program are completed. The tachometer is used in conjunction with the controller to control acceleration and deceleration of movements. The servo robot has a more sophisticated controller than the

nonservo. The controller has the capability of executing several hundred steps.

The servo classification can be divided into two groups: (1) *intelligent* and (2) *highly intelligent* servo robots. The main difference between the two servo classifications is that highly intelligent servo robots utilize external sensors. These sensors can provide the robot with certain decision-making capabilities. They help the robot determine its own actions and take corrective measures.

ROBOTIC SYSTEM CONFIGURATIONS

Robotic systems are available in many shapes and sizes. They are generally grouped in one of four major configurations, while some robots have more than one configuration. The different configurations are derived from their joint arrangement or from the various geometric arrangements of the robot's work area. The *jointed arm* or *jointed spherical* robotic system configuration is the most common configura-

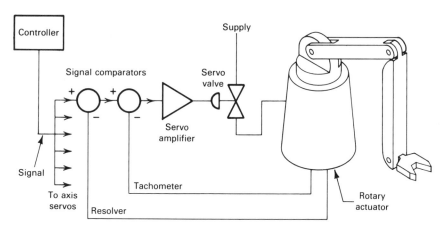

FIGURE 13–5
Servo robotic system.

tion. The robot is often described as anthropomorphic or humanlike in form because its movements closely resemble those of the human body. The jointed arm consists of rigid segments, joints, and a base. The rigid segments resemble a human's forearm and upper arms. The joints mimic the action of the wrist, elbow, and shoulder. The sweep represents the waist. Figure 13–6 shows the jointed arm configuration of a robotic system. The jointed-arm robot performs work in an irregular work space. The *work space* refers to the region the robot is capable of reaching. The jointed-arm robot provides a reach that is more flexible than many other types of robotic configurations.

The *Cartesian coordinate* robotic system consists of three intersecting perpendicular straight lines. This system is often referred to as the *X-Y-Z* system (see Figure 13–7). A smoother motion of the end effector can be achieved, allowing the robot to move directly to a designated point. Cartesian coordinate robots have advantages that include accuracy, repeatability, and load-carrying capacity. The weight-lifting capacity of a Cartesian coordinate robotic system does not vary with different locations within the work area.

The *cylindrical coordinate* robotic system, shown in Figure 13–8, consists of two slides mounted on a rotary base. Reach is accomplished by the movement of the arm of the robot. Vertical movement is accomplished by sliding action on a vertical post.

The *spherical robotic system configuration,* shown in Figure 13–9, resembles the turret of a tank. The robot has a pivot point that provides its vertical movement. Reach is accomplished by a telescoping boom that extends and retracts. Left and right movement is provided by a rotary axis. The movement of the three axes of this robotic system approximates a work space of a sphere.

In summary, the four basic robot configu-

FIGURE 13–6
Jointed-arm configuration of a robotic system.

rations are (1) *jointed-arm,* (2) *Cartesian,* (3) *cylindrical,* and (4) *spherical.* However, certain robot manufacturers may incorporate more than one configuration in a given model.

DEGREES OF FREEDOM OF A ROBOTIC SYSTEM

The degrees of freedom of a robotic system can be compared to the way in which the human body moves. For each degree of freedom, a joint is required. The degrees of freedom located in the arm define the configuration. Each of the four basic motion configurations discussed previously utilize three degrees of freedom in the arm. For applications that require flexibility, additional degrees of freedom are required in the wrist of the robot. Three degrees of freedom located in the wrist give the end effector more flexibility. A total of six degrees of freedom is needed to locate a robot's hand at any point in its work space. Although

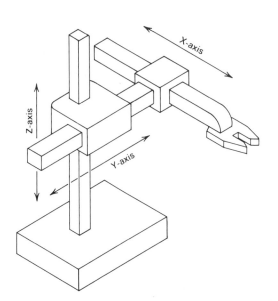

FIGURE 13–7
Cartesian coordinate configuration of a
robotic system.

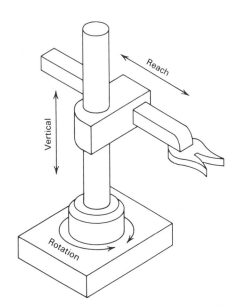

FIGURE 13–8
Cylindrical coordinate configuration of a
robotic system.

six degrees are needed for maximum flexibility, most robots employ three to five degrees of freedom. The more degrees of freedom, the greater complexity of motions.

In comparison, the movement of the human hand is controlled by 35 muscles. Fifteen of these muscles are located in the forearm. The arrangement of the muscles in the hand provides a great strength to the fingers and thumb for grasping objects. Each finger can act alone

or together with the thumb. This enables the hand to do many intricate and delicate tasks. Some of the grips of the human hand for moving objects are shown in Figure 13–10. It is difficult for robotic systems to duplicate many of these grips.

The hand has 27 bones; 8 bones are located in the wrist, 16 in the fingers, and 3 in the thumb. There are 22 degrees of freedom (joints) in the hand, with 7 in the wrist. From

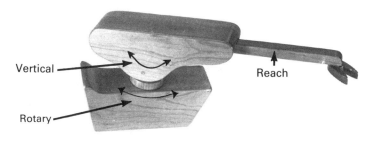

FIGURE 13–9
Spherical configuration of a robotic system.

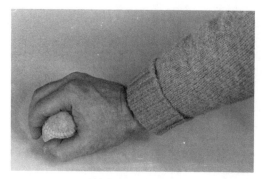

(A) Sperical grip.

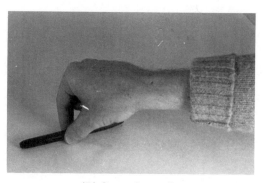

(B) Opposing grip.

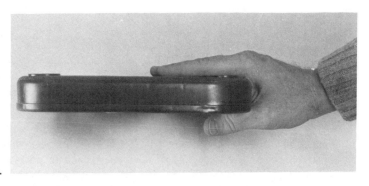

(D) Lateral grip.

FIGURE 13–10
Grips of the human hand used to move
objects.

Figure 13–11, it can be seen that the hand is a very complex multipurpose tool. Hands can be used to perform various repetitive tasks. The bones and joint arrangement give the human hand dexterity not found in robotic systems. The movements of a robotic system seem rather awkward and clumsy, since the robot is usually accomplishing these movements with only six degrees of freedom.

The three degrees of freedom located in the arm of a robotic system are the *rotational traverse,* the *radial traverse,* and the *vertical traverse.* The rotational traverse is the movement of the arm assembly about a rotary axis, such as the left and right swivel of the robot's arm about its base. The radial traverse is the extension and retraction of the arm or the in and out motion relative to the base. The vertical traverse provides the up and down motion of the arm of the robotic system.

The three degrees of freedom located in the wrist, which bear the names of aeronautical terms, are (1) *pitch,* (2) *yaw,* and (3) *roll.* The pitch or bend is the up and down movement of the wrist. The yaw is the right and left movement of the wrist, while the roll or swivel is

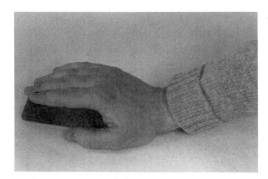

(C) Palm grip.

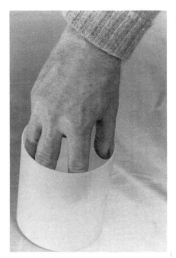

(E) Spread movement grip.

(F) Cylindrical grip.

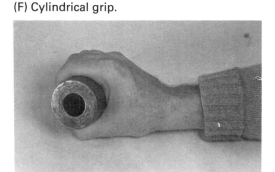

FIGURE 13–10 (Continued)

the rotation of the hand. Figure 13–12 illustrates the six basic degrees of freedom.

PROGRAMMING ROBOTIC SYSTEMS

The four major methods of programming robotic systems are (1) *manual*, (2) *lead-through*, (3) *walk-through*, and (4) *software* programming. Methods of programming involving voice and two-way communications are also being explored today.

Manual programming is best described as a machine setup. Programming is accomplished by an operator physically setting the necessary end stops, switches, cams, and electrical wires or hoses to complete a sequence of steps. This type of programming is characteristic of the less sophisticated robots known as *limited-sequence* or *pick-and-place* robots. Even though these robots are regarded as rather simple, they are capable of performing many of the tasks

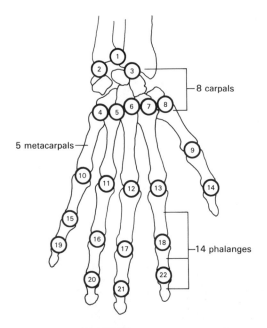

FIGURE 13–11
Degrees of freedom of the human hand.

found in manufacturing. If an appplication is suited for the less sophisticated robot, there is no reason to invest in one of the more complex models.

Lead-through programming involves the operator's use of a *teach pendant* to lead the robot through the desired positions or locations. As the robot's hand reaches each desired point in the sequence of motion, the point is recorded into memory. The points recorded in memory are used to generate the path the robot follows during operation. A teach pendant is shown in Figure 13–13.

Walk-through programming involves an experienced operator physically moving the robot's hand through the desired motions. While the operator is moving the robot through the desired path, points are recorded into memory. A single program may consist of several thousand points; therefore, magnetic tape or a floppy disc is generally used to store programs. Spraying and arc welding are the common ap-

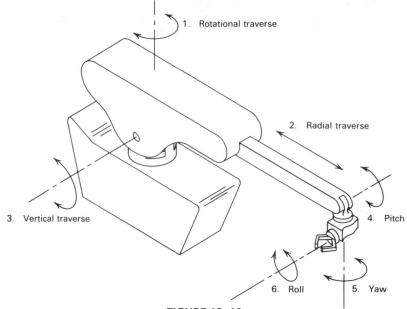

FIGURE 13–12
Six major degrees of freedom of a robotic system.

FIGURE 13–13
Teach pendant used for lead-through programming.

plications that utilize walk-through programming.

Software programming involves the programming of the robot by means of a computer. This method of programming is also known as *off-line* programming since the programming generally occurs away from the robotic system. Most robotic system manufacturers that use off-line programming have developed their own languages. Some common languages are AML (IBM Corporation), HELP (General Electric Corporation), Val (Unimation), AL (Stanford University), Rail (Automatix, Inc.), and MCL (McDonnell Douglas Corporation). Off-line programming has certain advantages over the other methods of programming. The computer provides greater flexibility, with high-level languages enabling robots to carry out complex operations. An advantage of off-line programming is that the robot does not have to be taken out of service during reprogramming.

Voice programming has not been used a great deal, but its utilization is certain to grow. Voice programming is accomplished by having an operator read or repeat a phrase of words several times. After this is completed, the electronic equipment computes the average voice frequency of the operator. After voice recognition is accomplished, the robot will respond to the operator's voice to carry out those commands it has been programmed to do. A robot will only respond to the commands of the voice it has been taught to recognize.

MOTIONS OF ROBOTIC SYSTEMS

A robotic system's end effector moves to or through a sequence of points. Three classifications of the patterns of motion are (1) *pick-and-place motion*, (2) *point-to-point motion*, and (3) *continuous-path motion*.

Limited-sequence robots use *pick-and-place motion*. Pick-and-place motion is a limited point-to-point motion, as shown in Figure 13–14. The number of points the robot is capable of duplicating is rather few. Programming is accomplished by manually setting mechanical stops or limit switches. For the

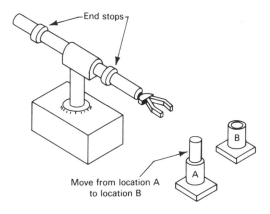

FIGURE 13–14
Pick-and-place motion.

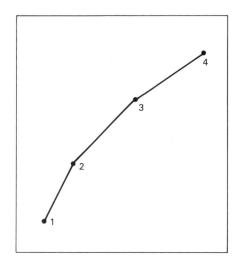

FIGURE 13–15
Point-to-point motion.

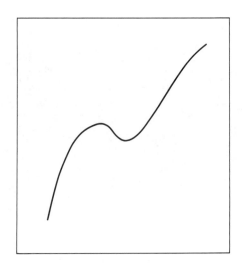

FIGURE 13–16
Continuous-path motion.

robot's end effector to arrive at some designated point, end stops on the various axes have to be adjusted.

Point-to-point (PTP) *motion* involves the movement of the robotic system through a number of discrete points, as shown in Figure 13–15. The programmer uses a combination of the robot axes to position the end effector at a desired point. Those positions or points are recorded and stored in memory. During the playback mode, the robot steps through the points recorded in memory. The path of motion is a straight line between the recorded points.

Continuous-path (CP) *motion* is an extension of the point-to-point method. The difference is that continuous path involves the utilization of more points. A continuous-path program can have several thousand points. Since more points are used, the distances between points are extremely close, as shown in Figure 13–16. Due to the large number of points, the robot is capable of producing smooth movements that give the appearance of continuous or contour movements. Continuous-

path motion is more concerned with control of the path movement rather than end-point positioning. Programming of the path of motion is accomplished by an operator physically moving the end effector of the robot through its path of motion. While the operator is moving the robot through its motion, the positions of the various axes are recorded on some constant time frame. Some continuous-path robots record up to 80 points per second. Programs are generally recorded on magnetic tape or disc.

SENSORS FOR ROBOTIC SYSTEMS

Robotic systems should be able to sense, evaluate, make decisions, and interact with their environment. With the perfection of sensors, robots will be able to achieve their full potential. *External sensors* are used for measuring displacements, forces, or other variables in the robot's environment. External sensors provide

robots with a higher level of intelligence. Four common external sensors in use today are (1) vision, (2) tactile, (3) proximity, and (4) voice.

Much research is being conducted on *vision sensing* by robot manufacturers. Vision sensing is being used for inspection, identification, and part orientation. There are several problems associated with vision sensing in the areas of orientation and parts assembly. One problem lies in the fact that interpretation and reaction to data are relatively slow. Another problem is that the human eye sees things in three dimensions, whereas most vision systems are only two-dimensional. With two-dimensional systems, it is difficult for instance to interpret visual information concerning parts that are stacked in bins. Interpretation is made easier when parts are presented in a single layer. With the increase in computer software capabilities and better vision systems, these problems should be overcome in the future.

Tactile sensing involves a sensor that makes physical contact with an object. Three types of tactile sensing are touch, force, and torque. *Force sensing* is extremely useful in the area of assembly, especially if clearance is close. Force sensing can prevent part damage, verify operations, and detect drift. *Touch sensing* can verify if an object is present or not. Touch sensors can be used to control the grip pressure of the end effector. *Torque sensing* can be used to indicate tool wear.

Proximity sensing is used to determine if an object is present. Proximity sensors have an advantage over tactile sensing in that physical contact is not required. Measurements can be taken at some distance from the object. In addition to using proximity sensors to avoid possible collision, they can be used for positioning the end effector to pick up and stack objects.

Voice sensing is in its infancy; however, voice recognition can be used to control and program robots. Voice is a natural means of communication, so it seems appropriate for this method of sensing to be utilized in the future.

MECHANICAL PARTS OF INDUSTRIAL ROBOTS

The mechanical parts of industrial robots are critical to their operation. Several special terms are used to define these mechanical parts. One important part is the basic mechanical unit or *manipulator*. The manipulator of a robot is a mechanism that usually has several moving joints and is used to grasp and move objects. This mechanism performs the actual work function of the machine.

Another basic mechanical part of an industrial robot is the *actuator*. An actuator is a motor that converts electrical, hydraulic, or pneumatic energy into mechanical energy to cause motion of the robot for performing work. Various types of motors are used as actuators. For example, dc stepping motors, such as those shown in Figure 13–17, are commonly used. Other mechanical parts of robots could include *limit switches* used to break or close electrical circuits and *relays* used for electromagnetic control of sequencing operations.

Electrical robots are usually driven by several dc stepping motors. DC stepping motors are rotary actuators that are used in nearly all high-power servomechanisms. They are more efficient and develop a very high torque. The dc stepping motor is used primarily to change electrical pulses into rotary motion that can be used to produce mechanical movement. The shaft of a dc stepping motor rotates a specific number of mechanical degrees with each incoming pulse of electrical energy. The amount of rotary movement or angular displacement produced by each pulse can be repeated precisely with each succeeding pulse from the

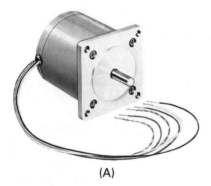

(A)

(B)

(C)

FIGURE 13–17
Actuators used with industrial robots.
(Courtesy of Superior Electric Co.)

drive source. The resulting output of this device is used to accurately locate or position the manipulator of an industrial robot.

The velocity, distance, and direction of a specific piece of equipment can be moved or controlled by a dc stepping motor. Motors of this type are energized by a dc drive amplifier that is controlled by a computer system.

CONTROL SYSTEMS FOR INDUSTRIAL ROBOTS

Various types of control systems are used for the operation of industrial robots. The control of industrial robots is accomplished by several electrical circuits. Some robots have arms controlled by external sensors, while others have mechanical limit switches to act as stops for pick-and-place operations. Servosystems may be controlled by sensors that control the motion of the robot's arm. Among the simplest control systems are nonservo or open-loop systems that use sequencers and mechanical stops to control the end-point positions of the robot arm. Robots of this type are the *pick-and-place* or *fixed-stop* robots. More complex robots, in terms of control, are programmable servo-controlled robots. These robots are the point-to-point or continuous-path types. These robots move in a series of steps from one point to another in a smooth, continuous motion. Programmable-controlled robots are typically used for arc welding and painting operations.

The *control unit,* such as the one shown in Figure 13–18, determines its flexibility and efficiency. Some robots have only mechanical stops on each axis, while others have microprocessor or minicomputer control with memory capability to store position and sequence data for controlling motion. Some important factors in the selection of a control unit are (1) speed of operation, (2) repeatability of the

FIGURE 13–18
Control unit of an industrial robot.

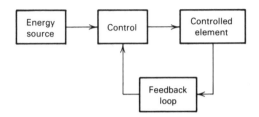

FIGURE 13–19
Closed-loop system diagram.

control operation, (3) accuracy of positioning, and (4) speed and ease of reprogramming.

Control of a robotic system is accomplished by some type of human input or by a physical change that occurs automatically. During production activity at an industry, control systems are continually at work. Control adjustments that alter machine operation must be made periodically. Automatic control is often accomplished by sophisticated and complex control systems. The control functions of automated manufacturing systems range from very simple on–off operations to complex automatic controls that sense a physical change and alter machine operation accordingly.

A wide variety of electronic and mechanical devices is used as control systems. The most basic type of control system is referred to as an *open-loop system*. Open-loop systems are used almost exclusively for manual control op-

erations. There are two variations of the open-loop system. When a system is simply turned off or on, it has *full control*. Switches, circuit breakers, fuses, and relays are used to achieve full control. Full control is designed to start or stop the system. In an electrical circuit, current stops when the circuit path is opened. Another type of open-loop control is *partial control*. In an open-loop system, partial control alters system operation rather than causing it to start or stop. In an automated manufacturing system, resistors, inductors, transformers, capacitors, semiconductor devices, and integrated circuits are commonly used to achieve partial control.

To achieve automatic control, there must be some type of interaction between a controlled element and the control section. In a closed-loop system, this interaction is called *feedback*. Both full and partial control can be achieved through a closed-loop system. Figure 13–19 shows the basic diagram for closed-loop

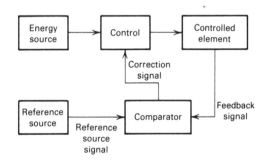

FIGURE 13–20
Closed-loop automatic-control system.

control. The feedback part of this diagram can be activated by electrical, thermal, light, chemical, or mechanical energy.

Figure 13–20 shows the block diagram of a closed-loop system with automatic correction control. In this system, energy from a source passes to the control element and to the controlled element. A feedback loop from the controlled element is applied to a *comparator*. The signal is then compared and sent to the control system. This signal is used to alter the system so that it conforms with operational data from the reference source. Systems of this type are designed to maintain the controlled element at a certain operating level regardless of its external variations or disturbances.

Many robotic systems used in industry today are of the closed-loop automatic-control type. Reference signals from a magnetic tape or disc of a microcomputer unit are fed into a comparator along with the feedback signal. An error-correction signal is then developed that will alter system control accordingly.

AUTOMATED MANUFACTURING SYSTEMS IN INDUSTRY

The advance of science and technology has brought about some very important changes in the manufacture of industrial products. These include improvements in such areas as product inspection techniques, quality control, detection procedures, automatic processing, sequence timing, and the use of microprocessors. At one time, industrial manufacturing operations were limited to systems and devices that were manually controlled. Gaseous tubes, magnetic contactors, and electrical switchgear served as the primary control devices at that time. Recent developments in solid-state electronics and microminiaturization have brought

FIGURE 13–21
Circuit board for a robot controller.

a number of significant changes to automated manufacturing. The internal circuit board of a robot controller, shown in Figure 13–21, illustrates the effect of miniaturization. Electromechanical, optoelectronic, hydraulic, and pneumatic systems are often combined in the control of a single machine. Industrial robotic systems are examples of machines that use several of these systems to achieve operation.

QUESTIONS

1. Look at the illustrations of Figure 13–2 and classify them according to the four basic robot configurations.

2. What are some applications of industrial robots?

3. What are some advantages of using robots in industry?

4. What are the three major components of a robotic system? Discuss each component.

5. What types of power supplies are used

with industrial robots? What are some applications of each type?

6. How are robotic systems classified? Briefly discuss each classification.

7. What are the four robotic system configurations? Discuss each configuration.

8. What is meant by the degrees of freedom of a robotic system?

9. How do the degrees of freedom of a robot's end effector compare to the human hand?

10. What are the degrees of freedom located in a robot's arm?

11. What are the degrees of freedom located in a robot's wrist?

12. What are the four major methods of programming industrial robots? Discuss each method.

13. What are the three patterns of motion of industrial robotic systems? Discuss each pattern.

14. What are the four common types of external sensors used with robotic systems? Discuss each type.

15. What are some important mechanical parts used with industrial robots?

16. What is a dc stepping motor and how is it used with industrial robots?

17. What are some factors to consider in the selection of a control unit for an industrial robot?

18. What is the difference between open-loop and closed-loop control systems?

19. Discuss the development of automated manufacturing systems in industry. Give examples.

Index